COLLEGE AND UNIVERSITY MATHEMATICS

COLLEGE AND UNIVERSITY MATHEMATICS

a functional approach

DONALD R. BARR
Naval Postgraduate School
Monterey, California

and

FLOYD E. WILLMORE
Wisconsin State University
Oshkosh, Wisconsin

ALLYN AND BACON, INC.

Boston

Dedicated to Robert Wonders

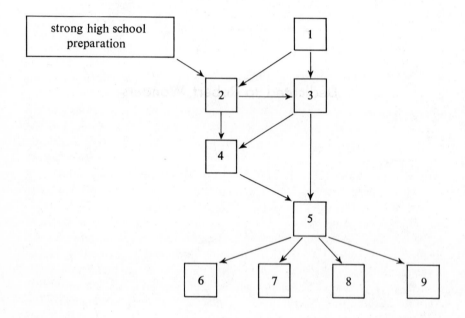

PREFACE TO THE INSTRUCTOR

THIS TEXT is primarily designed to serve as a pre-calculus course. However, the mathematics included here in no sense should be thought of as servicing this group only. The material allows considerable flexibility in designing a one (or two) semester course. The authors view Chapters 1, 3, and 5 as the heart of a one semester course, with inclusion of other chapters depending on the purpose of the course and the abilities and interests of the students involved. For students who have a strong high school background, it is possible to cover Chapters 2, 4, 5, and additional selected chapters. To cover the entire book takes the better part of two semesters.

One of the things which distinguishes this text from others in the field is the emphasis on bridging the gap between traditional notation and a set theoretic approach. We use set notions, not as an end in themselves, but as a language device to clarify certain concepts. After an understanding is gained, we feel free to eliminate details when they add nothing to clarity. Another distinguishing feature is the emphasis on student participation. The authors feel that mathematics is learned, not by *observing* mathematics, but by *doing* mathematics.

We also feel that consistently asking a student to prove a result which he has been assured is true takes a great deal of the excitement out of learning mathematics. The *real* challenge is to discover the result, and follow it with a proof verifying the conjecture. For this purpose, in addition to many problems of the routine type, we have included many exercises of the form "Investigate (prove or disprove)." (We have also not neglected to ask him to prove known results.)

The problems listed at the end of each section vary widely in difficulty. Some are routine problems which can be solved by some manipulative scheme discussed in the preceding material. Others are not routine. The classification of a problem as being "easy" or "hard" cannot be made until the student has tried to solve it. In fact, many times different students won't agree as to the difficulty of a problem. The good student should be able to solve all of the problems. In order to avoid discouraging students from *trying* the more difficult problems, the challenging problems have not been marked in any way, nor have they been put at the end of the problem set. Instead, they are scattered innocently among the easy problems.

It is not necessary for the instructor to view all of the theorems in this text as material for student consumption. In several places, theorems which are probably too involved for the student at this level are included for the purpose of completing the development. Possibly the student should be encouraged to read such proofs; he should not be expected to reproduce them. In such cases, the *result* is the important thing for him to know at this level.

Another feature of this text is the effort to capitalize on certain abstract mathematical concepts in order to eliminate difficulty in work that follows. For example, we emphasize that all of the "algebraic" structure used in real numbers transfers to the complex numbers. We feel that such innovations add greatly to an understanding of the foundations and applications of mathematics. We have also attempted to "interweave" our treatment of logic with the mathematical arguments in such a way that each motivates and clarifies the other. As much as possible, logical principles are discussed *as they arise*. The logical format of a number of proofs are listed *when these proofs are given*.

The authors wish to express their indebtedness to their colleagues for their many helpful suggestions concerning this book. Special thanks are due Mr. Norbert Kuenzi, who helped draft the original notes, and to Mr. Donald Voils, who assisted in the several revisions of the original material. We also wish to express a great indebtedness to Miss Mary Bork for her invaluable assistance in preparing the manuscript.

PREFACE TO THE STUDENT

IN READING this book, you should sit down with a pencil, a large supply of paper, and a trash can. (The trash can is for your scratch work—and there should be lots of it—not our book.) Whenever the text indicates a question, an exercise, or a "why," you should stop *reading* and start *writing*. To really understand the arguments and examples, you must actually "do" them yourself. When you have either solved the problem or tired of it (be sure not to tire too quickly), then read further. You will be surprised how easy and exciting mathematics can be if you are willing to participate. On the other hand, you will find it dull and difficult if you insist on being a spectator. *Mathematics is not a spectator sport.*

Among the exercises, you will find many routine problems designed to familiarize you with the material. There are also many challenging problems which you should be able to solve if you do not give up too easily. Real excitement in mathematics comes when you have "conquered" a difficult problem. Perhaps you will not be able to solve every problem, but you should at least launch a formidable "attack" which will enable you to understand and appreciate another student's result.

Learning mathematics is a great deal like meeting people for the first time. At first it may be difficult to associate each man with his name. But as you use his name more and more, the man and his name seem to be the same thing. You may have a similar experience as you learn math. It will be difficult at first to remember what all the names are naming and all the theorems are saying. But as you use them more and more, you will be able to recall them automatically. Don't expect this to happen overnight; in particular, don't expect it to happen without a great deal of personal involvement. To attempt to learn mathematics by merely attending outstanding lectures would be like learning to play football by watching television.

CONTENTS

CONTENTS

8 Linearity

0

ASSUMPTIONS

In order to have something familiar from which to construct examples as we develop the material in Chapter 1, we shall feel free to use what is considered to be common pre-college knowledge about the four number systems known as "the natural numbers," "the integers," "the rational numbers," and "the real numbers." We do this in such a way that it in no sense destroys the logical continuity of the development. In fact, the use of these number systems for examples and exercises throughout serves as a method of reinforcing the student's present knowledge, as well as preparing him for what is yet to come. By doing this, the student is familiar with these number systems when we begin to develop them in more detail in later chapters; thus, his understanding of the material is greatly enhanced.

The Natural Numbers, N

We shall denote the collection of *natural numbers* by the letter N. The student may know this collection by the name "positive whole numbers." N consists of the numbers, 1, 2, 3, 4, 5, 6, ... It is assumed that the student knows how to add, multiply, and in some cases divide two natural numbers in order to arrive at a third one. It is hoped that he also knows that a prime number is a natural number that cannot be divided evenly by anything except 1 and the number itself.

Example: a) 7 is prime, since the only natural number divisors of 7 are 1 and 7. *b)* 6 is not prime, since 3 divides into 6. That is, $6 = 3 \times 2$. *c)* 17 is prime. $17 = 1 \times 17 = 17 \times 1$ but there is no other way to multiply two natural numbers together to get 17.

Question: Which of the following natural numbers are prime? 3, 9, 21, 31, 40.

Remark: As a special convention, the number 1 is not considered to be prime, even though it satisfies the conditions mentioned above.

The Integers, Z

We shall denote the collection of integers by Z. This collection consists of all the whole numbers, positive, negative, and zero. $Z = \{..., -3, -2, -1, 0, 1, 2, 3, ...\}$. Again, the student is expected to know how to add, multiply, subtract, and in some cases divide two integers to arrive at a third integer. We regard the collection of natural numbers to be a subcollection of the integers. That is, each natural number is an integer.

The familiar concept of one integer being either smaller than or larger than any other integer will be used and is denoted by the symbol "$<$" or the symbol "$>$." ("$<$" is read "less than" and "$>$" is read "greater than.")

Example: $-4 < 0, 2 < 7, 5 > 0, -9 > -20, -36 < 0$.

The symbols "$\leq$" and "$\geq$" are used to abbreviate "less than or equal" and "greater than or equal" respectively.

Example: $3 \leq 5, 9 \geq -1, 7 \leq 7, 4 \geq 4, 4 \leq 9$.

This ordering concept allows the familiar interpretation of the integers as lying along a very long line with 0 in the "middle." (Whatever "middle" means!)

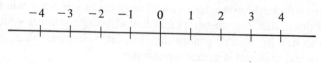

FIG. 0.1

The Rational Numbers, Q

We shall denote by Q the familiar collection of numbers known as the fractions, both positive and negative. The student should know how to divide any two non-zero rational numbers to arrive at a third rational number. He also should be able to add, multiply, and subtract such numbers.

Example: 5/8 and 2/3 are both rational numbers since they are given as the quotient of two integers. $5/8 \div 2/3 = 15/16$ and $5/8 \times 2/3 = 5/12$.

Remark: An integer is a rational number. For example, $3 = 3/1$ and $-5 = -5/1$. Thus zero is also in the collection Q since $0 = 0/1$.

Rational numbers are also considered to be ordered, and thus can be thought of as lying along a line.

FIG. 0.2

In fact, it seems at first that the rational numbers can correspond one to one with what we intuitively think of as *the line*. The idea of having these numbers lie on a line is a result of using them to record lengths of physical objects, and to compute various information about structures involving lengths. The order relation "$<$" is then a natural concept concerning the rational numbers. All the numbers lying to the "left" of zero are called *negative* and all those to the "right" are called *positive*.

The following is a list of <u>fundamental properties about order</u> that you should be familiar with, in order to work many of the exercises in Chapter 1.

1. If $x < y$, then for any z, $x + z < y + z$. (You can add the same number to both sides of an inequality and preserve the order.)
2. If $x < y$ and $z > 0$, then $xz < yz$. (You can multiply both sides of an inequality by a positive number and preserve the order.)
3. If $x < y$ and $z < 0$, then $xz > yz$. (You can multiply both sides of an inequality by a negative number and reverse the order.)
4. If $x < y$ and $y < z$, then $x < z$. (The order relation is *transitive*.)
5. If x and y designate rational numbers, then exactly one of the following is true: $x < y$, $x = y$, $x > y$. (Trichotomy Law)
Various other properties about order follow. Some of the more important ones are:
6. If $x > 0$, then $1/x > 0$.
7. If $xy > 0$, then ($x > 0$ and $y > 0$) or ($x < 0$ and $y < 0$).
8. If $xy < 0$, then ($x > 0$ and $y < 0$) or ($x < 0$ and $y > 0$).

(The ordinary "$\cdot$" or "juxtaposition" is used to indicate multiplication.) A useful convention to abbreviate "$x < y$ and $y < z$" is "$x < y < z$." Similarly with "$\leq$."

The Real Numbers, R

It was many years after the development of the rational numbers that it was discovered that there are simply not enough of them to completely correspond to what we intuitively call "the line." This discovery was made by using the well known Pythagorean formula, which states that "the square of the length of the hypotenuse of a right triangle is equal to the sum of the squares of the two legs." If we then try to compute the length of the hypotenuse of a right triangle whose legs have length 1 (one), we arrive at a length $\sqrt{2}$.

3

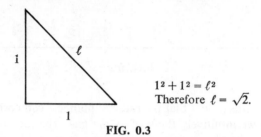

$$1^2 + 1^2 = \ell^2$$
Therefore $\ell = \sqrt{2}$.

FIG. 0.3

We will show later that $\sqrt{2}$ cannot be expressed as a fraction m/n, where m and n are integers. Many other numbers have been shown to be non-rational also, for example: $\sqrt{3}, \sqrt{5}, \sqrt{7}, \sqrt{11}, \sqrt{13}, \ldots, \sqrt{p}$ where p is prime. The famous number π is also irrational.

It follows, then, that in order to have enough numbers to correspond with what we call the line, we need more than the rational numbers. By a method which you shall have the opportunity to see later, we complete the rational number system by imbedding it in a larger system, in which there are enough numbers to cover the line. This number system is called the "real number system" and is denoted by R. All the order properties, addition properties, and multiplication properties with which you are familiar in the rational numbers are "transferred" to the reals. The new numbers are attached and fit into their proper place in such a way that they correspond one to one with what we call the real line.* All the real numbers which are not rational numbers are called "irrational numbers." Although they are no more "irrational" than the ones which can be expressed as the quotient of two integers, this unfortunate name has, for historical reasons, been given to them.

Exponents

In addition to the fundamental properties we have already mentioned, you should be familiar with the notational conventions which fall under the category of "exponents." These conventions are entirely a matter of definition, so let us list the definitions along with some of the properties which follow.

0.1 Definition: If n is any natural number and x is any real number, then

$$x^n = \overbrace{x \cdot x \cdots x}^{n \text{ times}}$$

---

* The process of assigning numbers to points on the real number line is discussed in the excellent book *Mathematics: The Man-made Universe* by Sherman K. Stein (W. H. Freeman and Company, 1963).

Example:
$$3^2 = 3 \cdot 3$$
$$5^4 = 5 \cdot 5 \cdot 5 \cdot 5$$
$$17^3 = 17 \cdot 17 \cdot 17$$

Immediate properties of exponents:

1. $x^m x^n = x^{m+n}$
2. $(x^m)^n = x^{mn}$
3. $(xy)^n = x^n y^n$
4. $(x/y)^n = x^n/y^n$
5. If $n > m$, then $x^n/x^m = x^{n-m}$
6. If $n < m$, then $x^n/x^m = 1/x^{m-n}$

For reasons you will later see, we make the following notation convention. It may seem a bit strange at first, but this strangeness will soon vanish and turn into a relationship of warm affection.

0.2 Definition: If $x \neq 0$ then $x^0 = 1$. (We assign no meaning to the symbol 0^0.)

Example: $5^0 = 1$, $9^0 = 1$, $(-7)^0 = 1$, $\pi^0 = 1$, $(-2)^0 = 1$.

Another useful convention is the following:

0.3 Definition: If n is a <u>negative integer</u> and $x \neq 0$, then $x^n = 1/x^{-n}$.

Exercise. Make an equivalent definition, but begin with "If n is a positive integer (natural number)...." *then* $x^{-n} = 1/x^n$

Summary

Although you have been using natural numbers, integers, rational numbers, and real numbers since early elementary school, they have many important properties with which you are not familiar. In later chapters we will develop many of these properties. But for now, we shall use some of the more familiar properties for the construction of examples designed to help you understand other concepts. Keep in mind that we consider the natural numbers to be imbedded in the integers, which are imbedded in the rational numbers, which are in turn imbedded in the real numbers. Keep in mind that the two distinct collections of numbers, the irrational numbers and the rational numbers together, comprise the entire set R of real numbers.

$$Q + Q^{-1} = R$$

Exercises 0.1

1. Calculate

   a) $3 + (-7) - 4(6 - 3)$

   b) $5 - (9 + 7 - 6)$

   c) $36^2 - 12^2$

   d) $3^3 - 7$

2. For what values of x will each of the following expressions yield positive numbers?

a) $x/3$

b) $x(-7)$

c) $(-3)/x$

d) $(x - 3)/2$

e) $(x - 1)/2x$

f) $x/(x - 1)(x + 2)$

For what values of x will they yield negative numbers?

3. Express each of the following as the quotient of two integers.

a) $2/3 - 5/8$

c) $1 - \dfrac{1}{(2 + 3/4)}$

e) $1 - \dfrac{1}{1 - \dfrac{1}{1 - 1/2}}$

b) $(3/7 + 2/3)/4$

d) $5/9 + \dfrac{(6 - 1/2)}{(2 + 1/4)}$

4. What number do you suppose is meant by the expression

a) $.314314314314 \ldots$?

b) $.333333 \ldots$?

5. Find all prime numbers less than 100.

6. Is 107 prime?

7. For what values of x will it be true that

a) $1 - \dfrac{x}{3} < 0$

c) $x/3 - 2 + (5x - 1)/2 > 0$

b) $2x > (x - 4)/2$

d) $x/4 - 7 > (x - 4)/7$

8. For what values of x will it be true that

a) $x^2 \geq 0$

b) $x^2 \leq 0$

c) $x - 1 \leq 2(x - 1)$

d) $x < 2x$

e) $(x - 1)/(x + 1) > 2$

9. Reduce each of the following expressions to the simplest form not involving zero or negative exponents.

a) $2^{-2} + 3^{-1}$

b) $(x^0 + x)^{-1}$

c) $(x + x^{-1})^3$

d) $(x^{-1} + x^{-2})/x$

e) $x/(x^{-1} + x^{-2})$

10. For what values of x will it be true that

a) $2x - 4^{-2} < 2^{-1}x + 1$

b) $(x - 1)^0 \leq x - 2$

11. Explain how the common "tape measure" utilizes the idea of imagining the rational numbers as lying along a line. Can you think of other useful applications of this idea? *clock, compass, odometer*

12. Write each of the following numbers as a product of primes.

a) 400

b) 378

c) 195

d) 127

13. Do you think it is possible that other people could come up with different answers in Exercise 12 than you did? (Perhaps, by computing differently.)

1

FOUNDATIONS

1.1 Introduction

In the present chapter we consider some of the most fundamental notions and basic structures to be found in the whole of mathematics. These objects also enjoy a position of great importance, and we shall see that an amazing amount of interesting work can be based on them. The major aim of this chapter is to develop the basic notions of sets, relations, and functions. In order to achieve this aim, it will be necessary to make several definitions. We urge the student to study these carefully, as we feel that it is crucial for him to know what he is talking about (Bertrand Russell's definition of mathematics notwithstanding).†

A mathematical system is usually made up of a conglomeration of several identifiable types of objects. These objects can be classified roughly in the following categories:

    1. A logic (generally unspecified, but usually assumed to be the "common sense" variety).‡

    2. Undefined terms and relations (necessary in order to avoid logically unsatisfactory circular definitions, that is, defining a word ultimately in terms of itself).

    3. Axioms (statements of assumed facts about the undefined terms and relations).

    4. Theorems (statements concerning the terms and relations derived from the axioms using logical reasoning).

---

† Russell defines mathematics as "the subject in which we never know what we are talking about nor whether what we are saying is true." G. A. Miller, "*Historical Introduction to Mathematical Literature*," p. 79, The Macmillan Company, New York, 1916.

‡ The situation is somewhat circular in that we would probably define "common sense" using our logic. Nevertheless, most mathematicians agree on what an acceptable logic is (*i.e.*, what types of arguments are to be considered valid)—with certain exceptions!

A good example of this kind of mathematical system is the system of plane (Euclidean) geometry. In that system, the logic used is the standard type. Some of the undefined terms usually taken are "point," "line," and "plane"; some of the undefined relations are "between" and "coincident." When studying (or inventing) a mathematical system, the investigator often formulates a "real world" (that is, "non-abstract") analogue or "model" which parallels, at least to some extent, the terms and axioms adopted in the system. Thus in the case of geometry, one may view the term "point" as a dot on the "plane," and one may have some intuitive notion about how he might expect the relation "between" to behave in the system. It is understood, however, that the model is at best only a method of gaining intuition and insight, and of communication with other investigators. The structure of the mathematical system is an entity in itself, independent of the model (or models) that "fit the system."

Logic, the Tool of Mathematicians

The study of mathematics is somewhat like the study of microbiology in that we wish to study certain objects in great detail. The creatures we study are ideas and their inter-relationship with one another. In order to study these ideas, we find it necessary to refine certain points of our language and to clarify for ourselves certain of our thinking processes. It would be impossible for a micro-biologist to carry his study very far with a foggy microscope. Similarly, it would be impossible to carry out our refined study of ideas without some precision tools.

Logic is the major tool of mathematics. We wish to discuss here certain concepts of logic which we shall use throughout the development of this text. From time to time, we will find it convenient to introduce additional logic and to elaborate on what has been given here.

Formation of Sentences

A *mathematical statement* or *sentence* is a phrase in our language which is considered to be either true or false. We do not allow a sentence to be both true and false. (A true sentence is said to have truth value T, and a false one F.) We will occasionally speak of an expression whose truth value cannot be determined as a result of its incompleteness. However, we will not call such an expression a sentence. A mathematical system usually involves many sentences. The logic we develop here deals with four ways of constructing new sentences from one or more given sentences. We wish to analyze the use of the words "not", "and", "or", and "implies." We would like to use these words to construct new expressions which are truly sentences in our system (*i.e.*, statements which are either true or false and not both).

Negation ("not")

If we consider a sentence "p", we wish to know what truth value to assign to the sentence "not p". We intuitively feel that if "p" is true, then its negation "not p" should be false, and that if "p" is false, then "not p" should be true. Furthermore, we feel that there are no other possibilities. Let us construct a table (called a truth table) which summarizes this information.

Negation Truth Table

p	not p
T	F
F	T

In the case of negation, it is fairly easy to decide how a truth value should be assigned to a newly constructed sentence, given the truth value of the original sentence. As we will see in the case of the connective "implies," this decision is not always so easy.

Conjunction ("and")

Let us now examine the connective "and". We want to decide how to assign a truth value to a new sentence constructed by placing the connective "and" between two old ones. If "p" and "q" are sentences, then the truth value of the new sentence "p and q" should depend on the truth values of "p" and "q". There are four possibilities to consider. Let us list these possibilities, and the truth value assigned to each new sentence, in a truth table.

Conjunction Truth Table

p	q	p and q
T	T	T
T	F	F
F	T	F
F	F	F

How do you feel about the way we have constructed this table? Does it seem reasonable in the first case that if "p" is a true statement, and if "q" is a true statement, we should consider "p and q" to be a true statement?

Example: "New York is a state" $= p$

                  "The President is a person" $= q$

9

"*p*" and "*q*" are each true in this case, and it seems reasonable that the statement, "New York is a state and the President is a person", is also true.

What about the next case? Here we have considered "*p*" to be true while "*q*" is false. The contention is that "*p* and *q*" is a false statement.

Example: *p* = "Wisconsin is a state"
              q = "New York is the capital of Maine"

It seems reasonable that the statement "Wisconsin is a state and New York is the capital of Maine" should be false. How do you feel about this? Can you think of other sentences using "and" which verify the rules of conjunction given in the truth table?

Disjunction ("or")

Next we consider the standard truth table for the connective "or." We leave it for the reader to convince himself that this is the "logical" way to construct this truth table. Notice that when a mathematician uses "or", he does not exclude the possibility of both sentences being true. This is somewhat in contrast with common usage.

Disjunction Truth Table

p	*q*	*p* or *q*
T	T	T
T	F	T
F	T	T
F	F	F

Implication ("if, then")

With the two connectives "and" and "or", it seemed reasonable to connect two sentences and then assign a truth value to the new sentence, in spite of possible differences in the context of the sentences which are connected. In ordinary conversation when one uses the expression, ". . . implies - - -," or the equivalent expression, "if . . . then - - -," the sentences being connected usually have a common context. However, we wish to assign a truth value to the sentence, "*p* implies *q*," which depends only on the individual truth values of "*p*" and "*q*," and which is independent of any common or uncommon context. This may seem a bit strange at first, but we would like to be able to combine any two arbitrary sentences using the connective "implies" as we did with "and" and "or." (When we have a sentence "*p* implies *q*," "*p*" is called the *hypothesis* and "*q*" the *conclusion*. The sentence "*p* implies *q*" is called the *implication*.)

Before we attempt to construct a truth table for this connective, let us analyze its use. This will help us decide how to assign truth values in the implication truth table. A few examples will help in making the necessary decisions.

Example: How do you feel about the statement: If "Washington was the first president," then "Adams was the second president." ? Both the hypothesis and the conclusion are true and it seems reasonable to consider the implication to be true.

Let us consider now a similar situation, in which the hypothesis and conclusion have no natural connection due to their context. How do you feel about the following statement: If "Washington was the first president," then "grass is green." ? Again, the hypothesis and the conclusion, are both true. It can be argued that the statement is a non-sense expression. However since both parts, the hypothesis and the conclusion, are sentences, and since we agreed that we would assign a truth value to the implication formed when any two arbitrary sentences are connected by the implication connective, we must make a decision. We also wish to be consistent in our pattern of truth value assignments, and to *have the assignment depend only on the truth values assigned to the components of the implication.* It seems then that one line of the truth table would be as follows:

p	q	p implies q
T	T	T

Example: How do you feel about the following sentence: If "a ball is round," then "all cats are green." ? In this case, the hypothesis is true and the conclusion is false. If we allow the implication to stand as a *true* sentence, then we are asking ourselves also to believe the conclusion. It is reasonably clear that the following should be a line in our truth table:

p	q	p implies q
T	F	F

Exercise: Construct other implications in which the hypothesis is true and the conclusion false, and decide how you feel about the truth of the implication.

Example: We would like to examine some statements of implication in which the hypothesis is false and the conclusion is true. That is, we wish to analyze the following line in the truth table:

p	q	p implies q
F	T	?

a) If "Washington was the 3rd president," then "Jefferson was the 3rd president."

b) If "all cats are red," then "some apples are green."

11

c) If "Abraham Lincoln was not a lawyer," then "Abraham Lincoln was once the president."

d) If "you are some kind of nut," then "you like mathematics."

The way we construct this line of the truth table is as follows:

p	*q*	*p* implies *q*
F	T	T

Perhaps you do not agree that this is the "logical" way to assign a truth value in this case, but we will elaborate on this decision after the next example.

Example: Consider the following statements:

a) If "All cats are green," then "All monkeys are blue."

b) If "Washington was the 5th president," then "Lincoln was the first president."

c) If "You have wings," then "I am a monkey's uncle."

Perhaps statements of this type are sufficiently familiar in everyday language to have you unhesitatingly agree to the last line of the implication truth table.

p	*q*	*p* implies *q*
F	F	T

In making the assignment of a truth value to some statements of implication, our intuition fails us. Some expressions seem to make no sense, although the components from which we constructed the implication are perfectly sensible. We are thus forced to have some seemingly nonsense sentences in our system if we are to be able to combine any two arbitrary sentences by implication. Let us take the position that "we won't bother them if they won't bother us". That is, we will allow these statements to be true provided we will never be confronted with phrases that apparently have both truth values.

We must examine how we intend to *use* implications. A consistent mathematical system consists of a large body of *true* statements (taken from various sources). We use our logic to enlarge this collection. The way we use implications is described in the following paragraph.

If the sentence "*p* implies *q*" is in our collection of truths, and if "*p*" is also in that collection, then we will deduce that "*q*" is among our collection of true sentences. Therefore, if a statement "*p*" is not in the collection of truths (*i.e.*, "*p*" is false), then allowing "*p* implies *q*" to be a true sentence can never do us any harm regardless of the truth value assigned to "*q*," since the statement "*p* implies *q*" would never in itself force us to accept the truth of "*q*." (Implications in which the hypothesis is false are said to be *vacuously true*.) Keeping these things in mind, you should be willing to accept the following truth table for the implication connective.

Implication Truth Table

p	q	p implies q
T	T	T
T	F	F
F	T	T
F	F	T

Alternate Notation

There are various notational devices used to indicate the connectives we have discussed. You should be familiar with the most common ones.

Negation: Instead of writing "not p" to indicate the negation of the sentence "p," it is common to use "$\sim p$" or "$\bar{p}$." In this text we shall use "$\sim p$" or "not p." It is also common to negate a sentence by negating the verb of the sentence. (This often is accomplished by drawing a slash through the verb.)

Example: The sentence, "the cat is green," is negated by any one of the following:

a) not-(the cat is green)
b) $\sim$(the cat is green)
c) The cat is not green
d) the cat i̸s green

Example: The sentence "5 = 6" is negated by any of the following:

a) not-(5 = 6)
b) $\sim$(5 = 6)
c) $5 \neq 6$

"*And*" *and* "*or*": It is common to use "$\wedge$" in place of "and" and "$\vee$" in place of "or."

Example: "p and q" is indicated by "$p \wedge q$" and "p or q" is indicated by "$p \vee q$."

"*Implies*": Other common expressions which are equivalent to "p implies q" are:

a) if p, then q
b) $p \Rightarrow q$ (read "p implies q")
c) p only if q
d) p is sufficient for q

Analyzing Sentences

It is often useful to translate a difficult argument into "abstract form" in order to analyze the validity of the argument.

13

Example: "Either the manager didn't notice the change, or else he approves of it. He noticed it all right, so he must approve of it."

In order to facilitate analyzing this argument, suppose we let some letter stand for each assertion. Let

N = "The manager noticed the change"
A = "The manager approves of the change"

With this we get: "$\sim N \lor A$" for the first sentence, and "N" for the second. Thus the entire argument is of the form: $(\sim N \lor A) \land N \Rightarrow A$. Do you agree with the conclusion that "A" *must* follow?

Example: The oxygen in the tube either combined with the filament to form an oxide, or else it vanished completely. The oxygen in the tube could not have vanished completely. Therefore, the oxygen in the tube combined with the filament to form an oxide.

Let

C = "The oxygen in the tube combined with the filament to form an oxide"
V = "The oxygen in the tube vanished completely"

Thus the argument is reduced to the following:

$$C \text{ or } V$$
$$\underline{\text{not } V}$$
$$\text{Therefore} \quad C$$

Do you think the conclusion "C" necessarily follows from the premises?

yes.

Exercises 1.1

1. Another logical connective which is often used is the connective "if." This is related to "implies" in that the sentence "q implies p" is equivalent to "p if q." Other statements which are equivalent to "p if q" are:
   a) $p \Leftarrow q$
   b) p is implied by q
   c) p is necessary for q

p	q	$p \Leftarrow q$
T	T	T
T	F	T
F	T	F
F	F	T

Make a truth table for the connective "if."

2. Another logical connective which is constructed by combining "if" and "implies" is the connective "if and only if."

Construct a truth table for "if and only if." Other statements equivalent to "p if and only if q" are:
   a) $p \Leftrightarrow q$
   b) p iff q (We will use this often! Don't forget what it means.)
   c) p is necessary and sufficient for q

T
F
F
T

3. Consider the expression "not-(p or q)" where "p" and "q" are sentences. Would the expression be a sentence? *yes.*
   a) Fill in the truth values for the following table:

p	q	not-(p or q)	not-$(p \wedge q)$
T	T	F	F
T	F	F	T
F	T	F	T
F	F	T	T

b) Do the same for the statement "not-(p and q)".

c) Construct a table for "q or not-p" and compare it with the "implies" table. What can you now deduce?

d) Construct a table for "p and not-q" and compare it with the "p implies q" table. What can you deduce from this? (*Hint:* Construct a table for "not-(p implies q)." $\sim (p \wedge q) \iff p \to q$ or $(p \wedge q) \iff \sim(p \to q)$

4.   One evening Gurney Gibson told his son Grant that if the cows were milked by 6:00, then he would let Grant use the car. Grant did not finish until 6:30, but he was allowed to take the car. *no — p is sufficient, but not necessary for q.*

Did Gurney lie to Grant? Does your answer agree with our construction of the "p implies q" truth table? (*i.e.*, the "if p, then q" table).

5.   In each of the following, translate the sentence into abstract statements and in each case decide if the conclusion is valid. The letters after each sentence are suggested names for sentences which appear.

a) Grant can have many friends only if he respects them as individuals. If he respects them as individuals then he cannot expect them all to behave alike. He does have many friends. Therefore, he does not expect them all to behave alike. (*F, R, E*) *valid*

b) The prisoner is to be condemned if he committed the crime. Either the prisoner was a model citizen or else he committed the crime. The prisoner was not a model citizen. Therefore, the prisoner is to be condemned. (*C, K, M*)

c) If you were at the scene of the crime and you possess a gun, then you committed the crime. You possess a gun. Therefore, you committed the crime. (*S, P, C*) *not valid*

d) It is not the case that he either forgot or wasn't able to finish. Therefore, he was able to finish. (*F, A*)

e) The granary is beyond the barn and the barn is beyond the shed. Therefore, the granary is beyond the shed. (*G$_b$, B$_s$, G$_s$*) *is beyond! transitive?*

f) The Gibsons plan a trip or business is bad. Business is bad or the crops were poor. The crops were not poor. Therefore, the Gibsons plan a trip. (*P, B, C*)

g) Grant did not feed the horses. Guy fed the horses and Gurney is not upset. Therefore, if Grant did not feed the horses, then Gurney is upset. (*P, B, C*) *not valid*

h) If the litmus paper turns red, then the solution is acid. Hence, if the litmus paper turns red, then either the solution is acid or something is wrong somewhere. (*R, A, W*)

i) If the first disjunct of a disjunction is true, the disjunction as a whole is true. Therefore, if both the first and second disjuncts of the disjunction are true, then the disjunction as a whole is true. (*F, W, S*) *valid*

6.   Show that the truth table for "p and (q and r)" is the same as for "(p and q) and r." Similarly for "or." This allows the use of sentences "p or q or r" and "p and q and r" with no parentheses, even though we logically connect only two sentences at a time. (Or do we?) *associative*

7.   Suppose each of the following is a true statement.

$p =$ "Today is Friday"
$q =$ "Yesterday was not Thursday"
$r =$ "I save money"

s = "I will graduate from the university"
t = "Food is not expensive"
u = "Canadians excel in athletics"
v = "My health suffers"

Determine the truth value of each of the following sentences.

a) not-p F
b) not-t F
c) not-s F
d) p or r T
e) p and not-q F
f) $p \Rightarrow$ not-q F

g) $s \Leftarrow t$ T
h) $\odot$ if not-r T
i) if not-t, then v T
j) u only if v T
k) u or not-t T
l) p and not-not-s T

m) $\sim p$ but (not-q or r) (Logically, "but" is equivalent to "and.")   F
n) r while v and t (What do you think is meant by "while"?)   T

r is true if v and t are true if
$r \Leftarrow (v \text{ and } t)$; if $(v \text{ and } t)$ then r

1.2 Fundamental Concepts

Equality

Equality, indicated by the equal sign "$=$" is one of the most fundamental and most used concepts in mathematics. It is therefore of utmost importance that the student understand clearly what is really meant by such vague but common expressions as: "two things are equal," "given two non-equal things," "given three things, two of which are distinct," etc. The concept of equality implied by such expressions establishes immediately a feeling of contradiction. How can there be *two* objects if they are equal? Equality should mean they are identically the same object. What possible sense can it mean to write $A = B$ indicating that "A" and "B" are identically the same thing, when clearly these letters look different?

You are familiar with the common occurrence of people having more than one name. Some of Gurney Gibson's close associates call him "Gurney." More formal associates call him "Mr. Gibson." His wife affectionately calls him "Gurn." In this sense we would say "Gurn = Gurney = Mr. Gibson." What we have in mind is that, although we have three names, they all name the same man. This is the concept of equality. If some object, a set, a number, a sentence, or whatever, has been designated by the name "A" and also by the name "B," then we say "A is equal to B" or "$A = B$." However, we would not say "A" = "B", meaning that the *names* "A" and "B" are themselves the same things. (Do not confuse the *name* of an object with the *object* itself.) Whenever one writes an equal sign between two characters, it means that the two characters have been designated as names for the same object. It follows that we may interchange any given name of an object for any other of its names. Thus we have the very important logic principle of *substitution*.

1.2-1 Substitution Rule: If A and B are different names for some object, then A can be replaced by B in any sentence involving A without affecting the truth value of the sentence.

You are also familiar with the confusion created when several associates in a crowd have the same name. For example, if the realm of a discussion included both Gurney Gibson and his brother Guy, it would be impossible to consider the name "Mr. Gibson" as being the name of both Gurney and Guy. If you did, you would find yourself writing such innocent statements as "Mr. Gibson = Mr. Gibson" and end up concluding such nonsense as "Gurney Gibson and Guy Gibson are the same person." Due to the lack of a sufficiently large list of convenient symbols for use as names of mathematical objects, it is necessary to use and re-use both the English and Greek alphabets. Nevertheless it is important that, in any given context, not more than one object be given a particular name. It is a common occurrence, however, that a given object may have more than one name. In fact, much of the content of mathematics consists of determining when a given name describes the same object as another name. This is due to the complex nature of some of our naming devices.

The concept of equality and its application, the substitution rule, are simple ideas and you should have no difficulty in their mastery. However, keep in mind that "equality" gives us *only* the substitution ability. Care should be taken not to assume more.

Sets, the Notion and the Notation

Our study of "set theory" will be based on the intuitive point of view. In a sense, we shall study models of set theory, rather than rigorously developing the theory axiomatically. The word "set" will be viewed as an undefined term, and many concrete examples (models) will be considered. In order to illustrate various set properties, we call upon the student's background and experience in using certain familiar number systems, although we intend to study these systems in more detail later. It is hoped that this approach will lead to a sound understanding of the theory, as well as giving the reader an accurate intuition concerning the properties of sets.

A *set* is a collection of objects. The objects in a particular set are called *members* or *elements* of the set. For example, the collection or aggregate of people reading this book is a set of which you are a member. As another example, this book is an element in the set of all books you have seen.

The mechanisms used to specify particular sets vary considerably from one context to another. One may describe a set in many ways, such as using

17

conditions stated in the language in sentence form, or using special symbols of various forms defined for that purpose. To make matters even more exciting, some phrases in the language which seem to describe sets do not in fact constitute legitimate set descriptions. An example of this is encountered in phrases of the type "the set of all sets" which admit contradictions such as the famous Russell paradox, which we shall examine later. One may technically prescribe that this situation does not occur by insisting that a set be a "well defined" collection of objects. This means that if A is to be considered a set, it must be possible to decide whether any given object is an element of A, or is not. However, we expect to know nothing more. That is, we do not consider one element to precede another, nor do we consider an element to be a member more than once. All we ask is that it be possible to determine whether a given object is a member. In practice it may be very difficult to decide whether an object α is an element of A (written "$\alpha \in A$" and read "α is an element of A" or "α in A.") But if A is a set, it must be at least theoretically possible to do so. For example, suppose we consider A to be the "set" of all positive integers n such that ← part of defining condition

$$x^n + y^n = z^n$$

for some non-zero integers x, y, and z. It is easy to see that $1 \in A$ and $2 \in A$, since

$$1^1 + 1^1 = 2^1 \text{ (taking } x = 1, y = 1, \text{ and } z = 2)$$

and

$$3^2 + 4^2 = 5^2 \text{ (taking } x = 3, y = 4, \text{ and } z = 5).$$

But in order for A to be considered a set, it must be possible to decide whether any given positive integer is in A. Is the number "googol" an element of A?§ We don't know. In fact, it is an open question in mathematics at present as to whether A has elements other than 1 and 2, or whether A is even a set! ‖

It should be pointed out that elements of a set need not be numbers. Indeed, elements may be people, cows, ideas, plants, sets, lines in the plane, three-toed Martians, or combinations of these or practically any other objects. Also note that we have not specified that a set necessarily contains any elements! In fact, there are sets which do not contain elements.

One of the unavoidable assumptions needed in a study of sets is the assumption that all the objects which we allow to be elements of our sets

§ Kasner used the name "googol" to express a "very large" number, 10^{100}. Actually, the name was given by his nine-year-old nephew. See Edward Kasner and James Newman, "*Mathematics and the Imagination*," p. 23, Simon and Schuster, New York, 1956.

‖ The famous mathematician Fermat theorized that no non-zero integral values of x, y, and z satisfy the equation $x^n + y^n = z^n$, if n is an integer greater than 2. No proof has ever been shown for this; Fermat himself stated that lack of marginal space in his copy of the Greek mathematician Diophantus' book prevented him from writing the proof. Several prizes have been offered in the past for a demonstration of Fermat's Theorem, one of $25,000. G. A. Miller, "*Historical Introduction to Mathematical Literature*," p. 153, The Macmillan Company, New York, 1916.

should be elements of some *universal set*. (A theory without this assumption would allow paradoxical statements, as we shall see later when we look at Russell's paradox.) When it is necessary, we shall call this universe U, but usually in a given context it is known what constitutes the universe. In such cases, no specific mention is made concerning its existence.

Sets Described by a List

If a set under consideration has relatively few members, one may write a description of it by simply listing names of the members. This list is usually enclosed in "braces".

Example: The set having the numbers 1, 2, and 3 as its only members is indicated by $\{1, 2, 3\}$.

Question: Does the set $\{1, 2, 3\}$ have the same membership as $\{2, 1, 3\}$? Remember that the set concept is a primitive notion for which we have no definition, and that all we expect of a description is that it indicates whether a given object is a member of the set.

Example: Consider the set having the numbers 6 and 7 as its only members. That is, the set $\{6, 7\}$. What can you say about the set $\{7, 6\}$?

Example: Consider the set having only the number 5 as a member, $\{5\}$. (Sets possessing only one member are sometimes called *singleton* sets.)

Example: The set of core memory addresses for a computer can be thought of as a set of numbers, each member of the set designating a particular core unit in the machine (hence the term "address"). For example, in a machine with 8,000 positions of core memory (called an "8K" machine by the people in the computing industry), the set of addresses might be the set described by

$$\{0000, 0001, 0002, - - -, 7998, 7999\}.$$

Example: The set of planets with orbits inside that of earth is the set $\{\text{Mercury, Venus}\}$.

Subsets

Now we are ready to investigate a set concept which can be defined in terms of the fundamental ideas we have discussed up to this point.

1.2-2 Definition: The set A is a *subset* of the set B if and only if every element of A is also an element of B. (This is denoted symbolically by writing "$A \subset B$." If it is not true that "$A \subset B$," we write "$A \not\subset B$.") (The symbol "$A \subset B$" is read "A is contained in B," or "A is a subset of B," and "$A \not\subset B$" is read "A is not contained in B.")

19

Remark: Definitions in general represent complete characterizations of the property under consideration, although commonly the wording used forms a single implication rather than a double implication. For example, our definition above which says

$$A \subset B \Leftrightarrow (x \in A \Rightarrow x \in B)$$

might commonly be written

$$A \subset B \text{ if } (x \in A \Rightarrow x \in B).$$

This can be confusing, so the student should be aware of this tradition. *In summary:* even though definitions in mathematics are often written using "if," they should be translated by the reader to "iff" form. Recall that our unusual word "iff" is an abbreviation for "if and only if."

Let us now consider some sets along with some of their subsets.

Example: $\{1,2,3,4\} = A$, $\{1,2\} \subset A$

$$\{4,3\} \subset A \qquad \{4\} \subset A$$

Question: What other sets are contained in A?

Example: $\{10, 13, 7\} = B$

yes, by def'n. ———→ $\{1, 2, 13\} \not\subset B$ $\{13, 7\} \subset B$ — no, B is a set not an element in a set.

Questions: Is $B \subset B$? Why? Is $B \in B$? Why not?

Example: $N \subset R$, $Q \subset R$, $N \subset Q$, $Z \subset Q$, $N \subset Z$. Recall that we denote by N, Z, Q, R, the number systems known as the Natural numbers, the Integers, the Rational numbers, and the Real numbers respectively.

One of the most common mistakes made by the novice set theorist is to confuse the *elements* of a set with certain of its *subsets*. If $A = \{1,2,3\}$, it is true that $1 \in A$, but false that $\{1\} \in A$. Also notice it is true that $\{1\} \subset A$ but false that $1 \subset A$.

A set may contain# elements which are themselves sets. However, we shall see later that a set cannot be an element of itself.

Example: Let $A = \{\{1\}, \{2, 3\}, \{1, 2, 3\}\}$

$$\{1\} \in A \qquad 1 \notin A \qquad \{1\} \not\subset A$$
$$\{2, 3\} \in A \quad \{\{1\}, \{2, 3\}\} \subset A \quad \{2, 3\} \not\subset A \quad 2 \not\subset A$$

The Empty Set

A useful concept which may at first seem a bit strange is the idea of empty sets. The existence of such an object is assumed (as an axiom) and its uniqueness will follow from another axiom.

Unfortunately, the common use of the word "contains" in set theory tends to lead to exactly the kind of confusion we are trying to avoid! In this instance we should properly use a different word (perhaps "possesses" would be better) since we use "contains" to express the "subset" concept which is different from the "element of" concept. It is, however, popular usage to use the same word in discussing the two different concepts, and the student must determine by the context which of the two ideas is intended.

1.2-3 Definition: Any set containing no element is called an *empty set*. That is, a set A is empty if and only if for every $x \in U$ (the universe) $x \notin A$.

We will assume that such sets exist, and anticipate the fact that there is only one and denote it by "$\emptyset$."

Example: "The set of all pages in this book written in Sanskrit" is an empty set.

We devote the remainder of this section to a discussion of the logic principles involved in the proofs to two theorems concerning the empty set $\emptyset$.

1.2-4 Theorem: For any set A, $\emptyset \subset A$.

Proof: According to the definition, we must show that every element in $\emptyset$ is also an element of A, where A is any set whatsoever. But since $\emptyset$ has no element, it is true that every element of $\emptyset$ is also in A. ☐

Remark: The above proof may at first seem confusing. The argument uses the fact that a false statement implies any statement. For example, the following implication is considered logically valid:

$$(2 + 2 = 5) \Rightarrow (\text{you like mathematics})$$

That is, in the event that 2 plus 2 were 5, then you do like mathematics. Here the false premise "$2 + 2 = 5$" implies *any* statement, and in particular it implies the (obviously true) conclusion that (you like mathematics). The logical structure of the proof is exactly the same: namely, for any set A,

$$x \in \emptyset \Rightarrow x \in A$$

is a valid implication, since "$x \in \emptyset$" is a false premise. (x *cannot* be an element of $\emptyset$, since $\emptyset$ has no elements.) This state of affairs is usually dealt with rather swiftly by the remark, "It is *vacuously* true that $\emptyset \subset A$, for any A." The word "vacuous" refers to the "false premise" type of argument that we used to prove the assertion.

1.2-5 Theorem: $A \subset \emptyset \Rightarrow (A \text{ is the empty set})$.

Proof: A must be the empty set, for if it were not, A would contain elements. But these elements of A cannot also be elements of $\emptyset$, since, by definition, $\emptyset$ does not contain elements. Thus if A were not the empty set, the premise $A \subset \emptyset$ wouldn't be true. ☐

Remark: Note that in order to prove this theorem, we are required to prove an implication of the form:

$$p \Rightarrow q$$

(p denotes the statement "$A \subset \emptyset$" and q denotes the statement "A is the empty set.") The actual proof succeeds in establishing instead the implication:

$$\text{not-}q \Rightarrow \text{not-}p$$

This implication is called the *contrapositive* of the original one, and is considered to be logically equivalent to the former.

For example, to prove

$$\text{it is raining} \Rightarrow \text{the ground is wet}$$

we may instead prove the contrapositive, namely

$$\text{the ground is not wet} \Rightarrow \text{it is not raining.}$$

Thus, the claim in the proof of 1.2-5 is, that by proving

$$A \text{ is not the empty set} \Rightarrow A \not\subset \varnothing$$

we have also proved the logically equivalent implication

$$A \subset \varnothing \Rightarrow A \text{ is the empty set.}$$

Exercises 1.2

1. Indicate at least five elements of the following sets, or indicate all elements if there are less than five.
   a) All integers between 0 and 51, each of which has 7 as its last digit.
   b) All square roots of the number 9.
   c) Shakespeare's plays.
   d) All square roots of 25 that are even numbers.
   e) All numbers which when added to a rational number x produce the sum x.

2. Which of the following are examples of empty sets?
   a) All states in the United States which are larger than Texas.
   b) All integers ending in 2 which are perfect squares.
   c) All living people who were born in the state of Wisconsin before 1800.
   d) All even integers ending in 3.

3. Determine which of the following statements are true and which are false. If false, correct the statement.
   T a) $3 \in \{2, 3, 4, 3, 1, 5\}$
   F b) $\{2\} \in \{2, 3, 4, 5\}$ $2 \in$
   F c) $\{3\} \in \{\{2, 3\}, \{5, 6\}, 3\}$ $3 \in$
   T d) $\{5, 6\} \in \{\{2, 3\}, \{5, 6\}, 3\}$
   F e) $3/4 \not\in \{Q, N, R, 2/3, Z\}$

4. Let

$A_1 = \{1, 3, 4, 5, 2, 1, 6, 5\}$ $A_4 = \{\{2, 5\}, \{5\}, \{6, 7\}\}$
$A_2 = \{2, 5, 6, 1\}$ $A_5 = \{\{4, 6\}, \{1, 2, 5, 6\}, 3\}$
$A_3 = \{5\}$ $A_6 = \{6, 5, 4, 3, 2, 1\}$

Between each of the following sets put in the appropriate symbol ($\in$, $\subset$, $=$, none of these):

a) $A_2 \subset A_1$ f) $A_3 \subset A_1$ k) $A_3 \subset A_6$
b) $A_2 \in A_5$ g) $A_3 \in A_4$ l) $6 \quad A_5$
c) $A_6 \subset A_1$ h) $A_4 \quad A_6$ m) $\{1, 6\} \subset A_2$
d) $\{2, 5\} \subset A_1$ i) $5 \quad A_4$ n) $\{3\} \quad A_5$
e) $\{2, 5\} \in A_4$ j) $\{5\} \in A_4$ o) $3 + 2 \in A_2$

5. What is the difference between $\emptyset$ and $\{\emptyset\}$? Note that writing braces around "$\emptyset$" is not "making something out of nothing," since $\emptyset$ is *not* nothing! (It is, among other things, a set.)

True or false:

a) $\{\emptyset\}$ is empty   c) $\emptyset \subset \{\emptyset\}$ e) $\{\emptyset,\emptyset\} \subset \{\emptyset\}$

b) $\emptyset \in \{\emptyset\}$ d) $\emptyset \in \emptyset$ f) $\{\{\emptyset\},\emptyset\}$ has two distinct elements

6. List all possible subset relations which exist among the sets N, Z, Q, R.

7. a) Let $A = \{2, 1, 3\}$. Find all subsets of A including $\emptyset$ and A.
    b) Let $A = \{1, 2, 3, 4\}$. Find all subsets of A. How many subsets has A?
    c) Let $A = \{1, 2, 3, - - -, n\}$. Can you suggest how many subsets A has?

8. Complete each of the following sentences.
    a) If $A \not\subset B$, then for some $x \in B$, x _____.
    b) If $A \subset B$, then for every $x \in A$, $x \in B$.
    c) If every $x \in A$ is also in B, then $A \subset B$.
    d) If some $x \in A$ is not in B, then $A \not\subset B$.
    e) If $x \in A$ and $A \subset B$, then $x \in B$.

9. A set may have no members. Is it possible then for a set to have no subsets?

10. Use the "substitution rule" to deduce that $a + b \in R$, where it is known that $a = x$, $b = y$, $A = R$, and $x + y \in A$.

11. Let $A \subset U$, $B \subset U$, $A \subset B$, $x \in A$, and $y \in B$.
    a) Is $x \in B$?   b) Can $y \in A$?
    c) Can there be a $z \in U$ such that $z \notin B$ and $z \notin A$?
    d) Must there be a $z \in U$ such that $z \notin B$ and $z \notin A$?
    e) Must there be a $z \in B$ such that $z \notin A$?

12. Let $A \not\subset B$, $B \not\subset C$.
    a) Can there be a $c \in C$ such that $c \notin B$?
    b) Must there be a $c \in C$ such that $c \notin B$?
    c) Can there be a $c \in C$ such that $c \notin A$?
    d) Must there be a $c \in C$ such that $c \notin A$?
    e) Can there be an $a \in A$ such that $a \notin A$?
    f) Do A and C name the same set?

13. Grant Gibson had always felt a little uncomfortable when he ran into mathematical statements which were "vacuously true" until the following incident occurred:

One night Grant came home from the movie at 11:30 P.M. His father met him at the door and told him he was going to be punished. When Grant asked "why?", Gurney explained that he had promised Mrs. Gibson: "If Grant arrives home after midnight, then he will get a licking." Gurney further explained that he had never broken a promise to Mrs. Gibson and that he must make this promise true by giving Grant a licking. Grant explained that he had arrived before midnight and that the promise his father had made would be "vacuously true" if he did not administer the punishment. Gurney agreed and Grant was not punished.

Did Gurney break his promise?

If Gurney had given Grant a licking, would he have broken the promise?

14. Why do you suppose we insist that a set cannot be an element of itself? (*Hint:* Read the next section.)

1.3 Set Descriptions and Form Statements

Form Statements *(open sentences)*

In order to expand our ability to describe sets, we wish to explore a special kind of expression which is very close to being a mathematical sentence, but which is not sufficiently complete to be assigned a truth value. You are perhaps familiar with "fill the blank tests." In playing this game, one is given a "statement form" in which a blank space appears. The "statement form," as it stands, is neither true nor false, but if a word is placed in the blank, it then is either true or false.

Example: "_____ is a man."

The expression is neither true nor false and therefore is not a sentence. However if a noun is selected from a universe of nouns and placed in the blank, the expression becomes a statement (and as such, has a truth value). Thus

"*George Washington* is a man",
"*Gauss* is a man"

are true, whereas

"*Martha Washington* is a man",
"*The White House* is a man"

are false.

We shall very often use form statements (also sometimes called "open sentences") in describing sets. It is traditional to use a letter of some alphabet instead of a blank space in such expressions.

Example: "$x \geq 5$" is a form statement and clearly cannot be determined to be true or false. However, by replacing "x" with a name for some number in the universe of real numbers, we arrive at a statement which is either true or false. For example,

$$\text{"}6 \geq 5\text{"}, \quad \text{"}12 \geq 5\text{"}, \quad \text{"}5 \geq 5\text{"}$$

are true, and

$$\text{"}0 \geq 5\text{"}, \quad \text{"}-7 \geq 5\text{"}, \quad \text{"}\pi \geq 5\text{"}$$

are false.

Let us indicate by "$p(x)$" that we have a form statement over some universal set U. If $a \in U$ then the statement "$p(a)$" is either true or false. Notice that in the expression "$p(x)$," it is not assumed that "x" is a word, but that it is a "hole" or "blank" in the sentence. When we replace the "x" by "a" where "a" names some object in our universe, the situation is quite different. It is typical for the novice mathematician to be confused by not being sure which concept is being used at certain times; however, the context should always make it clear. The "x" used in the form statement "$p(x)$" is called a *variable*. There is no reason to have used the symbol "x" in particular; in fact "y" or even "a" would have served equally well. The very important distinction between a variable being used in a form statement, and the name of an element ✳ of the universal set being used in a sentence, is one that must be mastered well in order to understand mathematics.

Brace Notation

Perhaps the most common method used to describe a set is the method sometimes referred to as "brace notation." In describing a set in this fashion, one has some form statement $p(x)$ over a given universe U. A set is then described by the notation $\{x: p(x)\}$. (Read: "The set of all x such that $p(x)$.") If a is an element of the universe and $p(a)$ is a true statement, then a is in the set. If $p(a)$ is a false statement, then a is not in the set. This descriptive device provides us with exactly the information we desire. That is, the ability to determine whether or not a given element is a member of the set being described. The form statement $p(x)$ in the description is called the "element selector" or sometimes the "set selector." Note the importance of the universal set in connection with this means of describing sets.

Example: Let $A = \{x: x \geq 5\}$. Suppose the universe is R.

"$2 \geq 5$" is a false statement, therefore $2 \notin A$.
"$6 \geq 5$" is a true statement, therefore $6 \in A$.
"$5 \geq 5$" is a true statement, therefore $5 \in A$.

Question: Is $5.001 \in A$? Is $4.9999 \in A$? no. $5 \frac{1}{1000} = \frac{5001}{1000}$

Example: Let $B = \{y: y > 1 \text{ and } y < 5\}$.

"$2 > 1$ and $2 < 5$" is a true statement, therefore $2 \in B$.
"$6 > 1$ and $6 < 5$" is a false statement, therefore $6 \notin B$. $U = R$

Remark: Note that we have not specifically described the universe in this case. You are expected to make an appropriate choice in situations such as this.

Question: How do you feel about the set $C = \{x: x > 1 \text{ and } x < 5\}$? Does $C = B$?   yes.

As was previously mentioned, it is sometimes possible to make a description which seems to describe a set but which does not. On the basis of studies of set theory, some of the unacceptable descriptions have been discovered. The most important fact which you must remember at this level is that a set cannot be a member of itself.

The famous Russell paradox makes this very clear.

1.3-1 (Russell's paradox)*

Let us define a collection M of sets called "normal" sets.

$$M = \{A: A \notin A\}$$

The question arises as to whether the "set" M is normal. We examine the two possible cases.

i) $M \in M$. It follows using the element selector in the brace notation that $M \notin M$.

ii) $M \notin M$. It follows then, since M satisfies the description that it is in the set. That is, $M \in M$,

In either case we arrive at a contradiction. This paradox is avoided if we do not allow the form statement "_____ $\in$ _____." That is, for any given set A, $A \in A$ is not a sentence and therefore has no truth value. Hence the form statement cannot be used as an element selector to describe a set.

The Power Set

Given a universe U, it is often desirable to discuss the subsets of U as being elements of some universe. U is one of the *subsets* of itself, but as we have seen, we cannot allow U to be one of its own *elements*. Thus, we find it necessary to consider a new universe.

1.3-2 Definition: Let A be a set. Then $2^A = \{B: B \subset A\}$ (*i.e.*, 2^A is the collection of all subsets of A). 2^A is called the *power set of A.*

Later, you shall be asked to show that if the number of elements in A is n, where n is some natural number, then the number of elements in 2^A is 2^n. The notation we have used to designate the power set was suggested by this fact.

Example:

$$2^{\{1,2\}} = \{\{1\}, \{2\}, \varnothing, \{1, 2\}\}$$
$$2^\varnothing = \{\varnothing\}$$
$$2^N \text{ is a large set!}$$

---

* Bertrand Russell discovered the paradox in 1903 while he and A. N. Whitehead were writing their "Principia Mathematica." The discovery of this and similar paradoxes has been the cause of a great deal of work and controversy in mathematics.

Exercises 1.3

1. True or False:

   T *a)* $\{x: x \geq 5\} \subset \{x: x \geq 2\}$

   F *b)* $\{x: x \geq 5 \text{ and } x \leq 9\} \subset \{y: y \geq 6\}$

   T *c)* $\{x: x \geq 0 \text{ and } x \in N\} \subset \{x: x \in Q\}$

2. Let $U = R$ and

   $A = \{x: x \geq 3\}$ $B = \{x: x \geq 5\}$ $C = \{x: x \geq 10\}$.

   True or False:

F *a)* $A \subset B$	F *e)* $B \subset C$	F *i)* $A \in C$
T *b)* $B \subset A$	T *f)* $C \subset B$	F *j)* $C \in A$
F *c)* $A \subset C$	T *g)* $5 \in B$	T *k)* $10 \in C$
T *d)* $C \subset A$	F *h)* $5 \in C$	F *l)* $C \in 10$

3. Let $U = R$ and

   $$A = \{x: x \geq 2 \text{ and } x \leq 7\}$$
   $$B = \{x: x \leq 5 \text{ and } x > 3\}$$
   $$C = \{x: x > 0\}.$$

   True or False:

T *a)* $A \subset A$	F *d)* $A \subset B$	T *g)* $A \subset C$ or $C \subset B$
F *b)* $A \in B$	T *e)* $B \subset A$	F *h)* $A \subset C$ and $C \subset B$
F *c)* $B \in A$	T *f)* $B \subset C$	

4. Write a brace description for the set consisting of:

   a) All rational numbers larger than 5. $\{x: x > 5 \text{ & } x \in Q\}$

   b) All real numbers larger than 7 and less than or equal to 12. $\{x: x > 7 \text{ & } x \leq 12\}$

   c) All real numbers whose square minus seventeen is equal to 36. (Can you give a list description of this set?) $\{x: x^2 - 17 = 36\} = \{\pm\sqrt{53}\}$

   d) All rational numbers whose square is less than two. $\{x: x \in Q \text{ & } x^2 < 2\}$

   $\{x: -1 \leq x \leq 1\}$

5. Let $A = \{4, 5, 7\}$.

   $$2^A = 2^{\{4,5,7\}}$$ How many elements are in 2^A? 8

6. Show that $A \in 2^A$. since $2^A = \{B: B \subset A\}$ & every set is subset of itself

7. Why is $A \subset A$ a *statement*, while $A \in A$ is not? a set cannot be an element of itself.

8. Let $A = \{a, b, \{c\}, \{d, e\}, f, g, h\}$.

   True or False:

F *a)* $a \in 2^A$	F *e)* $\{c\} \in 2^A$
T *b)* $\{a, b\} \in 2^A$	T *f)* $\{d, e\} \subset 2^A$
F *c)* $\{a, b\} \subset 2^A$	T *g)* $\{a, b, c\} \in 2^A$
T *d)* $\{\{a, b\}, \{f, g\}\} \subset 2^A$	T *h)* $\{\{c\}, \{d, e\}\} \in 2^A$

9. Let $U = \{1, 2, 3, 4, 5, 7, 8, 9, 10, 12\}$ $A C U$

    $A = \{1, 3, 5, 8, 12\}$ and $B = \{2, 4, 8, 10, 12\}$. $B C U$

Find the subset of U which has the following statement as the set selector (element selector).

a) If $x \in A$, then $x \in B$

b) If $y \in B$, then $y \notin A$

c) If $x \notin A$, then $x \notin B$

d) $x \notin A$ and $x \notin B$

e) $x \in A$ and $x \notin B$

f) $x \in A$ or $x \notin B$

a)

1.4 Sentences Using Variables and Quantifiers

Let us now pause to consider the way in which we use certain expressions in our language. Consider the following example.

Example: "For every animal x in Gurney Gibson's barn, x is a cow."

This sentence, if used in everyday conversation, would probably be in the form: "Every animal in Gurney Gibson's barn is a cow." However, it is necessary in mathematics to use structures of the first type; therefore we wish to carefully analyze the content of such sentences.

In the study of English grammar one often indicates that each word in a sentence is a particular part of speech. Let us indicate each part in our sample sentence.

Prep.	Adj.	Noun	?	Prep.	Noun	Noun	Noun
For	every	animal	x	in	Gurney	Gibson's	barn,

			?	Verb	Art.	Noun	
			x	is	a	cow.	

The question arises as to what part of speech can be assigned to the symbol "x" in our sentence. It seems to act very much like a noun in the second phrase of the sentence. Is it a noun? Is it a pronoun? Is it a verb? Since it seems to be much like a noun, let us ask ourselves what a noun is. A noun is a word which is the name of something. For example "Cleveland" is the name of a city in Ohio. When we see the word "Cleveland," we know specifically which object in the universe it designates. Which specific object in the universe does the word "cow" designate? At first it may seem that it doesn't designate a specific thing, since it does not name a single specific animal. It does, however, name a certain collection of animals, and the sentence, "Bess is a cow," means that a particular cow is a member of the collection. Back to the symbol "x" in our sentence. Does this symbol name a specific collection of animals? Does it refer to a specific animal? With some consideration, you will see that the symbol is not a noun. Perhaps it is a pronoun. Let us examine some sentences which contain pronouns and then decide whether "x" is a pronoun. In the sentence "Grant went to town and then he came home," the word "he" is a pronoun. In the phrase "he came home," the pronoun "he" does not directly indicate a specific person; however, it is known by context that "he" refers back to another word ("Grant") which is a noun and which does indicate a specific object. Next consider the sentence: "The students in the math class took out some fresh paper so they could take an examination." In this sentence, "they" is a pronoun, and the specific item that it specifies in the phrase "they could take an examination" is the set of students referred to earlier. It appears in our sample sentence "For every animal x in Gurney Gibson's barn, x is a cow.", that "x" stands some chance of being a pronoun. Let us examine more carefully the phrase "x is a cow". It is clear that "x" does not refer to a collection of cows, but rather it seems to designate a specific element in the collection. If "x" is a pronoun, we should be able to refer back in the context and determine which object is being designated. We see, however, that "x" only refers back to itself along with some information about it being an element from some given set, but we again do not know specifically which object. We see that "x" is not a pronoun in spite of the strong resemblance. What part of speech then is such a "word"; a word that merely seems to leave a hole, or blank space, in a sentence?

Let us pause to ask a new question which should perhaps have been asked earlier. Does our phrase form a sentence in the traditional sense by having all the proper components (*i.e.*, subject, predicate, and object)? What is the subject of the sentence (if it is a sentence)? What word or phrase is modified by the phrase "For every animal x"? Answers to these last questions will be left for people who study that sort of thing. As for the question about what part of speech to assign to "x" in our expression, we have called it a *variable*. (It is perhaps possible to subject our sentence to the acid test of English grammar and give it a proper "diagram" analysis in the traditional manner. Regardless of the outcome of such an attempt, we will use such structures.)

Let us decide what we mean by such expressions, and clarify some fine points of language which might cause difficulty.

The Quantifiers (Universal and Existential)

You have already seen how we use form statements to describe sets. A form statement $p(x)$ takes on a truth value when the name for some element in the universe replaces the variable in the form. It might be, in some cases, that each substitution allows a true statement. In these cases, we feel that the statement "For every x, $p(x)$" is a true sentence. On the other hand, if for some b in the universe $p(b)$ is false, we feel that the statement "For every x, $p(x)$" is false. In any case, it seems that a truth value can be assigned to the expression "For every x, $p(x)$" in spite of the blanks or holes in it.

29

Example: Let $U = \{4, 2, 3\}$ and consider the open sentence "x is a natural number." We notice that in this particular case every element in the universe makes the statement true. That is,

"4 is a natural number"
"2 is a natural number"
"3 is a natural number"

are all true sentences. Therefore, the statement "for every x, x is a natural number" is also true *with the understanding that "for every x" means "for every x in the universe U."*

Example: Let $U = \{1, 2, 3, 4, 5\}$ and let $p(x)$ be the statement form "$x + 1 \in U$." The statement "For all x, $x + 1 \in U$" is false, since $5 + 1 \notin U$. (However, the statement "For some x, $x + 1 \in U$" is true.)

We call the expression "for every x" the *universal quantifier* and the expression "for some x" the *existential quantifier*. Note that in each quantifier there is a variable, but in neither case could we use the quantifier for a statement form. Let us now describe what is meant by quantified statements being true.

1.4-1 Description: If $p(x)$ is a statement form, then the sentence "For every x, $p(x)$" is called a "universal generalization." If "For every x, $p(x)$" is a true sentence, then it will follow that "$p(a)$" is also a true sentence, provided "a" designates some member of the universe. (Other expressions which have the same meaning as "for every" are: "for each," "for all," and the symbol "$\forall$.")

1.4-2 Description: If $p(x)$ is a statement form, then the sentence "For some x, $p(x)$" is called an "existential assertion." If "For some x, $p(x)$" is a true sentence, then it will follow that for at least one member b of the universe, the statement "$p(b)$" is a true statement. There may be more than one such member, or there may be exactly one. (Other expressions which have the same meaning as "for some" are: "there exists" and the symbol "$\exists$.")

Example: Let $U = \{1, 2, 3, 4\}$. Then the sentence "for some x, $x + 2 = 4$" ($\exists x \ x + 2 = 4$) is a true sentence. The sentence "$\exists x \ x + 4 = 3$" is a false sentence.

We are now in a position to make more concise definitions of "$\subset$" and "$\varnothing$."

1.4-3 Definition: $A \subset B$ iff $\forall x \ x \in A \Rightarrow x \in B$.

1.4-4 Definition: $\forall x \ x \notin \varnothing$
Example: Let $U = \{1, 2, 3, 4, 5, 6, 7, 8\}, A = \{1, 2, 3\}, B = \{1, 2, 3, 4, 5\}$.

"$\forall x$ if $x \in A$, then $x \in B$"

is true since all of the following statements are true:

P   *q*   *p → q*

$$\begin{array}{cc}
\top & \top \\
\top & \top \\
\top & \top \\
F & \top \\
F & \top \\
F & F \\
F & F \\
F & F
\end{array}
\begin{array}{l}
\text{if } 1 \in A, \text{ then } 1 \in B \\
\text{if } 2 \in A, \text{ then } 2 \in B \\
\text{if } 3 \in A, \text{ then } 3 \in B \\
\text{if } 4 \in A, \text{ then } 4 \in B \\
\text{if } 5 \in A, \text{ then } 5 \in B \\
\text{if } 6 \in A, \text{ then } 6 \in B \\
\text{if } 7 \in A, \text{ then } 7 \in B \\
\text{if } 8 \in A, \text{ then } 8 \in B
\end{array}
\begin{array}{l}
\top \\ \top \\ \top \\ \top \\ \top \\ \top \\ \top \\ \top
\end{array}$$

Therefore, $A \subset B$.

Example: Let $U = N$, $A = \{5, 7, 4\}$, $B = \{1, 2, 3, 5, 7, 4\}$.

"$\forall x$ if $x \in A$, then $x \in B$" is true since each of the following statements is true:

$$\begin{array}{l}
\text{if } 1 \in A, \text{ then } 1 \in B \\
\text{if } 2 \in A, \text{ then } 2 \in B \\
\text{if } 3 \in A, \text{ then } 3 \in B \\
\text{if } 4 \in A, \text{ then } 4 \in B \\
\text{if } 5 \in A, \text{ then } 5 \in B \\
\qquad \vdots
\end{array}$$

Even though we cannot list *all* the statements which must be true in order for this generalization to hold, we do need to know they are true. Even with our limited knowledge of the set of natural numbers, we can "predict" that the complete list contains only true sentences. Therefore, we conclude that the generalization "$\forall x$ if $x \in A$, then $x \in B$" is also true, and thus by definition that $A \subset B$. Notice that it is necessary to check only those sentences in the above list in which the hypothesis is true, since any sentence with a false hypothesis is vacuously true.

Example: Let $U = N$, $A = \{1, 2, 3\}$, $B = \{2, 3, 6, 8, 10\}$. *the change*

"$\exists x \quad x \in A$ and $x \in B$" ← *note the implication from to conjunction*

is a true statement since "$2 \in A$ and $2 \in B$" is a true statement; although the statements

$$\begin{array}{l}
1 \in A \text{ and } 1 \in B \\
4 \in A \text{ and } 4 \in B \\
5 \in A \text{ and } 5 \in B \\
6 \in A \text{ and } 6 \in B \\
\qquad \vdots
\end{array}$$

are all false.

In order to prove an existential assertion, we need find only one true statement in the list; however there may be more than one.

Exercises 1.4

1. Let $U = \{1, 2, 3, 4\}$, $A = \{1, 2, 3\}$, $B = \{1, 2\}$.

   True or False:

   F *a)* $\forall x \quad x \in A$ and $x \in B$ T *e)* $\forall x$ if $x \in B$, then $x \in A$

   T *b)* $\exists x \quad x \in A$ and $x \in B$ F *f)* $\forall x \quad x \in A$ or $x \in B$

   F *c)* $\forall x$ if $x \in A$, then $x \in B$ T *g)* $\forall x$ if $x \notin A$, then $x \notin B$

   T *d)* $\forall x$ if $x \in B$, then $x \in B$ T *h)* if $4 \in B$, then $4 \in A$

2. $U = \{1, 2, 3, 4\}$ $A = \{1, 2, 3\}$ $B = \{1, 2\}$

   a) List all the statements which are asserted to be true by the statement, "$\forall x$ if $x \in B$, then $x \in A$." *(limited to converse, ie 1,2,3,4)*

   b) List all the statements which are asserted to be true by the statement, "$\forall x$ if $x \in A$, then $x \in B$."

   c) Is the statement, "$\forall x \quad x \in A$", true or false? Why? *no, $4 \notin A$*

3. Given: The statement,

   "$\forall x \quad x \in A \Rightarrow x \in B$" is true, where the universe is the set $\{1, 2, 3\}$.

   True, False, or Not enough information to decide:

   T *a)* $(1 \in A \Rightarrow 1 \in B)$ and $(2 \in A \Rightarrow 2 \in B)$ and $(3 \in A \Rightarrow 3 \in B)$

   b) $2 \in A$ or $2 \in B$

   F *c)* $2 \in A$ and $2 \notin B$

   d) $2 \in B$ and $2 \notin A$

   T *e)* $(1 \in A \Rightarrow 1 \in B)$ or $(2 \in A \Rightarrow 2 \in B)$

   f) $3 \notin A$ or $3 \in B$

   T *g)* not-$(1 \in A$ and $1 \notin B)$

4. Let $U = R$, the real numbers

   $A = \{x : x \geq 0 \text{ and } x < 5\}$ $B = \{x : x \geq 2\}$.

   True, False, or Not enough information to decide:

   T *a)* $0 \in A$ T *e)* $\exists x$ if $x \in A$, then $x \in B$

   F *b)* If $1 \in A$, then $1 \in B$ T *f)* If $5 \in A$, then $5 \in B$

   T *c)* If $2 \in A$, then $2 \in B$ F *g)* If $0 \in A$, then $0 \in B$

   T *d)* $\exists x \quad x \in A$ and $x \in B$ T *h)* If $-1/2 \in A$, then $-1/2 \in B$

5. Let $U = \{1, 2, 3, 4, 5\}$, $A = \{1, 2, 3\}$, $B = \{1, 2, 3, 4\}$.

   Prove that $\forall x$ if $x \in A$, then $x \in B$ *but $\forall x \quad x \in B \Rightarrow x \in A$ is false.*

6. In each of the following, rewrite it using quantifiers, then determine its truth value.

   a) Every real number is larger than some other real number.

   b) Everyone is related to someone else.

   c) Every man is married to some woman.

   d) Some integer is smaller or equal to every integer.

   e) Every integer has an opposite (a negative) integer.

   f) Some natural number is smaller than or equal to every natural number.

7. Let $U = \{a, b, c\}$ (a, b, and c all distinct)

$$A = \{a\} \qquad B = \{a, b\} \qquad C = \{b, c\}.$$

True or False:

  F *a)* $\forall x$ if $x \in A$, then $x \in B$ and $x \in C$

  T *b)* $\forall x$ if $x \in A$, then $x \in B$ or $x \in C$

  T *c)* $\forall x \quad x \in B \quad$ or $\quad x \in C$

  T *d)* $\exists x \quad x \in A \quad$ and $\quad x \in C$

  T *e)* $\exists x \quad x \in B \quad$ or $\quad x \in C$

  T *f)* $\exists x$ if $x \in B$, then $x \in A$

(Explain why it would change the answers if we had not indicated specifically that a, b, and c were all distinct.)

8. Let $U = \{a, b, c, d\}$ (a, b, c, and d not necessarily distinct)

$$A = \{a, b\} \qquad\qquad B = \{b, c\} \qquad\qquad D = \{a, b, d\}.$$

True, False, Undecidable:

  F *a)* $A \subset B$ F *c)* $B \subset A$ T *e)* $B \not\subset A$

  T *b)* $A \subset D$ T *d)* $D \not\subset B$

[handwritten: cannot decide because "c" may be another name for "a" in which case c) would be true, B ⊂ A]

9. Ask your English teacher to diagram the sentence: "For every animal x in Gurney Gibson's barn, x is a cow."

1.5 Axiom of Extent, Lemmas, Proofs of Generalizations, Uniqueness of the Empty Set

Equality of Sets

    Due to the primitiveness of the set concept, we must decide precisely when we will consider two different set descriptions as a description for the same set. When we are given a description of a set, we expect to determine only whether a given element is in the set described. We feel that if two different set descriptions allow exactly the same elements as members, then they describe the same set. We formalize this by the following axiom.

33

*Axiom of Extent*****

If $A \subset B$ and $B \subset A$,   then $A = B$.

One may feel that this fact can be deduced as a result of the definition for "$\subset$," using accepted substitution principles for equality and accepted valid arguments. However, any such attempt will end in failure. If you think you have such a "proof," you should examine it more carefully, because it is not valid. On the other hand, it is possible to prove the converse as follows:

1.5-1 Theorem: If $A = B$, then $A \subset B$ and $B \subset A$.

Before we attempt a proof of this theorem, let us see precisely what we must show. Under the assumption $A = B$ we need to arrive at two statements:

1) $A \subset B$

2) $B \subset A$

This requires that we go back to the definition of containment "$\subset$." We could proceed directly to prove each of the generalizations above; however, let us first prove a preliminary result which will take less effort to prove and from which our theorem will follow rather easily. When such a preliminary result is used to prove a theorem, the result is called a "lemma." A lemma is logically not different from a theorem, but due to the specialized role the result plays in the development, it is called a "lemma" rather than a "theorem."

1.5-2 Lemma: $A \subset A$ where A is a set. *nothing special about p*

Proof: If $p \in A$, then $p \in A$. (Recall that this statement is true regardless of the truth value of "$p \in A$.")

Hence $\forall x$ if $x \in A$, then $x \in A$.

Therefore by definition, $A \subset A$. ☐
                                                        , see p. 16-17

Let us now use this lemma and substitution logic for equality to prove the theorem.

Proof (of 1.5-1): Assume $A = B$. We know that $A \subset A$, and since we can substitute "B" where there is an "A", we arrive at the statement

$$A \subset B.$$

Also by a different substitution we have

$$B \subset A.$$

"Discharging" our assumption, we have:

If $A = B$, then $B \subset A$ and $A \subset B$. ☐

** In some texts this is referred to as a definition of set equality, but we feel that equality as a logical concept is quite independent of sets. We write "$a = b$" to mean only that "a" and "b" are names for the same object.

Proofs of Generalizations (*Test pattern principle*)

In our proof that $A \subset A$, we made use of a logic device which will be used time and time again. It is extremely important that this method be thoroughly mastered.

Let us consider the problem of proving a statement "$\forall x \quad p(x)$." In some situations, when our universe of discussion is sufficiently small, it is possible to test each member. For example, if $U = \{a, b, c\}$ and if each of the statements "$p(a)$," "$p(b)$," "$p(c)$" is true, then one can conclude that "$\forall x \quad p(x)$" is a true statement. This amounts to saying that there is nothing logically wrong with "trial and error" when it is possible to exhaust all possibilities. It is common to use a computer to check even a great number of possibilities for such "finite" problems. If the problem involves so many possibilities that it is not feasible (if even possible) to check them *all*, we can sometimes formulate an analogous problem with fewer possibilities.

However, very often one wishes to prove a generalization in which U is a very large set. It would then be impossible to test every member of U, especially if the set U had an infinite number of elements. The accepted method of proving such general statements as "for every x in U, $p(x)$" has been called "*the test pattern principle*."†† In using this method, one chooses an arbitrary element b from the universe U and proves by a series of logical steps that "$p(b)$" is a true statement. Clearly, it is not sufficient to prove "$p(b)$" in order to conclude "$\forall x \quad p(x)$," but this is almost what is done. The last step, however, is the most important one, and also the one which accounts for the name of the method. One surveys his proof of "$p(b)$" and concludes that the proof used no special property of the element b, except that b was a member of the universe U. Hence, by using the same *pattern*, one could prove the same result for any given member of U. The conclusion is that "$\forall x \quad p(x)$" is a true statement.

As we proceed, we will give many examples which may serve to make the proof of quantified statements more clear. We will find many occasions to make use of such proofs. It is hoped that the student will soon be able not only to read and understand such proofs, but also to make them himself. *yes!*

It is common practice in mathematics to make proofs of generalizations using this accepted logical method, but without pointing out specifically how and where the method is used. It is assumed that the reader will realize where this logic is being applied and will be able to follow the reasoning. On the other hand, many common phrases are used to alert the reader to the fact that this extremely important logic principle is about to be applied.

Some of these phrases are:

†† "High School Mathematics"—University of Illinois Committee on School Mathematics. University of Illinois Press, Urbana, 1960.

    1) "let x be an arbitrary element"
    2) "let x be fixed but unspecified"
    3) "select an arbitrary element y"

Of course in making use of this "generalization creating" principle, one need not restrict himself to a universe of numbers, but may say such things as:

    1) "let A be an arbitrary set"
    2) "let H be a fixed but unspecified region"
    3) "let X be given arbitrarily"

In fact, if you look closely at our lemma, you will see that we have made a general statement, and have not said anything special to signal that fact. However, it is hoped that the alert reader will realize what was intended. Our lemma, which merely stated that

$$\text{``}A \subset A\text{''}$$

is a general statement which really asserts

$$\text{``for every set } A, A \subset A\text{''}$$

where A is an element from the universe of sets (*i.e.*, $A \in 2^U$).

We are now in a position to prove a fact we have anticipated, namely, we will show that there is only one empty set. We will observe that this is a direct result of the axiom of extent which we elected to accept as a reasonable assumption.

1.5-3 Theorem: If $\forall x \quad x \notin A$ and $\forall x \quad x \notin B$, then $A = B$.
    Proof: Assume that $\forall x \quad x \notin A$ and $\forall x \quad x \notin B$. We must show

$$a) \ A \subset B \quad \text{and} \quad b) \ B \subset A.$$

    a) Let b be a fixed but unspecified element of U.

$$b \notin A, \quad \text{since} \quad \forall x \quad x \notin A.$$

Therefore $b \in A \Rightarrow b \in B$. ("$b \in A$" is false, and as you recall we chose to call any implication with a false hypothesis a true statement.)

Therefore $\forall x$ if $x \in A$, then $x \in B$ (*test pattern logic*).
Therefore $A \subset B$ (*definition of* "$\subset$").

    b) We leave this portion (which is similar to that for *a)*) as an exercise for the reader. $\square$

Perhaps the logic involved in the above proof was slightly unfamiliar, so let us illustrate generalization proofs in a more familar setting.
    Example: Let $A = \{x: x > 2\}$ $B = \{x: x > 1\}$.
    Claim: $A \subset B$
    Proof: Let $a \in A$, a arbitrary.

Now $a > 2$ (*definition of A*),
so $a > 1$ (*property of real numbers*)
therefore, $a \in B$ (*definition of B*).

Thus $\forall x$ if $x \in A$, then $x \in B$ (*generalization, i.e., test pattern*).
It follows that $A \subset B$ (*definition of "$\subset$"*).

Remark: It is crucial that the "general element" x not be assigned a specific value in the above argument. For example, suppose Glenda Gibson is asked to show that

$$\{x: x^2 - 3x = -2\} \subset N$$

(where N is, as usual, the set of natural numbers).
Glenda argues as follows:

"I observe that $1 \in \{x: x^2 - 3x = -2\}$, since the number 1 satisfies the conditions imposed in the description "$x^2 - 3x = -2$" (*i.e.*, it is true that $1^2 - 3(1)^2$ is equal to -2). But also $1 \in N$, since the number 1 is a member of the set

$$N = \{1, 2, 3, 4, \text{-}\text{-}\text{-}\}.$$

Thus I have shown that

$$x \in \{x: x^2 - 3x = -2\} \Rightarrow x \in N,$$

where x was taken to be the number 1."
Based only on this argument, Glenda still cannot conclude that

$$\{x: x^2 - 3x = -2\} \subset N,$$

because she has, in effect, only shown the general statement to hold for a particular choice of x (namely, $x = 1$). An attempt to apply test pattern logic would fail here, since the pattern established uses properties uniquely attributed to the number 1.

Exercises 1.5

1. Show (assume the universe is R)
    a) $\{x: x > 3\} \subset \{x: x > 0\}$
    b) $\{y: y \le -2\} \subset \{y: y \le 5\}$
    c) $\{x: x > 1\} \subset \{y: y > -1\}$

2. Show

    $$\{x: x > 3 \text{ and } x > 5\} = \{x: x > 5\}$$

    (*Hint:* Use the axiom of extent.)

3. Show
    a) $\{x: x > 1 \text{ and } x < 4\} \subset \{x: x > 0\}$
    b) $\{x: x > 2 \text{ and } x < 7\} \subset \{x: x > 1 \text{ and } x < 8\}$

4. Show that $A = \varnothing$ where $A = \{x: x < 2 \text{ and } x > 3\}$

5. What hidden generalities are implied but not stated in the axiom of extent as we stated it? ($A \subset B$ and $B \subset A \Rightarrow A = B$.)

6. Show that $A \subset B$ and $B \subset C$ implies that $A \subset C$. (This is called the *transitive property* of set inclusion.)

7. How would you show that an assertion is false?

8. Using your knowledge of real numbers, determine the truth value for each statement:

a) $\forall x \quad x + 1 = 5$

b) $\exists x \quad x + 1 = 5$

c) $\forall x$ if $x \geq 6$, then $x + 1 > 7$

d) $\forall$ if $x > 6$, then $x + 1 \geq 7$

e) $\exists x$ if $x \geq 4$, then $x + 1 > 5$

f) $\exists x$ if $x > 4$, then $x + 1 \geq 5$

9. Distinguish between

a) $\forall x \quad (x \in A \Rightarrow x \in B)$ and

b) $(\forall x \quad x \in A) \Rightarrow (\forall x \quad x \in B)$

(*Hint:* Construct some example sets A and B where one is true and not the other.)

1.6 Union, Intersection, Complementation, and Venn Diagrams

Let us introduce, in their simplest forms, two operations on sets which will later be generalized. For any given *pair* of sets we wish to determine new sets in certain ways.

1.6-1 Definition: $A \cup B = \{x : x \in A \text{ or } x \in B\}$.

($A \cup B$ is read "A union B" or "the union of A and B.")

1.6-2 Definition: $A \cap B = \{x : x \in A \text{ and } x \in B\}$.

($A \cap B$ is read "A intersect B" or "the intersection of A and B.")

Remark: Note that $A \cup B$ and $A \cap B$ are both sets.

Example: If $A = \{1, 2, 3\}$, $B = \{1, 4, 6\}$, then

$$A \cup B = \{1, 2, 3, 4, 6\}$$
$$A \cap B = \{1\}.$$

Example: If $X = \{3, 4, 5\}$, $Y = \{6, 7\}$, then

$$X \cup Y = \{3, 4, 5, 6, 7\}$$
$$X \cap Y = \varnothing.$$

Example: If $A = \{x : x > 0\}$, $B = \{x : x < 5\}$, then

$$A \cup B = \{x : x > 0 \text{ or } x < 5\}, \quad \text{and}$$
$$A \cap B = \{x : x > 0 \text{ and } x < 5\}.$$

There are many simple properties concerning these set operations with which you should be familiar. We list only a few and prove only two. We leave it as an exercise for the reader to prove the remaining ones.

1.6-3 Theorem. (*Some properties of sets*)

Let U denote the universal set, and suppose A, B, and C are subsets of U.
Then

$\cup$
- a) $A \cup B = B \cup A$ commutative property
- b) $A \cup \varnothing = A$) Identity property
- c) $A \cup U = U$
- d) $A \cup (B \cup C) = (A \cup B) \cup C$ Associative property
- e) $A \cap (B \cup C) = (A \cap B) \cup (A \cap C)$ Distributive property

$\cap$
- a') $A \cap B = B \cap A$ Commutative
- b') $A \cap \varnothing = \varnothing$) Identity
- c') $A \cap U = A$
- d') $A \cap (B \cap C) = (A \cap B) \cap C$ Associative
- e') $A \cup (B \cap C) = (A \cup B) \cap (A \cup C)$ Distributive

Proof: a) $x \in A \cup B$

$$\Leftrightarrow x \in A \text{ or } x \in B$$
$$\Leftrightarrow x \in B \text{ or } x \in A$$
$$\Leftrightarrow x \in B \cup A$$

therefore, $\forall x \quad x \in A \cup B$ if and only if $x \in B \cup A$, which implies that
$A \cup B \subset B \cup A$ and $B \cup A \subset A \cup B$. Therefore $A \cup B = B \cup A$. ☐
Proof: e') $x \in A \cup (B \cap C) \Leftrightarrow x \in A \text{ or } x \in B \cap C$

$$\Leftrightarrow x \in A \text{ or } (x \in B \text{ and } x \in C)$$
$$\Leftrightarrow (x \in A \text{ or } x \in B) \text{ and } (x \in A \text{ or } x \in C)$$
$$\Leftrightarrow x \in A \cup B \text{ and } x \in A \cup C$$
$$\Leftrightarrow x \in (A \cup B) \cap (A \cup C).$$

Hence we have shown both inclusions needed for set equality, and therefore
$A \cup (B \cap C) = (A \cup B) \cap (A \cup C)$. ☐

The reader should have no difficulty in verifying the remaining statements.

Complementation

Next we define a kind of "subtraction" between sets.

1.6-4 Definition: $A - B = \{x : x \in A \text{ and } x \notin B\}$.
    ("$A - B$" is read "A minus B" or *the relative complement of B in A.*)

Remark: If we complement a set *B* in the universe *U* we simply call it the *complement* of *B* and write $U - B = \overline{B}$ or $U - B = \sim B$.

Example: If $A = \{3, 4, 5, 7, 9\}$, $B = \{1, 2, 3, 4\}$, then $A - B = \{5, 7, 9\}$.

Example: If $U = \{1, 2, 3, 4, 5, 6, 7\}$,

and $\qquad A = \{1, 2, 3, 4\}$, $B = \{3, 4, 5, 6\}$,

then $$A - B = \{1, 2\}$$

$$B - A = \{5, 6\}$$

$$\overline{A} = U - A = \{5, 6, 7\}$$

$$\overline{B} = U - B = \{1, 2, 7\}.$$

Example: If $U = R$ and $B = \{x: x > 1\}$,

then $$\overline{B} = \{x: x \leq 1\}.$$

There are many immediate properties of sets related to complementation. Some of these are given in the following theorem.

1.6-5 Theorem. (More set properties)

Let *U* denote the universal set, and suppose *A*, *B*, and *C* are subsets of *U*. Then

a) $A = A - \varnothing$ $\qquad\qquad$ a') $A - A = \varnothing$

b) If $A \cap B = \varnothing$, then $A - B = A$

c) $(A - B) - C = A - (B \cup C)$

d) $(A - B) - C = (A - C) - B$

e) $(A - B) - C \subset A - (B - C)$

f) $A - U = \varnothing$

Proof (of *d*): Let $x \in (A - B) - C$.

We have the following successive steps.

$x \in A - B$ and $x \notin C$

$\Rightarrow (x \in A$ and $x \notin B)$ and $x \notin C$

$\Rightarrow (x \in A$ and $x \notin C)$ and $x \notin B$ ← *by what rule?*

$\Rightarrow x \in A - C$ and $x \notin B$

$\Rightarrow x \in (A - C) - B.$

Upon applying test pattern logic, we have

$$\forall x \text{ if } x \in (A - B) - C, \text{ then } x \in (A - C) - B$$

and so

$$(A - B) - C \subset (A - C) - B.$$

The second inclusion follows by an argument which is similar, exchanging the role played by B and C above. (This idea is often expressed by saying "Without Loss of Generality," or symbolically, "*WLOG*.")

Hence the conclusion

$$(A - B) - C = (A - C) - B$$

for any sets, A, B, and C. □

Venn diagrams

We now mention a graphical device (known as "Venn diagrams") which may aid in gaining an intuitive understanding of statements concerning sets. The idea, is to associate sets with regions of the plane. We try to do this in such a way that certain relationships between the sets under consideration are reflected in the relative sizes and positions of the regions. For example, suppose we are considering two sets, A and B, of numbers (*i.e.*, $A \subset R$ and $B \subset R$). We thus view R as the set of "all" elements in this discussion. That is, R is the universe. The universe R might be associated with a region in the plane (see Figure 1.1). The condition that A and B be sets of numbers (subsets

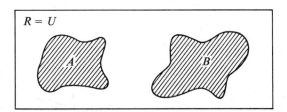

FIG. 1.1 The set R is viewed as the region enclosed in the large outer rectangle. The relationship "$A \subset R$" is interpreted graphically by drawing the region A inside this rectangle; this is done similarly for B.

of the universe R) is interpreted graphically by drawing regions for A and B inside the region representing the universe.

Suppose, in addition, we know that $B \subset A$. Then the diagram can be changed from that shown in Figure 1.1, so as to include this information. This is done in Figure 1.2, where "$B \subset A$" is interpreted by drawing the region "B" inside the region "A."

Example: Suppose the problem under consideration involves animals. Then we can take our universe U to be the "set of all animals." (Do you

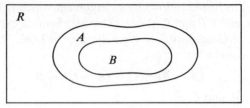

FIG. 1.2

think this description is acceptable? That is, is U well defined? If not, take any convenient set of objects which contains the animals under consideration.) Suppose A is the set of all dogs, B is the set of all cats, C is the set of all mammals. Then the Venn diagram in Figure 1.3 can be used to interpret the following facts:

$$A \subset U \qquad B \subset U \qquad C \subset U$$
$$A \subset C \qquad B \subset C$$

A and B don't have any members in common.

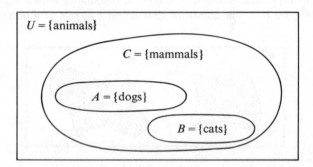

FIG. 1.3

Using Venn diagrams, certain statements about sets are made "intuitively obvious." For example, consider the (true) implication

$$A \subset B \text{ and } B \subset C \Rightarrow A \subset C$$

Using Venn diagrams, we can interpret this by Figure 1.4.

Of course, the usual caution about using graphical devices in formal proofs holds for Venn diagrams. Thus the "diagramatic verification" of the implication is *not* a proof. (The proof should proceed exactly as you did in Problem 6 of the last section, using the definitions involved.)

Figure 1.5 shows a Venn diagram interpretation of the difference $A - B$ of two subsets A and B of U.

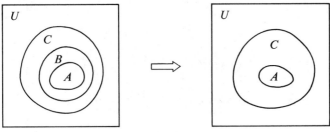

FIG. 1.4

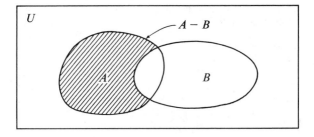

FIG. 1.5   The shaded region represents the set $A - B$.
It contains the elements which are elements of A but not
also elements of B.

A Venn diagram interpretation of the complement of a set A in U is
given in Figure 1.6. The shaded region represents the set of all points (in U)
that are not in A.

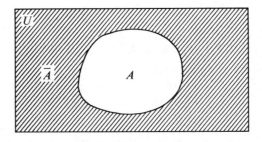

FIG. 1.6   The shaded region represents the
set of all points (in U) that are not in A. Note
that together A and $\overline{A}$ make up U, that is, that
$A \cup \overline{A} = U$.

Venn diagrams can also be used to represent unions and intersections.
Such diagrams are shown in Figures 1.7 and 1.8.

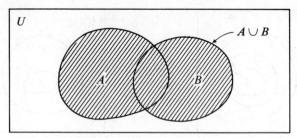

FIG. 1.7 The shaded region consists of points that are in at least one of the sets A and B. Thus the union of A and B is a set consisting of the points in A together with those in B.

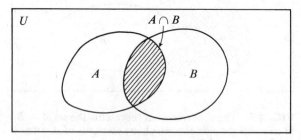

FIG. 1.8 The shaded region represents the set of points that are in both A and B. Thus the intersection of A and B is the set consisting of the points that A and B have in common.

Exercises 1.6

1. Let $U = \{1, 2, 3, 4, 5, 6, 7, 8, 9, 10\}$ $A = \{1, 3, 5, 7, 9\}$ $B = \{2, 4, 6, 8, 10\}$ $C = \{1, 3, 4, 6, 7, 9, 10\}$ $D = \{1, 2, 4, 5, 7, 8, 10\}$.

   Find each of the following sets:

   a) $A \cap B$ e) $A \cup C$ i) $A - B$

   b) $B \cup C$ f) $B \cap C$ j) $A \cap D - C$

   c) $C \cap D$ g) $C \cup D$ k) $(A \cup C) - (A \cap C)$

   d) $A \cap C$ h) $D \cup A$ l) $U - (A \cap D)$

2. Let U be R the real numbers. Let

   $A = \{x : x \geq 3\}$ $B = \{x : x \leq 18\}$ $C = \{x : 3 < x \text{ or } x < -5\}$
   $D = \{x : x < 3 \text{ and } x < 5\}$.

   Give a brace description for each of the following:

   a) $A - B$ c) $A \cup C$ e) $C - B$

   b) $C \cap D$ d) $B \cap C$ f) $D \cup B$

3. Draw Venn diagrams illustrating the set properties given in Theorem 1.6-5.

4. Prove the properties given in Theorem 1.6-5.

5. Draw a Venn diagram which will illustrate that the converse of part e) Theorem 1.6-5 is not a valid inference. (By the converse, here, we mean the set inclusion which would be needed to deduce equality.)

6. Investigate (prove or disprove):

   a) $A \subset A \cup B$ e) $A \subset B$ implies $A \cup B = B$

   b) $A \cap B \subset A$ f) $\overline{A} - \overline{B} = B - A$

   c) If $A - B = \emptyset$, then $A = B$ g) $A \subset B \Rightarrow A \cup (B - A) = B$

   d) If $A \cap B = \emptyset$, then $B \cap \overline{A} = B$

7. Draw a Venn diagram for three non-empty sets A, B, and C so they will have the following properties:

   a) $A \subset B$, $C \subset B$, and $A \cap C = \emptyset$

   b) $A \subset C$, $A \not\subset B$, and $B \cap C = \emptyset$

   c) $A \subset B$, $C \not\subset B$, $A \cap C \neq \emptyset$

   d) $A \subset (B \cap C)$, $B \subset C$, $C \neq B$, and $A \neq C$

8. Show that $\overline{\overline{A}} = A$ for all $A \subset U$.

9. Investigate (prove or disprove):

   a) $A \subset B$ iff $\overline{\overline{B}} \subset \overline{A}$ c) $A \subset B$ iff $\overline{B} \subset \overline{A}$

   b) $A = B$ iff $\overline{A} = \overline{B}$ d) $A \subset B$ and $A = \emptyset \Rightarrow \overline{B} = \emptyset$

10. Define $A \triangle B$ (called the "symmetric difference") as follows:

$$A \triangle B = (A - B) \cup (B - A)$$

Investigate (prove or disprove):

   a) $A \triangle B = B \triangle A$

   b) $A \triangle (B \cup C) = (A \triangle B) \cup (A \triangle C)$

   c) $A \triangle (A \cap B) = A - B$

   d) $A \triangle (A \cap B) = A \cap \overline{B}$

   e) $A \triangle (B \cap C) = (A \triangle B) \cap (A \triangle C)$

1.7 Abbreviations in Set Descriptions and Quantified Sentences. Negation of Quantified Sentences. De Morgan's Laws

Abbreviation Conventions

There are several common abbreviations which are used to restrict the universe under consideration. It is important to understand exactly what is meant when these conventions are used.

1.7-1 Conventions. Let $p(x)$ be a form statement over a universe U, and let $A \subset U$.

Then

    a) $\{x \in A: p(x)\} = \{x: x \in A \text{ and } p(x)\}$
    b) $\forall x \in A \; p(x)$ iff $\forall x \quad x \in A \Rightarrow p(x)$
    c) $\exists x \in A \; p(x)$ iff $\exists x \quad x \in A \text{ and } p(x)$

    Example: Let $U = R$

then

$$\{x \in N: x > 5\} = \{x: x \in N \text{ and } x > 5\} = \{6, 7, 8, 9, \cdots\}.$$

Note that $\{x \in N: x > 5\} \subset \{x: x > 5\}.$

Also $\{x \in N: x > 5\} \subset N.$

    In fact, $\{x \in N: x > 5\} = \{x: x > 5\} \cap N$, and in general $\{x \in A: p(x)\} = \{x: p(x)\} \cap A$.

    Example: Let $U = R$.

     $\forall x \in N \quad 5 + x \in N$ iff $\forall x \quad x \in N \Rightarrow 5 + x \in N.$

    Example: Let $U = R$.

     $\exists x \in Q \quad (3/4)x = 5$ iff $\exists x \quad x \in Q \text{ and } (3/4)x = 5.$

    There are many other common abbreviations. For example, if $U = R$, then

$$\forall x \neq 0 \quad 5 + x \neq 5$$

means $\forall x$ if $x \neq 0$, then $5 + x \neq 5.$

This is a true generalization which would be false if the restriction were lifted.

    Note that the truth of the restricted generalization "$\forall x \in A \; p(x)$" asserts nothing about the existence of an element in A. In fact "$\forall x \in \varnothing \; p(x)$" is vacuously true regardless of the statement $p(x)$. However, if "$\exists x \in A \; p(x)$" is true, then it follows that $A \neq \varnothing$.

Negation of a Quantified Statement

    If $p(x)$ is a form statement then the statement

         not-$(\forall x \; p(x))$ is equivalent to $\exists x$ not-$p(x)$

and

         not-$(\exists x \; p(x))$ is equivalent with $\forall x$ not-$p(x)$.

It follows immediately that

         not-$(\forall x \in A \; p(x))$ iff $\exists x \in A$ not-$p(x)$

and

         not-$(\exists x \in A \; p(x))$ iff $\forall x \in A$ not-$p(x)$.

Example: $\forall x \in R \quad x + 0 = x$ is negated by

$$\exists x \in R \quad x + 0 \neq x.$$

Example: $\exists x \in R \quad 5 + x = 7$ is negated by

$$\forall x \in R \quad 5 + x \neq 7.$$

Open Sentences (form statements) with more than One Variable

We have discussed (form) statements which are incomplete and therefore have no truth value. Some of these are sufficiently complete, however, that by inserting the name of some element from the universe U in a blank space, they become true or false. Such form statements can be used as element selectors to describe sets. Alternatively, the blank space (variable) could be properly quantified and a complete sentence would result.

We now wish to consider form statements in which two (or more) "kinds" of blank spaces appear.

Consider the expression

$$x + y = 6.$$

None of the following assertions can be called true or false:

$$x + 2 = 6$$
$$x + 3 = 6$$
$$3 + y = 6$$
$$2 + y = 6$$

However, each of the following statements has a truth value:

$$2 + 2 = 6$$
$$5 + 3 = 6$$
$$4 + 2 = 6$$
$$3 + 3 = 6$$

If we write $\forall x \quad x + y = 6$, we still do not have a complete sentence because each assertion implied by the generalization is still incomplete. On the other hand, if we quantify *each* variable in some order, we can then determine a truth value. For example,

$$\forall x \forall y \quad x + y = 6 \qquad \text{is a false sentence,}$$
$$\forall x \exists y \quad x + y = 6 \qquad \text{is a true sentence,}$$
$$\exists x \forall y \quad x + y = 6 \qquad \text{is a false sentence,}$$
$$\exists x \exists y \quad x + y = 6 \qquad \text{is a true sentence.}$$

47

Notice that the order in which the quantifiers appear can change the truth value of the sentence.

Let us designate a form statement with two variables by $P(x, y)$. If we quantify one variable, the assertion which results is still only a form statement (in the other variable).

Example: "$Q(x)$" = "$\forall y\, P(x, y)$."

The resulting form statement might in turn be quantified. Then we would have a sentence. Thus,

$$\text{"}\exists x\; Q(x)\text{"} = \text{"}\exists x\, (\forall y\, P(x, y))\text{"}$$

is either true or false.

This would ordinarily be written without the extra grouping symbols. That is, it is understood that "$\exists x \forall y\, P(x, y)$" means "$\exists x\, (\forall y\, P(x, y))$."

There is no need to be restricted to form statements with only two variables.

Example: Let $P(x, y, z, u)$ be a form statement and consider the statement, $\forall x \forall y \exists z \exists u\, P(x, y, z, u)$ which, of course, is understood to mean:

$$\forall x\, (\forall y\, (\exists z\, (\exists u\, P(x, y, z, u)))).$$

Example: Let $U = R$. Then

$$\forall x \forall y \forall z \quad (x + y)z = xz + yz$$

and

$$\forall x \forall y \quad x + y = y + x$$

are familiar statements about operations on the real numbers.

In order to emphasize the importance of the order in which the quantifiers appear for each variable, let us consider another example.

Example: $\forall x \exists y\, x + y = 0.$

The truth of this statement asserts the truth of the following list of statements:

$$\exists y \quad 5 + y = 0$$
$$\exists y \quad -4 + y = 0$$
$$\exists y \quad \pi + y = 0$$

along with many more which are seen to be true. However, if

$$\exists y \forall x \quad x + y = 0 \quad \text{is to be true,}$$

then there is some fixed $p \in R$ such that the following statement is true:

$$\forall x \quad x + p = 0$$

which in turn asserts that the following statements are true:

$$5 + p = 0$$
$$6 + p = 0$$
$$\pi + p = 0$$

and many more. But we know these statements are not all true for the same fixed p.

48

Domains of the Variables

The abbreviation conventions for open sentences of the form $p(x)$ are easily extended to those of the form $P(x, y)$. Thus it is possible to restrict each variable to a specific set.

Example: Let A, B, C be subsets of some universe U, and $P(x, y, z)$ be a form statement over U. Then the sentence

$$\forall x \in A \quad \exists y \in B \quad \forall z \in C \ P(x, y, z)$$

is understood to mean

$$\forall x \ (\text{if } x \in A, \text{ then } (\exists y \quad y \in B \text{ and } (\forall z \text{ if } z \in C, \text{ then } P(x, y, z)))).$$

Here it is said that "x varies over A" or "A is the domain of the variable x." Similarly for y and B, and z and C.

Example: The following are true statements about the universe R.

$$\forall x > 0 \quad \exists y < 0 \quad x + y = 0$$
$$\forall x \neq 0 \quad \exists y \quad \quad xy = 1$$

Another simple but useful convention which we shall employ is illustrated by the following example.

Example: If $P(x, y, z)$ is a form statement in three variables then the following abbreviations may be used.

$\forall x, y, z \quad P(x, y, z)$	means	$\forall x \forall y \forall z \quad P(x, y, z)$
$\forall x, y \ \exists z \quad P(x, y, z)$	means	$\forall x \forall y \exists z \quad P(x, y, z)$
$\exists x, y, z \quad P(x, y, z)$	means	$\exists x \exists y \exists z \quad P(x, y, z)$

Negation of Multiply Quantified Sentences

The negation of a sentence with several quantifiers comes as a direct result of the way grouping symbols are understood to be placed in such sentences.

Example: The following are equivalent statements.

$$\text{not-}(\forall x \forall y \exists z \ P(x, y, z))$$
$$\exists x \ \text{not-}(\forall y \exists z \ P(x, y, z))$$
$$\exists x \exists y \ \text{not-}(\exists z \ P(x, y, z))$$
$$\exists x \exists y \forall z \ \text{not-}P(x, y, z)$$

Thus the overall effect of negation is to replace each "$\forall$" by "$\exists$," each "$\exists$" by "$\forall$," and "P" by "not-P."

49

De Morgan's Laws

It is interesting to note that negation of a statement can be interpreted in terms of complementation of a certain set.

Consider for example, a form statement $p(x)$ over some universe U and the set

$$T = \{x: p(x) \text{ is true}\}.$$

Then the statement

$$\forall x\, p(x)$$

is equivalent to the statement

$$T = U.$$

The negation of the statement "$T = U$", is the statement "$T \neq U$" which is, of course, equivalent to

$$\text{not-}(\forall x\, p(x)).$$

As previously mentioned, this universal statement is negated by saying

$$\exists x\ \text{not-}p(x).$$

On the other hand "$T \neq U$" is equivalent with saying

$$\bar{T} \neq \varnothing.$$

We see that any element $b \in U$ which satisfies $p(b)$ is in T, and if not, it is in $\bar{T}$. That is,

$$T = \{x: p(x)\} \qquad \text{if and only if} \qquad \bar{T} = \{x: \text{not-}p(x)\}.$$

We can use this information to deduce a famous theorem.

1.7-2   Theorem (De Morgan's Laws)

If A and B are subsets of some universe, then

a) $\overline{A \cup B} = \bar{A} \cap \bar{B}$ and   b) $\overline{A \cap B} = \bar{A} \cup \bar{B}$

Proof: $A \cup B = \{x: x \in A \text{ or } x \in B\}$ has as its complement

$$
\begin{aligned}
\overline{A \cup B} &= \{x: \text{not-}(x \in A \text{ or } x \in B)\} \\
&= \{x: \text{not-}(x \in A) \text{ and not-}(x \in B)\} \qquad \text{(why?)} \\
&= \{x: x \notin A \text{ and } x \notin B\} \\
&= \{x: x \in \bar{A} \text{ and } x \in \bar{B}\} \\
&= \bar{A} \cap \bar{B}.
\end{aligned}
$$

Note that the assertion $\overline{A \cup B} = \bar{A} \cap \bar{B}$ rests directly upon the fact that not-(p or q) iff not-p and not-q. This logic analogue of the set theoretic result is also called De Morgan's Law.

The proof for the b) part is left as an exercise. □

Exercises 1.7

1. "Abbreviate" each of the following set descriptions:
   a) $\{x: x \in Q$ and $x > 5\}$
   b) $\{x: x \in N$ and $x^2 \geq 25\}$
   c) $\{x: x \neq 0$ and $x > -5\}$

2. "Unabbreviate" each of the following:
   a) $\{x \in N: x^2 > 7\}$
   b) $\{x \in Q: 0 < x < 5\}$
   c) $\{x \neq 5: x > 2\}$

3. "Unabbreviate" each of the following generalizations:
   a) $\forall x \in N \quad x^2 \geq x$ d) $\exists x < 0 \quad x + 7 = 0$
   b) $\forall x \in Q \quad \sqrt{x} \in R$ e) $\forall x > 0 \quad x + 2 > 0$
   c) $\exists x \in R \quad x^2 = 5$

4. "Abbreviate" each of the following:
   a) $\forall x \quad x \in N \Rightarrow 2 + x \in N$
   b) $\exists x \quad x \in A$ and $6x^3 + 2x - 1 > 0$
   c) $\forall x$ if $x \in Q$, then $x + 5 \in Q$

5. Decide in each case whether the statement is true or false. If false, make it true by a proper negation.
   a) $\forall x \in R \quad x + 1 > 0$ e) $\forall x$ if $x \in Q$, then $5x = 7$
   b) $\exists x \in R \quad x + 7 = 0$ f) $\exists x$ if $x \in N$, then $(1/3)x \in N$
   c) $\exists x \in N \quad x + 1/3 > -1$ g) $\forall x > 2 \quad x - 1 \geq 2$
   d) $\forall x \in N \quad 5 + x > 7$

6. Which of the following are sentences and which are only forms? If it is only a form, make it into a sentence by inserting one or more quantifiers. Indicate whether your sentence is true or false.
   a) $x + y = 7$ e) $\forall x \forall y \quad P(x, y, z)$
   b) $\forall x \quad x - y = 3$ f) $\exists x \forall z \quad P(x, y, z)$
   c) $\forall x \exists y \quad x + y = 9$ g) $\forall x \quad x - y \in N$
   d) $\exists y \exists x \quad xy = 0$
   (In this exercise, let $U = R$, the real numbers.)

7. Given that $U = R$ and $\forall x \forall y \forall z \, P(x, y, z)$, which statements follow as a result?
   a) $P(1, 2, 3)$ d) $\forall y \forall z \quad P(5, y, z)$
   b) $\forall z \quad P(1, 2, z)$ e) $\forall z \quad P(2, 2, z)$
   c) $P(1, 1, 1)$ f) $\forall y \forall z \forall x \quad P(x, y, z)$

8. Negate each of the following statements:

    a) $\forall x \forall y \exists z \ \ P(x, y, z)$ *c*) $\forall x > 0 \ \ \exists n \in N \ \ P(x, n)$

    b) $\exists x \in R \ \ \forall y \in N \ \ xy = 0$ *d*) $\forall x$ if $x \in S$, then $\exists y \ x + y \neq 0$

9. Use the two quantifiers "$\forall$," "$\exists$," and set notation to write sentences which are equivalent with the following.

$$S = \{\text{all sophomores}\} \quad J = \{\text{all juniors}\} \quad P = \{\text{all seniors}\}$$

    a) Sophomores like Greek only if they like mathematics.

    b) Some seniors like Greek, but no senior likes both French and mathematics.

    c) Every instant of the day is after some instant of the day.

    d) Some seniors who like mathematics do not date Glenda.

    e) Some juniors who do not like French date both Betty and Glenda.

    f) If all sophomores like Greek, then some freshmen do.

10. Use the two quantifiers "$\forall$," "$\exists$" along with the standard symbols of arithmetic, and set notation, to write sentences which are equivalent with the following. (The universe is R.)

    a) There is a number which is less than 7 and greater than 3.

    b) Given any number x, there is a smaller number y.

    c) There is no largest number.

    d) There are numbers x, y, and z such that the difference of x and y is less than the product of x and z.

    e) If the sum of two numbers which are neither zero is zero, then one of the numbers is greater than zero.

11. Complete the proof of De Morgan's Laws.

12. Determine in each case whether the sentence is true or false. ($U = R$, the real numbers.)

    a) $\forall x \exists y$ if $x < y$, then $y > 0$ *d*) $\forall x \forall y$ if $x < y$, then $y > 0$

    b) $\exists y \forall x$ if $x < y$, then $x < 0$ *e*) $\exists x \exists y$ if $x < y$, then $y > 0$

    c) $\exists y \forall x$ if $x < y$, then $x > 0$

13. *a*) Write the following sentences using set notation and the symbols "$\forall$" and "$\exists$."

    1) Every boy kissed some girl.

    2) Some girl kissed every boy.

    b) At Glenda Gibson's 16th birthday party which was attended by seven boys and six girls, including Glenda and her brother Grant, "every boy kissed some girl." Which of the following are valid conclusions? If the conclusion is not valid, then state whether or not the statement is definitely false.

    1) Some girl kissed every boy.

    2) Glenda was kissed by some boy.

    3) No one kissed Grant.

    4) Some girl was kissed twice.

    c) At Glenda's 17th birthday party which was attended by the same people that attended her 16th birthday party, "some girl kissed every boy." Which of the following are valid conclusions? If the conclusion is not valid, then state whether or not the statement is definitely false.

    1) Every boy kissed some girl.
    2) Glenda was kissed by some boy.
    3) No one kissed Grant.
    4) Some girl was kissed twice.

1.8 Subsets of the Real Numbers and Their Graphs

Let us now restate carefully some of the properties of real numbers which we stated in Chapter 0.

1. $\forall x, y, z$, if $x < y$, then $x + z < y + z$
2. $\forall x, y, z$, if $x < y$ and $z > 0$, then $xz < yz$
3. $\forall x, y, z$, if $x < y$ and $z < 0$, then $xz > yz$
4. $\forall x, y, z$, if $x < y$ and $y < z$, then $x < z$
5. $\forall x, y$, exactly one of the following is true:

$$x < y, \quad x = y, \quad x > y$$

Graphs

Since we already have in our minds the concept of the real numbers lying along a line, we find it convenient to use figures or "graphs" on a line to represent sets of real numbers, rather than using Venn diagrams or other devices.

Example: Graph the set $\{x \in R: x \geq 2\}$ (see Figure 1.9).

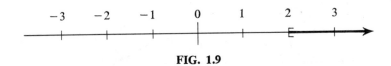

FIG. 1.9

The arrow indicates that the graph extends indefinitely along the line to the right. The squared brace on the left indicates that 2 *is* an element of the set.

Example: Graph $\{x \in R: x \geq 0 \text{ and } x < 3\}$ (see Figure 1.10).

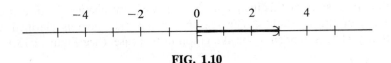

FIG. 1.10

Here the darkened portion of the line indicates the set. The curved brace on the right indicates that 3 *is not* in the set, while the squared brace on the left indicates that 0 *is* in the set.

Example: Graph $A \cup B$, where $A = \{x \in R: x < -1\}$, and $B = \{x \in R: 2 \leq x \text{ and } x \leq 4\}$ (see Figure 1.11).

FIG. 1.11

The use of the real number line to obtain a "pictorial" or "graphical" representation of simple sets of numbers can be quite helpful. Actually, the assumptions involved (such as using a "straight" line rather than a "curved" one and using a standard "unit" distance between integers throughout) are not necessary. On the other hand, these assumptions do not hurt anything, and they do lead to a simple way of associating numbers with points. As an example of how one can use the real number line to gain insight into a problem involving real numbers, let us consider a simple statement about inequality. Suppose we have the (true) statement "2 < 3." In terms of the real number line, this statement can be interpreted as "the point corresponding with 2 is to the left of the point corresponding with 3." (We refer to "the point on the graph corresponding with the number k" as simply "the point k." That is, we consider the number associated with a point to be a label or name of the point.)

Consider the result on the graph when one multiplies a number k by a negative number, say -1 for convenience. The result $(-k)$ is a second point equally spaced from zero. (In this case, we refer to $-k$ as the reflection of k through 0.) (See Figure 1.12.)

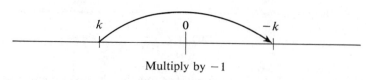

Multiply by -1

FIG. 1.12

Let us return to the inequality 2 < 3. The reader may recall that if we multiply both sides of this inequality by -1, we must change the direction, or sense, of the inequality. The reason for this statement is clarified by observing what is happening on the graph in this case. (See Figure 1.13.)

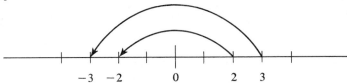

FIG. 1.13 Multiply both sides by -1 (*i.e.*, 2 is to the left of 3 on the graph but -3 lies to the left of -2 on the graph).

$$-3 < -2 \text{ but } 2 < 3$$

In this case it is seen that multiplication (or division) by a negative number results in a reflection on the graph. This reflection results in images that have positions interchanged with respect to the relative positions of the original points.

It should be noted that the use of graphs is to be limited to the role of gaining intuition about, and insight into, the properties of various mathematical objects. The situation here is very much like the role of Venn diagrams, or of the pictorial "constructions" used in plane geometry. One uses these constructions in order to help communicate ideas to others, and in order to gain facility in understanding relationships between the various objects under consideration. The student should realize, however, that the "drawing" of a triangle, for example, is not itself a triangle. It is merely a model, or concrete analogue, of a triangle. The triangle itself is exactly the mathematical object under consideration. So it is with graphs. Solution sets and numbers are abstract mathematical objects having certain properties. Although we may picture the set on a graph, the fact is that the dots we draw are not numbers (they are not even points, for that matter).

All of this is to say that graphs and diagrams are useful devices, but they are not the mathematical objects to which they are analogous. For this reason, one should not attempt to use the pictorial devices in any essential way in proofs or other formal discussions. On the other hand, we do not wish to discourage this kind of thinking. The graphical interpretations very often lead one into a useful physical application of the mathematical objects being studied.

Intervals

Some special subsets of the real numbers are discussed so frequently that they are given special names. These special sets are called *intervals* and are defined as follows.

1.8-1 Definition: Let a, b be real numbers. Then

$$(a, b) = \{x: a < x < b\}$$
$$[a, b] = \{x: a \leq x \leq b\}$$
$$(a, b] = \{x: a < x \leq b\}$$
$$[a, b) = \{x: a \leq x < b\}$$
$$(a, \infty) = \{x: a < x\}$$
$$[a, \infty) = \{x: a \leq x\}$$
$$(-\infty, a) = \{x: x < a\}$$
$$(-\infty, a] = \{x: x \leq a\}.$$

Note that ∞ and $-\infty$ are not meant to be numbers, but rather symbols which, when used in the interval notation, convey a certain idea. We shall avoid writing symbols such as $[-\infty, a)$ and $[a, \infty]$.

These symbols correspond very closely with the techniques used to graph the subsets they name.

Example: Graph the set $[5, 20]$ (see Figure 1.14).

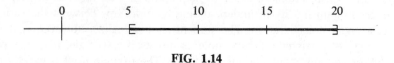

FIG. 1.14

Example: Graph the set $(1, \infty)$ (see Figure 1.15).

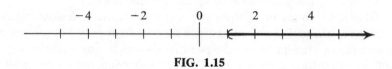

FIG. 1.15

Example: Graph the set $(-\infty, 0] \cup (2, 5)$ (see Figure 1.16).

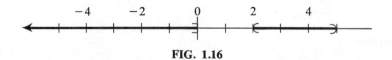

FIG. 1.16

Note: If $a < b$, then $(b, a) = \varnothing$ and $[b, a] = \varnothing$. If $a = b$, then $(a, b) = (a, a) = \varnothing$, but $[a, b] = [a, a] = \{a\}$. One usually avoids discussions involving an interval from b to a, if a is to the left of b.

Assumed Quantification and Solution Sets

A problem that sometimes arises and causes confusion in dealing with variables is the fact that common usage and convenience demands that the explicit designation of some quantifiers and restrictions of the variables be omitted. It is then necessary to realize that the variable is *assumed* to be quantified and to be aware of the understood domain of the variable. It is usually the case that with careful analysis, the context of the material makes the assumed quantification clear. For example, in dealing with the algebra of the real numbers, it is common to see such statements as "$x + y = y + x$" where it is understood that the complete sentence reads "$\forall x \in R \; \forall y \in R$, $x + y = y + x$."

Certain expressions used in mathematics called "identities" provide a common example of implied quantification. To say that the expression "$(x + y)(x - y) = x^2 - y^2$ is an identity" is equivalent to the statement

$$\forall x \in R \; \forall y \in R \quad (x + y)(x - y) = x^2 - y^2.$$

To say that the equation "$3x - 2 = 5$ has a solution" is the same as saying

$$\exists x \in R \quad 3x - 2 = 5.$$

Sometimes, in a discussion, a form statement appears with no quantifier either explicit or understood. In such cases, it is possible that the form statement is implicitly intended as an element selector in a set description. For example, when one says to solve the equation $3x^2 - 4 = 8$, what is intended is to explicitly determine the membership of the set

$$\{x : 3x^2 - 4 = 8\}.$$

This set of numbers is called the *solution set* associated with the given equation.

The task of solving an equation can be viewed as that of trying to find a simpler description of the solution set. For example, suppose we wish to "solve" the equation

$$3x = 6. \tag{1}$$

In the first place, we need to clarify what is meant by the expression "solve equation (1)." The reader has, of course, arrived at "the answer":

$$x = 2 \tag{2}$$

In this case it seems that the job of solving equation (1) is essentially that of finding a real number (or real numbers) which, when multiplied by 3, will yield 6 (provided the variable "x" in statement (1) is assumed to have R as its domain). We claim in this case, that the unique real number which satisfies the given condition is the number 2, so we claim equation (2) as the "answer."

From the standpoint of set descriptions, the task of solving equation (1) can be assigned by saying: "Find a simpler description of the set described by

$$\{x \in R\colon 3x = 6\}"$$

or perhaps more specifically by, "Give a list description of the set

$$\{x \in R\colon 3x = 6\}."$$

In this case, we can describe the set by listing it as

$$\{2\}.$$

Actually we are doing nothing more than claiming that

$$\{x\colon 3x = 6\} = \{2\}.$$

In this case, the list description on the right is called the *solution set* for equation (1). Its member, 2, is called the *solution* of the equation.

Example: In order to find the solution of the equation

$$2x^2 - 3x = 2,$$

we merely describe the set

$$\{x\colon 2x^2 - 3x = 2\}$$

by a list. That is, the solution is

$$\{-1/2, 2\}.$$

Example: Find $\{x \in R\colon 3x < -5\}$. The reader should verify that an acceptable solution set in this case is the set of all real numbers strictly less than $-5/3$ (*i.e.*, the set $(-\infty, -5/3)$).

Remark: Set descriptions are called "equivalent" provided that they describe equal sets. Inasmuch as equations can serve as descriptions of the corresponding solution sets, we can in particular refer to two equations as being equivalent, provided they describe the same solution set. Thus we may say that the equations $5x - 2 = 1$ and $10x = 6$ are equivalent equations. The same remark can be made about inequalities. The usual techniques used in solving equations, such as "multiplying both sides by the same non-zero number" or "adding the same number to both sides" are in fact operations on equations which yield equivalent equations. Thus, since we are seeking the solution set, these operations are used to obtain a simpler (equivalent) equation from which the solution set can be listed or described in simple form.

Example: Solve the inequality $2x - 1 \geq 5$. The solution is

$$x \geq 3.$$

The meaning intended is the following set equality.

$$\{x\colon 2x - 1 \geq 5\} = \{x\colon x \geq 3\}$$

That is, any number which satisfies one description will also satisfy the other.

Solving Inequalities

One of the situations in mathematics in which the set ideas of union and intersection are useful, is in the solution of real number inequalities.

Example: Solve the inequality $(x - 1)/x > 0$. That is, determine the membership of the set

$$S = \{x: (x - 1)/x > 0\}.$$

From real number properties we deduce the following steps:

$\{x: (x - 1)/x > 0\}$

$$= \{x: (x - 1 > 0 \text{ and } x > 0) \text{ or } (x - 1 < 0 \text{ and } x < 0)\}$$
$$= \{x: x - 1 > 0 \text{ and } x > 0\} \cup \{x: x - 1 < 0 \text{ and } x < 0\}$$
$$= \{x: x > 1 \text{ and } x > 0\} \cup \{x: x < 1 \text{ and } x < 0\}$$
$$= \{x: x > 1\} \cup \{x: x < 0\}$$
$$= (-\infty, 0) \cup (1, \infty).$$

The graph of this solution set gives a nice intuitive interpretation of the result (see Figure 1.17).

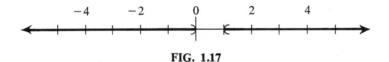

FIG. 1.17

Example: Solve the inequality $(x^2 - 4)/(x - 1) < 0$. That is, give a simpler description of the set

$$S = \{x: (x^2 - 4)/(x - 1) < 0\}$$
$$= \{x: (x - 2)(x + 2)/(x - 1) < 0\}.$$

If we let $A = \{x: x - 2 > 0\}$ $A' = \{x: x - 2 < 0\}$

$B = \{x: x + 2 > 0\}$ $B' = \{x: x + 2 < 0\}$

$C = \{x: x - 1 > 0\}$ $C' = \{x: x - 1 < 0\}$

then by considering all possibilities on a, b, and c for which the quotient ab/c is negative, we see that:

$S = (A \cap B \cap C') \cup (A \cap C \cap B') \cup (B \cap C \cap A') \cup (A' \cap B' \cap C')$

$= \{x: x > 2 \text{ and } x > -2 \text{ and } x < 1\} \cup \{x: x > 2 \text{ and } x > 1 \text{ and } x < -2\}$

$\{x: x > -2 \text{ and } x > 1 \text{ and } x < 2\} \cup \{x: x < 2 \text{ and } x < -2 \text{ and } x < 1\}$

$$= \emptyset \cup \emptyset \cup \{x\colon x > 1 \text{ and } x < 2\} \cup \{x\colon x < -2\}$$
$$= \{x\colon 1 < x < 2\} \cup \{x\colon x < -2\} = (-\infty, -2) \cup (1, 2).$$

(See Figure 1.18.)

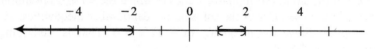

FIG. 1.18

Exercises 1.8

1. Determine in each case a simpler name for the set of real numbers described.
   a) $\{x\colon x + 8 = 7\}$ d) $\{x\colon x^2 + 9x + 20 = 0\}$
   b) $\{x\colon 8x + 2(3 - 4x) = 9\}$ e) $\{x\colon 6x = 7x\}$
   c) $\{y\colon y/3 + y/4 = 13 - 7/2\}$

2. Solve the following equations.
   a) $4 - 2(x - 3) = 1 - (1 - x)$
   b) $(3 - y)/11 + (4 + y)/2 = (1 + y)/4$
   c) $(2z + 1)/(3z - 2) = (6z + 1)/(9z + 2)$
   d) $z^2 - 17z + 70 = 0$

3. Determine a simpler name for each set, and graph the set.
   a) $\{x\colon 5(x - 1) > 6x - 3(x - 2)\}$
   b) $\{x\colon 9 - 3(2x + 4) < x/2 - (3x + 1)/3\}$
   c) $\{x\colon 4x + 5 > 2x - 7\}$
   d) $\{x\colon (5 - 3x)/7 < (x + 5)/9\}$
   e) $\{x\colon x^2 + 25 - 10x \geq 0\}$

4. Solve each of the following inequalities and graph the solution set.
   a) $(x - 8)(x + 7) > 0$ d) $(z - 2)(z + 3)/z < 0$
   b) $x(x + 4) > 3 + 3(9 + x)$ e) $(2x - 3)/(x + 4) > 0$
   c) $(2y + 3)/(3y - 3) \leq 0$ f) $(3x - 1)/(2x + 3)(7x) < 0$

5. Determine the proper quantifiers in the following statements. (Is the statement an equation, an identity, or a restricted identity?)
   a) $x + 2 = 2 + x$ d) $(x^2 + 3x)x^2 = x^4 + 3x^3$
   b) $(x + 2)/x = 1 + 2/x$ e) $\dfrac{x^3 - x^2 - x - 1}{x - 1} = x^2 + 2x + 1$
   c) $(x^2 - 4)/(x - 2) = x + 2$ f) $x^2 - 3x = x$

6. Graph the following sets:
   a) $[2, 7]$ e) $(4, 5) \cap [5, 6)$
   b) $(-\infty, 9)$ f) $(-\infty, 9] \cap [0, 12)$
   c) $[0, \infty)$ g) $([-4, 2) \cup (3, 5)) \cap (-2, 6)$
   d) $[-5, -3] \cup [2, 7)$

7. Solve and graph the solution set:

   a) $(x - 3)(x + 4)/(2x - 3) \leq 0$

   b) Notice that at $x = 3$, $x = -4$, and $x = 3/2$, something critical happens with regard to real numbers being in or out of the set. Can you generalize this?

8. Solve and graph the solution set:

   a) $(x - 1)(x + 2) \leq 0$ d) $(x^2 - 1)(x + 2) < 0$

   b) $(2x - 3)(x - 1) \geq 0$ e) $(x - 3)(x + 3)(x - 1) < 0$

   c) $2(x - 4)(2x + 1) < 0$ f) $(3x - 1)(2x - 4)/3(x + 1) \geq 0$

9. Solve and graph the solution set:

   a) $12x^2 - 2x - 2 > 0$ b) $10x^2 - 3x - 1 \leq 0$

10. Show that $\overline{(-\infty, a]} = (a, \infty)$.

1.9 Cartesian Products

In this section we will introduce a "multiplication" operation on sets. The result will be a set, although not of the same "kind" as the original sets entering into the product. A large part of the work of mathematics concerns such "product sets," so we shall discuss notation and terminology associated with them. Before we can discuss product sets, we must introduce the preliminary concept of an ordered pair.

Ordered Pairs

With respect to the primitive set idea, there is no concept of an assignment of the order in which the elements appear. The idea of order is fairly fundamental, so we would like to introduce objects which are somewhat like sets, but have additional properties concerning order. We could, if we wished, begin in somewhat the same way we did with sets. That is, we could describe what we have in mind and then accept it as a primitive concept. However, we prefer to keep the primitive notions at a minimum, and whenever possible define new structures or ideas in terms of what we have already developed. The following definition is made for the purpose of constructing objects which we will call "ordered pairs." The definition interests us primarily because it allows us to define the "ordered pair" in terms of previous notions, without introducing a new undefined term. What we really are interested in is a property they possess, allowing us to introduce the concept of order.

1.9-1 Definition: The *ordered pair* (a, b) is defined by:

$$(a, b) = \{\{a\}, \{a, b\}\}.$$

Remark: "*a*" is called the first component and "*b*" is called the second component of the ordered pair (a, b).

We leave it as an exercise to show that ordered pairs have the following property, and emphasize the fact that this definition is useful only in that we have avoided the introduction of another primitive notion.

1.9-2 Theorem: An ordered pair is ordered. That is:

$$(x, y) = (a, b) \qquad \text{if and only if} \qquad x = a \text{ and } y = b.$$

The proof is left as an exercise.

1.9-3 Definition: The Cartesian Product (or simply the product) $A \times B$ of two sets A and B is the *set* described by:

$$A \times B = \{(a, b): a \in A \text{ and } b \in B\}$$

Note that in taking the product of two sets, we obtain the set of all ordered pairs that can be formed in the manner indicated in the definition. Each ordered pair (a, b) is made up of two components, one from each set entering into the product, in a certain order (hence the name *ordered* pair).

Example: $\{1, 2\} \times \{1, 4\} = \{(1, 1), (1, 4), (2, 1), (2, 4)\}$

$\{1\} \times \{2, 3\} = \{(1, 2), (1, 3)\}$.

Example: Note that $\{\text{Gurney}\} \times \{\text{Gibson}\} = \{(\text{Gurney, Gibson})\}$ while $\{\text{Gibson}\} \times \{\text{Gurney}\} = \{(\text{Gibson, Gurney})\}$. Thus we see that apparently in general

$$A \times B \neq B \times A$$

since the ordered pairs (Gurney, Gibson) and (Gibson, Gurney) are not the same.

Example: $\{1, 2, k\} \times \{*, 5\} = \{(1, *), (2, *), (k, *), (1, 5), (2, 5), (k, 5)\}$ where it is assumed, of course, that "1," "2," "*k*," " * ," and "5" are the names of elements from some acceptable universe.

Now, an interesting situation arises when one of the sets entering into a product is itself a product. Suppose, for example, that three sets of integers are given as follows:

$$A = \{1\}$$
$$B = \{2, 3\}$$

and $$C = \{3, 4\}$$

Since $A \times B = \{(1, 2), (1, 3)\}$ is a set, it is perfectly acceptable to write

$$(A \times B) \times C = \{(1, 2), (1, 3)\} \times \{3, 4\}$$

so that the result will be a set consisting of four ordered pairs.

It might be of interest to investigate some of the products that can be formed using the sets A, B, and C introduced above. Some of the possible products among these sets are listed below.

a) $A \times B = \{(1, 2), (1, 3)\}$

$b)$ $(A \times B) \times C = \{(1, 2), (1, 3)\} \times \{3, 4\}$
$$= \{((1, 2), 3), ((1, 2), 4), ((1, 3), 3), ((1, 3), 4)\}$$

$c)$ $B \times C = \{(2, 3), (2, 4), (3, 3), (3, 4)\}$

$d)$ $A \times (B \times C) = \{(1, (2, 3)), (1, (2, 4)), (1, (3, 3)), (1, (3, 4))\}$

Note that we do not have the "associativity property" for product sets. (That is, $(A \times B) \times C$ isn't the same as $A \times (B \times C)$.)

Since various sets of ordered pairs are of such great importance, there is a great deal of terminology and notation used in connection with them. We have mentioned before that it is often convenient to assume the objects in a given discussion all belong to some set; the *universal set*. That is, if U denotes the universal set, then in a discussion of sets A and B we assume that $A \subset U$ and $B \subset U$. However, if this is the case, the set $A \times B$ is not a subset of the universal set U. It seems that the corresponding universal set containing such product sets might be taken to be $U \times U$ or some other "large" set of ordered pairs. In doing this, apparently we have two "universes" in our discussion—one being U, the universe containing the members of A, B, and similar sets; the other being $U \times U$ containing the members of $A \times B$ and possibly other ordered pairs. In order to aid in the problem of conveying information concerning whether a set T is in the universe of elements a, b, c, etc., or in the universe of ordered pairs (a, b), (c, b), etc., we make the following definition.

1.9-4 Definition: A subset of a product set $A \times B$ is called a *relation in $A \times B$*, or simply a *relation* if the context makes the universe $A \times B$ understood.

Note that calling a set T a "relation" identifies it as being a subset of the product universal set $A \times B$. Note also that *any* subset of $A \times B$ is by definition, a relation. Thus, in general, there may be many distinct relations in a given universal set $A \times B$.

Example: Suppose $A = \{1, 2\}$ and $B = \{2, 4, 6, 8\}$.

Then $R_1 = \{(1, 6)\}$

$R_2 = \{(2, 2), (2, 4), (2, 6), (2, 8)\}$

$R_3 = \varnothing$

$R_4 = \{(1, 4), (2, 4)\}$

all are relations in $A \times B$. In fact, in this particular case there are $2 \cdot 4 = 8$ distinct ordered pairs in $A \times B$, so that it is possible to determine $2^8 = 256$ distinct relations in this product universal set!

Suppose we have a relation T in $A \times B$. We know that T is a subset of $A \times B$, although we don't know how large it is. It might be a $A \times B$ itself (for $A \times B$ is a subset of $A \times B$), or it might be $\varnothing$ (recall that $\varnothing$ is a subset of any set). These two relations ($A \times B$ and $\varnothing$) are relatively uninteresting subsets of $A \times B$, and they are often called the *trivial relations*. Besides the trivial relations, we will have occasion to consider several other special kinds of relations, such as *order relations, functions,* and *equivalence relations.* Before doing so, however, we return to our consideration of the sets A and B as "universes" in addition to the universe $A \times B$.

We note that (by definition) the first component of an ordered pair in any relation $T \subset A \times B$ must come from the set A, while the second component comes from the set B. Thus, A serves as a "universal set" for the first components of the members of any relation in $A \times B$, while B serves as a "universe" for the second components of the members of any relation in $A \times B$. In discussing relations, it is helpful to distinguish between these "universes" by giving them special names.

1.9-5 Definition: Given a relation T in $A \times B$, the *domain* of T is the set

$$D_T = \{a: (a, b) \in T \text{ for some } b \in B\}.$$

The *range* of T is the set

$$R_T = \{b: (a, b) \in T \text{ for some } a \in A\}.$$

Remarks: Note that $D_T \subset A$ and $R_T \subset B$.

Note that $T \subset D_T \times R_T$. (Why not equality?)

Note that, in particular, we might have $A = B$. (In fact, this is the case in many important applications of relations.)

Example: Suppose $U = \{p, q, r\}$. Then

$$M = \{(p, q), (p, r), (q, r)\}$$

is a relation in $U \times U$. The domain and range of this relation are

$$D_M = \{p, q\}$$

and

$$R_M = \{q, r\}$$

respectively.

Example: Given $U = \{1, 2, 3, \cdots, 10\}$. Define the relation T in $U \times U$ by the description

$$T = \{(a, b): a = b + 2\}.$$

(Let "$\#(S)$" denote the number of distinct elements in a set S.) The reader should verify each of the following:

a) $\#(T) = 8$ b) $\#(D_T) = \#(R_T)$ c) $D_T \neq R_T$

     d) $D_T \neq U$ e) $R_T \neq U$

(*Hint:* You might find it helpful to describe T by a list.)

Form statements with two variables make excellent element selectors in descriptions of sets of ordered pairs.

Example: Let $S = \{(x, y): x + y = 6\}$, $S \subset R \times R$, and some of the elements of S are

$$\{(3, 3), (4, 2), (2, 4), (5, 1), \cdots\}.$$

For any given ordered pair (a, b) in $R \times R$, it can be determined whether the statement "$a + b = 6$" is true or false.

For instance,   "$2 + 3 = 6$" is false; therefore $(2, 3) \notin S$

"$4 + 2 = 6$" is true; therefore $(4, 2) \in S$.

Very often in discussing certain relations, the following notation is useful.

1.9-6 Notation Convention: Let T be a relation between A and B (*i.e.,* $T \subset A \times B$). Then aTb means $(a, b) \in T$. ("aTb" is read "a is T-related to b," or simply "a is T to b.")

Example: Consider the "$<$" relation in $R \times R$.

$3 < 5, 3 < 7$, and $2 < 7$ means that the ordered pairs $(3, 5)$, $(3, 7)$, and $(2, 7)$ are all elements of the relation $<$.

Question: What are some other members of $<$?

An important and useful concept is the idea of the "inverse" of a relation.

1.9-7 Definition: If T is a relation in $A \times B$, then the relation in $B \times A$ defined by:

$$T^{-1} = \{(y, x): (x, y) \in T\}$$

is called *T-inverse* or the *inverse of T*.

Note that T^{-1} is formed by interchanging the first and second components in all the ordered pairs in T. Thus,

$$D_{T^{-1}} = R_T \qquad \text{and} \qquad R_{T^{-1}} = D_T.$$

Example: Let $A = \{1, 2, 5\}$, $B = \{3, 4\}$, and let $T = \{(1, 3), (1, 4), (5, 4)\}$. Then

$$T^{-1} = \{(3, 1), (4, 1), (4, 5)\}.$$

Example: Suppose $A = \{\text{John, Grant}\}$ and $B = \{\text{Grant}\}$ and let $T = \{(\text{John, Grant})\}$

then
$$T^{-1} = \{(\text{Grant, John})\}.$$

Question: Would it ever be possible to have $T = T^{-1}$?

In the remainder of this section, we investigate the particular case of two sets of real numbers entering into a product. The question arises as to what kind of graphical interpretation can be made for the product, given the "real line" graphs of the sets entering into the product.

Suppose, for example, that the following two sets are under consideration:

$$A = \{2, 4, 6, 8\} \qquad B = \{1\}$$

Now suppose the graphs of A and B are sketched in the usual manner (see Figure 1.19). A list for $A \times B$ is:

$$A \times B = \{(2, 1), (4, 1), (6, 1), (8, 1)\}$$

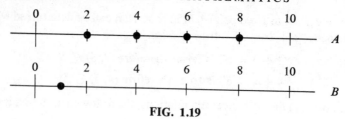

FIG. 1.19

We want to "combine" the individual graphs of A and B in some manner to get a graphical representation of the product set $A \times B$. This could be done in many ways, but we discuss here only two of these. One way to graphically represent the ordered pair (2, 1) (for example) would be to draw a line (or arrow) between the corresponding points on the two number lines. Using this scheme, a "graph" of $A \times B$ would appear as in Figure 1.20.

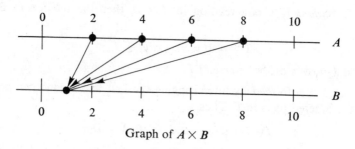

Graph of $A \times B$

FIG. 1.20

This scheme is often used in association with the notion of "mappings," where the arrows are supposed to indicate how each point of A is mapped onto some particular point of B. We shall make limited use of this scheme of graphing $A \times B$, since if A and B have many elements, the mass of arrows involved would tend to be confusing (if not impossible). Later, we will have occasion to return to mappings.

A more workable scheme of graphing product sets of the form $A \times B$ is to make use of the *Cartesian Coordinate System*. In this system, we avoid the necessity of joining the elements of A to elements of B by arrows. The idea is to form the two lines upon which A and B are graphed at right angles, intersecting at the zero points of both lines (see Figure 1.21).

The elements of $A \times B$ are then graphed as points of intersection of lines (sometimes called *lattice lines*) parallel to the real number lines upon which A and B are graphed. In this way, one sets up a correspondence between certain points in the plane and ordered pairs in the product set $A \times B$.

Remark: Actually, the Cartesian coordinate system can be viewed as

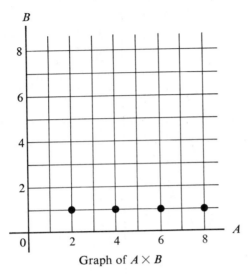

Graph of $A \times B$

FIG. 1.21

setting up a correspondence between the "plane" and $R \times R$. It is to be again emphasized that the dots we place on a sheet of paper are merely to serve as *representations* of points in the plane. Strictly speaking, we shouldn't refer to dots, lines, etc., drawn on the paper as *graphs:* they are merely visual representations, or *sketches* of the true (idealistic) graphs. The term *graph* is then reserved to designate the set of points in the plane which correspond with the ordered pairs of real numbers in the product set (through the correspondence defined by our coordinate system).

There is no reason why one couldn't use other schemes (coordinate systems) to set up a correspondence between points in the plane and ordered pairs of real numbers (*i.e.*, elements of $R \times R$). For example, one could set up a system in which the lines do not intersect at right angles, or in which the lines are replaced by curves of some sort, or other variations as well. We shall see later that other systems *are* commonly used, and that there are good reasons to use the Cartesian coordinate system in many cases.

There is some terminology associated with the coordinate system we have introduced which is considered standard. We mention here some of the most commonly used terms. The real number lines upon which A and B are graphed are called *axes*. The intersection of the axes (*i.e.*, the point corresponding to the pair $(0, 0)$) is the *origin*. The four parts of the plane separated by the axes are *quadrants*. These quadrants are numbered I, II, III, and IV, as shown in Figure 1.22.

The point in the plane corresponding with the ordered pair (a, b) is called "the point (a, b)," and the numbers a and b are called coordinates of the point. In particular, a is called the *abscissa* and b the *ordinate*. Finally, as

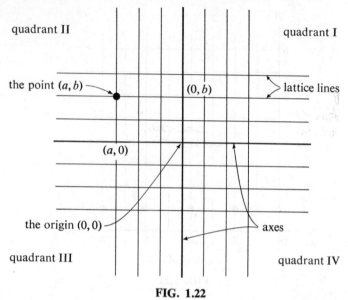

FIG. 1.22

remarked above, the array associated with the elements of $A \times B$ is called the *graph* of $A \times B$ (or more precisely, a *sketch* of the graph of $A \times B$).

Confusion in a Precise Subject

As you may have noticed, we have used the notation "(a, b)" to denote an ordered pair and also to denote a particular set of real numbers where a and b are real numbers. This may seem to introduce confusion into a subject in which precision is our major concern. However, due to the lack of a sufficiently large collection of parenthetical marks (marks like "(", "{", "[", "⟨") we are forced to use the ones we have to indicate a great many things. This often results in the kind of confusion we seem to have introduced here. It is hoped, however, that whenever a given symbol could mean any one of several things, the alternatives will be sufficiently different in character that the context will make it clear just which mathematical object or concept is intended.

Example: If we write "$[(1, 2) \cup (5, 6)] \times [2, 4]$" it may not at first be clear whether "$(1, 2)$" is to indicate the ordered pair with first component 1 and second component 2 or the set $\{x: 1 < x < 2\}$. However, since the union of two ordered pairs holds no particular interest for us, we conclude that an interval is intended. Also, note that the brackets "[ ]" in the expression "$[(1, 2) \cup (5, 6)]$" are intended only as grouping symbols, while in the interval notation "[2, 4]" they indicate that the end points are included in the interval.

The novice mathematician may at first be somewhat bewildered by this imprecision, but will soon learn to appreciate the difficulty which has been avoided; namely, that of creating a huge collection of distinct symbols.

Exercises 1.9

1. We have stated that the precise definition for an ordered pair was a device used solely to avoid the introduction of a new undefined term. Why is it desirable to avoid new undefined terms whenever possible?

2. Let $A = \{3, 4, 5\}$, $B = \{1, 2, 3\}$.
    List and graph $A \times B$.

3. If $A \times B = \{(1, 1), (2, 5), (3, 4), (9, 1), (1, 5), (9, 5)\}$, then find A and B. (Double check this. This is a trick question!)

4. Let $T = \{(1, 1), (1, 5), (1, 3), (4, 4), (4, 5)\}$. Find T^{-1}. Graph T and T^{-1}. Describe the sets D_T, $D_{T^{-1}}$, R_T, $R_{T^{-1}}$.

5. What is the difference between the set $\{1, 3\}$ and the ordered pair $(1, 3)$?

6. Let $A = \{x : 2 \le x \le 3\}$, $B = \{x : 0 \le x \le 2\}$. Graph $A \times B$ and $B \times A$. Note that $A \subset R$ and $B \subset R$.

7. Let $A = \{x : -1 \le x \le 2\}$, $B = \{x : 0 < x < 3\}$. Graph $A \times B$ and $B \times A$.

8. Graph:
    a) $[-1, 2] \times [0, 4]$
    b) $(0, 3) \times (0, 3)$
    c) $[1, 2] \times [2, 3]$
    d) $[2, 3] \times [1, 2]$
    e) $[(1, 2) \cup (3, 4)] \times (1, 3)$
    f) $(0, \infty) \times [1, 2]$
    g) $[0, 2] \times (-\infty, 1)$

9. a) Prove that $A \times B = B \times A \Rightarrow A = B$ provided $A \ne \varnothing$ and $B \ne \varnothing$. What if $A = \varnothing$ or $B = \varnothing$?
    b) Is it possible to find a set M such that $M \times M = M$?

10. Show that $A = B \Rightarrow A \times B = B \times A$.

11. How many elements are there in $A \times B$ if A contains m elements and B contains n? Why?

12. Show that $A \subset X \Rightarrow A \times B \subset X \times B$.

13. a) List all four-element relations in $A \times B$ where $A = \{1, 2, 3\}$ and $B = \{4, 5\}$.
    b) List all five-element relations in $A \times B$.

14. Let $A = \{1, 2, 3, 4\}$ $B = \{3, 4, 5, 6\}$.
    List the ordered pairs in T where T is completely described by:
    a) 1T4, 2T5, 2T6.
    b) 4T6, 4T3, 3T3, 2T3.
    c) 1T3, 2T4, 3T5, 4T6.
    d) 1T3, 2T3, 3T6.
    How many relations are there in $A \times B$?

15. Graph each of the following relations and their inverses in $R \times R$ and find their domains and ranges:

  a) $f_1 = \{(x, y): x \in (-3, 5] \text{ and } y = 2x\}$
  b) $f_2 = \{(x, y): y \in (-6, 5) \text{ and } y = x^2\}$
  c) $f_3 = \{(x, y): x \in [-3, -2) \text{ and } y = x^3\}$

16. Prove that ordered pairs are ordered, using the following sequence of steps. Let $\{A, B\} = \{C, D\}$ where A, B, C and D are sets.

  a) Show that $A \cap B = C \cap D$.
  b) Show that $A \cup B = C \cup D$.
  c) Apply a) and b) to the sets $\{\{x\}, \{x, y\}\} = \{\{a\}, \{a, b\}\}$.
  d) Conclude that if $(x, y) = (a, b)$ then $x = a$ and $y = b$.

1.10 Relations and Their Properties

A reasonable question which one might ask is: "Why call a set of ordered pairs a relation?" A relation is a subset of $A \times B$. Sometimes it is called a "relation between A and B" or a "relation from A to B." A given relation $T \subset A \times B$ describes a certain connection between elements in A with elements in B.

Example: Let $A = \{1, 2, 3\}$ $B = \{4, 5, 6, 7\}$

and let $\qquad\qquad T = \{(1, 4), (1, 5), (3, 7)\}$.

This simple relation can be "diagramed" as in Figure 1.23.

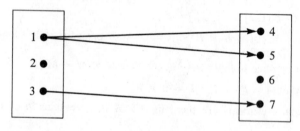

FIG. 1.23

Here we might say that 1 in A is "related" to 4 and to 5 in B, and that 3 in A is "related" to 7 in B, where "related" means with respect to the relation T. We see that 2 in A and 6 in B are not related to anything by the relation T.

It is possible for every element in A to be related to every element in B. This relation is given by the trivial relation $A \times B$. On the other hand, the trivial relation $\varnothing$ between A and B is the relation in which everything in A is related to nothing in B. (Or is it, nothing in A is related to everything in B?)

1.10-1 Definition: Let $T \subset A \times B$ and let $S \subset A$. Then

$$T[S] = \{y \in B: \exists x \in S \ (x, y) \in T\}.$$

($T[S]$ is called the *trace* of S under T or the *image set* of S through T.)

Example: Let $A = \{1, 2, 3, 4\}$, $B = \{5, 9, 11, 8\}$,

$$T = \{(1, 5), (1, 9), (2, 9), (3, 5), (3, 11)\},$$

$$S_1 = \{1, 2, 4\}, \quad \text{and} \quad S_2 = \{2, 3\}.$$

Then

$$T[S_1] = \{5, 9\} \quad \text{and} \quad T[S_2] = \{9, 5, 11\}.$$

Further,

$$T[\{1\}] = \{5, 9\}, \quad T[\{2\}] = \{9\}, \quad \text{and}$$

$$T[\{3\}] = \{5, 11\}.$$

Example: Let $A = [0, 1]$, $B = [0, 1]$, and

$$T = \{(x, y): y = 7x\} \cup \{(x, y): y = x - 1/2\}.$$

The graph of T is given by Figure 1.24.

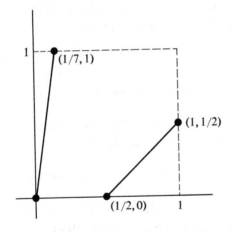

FIG. 1.24

Note that $T[\{1/4\}] = \varnothing$ (*i.e.*, $1/4$ is not related to anything), and that $T[[0, 1/7]] = [0, 1]$ (*i.e.*, each number in $[0, 1]$ is related to some number in $[0, 1/7]$). Similarly,

$$T[[1/2, 1]] = [0, 1/2]$$

and

$$T[(0, 1/2)] = (0, 1]. \quad \text{(Verify this!)}$$

Note that if $T \subset A \times B$ then T^{-1} is a relation in $B \times A$ and hence if $K \subset B$, then $T^{-1}[K]$ is given by the definition 1.10-1.

1.10-2 Question: Which if any of the following statements are true for an arbitrary relation T?

a) $T^{-1}[T[S]] \subset S$

b) $T[T^{-1}[K]] \subset K$

c) $S \subset T^{-1}[T[S]]$

d) $K \subset T[T^{-1}[K]]$

e) $T^{-1}[T[S]] = S$

f) $T[T^{-1}[K]] = K$

Singled Valued Relations

Some relations have a special property known as "single valuedness" which makes them extremely useful in describing certain mathematical ideas. In fact, it is one of the single most important ideas in mathematics!

1.10-3 Definition: Let $T \subset A \times B$ and let $x \in A$. We say that T *is unique at* x if and only if

$$a \in T[\{x\}] \text{ and } b \in T[\{x\}] \Rightarrow a = b.$$

(*I.e.,* the trace of $\{x\}$, $T[\{x\}]$, is either empty or contains only one element.)

Note: The statement "$a \in T[\{x\}]$ and $b \in T[\{x\}] \Rightarrow a = b$" has some quantifiers missing. How should it be read to be complete?

1.10-4 Definition: A relation T in $A \times B$ is called a *function* iff

$$\forall x \in A, \qquad T \text{ is unique at } x.$$

(In this case T is also called a *single valued relation* [*i.e.,* a function is a single valued relation].)

Example: If $A = \{1, 2, 3\}, \qquad B = \{4, 5, 6\}$,

and

$$T_1 = \{(1, 5), (2, 4)\}.$$

Then

$$T_1[\{1\}] = \{5\}, \qquad T_1[\{2\}] = \{4\}$$

and

$$T_1[\{3\}] = \varnothing.$$

Hence we see that T_1 is a function. Suppose also that

$$T_2 = \{(1, 4), (1, 5), (2, 6), (3, 6)\}.$$

Then

$$T_2[\{1\}] = \{4, 5\}, \qquad T_2[\{2\}] = \{6\}, \qquad T_2[\{3\}] = \{6\}$$

so T_2 is *not* a function. (T_2 is not unique at 1.)

If we let

$$T_3 = \{(1, 4), (2, 4), (3, 4)\},$$

then

$$T_3[\{1\}] = \{4\}, \qquad T_3[\{2\}] = \{4\}, \qquad \text{and} \qquad T_3[\{3\}] = \{4\}.$$

Hence T_3 is a function. (T_3 is unique at each point in A.) Note that unlike the function T_1, T_3 has A as its domain. We say in such cases that "T_3 is a function from A to B."

Example: $T = \{(1, 4), (2, 3), (3, 3), (4, 4)\}$ is a single valued relation (a function).

$$H = \{(1, 3), (1, 5), (2, 2)\}$$

is not single valued (not a function).

The definition stipulates that a relation is a function if no two distinct ordered pairs have the same first component. This uniqueness or single valuedness property of functions allows us to prove the following very useful result.

1.10-5 Theorem: Let $F \subset A \times B$ be a function. If $x \in D_F$, then there exists exactly one $y \in B$ such that $y \in F[\{x\}]$.

Proof: The *existence* follows immediately from the fact that $x \in D_F$; since

$$x \in D_F \Rightarrow (x, y) \in F \text{ for some } y \in B.$$

Therefore

$$y \in F[\{x\}] \text{ for some } y \in B.$$

The *uniqueness* follows from the uniqueness property of F. That is, if $F[\{x\}]$ contains more than one element, then the statement

$$a \in F[\{x\}] \text{ and } b \in F[\{x\}] \Rightarrow a = b$$

will fail to be true. []

(Explain the logic used in the uniqueness proof above.)

The following notation is used in connection with functions.

1.10-6 Notation Convention: If $F \subset A \times B$ is a function, and if $x \in D_F$, then the unique element in $F[\{x\}]$ is denoted by "$F(x)$." That is

$$F[\{x\}] = \{F(x)\}$$

"$F(x)$" is read "F of x," "F evaluated at x," or "the value of F at x." $F(x)$ is also sometimes denoted by "xF" (read "x through F"). Thus, if $F[\{x\}] = \{y\}$, then $y = F(x)$, or $y = xF$.

Remark: This notation would be illogical in dealing with a relation which wasn't a function. For example, if $T[\{x\}] = \{a, b\}$ and $a \neq b$, then we would not know whether $T(x)$ meant to designate a, or if it was intended to designate b.

Remark: If $F \subset A \times B$ and F is a function, then

a) If $x \in D_F$, then

$$F[\{x\}] \subset B, \quad \text{but} \quad F(x) \in B.$$

b) If $x \notin D_F$, then

$$F[\{x\}] = \varnothing \subset B, \quad \text{but } F(x) \text{ is not defined.}$$

If F is not a function, then $F(x)$ is not defined for all x.

Example: Suppose $A = \{1, 2, 3\}$, $B = \{4, 5, 6\}$,

and
$$F = \{(1, 4), (2, 5), (3, 5)\}.$$

Clearly F is a function, and

$$F(1) = 4, \qquad F(2) = 5, \qquad \text{and} \qquad F(3) = 5.$$

Example: If $A = \{1, 2, 3\}$, $B = \{4, 5, 6\}$, and $F(1) = 6$, $F(2) = 5$, and $F(3)$ is undefined. Then $F = \{(1, 6), (2, 5)\}$.

In general, what we know about a function F is that, the collection of ordered pairs which makes up the function is the set

$$F = \{(x, F(x)): x \in D_F\}.$$

Let us list now some equivalent descriptions of functions, any one of which could have been used for the definition of a "function."

1.10-7 Theorem: (Characterizations of Functions.)

    a) A relation $F \subset A \times B$ is a function iff

$$(a, x) \in F \text{ and } (a, y) \in F \Rightarrow x = y.$$

    b) A relation $F \subset A \times B$ is a function iff

$$(a, b) \in F \text{ and } y \neq b \Rightarrow (a, y) \notin F.$$

(Note the missing quantifiers.)

    Proof: *a)* $\overset{\Rightarrow}{(\text{only if})}$ Assume that F is a function, and assume that

$$(a, x) \in F \qquad \text{and} \qquad (a, y) \in F.$$

Clearly $a \in D_F$. Since $(a, x) \in F$ and $(a, y) \in F$, it follows that

$$x \in F[\{a\}] \qquad \text{and} \qquad y \in F[\{a\}].$$

But since F is unique at a, it must be the case that

$$x = y.$$

Hence $(a, x) \in F$ and $(a, y) \in F \Rightarrow x = y$.

    $\Leftarrow$
    (if)   Assume that

$$(a, x) \in F \text{ and } (a, y) \in F \Rightarrow x = y.$$

Let $z \in A$.

If $z \notin D_F$, then $F[\{z\}] = \varnothing$.
If $z \in D_F$, then let

$$a \in F[\{z\}] \qquad \text{and} \qquad b \in F[\{z\}].$$

It follows that

$$(z, a) \in F \qquad \text{and} \qquad (z, b) \in F.$$

But by hypothesis, $a = b$, therefore F is unique at z. Hence, $\forall z$, F is unique at z, so F is a function.

b) Left for the reader to enjoy.▯

Example: Suppose $U = \{1, 2, 3, 4\}$.

Then
$$F_1 = \{(1, 1)\}$$
$$F_2 = \{(1, 2), (2, 3)\}$$
$$F_3 = \{(1, 1), (2, 2), (3, 3), (4, 3)\}$$
and
$$F_4 = \{(1, 4), (2, 4), (3, 1), (1, 4)\}$$

are functions in $U \times U$.

Question: Let $A = \{1, 2, 3, 4\}$, $B = \{3, 4, 5, 6, 7\}$. Which of the following relations are functions?

$$F_1 = \{(1, 3), (2, 5), (3, 6), (4, 7)\}$$
$$F_2 = \{(1, 4), (2, 4), (3, 5), (4, 5)\}$$
$$F_3 = \{(1, 3), (1, 4), (2, 3), (3, 4), (4, 6)\}$$
$$F_4 = \{(1, 3), (3, 3)\}$$
$$F_5 = \{(4, 7), (3, 7), (3, 6)\}$$

Answer: F_1, F_2, F_4.

Exercises 1.10

1. Which of the following relations are single valued?
   a) $T = \{(1, 3), (5, 7), (7, 4), (3, 4)\}$
   b) $P = \{(1, 4), (1, 5), (1, 6), (6, 1)\}$
   c) $S = \{(5, 9), (9, 5)\}$
What about the inverse relation in each case?

2. List the domain and range of each of the relations in exercise 1.

3. Let $A = \{1, 2, 3, 4, 5\}$, $B = \{1, 5, 7, 9, 12, 13\}$
   $$T_1 = \{(1, 1), (2, 5), (3, 9)\}$$
   $$T_2 = \{(2, 1), (2, 5), (3, 9), (3, 12)\}$$
   $$T_3 = \{(1, 1), (3, 1), (5, 1), (4, 1)\}$$
   $$T_4 = \{(1, 1), (2, 5), (3, 7), (4, 9), (5, 7)\}$$
and let
   $$S_1 = \{1, 2\} \qquad S_2 = \{2, 3, 4\} \qquad S_3 = \{1, 2, 3\} \qquad S_4 = \{3, 4, 5\}.$$
   a) Determine the trace for each set S_i under each relation T_i.
   b) For each relation T_i, is T_i a function?
   c) Is T_i^{-1} a function?

75

4. Let $A = \{1, 2, 3, 4, 5, 6\}$ and $T \subset A \times A$ be given by

$$T = \{(1, 2), (2, 3), (3, 5), (3, 6), (4, 3), (4, 1)\}.$$

Let $S_1 = \{1, 2, 3\}$ $S_2 = \{4, 5, 6\}$. Find $T^{-1}[T[S_i]]$ and $T[T^{-1}[S_i]]$ for $i = 1, 2$.

5. List a relation in $N \times N$ which is
   a) a function
   b) not a function
   c) unique at some point but not at another.

6. If $F = \{(1, 2), (2, 5), (3, 9), (5, 7)\}$, then F is a function. What is $F(1)$, $F(2)$, $F(3)$, $F(5)$?

7. Let $f \subset N \times N$ be defined by $\forall x \in N$ $f(x) = x + 2$. List some of the ordered pairs which appear in f. What is R_f? Is f^{-1} a function?

8. Is $\emptyset$ a function in $U \times U$? What are its domain and range?

9. Is it possible for different functions to have identical domains and ranges? Prove your answer.

10. Answer Question 1.10-2.

11. (Investigate) For any relation $T \subset A \times B$, prove or disprove that:
   a) $R_T = T[D_T]$
   b) $T \subset A \times T[D_T]$
   c) $T = D_T \times R_T$
   d) $T^{-1}[R_T] = D_T$

12. Consider $f \subset R \times R$ defined by

$$f(x) = x^2 + 1.$$

Find:
   a) $f(2)$
   b) $f(3)$
   c) $f(7) - f(4)$
   d) $f(2 + 3)$
   e) $f(3 \cdot 4)$
   f) $f(b + 2)$ for an arbitrary b
   g) $(f(4)) \cdot 3$

13. Consider $f \subset R \times R$ defined by

$$\forall x \in R \quad xf = 2x - 4.$$

Find:
   a) $2f$
   b) $3f$
   c) $(2 + 1)f$
   d) $(2 \cdot 3)f$
   e) $2(3f)$
   f) $(a + 1)f$ for arbitrary $a \in R$
   g) $(4a)f$ for arbitrary $a \in R$

14. Let $f \subset R \times R$ be given by $f(x) = 2x + 1$. Determine the following "traces" under f of the given subset of R.
   a) $f[(2, 3)]$ b) $f[[1, 2]]$ c) $f[(-1, 3]]$

15. Let $f \subset R \times R$ be given by $f(x) = x^2 - 1$. Determine:
   a) $f[(-1, 2)]$ b) $f[[1, 2]]$ c) $f[[-2, 2]]$

1.11   Maps and Their Graphs

"Functions Are" vs. "Functions Do"

The word "function" as it is commonly used in the English language seems to be far removed from the notion of sets of ordered pairs. It may seem that we have selected a very strange name for sets of ordered pairs T, with the special property that

$$(a, b) \in T \text{ and } (a, c) \in T \Rightarrow b = c.$$

In mathematics we are interested, for the most part, in what functions *do* rather than what they *are*. That is, we are interested in their properties more often than specifically how they are constructed. However, we do find it useful on occasion to look very carefully into a function in order to derive some of its properties.

What we have in mind for a function to "do" is to "associate" each member of some given set (the domain of the function) with some specific member of another set (not necessarily different). That is, we expect a function to have the property that given any element in its domain, there is a unique element in its range which is determined by the function. On the other hand, if we know, for a given set, that each of its elements is assigned to a unique member of some given set, then we expect a function to be determined. Sets of ordered pairs (relations) which are single valued have this property. We have chosen to state specifically what a function *is* rather than to leave "function" as one of the possibly confusing undefined terms. Therefore we have defined a function as a special kind of relation. A function can be thought of as some sort of selecting or assigning rule or machine. If one wishes to know exactly how the machine is constructed, then he may look at the internal structure which happens to be a collection of ordered pairs. All the selections which the function makes are determined by this structure. On the other hand, if one knows all the selections which the function makes, then the set of ordered pairs from which the function is constructed can be determined.

Example: If $F = \{(1, 2), (3, 5), (7, 9)\}$, all of the following things are determined:

$$D_F = \{1, 3, 7\} \qquad R_F = \{2, 5, 9\}$$

and
$$F(1) = 2, \qquad F(3) = 5, \qquad F(7) = 9.$$

Example: If we know that $D_f = \{2, 4, 6, 8\}$ and that

$$f(2) = 6, \qquad f(4) = 9, \qquad f(6) = 7, \qquad f(8) = 8,$$

then all of the following things are determined:

$$R_f = \{6, 9, 8, 7\}$$
$$f = \{(2, 6), (4, 9), (6, 7), (8, 8)\}.$$

We concede that a definition of functions could be given in terms of what a function *does*, but we find it more natural to say what a function *is*, and then to examine and elaborate upon some of the resulting properties. Viewing a function in terms of what it does, is viewing it as a "rule" which defines a correspondence between members of a set A and some of the members of a set B. Thus we might view a function f as a "projector" which projects each point in D_f to a point in R_f. That is, the function f can be viewed as projecting each "pre-image" point in A to its "image" in B. As a result of this "assigning" property possessed by functions, they are often called *maps* or *mappings*. The following notation suggested by the mapping point of view, is useful in discussing functions.

1.11-1 Notation Convention: The symbol "$f:A \to B$", means that

1) f is a function,
2) $D_f = A$,
3) $R_f \subset B$.

("$f:A \to B$" is read "f is a function from A into B.")

In the mapping framework, one sees an alternate to graphs using the Cartesian coordinate system. If we imagine f as a rule which projects each pre-image to its image, it is natural to construct a graphical model as in Figure 1.25.

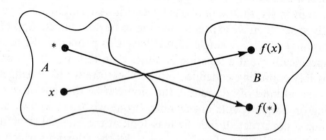

FIG. 1.25 f is viewed as a rule which "maps" each point of A to some unique point of B. Thus $* \in A$ is mapped to $f(*) \in B$ by the function f.

This type of graphical interpretation lets one imagine domains and ranges that are completely abstract, while the use of the Cartesian coordinate system is most useful when these sets are subsets of R. On the other hand, this type of graph does not lead to easy graphical interpretations of such properties of functions as symmetry. It will be seen that each type of graph has its advantages and disadvantages, and, of course, when making a graphical interpretation of a function, one should use the type of graph that best fills the needs of the particular problem involved.

It should be noted that the all-important characteristic of the function, whether it be viewed as a set of ordered pairs, or as a rule of correspondence, is that *with each point in the domain there is assigned a unique corresponding point in the range.* Suppose $f \subset A \times B$ is a function with a domain A. Then the statement

$$(a, b) \in f$$

(using the ordered pair terminology) can be translated to

$$b \text{ is the image of } a$$

(using the mapping terminology). Both of these statements can be simply rephrased as

$$b = f(a).$$

In all of these statements, it is asserted that b is the unique point in R_f associated with a.

It should be clear that the two outlooks on functions that we have discussed are equivalent, and we can translate from each point of view to the other simply by modifying the notation and terminology as appropriate. It seems that, as in the case of the various possible graphical interpretations of a function, each point of view has its advantages. Some mathematicians take the "rule of correspondence" definition as basic and call the corresponding set of ordered pairs the "graph" of the function. However, this approach does not appear to be standard at the present time.

Example: Suppose $f: A \to B$ is a function which maps $A = [0, 1)$ into $B = R$ as follows:

$$f(x) = 3, \qquad \forall x \in [0, 1).$$

The graph of this function is sketched in Figure 1.26.

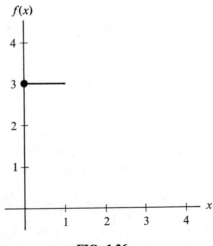

FIG. 1.26

We could also interpret the function graphically as in Figure 1-27.

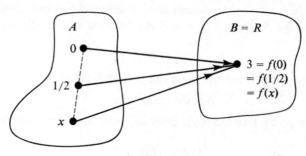

f maps $[0, 1)$ into $\{3\}$.

FIG. 1.27

As a set of ordered pairs, f could be described by

$$f = \{(x, 3): x \in [0, 1)\}$$

or by

$$f = [0, 1) \times \{3\}.$$

Note that we are dealing here with a function, since every point of $[0, 1)$ is mapped to a unique image point. It just happens in this case that all of the images of points of $[0, 1)$ are the same.

Maps in $R \times R$

It is interesting and useful to consider the condition on a relation F in $R \times R$ in order for it to be a function in light of the Cartesian graph of F. Recall that the graph of a product set $R \times R$ is a set of points in the plane corresponding to the ordered pairs in $R \times R$. Thus, it is natural to take the graph of any subset T of the product set $R \times R$ to be the set of points in the plane corresponding with the elements of T. Now inasmuch as a function F is a relation, we may consider its graph. The condition

$$(a, b) \in F \text{ and } x \neq b \Rightarrow (a, x) \notin F$$

asserts that in the graph of F, for each point $a \in D_F$ there is precisely *one* point in the plane that is on the vertical lattice line intersecting the horizontal axis at the point $(a, 0)$.

Example: Given the graphs in Figure 1.28 of relations in $[0, 1] \times [0, 1]$, only (*a*) and (*c*) are graphs of functions.

The relation whose graph is sketched in (*b*), for example, is not a function since there are points in $D_F = [0, 1]$ (1/2 for instance) for which the corre-

sponding vertical lattice line intersects the graph at more than one point.
Question: In each case in Figure 1-28, is the inverse relation a function?

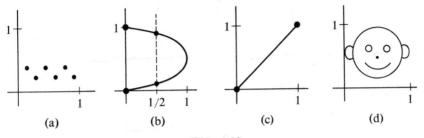

(a)   (b)   (c)   (d)

FIG. 1.28

The graph in (c) above is a segment of a straight line. The entire line
can be considered to be the graph of the function F defined by

$$F = \{(x, y): y = x\}$$

in $R \times R$ (see Figure 1.29).

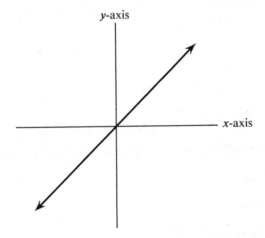

FIG. 1.29 The graph of the function F in
$R \times R$ described by $y = x$ is a straight line
extending into quadrants I and III.

Example: Suppose the universal set is R. Consider the relation K in
$R \times R$ defined by

$$K = \{(x, y): y = 3\}.$$

81

We see that an ordered pair (a, b) of real numbers is an element of K iff $b = 3$. The graph of K is sketched in Figure 1.30. Note that K is a function.

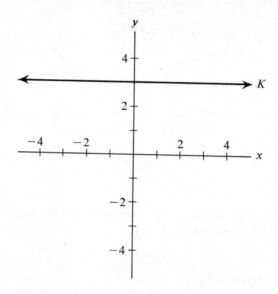

FIG. 1.30 The graph of the function described by the equation $y = 3$ is a lattice line.

Question: Is K^{-1} a function?

Maps with Special Properties

In connection with the notation "$f: A \to B$" where it is understood that

1) f is a function
2) $D_f = A$
3) $R_f \subset B$

we make the following definitions.

1.11-2 Definition: A function $f: A \to B$ is called *onto* iff

$$R_f = B.$$

This is denoted by   "$f: A \xrightarrow[onto]{} B$."

(An *onto* map is sometimes called a "surjection.")

Thus, in an *onto* map, every element b of B appears in at least one ordered pair of the form (a, b) in f.

Example: Let $A = \{1, 2, 3\}$, $B = \{4, 5, 6\}$ and let

$$F(1) = 4 \qquad F(2) = 4 \qquad F(3) = 5$$
$$f(1) = 4 \qquad f(2) = 5 \qquad f(3) = 6.$$

Both F and f are functions from A into B, but f is *onto* B while F is not.

It is of interest to know in general whether a given function F associates more than one point in its domain with any given point in its range. If it does *not*, we say that F is *"one-to-one."*

1.11-3 Definition: A function F: $A \rightarrow B$ is *one-one* iff

$$(a, b) \subset F \text{ and } (c, b) \subset F \Rightarrow a = c.$$

This is denoted by   *"F: $A \overset{1\text{-}1}{\rightarrow} B$."*

(1-1 maps are sometimes called "injections.")

Thus, a *one-one* function F in $A \times B$ is one which associates distinct pre-images in A with distinct images in B.

The notions of *"1-1"* and *"onto"* are independent of each other. That is, there are functions which are *1-1* but not *onto*, others are *onto* but not *1-1*, some that are both, still others that are neither (see Figure 1-31).

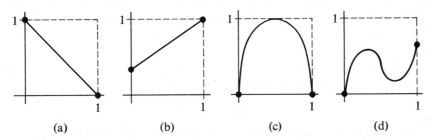

FIG. 1.31 Graphs (a), (b), (c), and (d) above are all graphs of functions in $[0,1] \times [0,1]$. The function graphed in (a) is *1-1* and *onto*; (b) is *1-1* but not *onto*; (c) is *onto* but not *1-1*; and (d) is neither. These examples show that the notions of "1-1" and "onto" are independent of each other.

Examples: Consider the following relations in $\{1, 3, 7, 5\} \times \{2, 4, 6, 8\}$:

$$R_1 = \{(1, 2), (3, 2), (5, 2), (7, 2)\}$$
$$R_2 = \{(1, 2), (1, 4), (1, 6), (1, 8)\}$$
$$R_3 = \{(1, 2), (3, 4), (5, 6)\}$$
$$R_4 = \{(1, 4), (3, 2), (7, 8), (5, 6)\}.$$

Which are functions? Which are functions *from* $\{1, 3, 5, 7\}$ into $\{2, 4, 6, 8\}$? Which are *1-1* and which are *onto*?

Solution: R_1: $\{1, 3, 5, 7\} \rightarrow \{2, 4, 6, 8\}$ is a function, but is neither *one-one* nor *onto*. R_2 is not a function. However, notice that R_2^{-1}: $\{2, 4, 6, 8\} \rightarrow \{1, 3, 5, 7\}$ is a function, but is neither *one-one* nor *onto*. R_3 is a function but it does not map $\{1, 3, 5, 7\}$ into $\{2, 4, 6, 8\}$, since $7 \not\subset D_{R_3}$. However, R_3 is a *one-one* function from $\{1, 3, 5\}$ into $\{2, 4, 6, 8\}$. R_4 has domain $\{1, 3, 5, 7\}$ and is both *one-one* and *onto* as a function

$$R_4: \{1, 3, 5, 7\} \rightarrow \{2, 4, 6, 8\}.$$

It is of special interest to consider functions which are both *one-one* and *onto*. Suppose we have a *1-1* and *onto* function F in a product universe $A \times B$. Using the definition of the three attributes of F (F is a function, F is *1-1*, F is *onto*) we make the following assertions.

1) For each element a in the domain A of F, there is exactly one ordered pair in F of the form (a, b), where $b \in B$.

2) For each element b in the range B, there is exactly one ordered pair in F of the form (a, b).

If we put 1) and 2) together, we may say that any *1-1* and *onto* function $F: A \rightarrow B$ is composed of ordered pairs in which each element of A is "paired" with a unique element of B, and each element of B is paired with a unique element of A. This situation is described briefly by saying that F is a *one-one correspondence between A and B*. Intuitively, this term describes the fact that the elements of F determine a "matching" between the elements of A and those of B.

Example: Suppose $A = \{1, 2, 3, - - -, 50\}$, and $B = \{$names of states in the U.S.A.$\}$. We can define a function F in $A \times B$ by

$$(a, b) \in F \qquad \text{iff}$$

b is the *a*th name in the alphabetical list of the states in the U.S.

Thus, for example,

$$\text{(1, Alabama), (2, Alaska), and (3, Arizona)}$$

are elements of F. We see that F is *1-1* and *onto*, so F is a *1-1* correspondence between A and B. Note that each state is paired with exactly one integer, so that we could refer to "state number 3" for example when we were talking about "Arizona." Thus, the set $\{1, 2, \cdots, 50\}$ could be used as "labels" for the elements of B. This might be of some advantage in certain contexts, since the "labels" in A might be simpler and easier to handle in those situations.

1.11-4 Definition: If $F: A \rightarrow B$ and F is both *one-one* and *onto*, then F is called a *"one-one* correspondence between A and B." This is denoted by

$$\text{"} F: A \xrightarrow[onto]{1\text{-}1} B. \text{"}$$

(*One-one* and *onto* functions are sometimes called "bijections.")
   Example: Let $F: N \to Z$ be given by

$$F(n) = \frac{n}{2}, \qquad \text{if } n \text{ is even.}$$

$$F(n) = -\frac{n-1}{2}, \qquad \text{if } n \text{ is odd.}$$

(See Figure 1.32.)

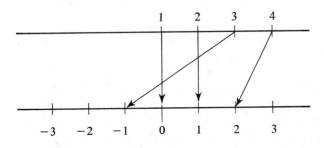

FIG. 1.32

Then F is a *one-one* correspondence between the set of natural numbers N, and the set of integers Z.

   Note that the act of counting objects may be viewed as setting up a *1-1* correspondence between the objects and a subset of N. The value of this procedure lies in the fundamental idea that if there is a *1-1* correspondence between two sets, the sets contain precisely the same "number" of objects. Thus, in counting the number of C's on his transcript, Grant Gibson finds that there is a *1-1* correspondence between the set of all courses in which he earned a "C" and the set $\{1, 2\}$, and thus concludes that he has received the grade "C" in *two* classes. (Obviously with this kind of thinking on his part, neither of these classes was his math class.)

   Let us now consider the relations in $[0, 1] \times [0, 1]$ associated with the graphs in Figure 1.33, with the aim of seeing how they relate $[0, 1]$ to $[0, 1]$.

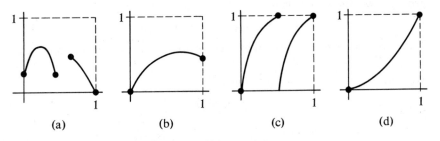

FIG. 1.33

The relation pictured in

    (a) is a function but not *from* $[0, 1]$.

    (b) is a function from $[0, 1]$ into $[0, 1]$ but not *onto* and not *one-one*.

    (c) is a function from $[0, 1]$ *onto* $[0, 1]$ but not *one-one*.

    (d) is a *one-one* correspondence between $[0, 1]$ and $[0, 1]$.

Question: How can one tell from the graph of a function $f \subset R \times R$ whether the relation $f^{-1} \subset R \times R$ is a function?

We devote the final part of this section to an investigation of a connection between the *1-1* and *onto* properties of a function, and the condition that its inverse also be a function.

1.11-5 Theorem: The inverse of a function $f: A \to B$ is a function $f^{-1}: B \to A$ iff f is *1-1* and *onto*.

Proof: Note that we must show two things:

    a) that $f: A \xrightarrow[onto]{1\text{-}1} B \implies f^{-1}: B \to A$ is a function, and

    b) that $f^{-1}: B \to A$ a function $\implies f: A \xrightarrow[onto]{1\text{-}1} B$.

Part a) Suppose that f is a *1-1* and *onto* function from A into B. Then for any point $b \in B$, there is exactly one ordered pair of the form (a, b) in f (for if there were another, say (c, b), $c \neq a$, then we would have two points, c and a, in A mapping to the image b under f, and hence f would not be *1-1*). Thus for each $b \in B$, there is a unique point $a \in A$ such that $(b, a) \in f^{-1}$. By definition, this means that f^{-1} is a function with $D_{f^{-1}} = B$. But this is exactly what is meant by the symbol "$f^{-1}: B \to A$."

    Part b) Suppose that $f^{-1}: B \to A$ is the inverse function associated with $f: A \to B$.

We must show that f is *1-1* and *onto*. The *onto* property follows immediately from the fact that $R_f = D_{f^{-1}}$, since $D_{f^{-1}}$ is B. The *1-1* property of f follows from the assumption that f^{-1} is a function, since this implies that for each $b \in B$, there is a unique image $a = f^{-1}(b)$ under f^{-1}, which in turn implies that b is the only image of the point a under f. $\square$

Remark: Actually, under the conditions that f is *1-1* and *onto*, it follows that f^{-1} is also a *1-1* and *onto* function.

Remark: The condition in the Theorem that f is *onto* may be relaxed, provided we assert only that

$$f^{-1}: R_f \to A \qquad \text{is a function.}$$

Note that the *onto* property was used in the proof only to establish that $D_{f^{-1}} = B$.

We may assume that, given any function

$$f: A \to B,$$

we have

$$f: A \xrightarrow[onto]{} R_f \qquad \text{(see Exercise 12).}$$

Exercises 1.11

1. Sketch the graph (by plotting numerous points if necessary) of the relation in $R \times R$ described by:

   a) $\{(x, y): x = 2 \text{ and } y = 2\}$ e) $\{(x, y): x^2 + y^2 = 1\}$

   b) $\{(x, y): x = 2\}$ f) $\{(x, y): x^2 + y^2 < 1\}$

   c) $\{(x, y): y = 2\}$ g) $\{(x, y): y = x^2\}$

   d) $\{(x, y): y = 2 + x\}$ h) $\{(x, y): x = y^2\}$

2. a) Which of the relations in Exercise 1 are also functions?

   b) In each case determine the domain and the range.

   c) Which are *onto R*?

   d) Which are *1-1*?

   e) Which are *1-1* correspondences?

3. Let $f: R \rightarrow R$ be defined by

$$f(x) = 3x^2 + 2x + 1.$$

   a) Compute $f(0), f(1/2), f(1), f(2), f(3), f(-1/2), f(-1), f(-2), f(-3)$.

   b) Use these computations to sketch a graph in $R \times R$ of f.

4. Let $g: R \rightarrow R$ be defined by

$$g(x) = -x^2 + 2.$$

   a) Compute $g(0), g(1), g(2), g(3), g(-1), g(-2), g(-3)$.

   b) Use these computations to sketch a graph of g.

5. Suppose $A = \{a, b, c\}$ and $B = \{1, 2\}$.

   a) How many functions are there in $A \times B$? (Don't forget $\varnothing$.)

   b) How many *1-1* functions are there in $A \times B$?

   c) How many functions *onto B*?

   d) How many *1-1* and *onto* functions from A to B?

   e) Try to generalize these results to a product universal set $A \times B$ where $\#(A) = m$ and $\#(B) = n$.

6. Decide whether the relation is a function.

   a) $\{(x, y): x^2 - y^2 = 1\}$ d) $\{(x, y): y^2 = x\}$

   b) $\{(x, y): x^2 - y^2 < 1\}$ e) $\{(x, y): y = x^2\}$

   c) $\{(x, y): y = x\}$

7. Graph each relation in $R \times R$.

   a) $\{(x, y): x = 5\}$ c) $\{(x, y): x = 0\}$

   b) $\{(x, y): y = 2\}$ d) $\{(x, y): y = 3x\}$

8. Give a "mapping" interpretation of

   a) The condition that f is *onto*.

   b) The condition that f is *1-1*.

9. *a*) Show that any function from a nonempty set *A* into a singleton set *B* is *onto*.

b) Can such a function also be *1-1*?

c) Give an example of such a function and its inverse (which is also necessarily a function).

10. *a*) Show that if $f: A \xrightarrow[onto]{1-1} B$, then

$$f^{-1}: B \xrightarrow[onto]{1-1} A.$$

b) If $f: A \xrightarrow[onto]{1-1} B$, then what can you say about the number of elements in *A* compared with *B*?

11. *a*) Suppose that $f: A \to B$. Explain why it is true that

$$a = b \implies f(a) = f(b).$$

b) Under what conditions (on *f*) will the converse of the implication in *b*) also be true?

12. Prove that if

$$f: A \to B,$$

then there is a subset *C* of *B* such that

$$f: A \xrightarrow[onto]{} C.$$

1.12 Binary Operations, Restriction of Functions, and Closure

There is a particular class of functions known as "binary operations" which will interest us a great deal when we begin to develop number systems. You are familiar with the operation of adding two numbers, with a resulting third number. Similarly with subtraction, multiplication, and division. We would like to decide precisely what we mean by such "operations" and then extend the concept to a more general setting.

The operations we have in mind deal with one set and have the following properties:

i) If two, not necessarily distinct, elements are selected from the set, then the operation assigns them to some element of the set.

ii) For some operations, the order is important (for example, in subtraction) while for others it is not (for example, in addition).

We wish to make a definition that will allow addition, subtraction, multiplication, and division to be *binary operations*. This will also allow us to generalize the underlying ideas involved.

1.12-1 Definition: Let S be a set. Then any function

$$\varphi: S \times S \to S$$

is called a *binary operation* on S.

1.12-2 Notation Convention: Usually, if φ is a binary operation on S, and if

$$(a, b) \in D_\varphi,$$

then the unique value φ takes at (a, b) is designated by

$$a\varphi b.$$

Thus, if $\varphi((a, b)) = c$, then we write $a\varphi b = c$.

Example: The operation "$+$" on N is a binary operation. That is,

$$+: N \times N \to N.$$

Thus, $+((5, 3)) = 8,$ $+((4, 1)) = 5,$ $+((1, 4)) = 5,$

but one usually writes

$$5 + 3 = 8, \quad 4 + 1 = 5, \quad 1 + 4 = 5.$$

Example: The operation "$-$" on Z is a binary operation. Thus,

$$-((5, 3)) = 2, \quad -((4, 1)) = 3, \quad -((1, 4)) = -3,$$

but usually written

$$5 - 3 = 2, \quad 4 - 1 = 3, \quad 1 - 4 = -3.$$

Example: Let $S = \{a, b\}$ and $\odot$ be defined by:

$$a \odot a = a \quad\quad a \odot b = b$$
$$b \odot a = a \quad\quad b \odot b = b$$

The ordered pairs in $\odot$ are given in the list

$$\odot = \{((a, a), a), ((a, b), b), ((b, a), a), ((b, b), b)\}.$$

Upon looking at a binary operation as a set of ordered pairs, it becomes evident that the simpler notation is desirable.

Example: Let $S = \{$Gurney, Glenda, Grant$\}$.

Let $\oplus: S \times S \to S$, be defined by:

$$\text{Gurney} \oplus \text{Gurney} = \text{Gurney}$$
$$\text{Gurney} \oplus \text{Glenda} = \text{Glenda}$$
$$\text{Glenda} \oplus \text{Gurney} = \text{Gurney}$$
$$\text{Glenda} \oplus \text{Glenda} = \text{Glenda}$$
$$\text{Grant} \oplus \text{Grant} = \text{Grant}$$
$$\text{Grant} \oplus \text{Glenda} = \text{Glenda}$$
$$\text{Glenda} \oplus \text{Grant} = \text{Grant}$$
$$\text{Grant} \oplus \text{Gurney} = \text{Gurney}$$
$$\text{Gurney} \oplus \text{Grant} = \text{Grant}$$

What are the ordered pairs in $\oplus$?

Question: What are some of the ordered pairs in the binary operation "$\times$" on the natural numbers N with which you are familiar?

Binary Operations with Special Properties

There are in general many binary operations on any given set. Some special properties of some binary operations make them more interesting and more useful than other binary operations. We list here two such special properties.

1.12-3 Definition: If φ is a binary operation on S and if

$$\forall x \in S \quad \forall y \in S \quad x\varphi y = y\varphi x,$$

then we say φ is a *commutative operation.* If

$$\forall x, y, z \in S \quad x\varphi(y\varphi z) = (x\varphi y)\varphi z,$$

then we say that φ is an *associative operation.*

You can easily verify that addition on N is both commutative and associative, whereas subtraction is neither.

Restrictions of Functions

If $f: A \to B$, and $S \subset A$, then there is a naturally induced function $g: S \to B$. This is obtained by simply taking the same values for g as were given for f on the set S. This process is known as "restricting" the function f. The precise idea is given in the following definition.

1.12-4 Definition: Let $f: A \to B$, and let $S \subset A$. Then

$$f|_S$$

(called "f restricted to S" or "the restriction of f to S") is the function $g: S \to B$, defined by

$$\forall x \in S \quad g(x) = f(x).$$

Example: Let $A = \{1, 2, 3, 4\}$, $B = \{17, 31, 40, 41\}$,

$$S = \{1, 2\}, \text{ and}$$

$$f = \{(1, 17), (2, 17), (3, 31), (4, 40)\}.$$

Then

$$f|_S = \{(1, 17), (2, 17)\}.$$

Example: Let $A = \{4, 5, 17\}$, $B = \{a, b, c\}$, $S = \{4, 5\}$, and

$$f(4) = a, \quad f(5) = b, \quad f(17) = c.$$

Then

$$f|_S(4) = a, \qquad f|_S(5) = b$$

but $f|_S(17)$ is undefined, since $17 \not\subset D_{f|_S} = S$.

Question: If $f: N \to N$ is defined by

$$\forall n \in N \qquad f(n) = 6n - 1,$$

then what are the ordered pairs in the function

$$f|_{\{2,4,9,11\}}?$$

Extension of Functions

Similar to the idea of restricting a function is that of extending a function.

1.12-5 Definition: Let f and g be functions such that

$$D_f \subset D_g.$$

Then g is called an *extension* of f if and only if

$$\forall x \in D_f \qquad g(x) = f(x).$$

That is

$$f = g|_{D_f}.$$

Remark: A function can be extended in many ways, but the restriction of a function is unique.

Example: Let $D_f = \{1, 2, 3\}$ and let

$$f(1) = 5, \qquad f(2) = 7, \qquad f(3) = 4.$$

If we define two functions g_1 and g_2 by:

$$g_1(1) = 5, \qquad g_1(2) = 7, \qquad g_1(3) = 4,$$
$$g_1(5) = 11, \qquad g_1(4) = 12$$

whereas

$$g_2(1) = 5, \qquad g_2(2) = 7, \qquad g_2(3) = 4,$$
$$g_2(5) = 13, \qquad g_2(4) = 12$$

then g_1 and g_2 are both extensions of f to $\{1, 2, 3, 4, 5\}$, but

$$g_1 \neq g_2. \qquad \text{Note, however, that}$$
$$g_{1|D_f} = g_{2|D_f} = f.$$

Closure of a Set under Binary Operations

Putting the two previously developed ideas together, we can discuss the notion of "closure" under an operation. A binary operation is given as a concept relating to a given set S. If $A \subset S$, then one might ask: "Is the restriction of the binary operation to the set A (or more precisely to $A \times A$) again a binary operation?" In general the answer is "no", but in case it *is*, we say that the set A is "closed" under the operation. We state this more precisely as follows.

1.12-6 Definition: Let φ be a binary operation on S (*i.e.*, $\varphi: S \times S \to S$), and let $A \subset S$. Then if $\varphi|_{A \times A}$ is a binary operation on A, we say that A *is closed under* φ.

Example: Let $S = \{a, b, c\}$ (all distinct). Let * be an operation on S defined by the following table.

*	a	b	c
a	b	a	c
b	a	b	b
c	c	a	a

That is,

$$* = \{((a, a), b), ((a, b), a), ((a, c), c), ((b, a), a),$$
$$((b, b), b), ((b, c), b), ((c, a), c), ((c, b), a), ((c, c), a)\}.$$

Let *' be * restricted to $\{a, b\}$. Then *' is given by the following table.

*'	a	b
a	b	a
b	a	b

Now *' is a binary operation since *' is a function from $\{a, b\} \times \{a, b\} \to \{a, b\}$. Hence, $\{a, b\}$ is closed under *. Let *'' be * restricted to $\{a, c\}$. Then *'' is given by the following table.

*''	a	c
a	b	c
c	c	a

Clearly *'' is not a function from $\{a, c\} \times \{a, c\} \to \{a, c\}$, hence $\{a, c\}$ is not closed under *. What about closure of $\{b, c\}$ under *?

Example: Addition is a binary operation on Z, but if we select only elements in $N \subset Z$ and add them, we always get sums in N. Thus N is closed under addition.

Example: Subtraction is a binary operation on Z, but if we select any two elements from $N \subset Z$, we cannot be certain that the difference is in N. Thus, N is *not* closed under subtraction.

Example: Let $S = \{\text{pig, cow}\}$. Define $\oplus$ a binary operation on S by

$$\text{pig} \oplus \text{pig} = \text{pig}$$
$$\text{pig} \oplus \text{cow} = \text{pig}$$
$$\text{cow} \oplus \text{pig} = \text{cow}$$
$$\text{cow} \oplus \text{cow} = \text{pig}$$

Then $\{\text{pig}\} \subset S$, is closed under $\oplus$ but $\{\text{cow}\} \subset S$ is not. (Note that $\oplus$ is not commutative in this case.)

Exercises 1.12

1. Let $f = \{(1, 3), (2, 5), (3, 3), (4, 7)\}$.
    a) List the ordered pairs in $f|_{\{2,3\}}$ and $f|_{\{1,3,4\}}$.
    b) List two functions g_1 and g_2 whose domain is $\{1, 2, 3, 4, 5, 6\}$ such that $g_1 \neq g_2$ but
    $$g_i|_{\{1,2,3,4\}} = f, \quad i = 1, \quad \text{and} \quad i = 2.$$

2. Let $f: R \to R$ be given by
    $$f(x) = 2 - x^2.$$
    Let $S = \{1, 5, 6, 7\}$. List all the ordered pairs in $f|_S$.

3. Let $S = \{a, b, c\}$ and define the binary operation $\oplus$ on S by the following $\oplus$ table.

$\oplus$	a	b	c
a	a	b	a
b	b	a	c
c	a	c	a

Determine:
    a) $a \oplus b$ *c)* $b \oplus c$ *e)* $\oplus((b, b))$
    b) $c \oplus c$ *d)* $\oplus((a, c))$ *f)* $\oplus = \{ \qquad \qquad \}$

Is $\oplus$ a commutative operation? Is $\oplus$ an associative operation? Make a table for $\oplus$ restricted to $\{a, b\}$. Is $\{a, b\}$ closed under $\oplus$?

4. Let $S = \{a, b\}$ and define $\odot$ by:
    $$a \odot b = a \qquad a \odot a = a$$
    $$b \odot a = a \qquad b \odot b = b$$
    Make a $\odot$ table. Is $\odot$ commutative or associative?

5. Define $+$ on $\{E, 0\}$ by

$+$	0	E
0	E	E
E	0	0

Show that $+$ is neither associative nor commutative. Show that no non-empty proper subset of $\{E, 0\}$ is closed under $+$.

6. Let $f = \{(0, 1), (5, 9), (10, 10), (3, 9)\}$, $S = \{0, 5, 10\}$. What is
   a) $f|_S(0)$ b) $f|_S(10)$ c) $f|_S(5)$ d) $f|_S(3)$?

7. Is Z closed under division? Is Q closed under division?

8. Suppose $T = \{a, b\}$ and $S = 2^T$.
   a) Show that Union "$\cup$" is a binary operation on S.
   b) Show that Intersection "$\cap$" is a binary operation on S.
   c) Suppose $M = \{T, \{a\}\}$.
             Is "$\cup$" closed on M?   Is "$\cap$" closed on M?
   (For a set to be closed under an operation means the same as the operation being closed on the set!)
   d) Are intersection and union associative and commutative?

9. Let $Z_5 = \{0, 1, 2, 3, 4\}$. Define $\oplus$ by the following Table.

$\oplus$	0	1	2	3	4
0	0	1	2	3	4
1	1	2	3	4	0
2	2	3	4	0	1
3	3	4	0	1	2
4	4	0	1	2	3

a) Is $\oplus$ associative or commutative?
b) Does Z_5 have any subsets which are closed under $\oplus$?
c) List the elements in $\oplus|_{A \times A}$, where $A = \{0, 2, 4\}$.
d) $3 \oplus 2 = ?$ $4 \oplus 3 = ?$
    $\oplus((3, 3)) = ?$ $\oplus((2, 2)) = ?$

1.13 Cardinality and Composition

A major concern of mathematics is the search for ways to analyze and investigate the concept of "amount." The seemingly simple question "how many?" deserves some attention at this point. You are perhaps accustomed to answering such a question by stating the name of some number, but how would you explain to someone who had no concept of "counting numbers"?

Gurney Gibson was faced with a similar problem when his fifth cousin Ole Gibson from Sweden came to visit. He was trying to explain to Ole that he had the same number of sheep as he had pigs. Due to the fact that they spoke different languages, his explanations were to no avail. His son Grant, however (being a brilliant young lad), devised a plan to get the message across, in spite of the language barrier. This is what they did: Grant rounded up all the sheep and put them in a pen while Gurney rounded up all the pigs and put them in the pen. They then tied each sheep to exactly one pig. They let Ole check carefully all the animals in the pen so he could see that there was no sheep which was not tied to a pig and no pig which was not tied to a sheep, and no sheep was tied to two or more pigs, and no pig to two or more sheep. Even though Gurney will never know for sure, he is quite confident that Grant's plan convinced Ole that he had the same number of sheep as he had pigs. Do you feel that his demonstration was convincing?

Let us then make the following definition which we feel "pins down" the idea that two sets have the same number of elements.

1.13-1 Definition: Two sets A and B are said to be cardinally equivalent (denoted by $A \# B$) if there is a *1-1* correspondence between A and B.

Example: If $A = \{3, \pi, 2, 19, 18\}$, $\quad B = \{2\pi, 6, 21, 40, 9\}$

then $$A \# B$$

since

$$T = \{(3, 2\pi), (\pi, 6), (2, 21), (19, 40), (18, 9)\}$$

is a *1-1* correspondence between A and B.

Note: There are many *one-one* correspondences between A and B, but to prove cardinal equivalence it is sufficient to display only one.

The idea that cardinally equivalent sets necessarily have the same number of elements is based on the "one-for-one pairing" of elements from each set, the possibility of this pairing being guaranteed by the *1-1* correspondence. That this is not completely obvious in all cases is seen in the following example.

Example: Suppose E denotes the set of even integers

$$\{ \cdots, -4, -2, 0, 2, 4, 6, \cdots \}.$$

Then a *1-1* correspondence between Z and E is established by the function

$$F = \{(x, y): y = 2x, \text{ and } x \in Z\}$$

in $Z \times E$. Thus, for example, $1 \in Z$ corresponds to $2 \in E$, since $2 = F(1)$ (so that $(1, 2) \in F$). Similarly, $(2, 4), (3, 6), (4, 8), \cdots$ are elements of F. The student should verify that F is a *1-1* correspondence between Z and E. Since this is true, we must have the same "number" of elements in Z as in E! (That

95

is, there are "as many" *even* integers as there are integers!) Does this seem paradoxical? (Does it make sense to talk about "the number of integers"?)

Example: Let $A = (0, 1)$, $B = (5, 6)$ (A and B are intervals). Then $A \# B$.

Proof: Define $f: A \to B$ by the following:

$$\forall x \in A \quad f(x) = 5 + x.$$

Let us now show that

$$f: A \xrightarrow[onto]{1\text{-}1} B.$$

Clearly, f is a function and $D_f = A$. Let $f(x) = f(y)$ for $x, y \in A$. Then

$$x + 5 = y + 5$$

so that $\qquad\qquad x = y.$

Hence f is *1-1*. Let $z \in B$. Then

$$5 < z < 6,$$

so that $\qquad\qquad 0 < z - 5 < 1.$

Hence $\quad z - 5 \in D_f \quad$ and $\quad f(z - 5) = (z - 5) + 5 = z.$

Therefore $\qquad\qquad z \in R_f \quad$ and $\quad f$ is *onto*.

We have shown all the necessary things in order to conclude that f is a *1-1* correspondence between A and B. Thus by definition $A \# B$.

Example: Let $A = [0, 1]$, $B = [0, 5]$. Then $A \# B$.

Proof: Let $f: A \to B$ be defined by

$$\forall x \in A \quad f(x) = 5x.$$

Note that f is well defined. That is, for any number x in the interval $[0, 1]$, there exists a unique image, namely, the number $5x$. Note also that if $0 \le x \le 1$, then $0 \le 5x \le 5$. (proof of *onto*) If $y \in B$, then $1/5y \in A$ and $f(1/5y) = y$. (proof of *one-one*) Assume $f(x) = f(z)$.

Then $\qquad\qquad 5x = 5z,$

from which $\qquad\qquad x = z,$

and hence $\qquad \forall x, z \in A \quad f(x) = f(z) \implies x = z.$

We have shown that

$$f: A \xrightarrow[onto]{1\text{-}1} B.$$

Therefore $A \# B$.

If $A \# B$, then clearly $B \# A$

since $\qquad f: A \xrightarrow[onto]{1\text{-}1} B \implies f^{-1}: B \xrightarrow[onto]{1\text{-}1} A.$

Question: If $A \# B$ and $B \# C$, then does it follow that $A \# C$? If so, how would you prove it? (We shall return to this below.)

Note that the assertion that A and B are cardinally equivalent does not imply that we can actually *exhibit* a *1-1* correspondence between A and B, but only that such a correspondence *exists*. (Of course, as was mentioned earlier, one of the most common methods of proving the *existence* of an object is to actually produce such an object.)

Composition of Relations

Recall that a relation in $A \times B$ "relates" A and B by "connecting" or "pairing" their respective elements. Consider that a set A is related to B by a relation T_1 and that B is in turn related to a set C by the relation T_2.

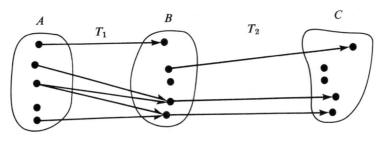

FIG. 1.34

The diagram (Figure 1.34) suggests that in a very natural way a relation is induced between A and C. If there is a path from an element in A to an element of C, then these elements are taken to be related. The following definition makes this idea precise.

1.13-2 Definition: If $T_1 \subset A \times B$ and $T_2 \subset B \times C$, then $T_1 \circ T_2 \subset A \times C$ is given by

$$T_1 \circ T_2 = \{(x, z): (x, y) \in T_1 \text{ and } (y, z) \in T_2 \text{ for some } y \in B\}$$

("$T_1 \circ T_2$" is read "T_1 composed with T_2.").

Remark: Using the notation given in Definition 1.9-7, the set description for $T_1 \circ T_2$ could be replaced by the statement

$$x T_1 \circ T_2 z \iff x T_1 y \text{ and } y T_2 z \text{ for some } y \in B.$$

Example: Let $A = \{a, b, c\}$, $B = \{1, 2, 3\}$, $C = \{5, 10, 15\}$, and

$$T_1 = \{(a, 1), (a, 2), (b, 3)\},$$
$$T_2 = \{(1, 5), (1, 10), (3, 10)\}.$$

Then

$$T_1 \circ T_2 = \{(a, 5), (a, 10), (b, 10)\}.$$

Example: Let $A = \{1, 7, 9\}$, $B = \{\text{Apple, pig}\}$
$C = \{\text{Glenda, Gurney, Grant}\}$, and suppose T_1 and T_2 are such that

$$1T_1 \text{ apple}, \qquad 1T_1 \text{ pig}, \qquad 7T_1 \text{ pig}$$

and

$$\text{apple } T_2 \text{ Gurney} \qquad \text{pig } T_2 \text{ Grant}.$$

Then

$$1T_1 \circ T_2 \text{ Gurney}, \qquad 1T_1 \circ T_2 \text{ Grant}, \qquad 7T_1 \circ T_2 \text{ Grant}.$$

Question: Does $T_1 \circ T_2 = T_2 \circ T_1$?
Question: If $R_{T_1} \cap D_{T_2} = \varnothing$, then what is $T_1 \circ T_2$?

Composition as an Associative Binary Operation On the Collection of All Relations

If A and B are subsets of some universe U, then any relation $T \subset A \times B$ can also be considered to be a relation $T \subset U \times U$. We notice then that composition of relations "$\circ$" is a binary operation on the collection of all relations. That is, if $T \subset U \times U$ and $S \subset U \times U$, then $T \circ S \subset U \times U$. Note that in general, $T \circ S \neq S \circ T$ (why?) which suggests also the question of associativity.

1.13-3 Theorem: If $S \subset U \times U$, $T \subset U \times U$, and $V \subset U \times U$, then

$$(S \circ T) \circ V = S \circ (T \circ V).$$

Proof: Assume $(x, v) \in (S \circ T) \circ V$.

Therefore $\exists y \quad (x, y) \in S \circ T$ and $(y, v) \in V$,

$\quad\quad \exists y (\exists z \quad (x, z) \in S$ and $(z, y) \in T)$ and $(y, v) \in V$,

$\quad\quad \exists z \quad ((x, z) \in S)$ and $(\exists y \quad (z, y) \in T$ and $(y, v) \in V)$,

$\quad\quad \exists z \quad (x, z) \in S$ and $(z, v) \in T \circ V$,

from which $\quad\quad (x, v) \in S \circ (T \circ V)$.

Hence $\quad\quad (S \circ T) \circ V \subset S \circ (T \circ V)$.

The proof of the reverse inclusion is similar. Therefore

$$(S \circ T) \circ V = S \circ (T \circ V). \ \square$$

Composition of Functions

Since a function is a relation, composition of functions is automatically defined. It is not difficult to show that the collection of functions is closed under composition. That is, if f and g are functions, then $f \circ g$ is a function.

98

We have seen that one may view a function as a set, or as a rule, with a certain property (the "unique image" property). In this and a later section, we shall discuss how one can view functions simply as elements of a set $\mathcal{F}$ of functions. (For historical reasons, a set $\mathcal{F}$ of functions is often called a "function space" by mathematicians.) It will turn out that we can define operations (such as addition and multiplication) on the class of functions, and thus we could ask questions about the closure of the class under the operations in question. We shall also investigate whether these operations are commutative, associative, etc. The point to remember as we proceed in this section is that we can consider functions to be (abstract) elements in a set, and that we can talk about performing operations on these elements to obtain other such elements.

There is some confusion which exists in the notation surrounding composition of functions. If composition were a commutative operation, the confusion would not occur; however, since it does, it is best that you be prepared for it. In stating our definition of "$T \circ S$" it was very natural to think in terms of the notation "$aT \circ Sb$" as meaning that a is T related to something that is S related to b. Our habit of reading from left to right, and consequently our habit of drawing functional diagrams with arrows running from left to right, along with having the domain elements of functions given on the left as first components in the ordered pairs, led us naturally into our definition. If we restrict ourselves to functions, then our definition corresponds very well with the notation "xf" as being the image of x under f. If we compose two functions f and g, then $(x)f \circ g = ((x)f)g$. That is, we merely follow x along through the functions from left to right as our definition stated we should. However, we also have the habit of writing $f(x)$ to indicate the image of x under f. When using this notation in connection with composition, we like to have $f \circ g(x) = f(g(x))$. As a result, we are forced to write "$f \circ g$" when perhaps we really mean "$g \circ f$." There is of course, no confusion when we are talking about the image of some point. That is, if one writes "$(x)f \circ g$" it is clear that he means "$((x)f)g$" and if one writes "$f \circ g(x)$" it means "$f(g(x))$." Confusion arises when the discussion involves only the functions, where one needs to write simply "$f \circ g$" (which in general does not equal "$g \circ f$"). It is always the case, then, that the reader must be told in advance how the writer is writing his compositions. We shall endeavor to make this clear when writing symbols of the form "$f \circ g$."

Composition and Cardinality

Example: Consider functions f and g in $R \times R$ defined by

$$f(x) = 2x + 1 \quad \text{and} \quad g(x) = x^2 - 1.$$
$$f(2) = 5 \quad \text{and} \quad g(5) = 24$$

hence
$$g \circ f(2) = g(f(2)) = g(5) = 24.$$

$$2 \xrightarrow{f} 5 \xrightarrow{g} 24$$

or perhaps a better diagram for our "backwards" composition would be

$$24 \xleftarrow{g} 5 \xleftarrow{f} 2.$$

Example: Give a formula which describes $g \circ f(x)$ and $f \circ g(x)$ where
$$f(x) = 2x + 1 \text{ and } g(x) = x^2 - 1.$$

We solve this as follows:

Given an arbitrary $a \in R$, we trace a through f then g

$$g \circ f(a) = g(f(a)) = g(2a + 1) = (2a + 1)^2 - 1 = 4a^2 + 4a.$$

Hence, $\qquad \forall x \quad g \circ f(x) = g(f(x)) = 4x^2 + 4x.$

Similarly, if $b \in R$, then

$$f \circ g(b) = f(g(b)) = f(b^2 - 1) = 2(b^2 - 1) + 1 = 2b^2 - 1.$$
Hence

$$f \circ g(x) = f(g(x)) = 2x^2 - 1 \qquad \text{for all } x \in R.$$

We are now in a position to answer a question we posed earlier.

1.13-4 Theorem: If $A \# B$ and $B \# C$, then $A \# C$.

Proof: We know that there exist f and g such that

$$f: A \xrightarrow[\text{onto}]{1\text{-}1} B \qquad \text{and} \qquad g: B \xrightarrow[\text{onto}]{1\text{-}1} C. \qquad \text{(Why?)}$$

We shall show that

$$f \circ g: A \xrightarrow[\text{onto}]{1\text{-}1} C.$$

(Here we mean $x \in A \Rightarrow (x)f \circ g \in C$.)

i) $f \circ g$ is a function (see Exercise 10) and $D_{f \circ g} = A$ (see Exercise 14).

ii) $z \in C \Rightarrow (z)g^{-1} \in B \Rightarrow ((z)g^{-1})f^{-1} \in A \Rightarrow z \in R_{f \circ g}.$ Therefore $f \circ g$ is *onto*.

iii) Let $(x, y), (z, y) \in f \circ g.$

Therefore $\qquad (x, p) \in f$ and $(p, y) \in g$ for some $p,$

and $\qquad\qquad (z, q) \in f$ and $(q, y) \in g$ for some $q.$

But since g is *one-one*, $p = q$. It follows, since f is *one-one* that $x = z.$
Therefore $f \circ g$ is *one-one*. ☐

Exercises 1.13

1. Show that $A \# B$ where

$$A = \{\pi, 3/4, 7, 21\}$$
$$B = \{\text{Gurney, Glenda, Grant, Ole}\}$$

2. Find two sets A and B which are not cardinally equivalent.

3. Show that every set is cardinally equivalent to itself.

4. Show that $[0, 1] \# [0, 25]$.

5. Let $T = \{(1, 2), (5, 7), (5, 5), (6, 7), (7, 9)\}$
   $S = \{(9, 5), (6, 3), (7, 7), (4, 1)\}$, then give a list description of
   a) $T \circ S$ b) $S \circ T$ (Left to right composition.)

6. If T and S are defined by:

   $a\ T\ b$ $1\ T\ 7$ $5\ T\ a$ $7\ T\ b$ $7\ T\ 9$

   $5\ S\ a$ $b\ S\ 7$ $b\ S\ 48$ $9\ S\ 9$

then list the ordered pairs in $S \circ T$ and $T \circ S$.

7. Let $f: R \to R$ and $g: R \to R$ be defined by:
   $$(x)f = 6x + 3 \quad \forall x \in R$$
   $$(x)g = 9x^2 + 1 \quad \forall x \in R$$

Determine:
   a) $(x)f \circ g$ b) $(x)g \circ f$

8. Determine a formula for $f \circ g(x)$ and $g \circ f(x)$ where
   a) $f(x) = 6x + 2$, $g(x) = 3x^2 + x + 1$
   b) $f(x) = 4 - x^2$, $g(x) = 2x + 2$
   c) $f(x) = x$, $g(x) = 7x^2 - 4$
   d) $f(x) = 3 + x^3$, $g(x) = 2x$

9. Let $y = f(x)$ and $z = g(x)$. Determine $f \circ g(3)$ and $g \circ f(3)$ where
   a) $y = 7x - 3$, $z = x^2 + 2$ c) $y = 2 - 3x^2$, $z = 4x^2 - 1$
   b) $y = 6x^2$, $z = x + 1$ d) $y = 4$, $z = 7x$

10. Show that the collection of functions is closed under "$\circ$."

11. Show that if f and g are 1-1 functions, then $f \circ g$ is 1-1 and $(f \circ g)^{-1} = g^{-1} \circ f^{-1}$.

12. Show that if $f: A \overset{1\text{-}1}{\to} B$ and $g: B \overset{1\text{-}1}{\to} C$, then $f \circ g: A \overset{1\text{-}1}{\to} C$.

13. Is $(0, 1) \# R$? (*I.e.*: are there as many real numbers between 0 and 1 as there are real numbers?)

14. Show that if $f: A \to B$ and $g: C \to D$, then $D_{f \circ g} = A$ iff $R_f \subset C$.

15. Give examples to show that the following statements are false.
   a) $f: A \overset{1\text{-}1}{\to} B$ and $g: B \underset{onto}{\longrightarrow} C \Rightarrow f \circ g: A \overset{1\text{-}1}{\to} C$

   $f: A \overset{1\text{-}1}{\to} B$ and $g: B \underset{onto}{\longrightarrow} C \Rightarrow f \circ g: A \underset{onto}{\longrightarrow} C$

   b) $f: A \underset{onto}{\longrightarrow} B$ and $g: B \overset{1\text{-}1}{\to} C \Rightarrow f \circ g: A \overset{1\text{-}1}{\to} C$

   $f: A \underset{onto}{\longrightarrow} B$ and $g: B \overset{1\text{-}1}{\to} C \Rightarrow f \circ g: A \underset{onto}{\longrightarrow} C$

16. Show that if $f: A \to B$ and $g: B \to A$ and if $f \circ g = \{(x, x): x \in A\}$, then f is 1-1 and g is *onto*.

101

17. Give examples of functions such that

   a) $f: A \xrightarrow{1-1} B$ and $g: B \xrightarrow[onto]{} A$ but $f \circ g \neq \{(x, x): x \in A\}$.

   b) $f: A \rightarrow B$ (not *onto*) and $g: B \rightarrow A$ (not *1-1*) but
   $$f \circ g = \{(x, x): x \in A\}$$
   and
   $$g \circ f = \{(x, x): x \in B\}.$$

18. Suppose $f: A \xrightarrow[onto]{1-1} B$ and $g: B \xrightarrow[onto]{1-1} C$, so that $f \circ g$ has an inverse $(f \circ g)^{-1}: C \rightarrow A$. What can you say about $(f \circ g)^{-1}$ in terms of f^{-1} and g^{-1}? (Compare with Exercise 11.)

19. Investigate:

   a) If $\#A = n$ for some $n \in N$ and if $f: A \xrightarrow[onto]{} A$, then f is *1-1*.

   b) If $\#A = n$ for some $n \in N$ and if $f: A \xrightarrow{1-1} A$, then f is *onto*.

   c) If A is infinite, then a), b) need not hold.

20. If A and B are nonempty sets, show that $A \times B \,\#\, B \times A$.

21. Let f and g be defined by
   $$\forall x \quad f(x) = x + 1 \qquad \forall x \quad g(x) = x^2.$$
   a) How would $f \circ g$ be defined?
   b) How about $g \circ f$?
   c) How would you describe f^{-1} and g^{-1}?

22. Let f and g be defined by
   $$f(x) = x^2 + 2x + 1 \qquad g(x) = 3.$$
   How would you describe:

   a) $f(1/x)$ b) $f(x^2)$ c) $f(2x)$ d) $f(x - 1)$

   Do the same for g.

23. If $g(x) = f(1/x)$, and $f(x) = 2x + 1$, then
   a) $g(3) =$ c) $g(5) =$
   b) $g(1/x) =$ d) $g(1/5) =$
   e) g may be thought of as a composition of what two functions?

24. If $f(x) = x^2 + 3x$, then true or false. If false, correct the statement.
   a) $f(1/x) = 1/x^2 + 3x$ c) $f(-x) = -f(x)$
   b) $f(2x) = 2f(x)$ d) $f(x + y) = f(x) + f(y)$

2

ADVANCED
FOUNDATIONS

2.1 Simple Proofs in the Abstract

Since the study of mathematics is heavily involved with deciding whether a particular statement can be deduced as a result of other statements, it is worthwhile to hesitate once again and examine the logical machinery used to make such decisions,

It is helpful if, in the process of learning to reason deductively, we "strip" our system of any mathematical meaning, leaving only logical inference patterns to be studied. Some students find this very frustrating while others enjoy it immensely; however, in either case, one's understanding of the deductive process is enhanced by such "exercise in the abstract."

Some Basic Rules of Reasoning

We wish to discuss some specific logical arguments which can be used to add more "true sentences" to a given collection of "truths." The axiomatic method used throughout mathematics consists of beginning with a collection of facts considered to be true and then transforming this collection into a larger body of true sentences by using logical processes. In this section we examine some fundamental "valid arguments" which we feel can logically be used to extend a mathematical system. To illustrate these arguments we will use a *one-line (inference) diagram*. A one-line diagram consists of a single horizontal line with a list of statements above the line (considered to be true statements) and a single statement below the line (considered to be a logical consequence of the statements above the line). In short, we feel that the statement below the line is inferred by those above.

Example:

$$\frac{\text{Glenda and Grant have the same father, Gurnie is Grant's father}}{\text{Gurnie is Glenda's father}}.$$

We wish, moreover, to list only inference patterns or "structural inferences" that indicate which sentences can be deduced as a result of their interrelationship with other true sentences, through the four basic connectives "and," "or," "not," "implies." It is important to keep in mind that the symbols we use to indicate sentences are "sentential variables" and are used only to make a *pattern*. They do not name specific sentences.

We have already discussed the way in which we expect to arrive at a new truth when the sentence "p" is among our true sentences along with the sentence "$p \Rightarrow q$." (See Section 1.1.) In this case, we feel that "q" should also be listed among our body of truths. The following example is a one-line diagram indicating this method of deducing a true sentence.

Example: $$\frac{p,\, p \Rightarrow q}{q}$$

Observe that "p" and "$p \Rightarrow q$," the sentences considered to be true, are listed above the line and the new sentence "q" (considered to be true by logical inference) is below the line. What we mean, of course, is that if we find a particular sentence in our body of mathematical facts and also a sentence produced by connecting the given sentence to another by the connective "implies," then the second sentence in the implication follows as a result. The sentence which is denoted by "p" is entirely arbitrary, but in any given context, the p must be replaced by the same sentence throughout the pattern.

Let us now introduce certain rules of reasoning which we will use and which we hope you agree are logical. If you do not agree in every case that the rule is the "common sense, intuitive" thing, then it is up to you to train your "common sense intuition," since in every case we have chosen the prevailing point of view used by mathematicians and logicians.

The following, in the form of one line diagrams, is a list of some basic rules for introducing and eliminating the four connectives discussed in Section 1.1.

Logic Axioms

LA 1. $\dfrac{p}{\text{not-(not-}p)}$ (DD 1. *double denial 1*)

LA 2. $\dfrac{\text{not-(not-}p)}{p}$ (DD 2. *double denial 2*)

LA 3. $\dfrac{p}{p \text{ or } q}$

LA 4. $\dfrac{p \text{ or } q, \text{ not-}q}{p}$

LA 5. $\dfrac{p, q}{p \text{ and } q}$

LA 6. $\dfrac{p \text{ and } q}{p}$

LA 7. $\dfrac{q}{p \Rightarrow q}$

LA 8. $\dfrac{p \Rightarrow q, p}{q}$ *(modus ponens)*

LA 9. $\dfrac{p \Rightarrow q, \text{ not-}q}{\text{not-}p}$ *(modus tolens)*

LA 10. $\dfrac{p \text{ and } q}{q \text{ and } p}$

LA 11. $\dfrac{p \text{ or } q}{q \text{ or } p}$

Question: Do these inference patterns agree with the truth tables in Section 1.1?

Example: Suppose we had a mathematical system in which the following statements appeared among the axioms or existing theorems.

1. Blobs are blurbs.
2. Blobs fit or golns grit.
3. Golns don't grit.

It would then be possible to add:

4. Blobs are blurbs or cows fly.

Proof: $\dfrac{\text{Blobs are blurbs}}{\text{Blobs are blurbs or cows fly}}$ (LA 3.)

Also, we could deduce:

5. Blobs fit.

Proof: $\dfrac{\text{Blobs fit or golns grit, Golns don't grit}}{\text{Blobs fit}}$ (LA 4.)

We could also deduce:

6. Blobs are blurbs and golns don't grit.

Proof: (LA 5)   and statements (1) and (3).).

Remark: Usually a mathematical proof would not include the diagram structure, but would merely indicate, as we have done in this case, which statements have been used and give a hint as to the logic involved.

Once we have deduced a theorem, then it may be used above the line in a proof in order to deduce another result. Thus we may now add:

7. Blobs fit and blobs are blurbs.

Proof: (Statement (5), (1), and LA 5.)

It may be the case that in trying to prove a particular fact, one cannot find an acceptable logic pattern from which he can immediately deduce the fact. However, sometimes one can deduce a new intermediate fact (a lemma) and then use it, as we did in the previous example to deduce (7). If we had tried to arrive at (7) without previously deducing (5) we would not have had a pattern in our list that would allow us to deduce (7).

Exercises 2.1

1. Let the following list be a collection of axioms for some mathematical system.
   a) Cats are not red.
   b) Dogs are blue.
   c) Pigs are green implies cats are red.
   d) Dogs are blue implies canaries are pink.

Which of the following statements follow logically from the axioms?
   1) Dogs are green.
   2) Cats are not red or dogs are green.
   3) Canaries are pink.
   4) Canaries are pink implies dogs are blue.
   5) Pigs are not green.

Indicate a reason for the statements which follow logically by giving one Logic Axiom and the mathematical statements used to make the deduction.

2. Let the following be a collection of axioms for some mathematical system.
   a) If a line is long, then it is straight.
   b) A plane is flat.
   c) If a plane is flat, then a line is long.
   d) A point is small or a plane is not flat.

Deduce some theorems and then prove them.

3. Consider the following as a list of axioms for a mathematical system.
   a) A and B
   b) A implies C
   c) C implies not-D
   d) D or F
   e) H implies not-B

Prove the following theorems according to the previously given rules by indicating one inference pattern along with the necessary number of known facts from the mathematical system. (It may first be necessary to deduce a lemma in some cases.)
   1) A 3) F 5) C implies A
   2) C 4) not-H

Conjecture and prove other theorems about the system. Can you conjecture a statement which can be neither proved nor disproved? (To disprove a statement *p* is to prove the statement not-*p*.)

2.2 Extending the Logic

In general, a mathematical proof involves thinking patterns which are more complex than the simple arguments that we diagrammed in the previous section. A proof will often involve a discussion which indicates how a given sentence will fit into a certain logic inference, along with an explanation about why the inference pattern is valid. We now turn our attention to the process of deriving and proving other useful, and more sophisticated, valid inference patterns. A workable approach to mathematics would be to have a very long list of valid inference patterns and then to test all of the mathematical facts against each pattern to see if any new results could be obtained. Although this is not what is done altogether, it is done to a limited extent. Let us temporarily approach our subject from this point of view. We thereby use our small list of valid arguments along with some very primitive thinking processes to extend to a larger list of valid arguments.

A Comparison of Mathematical Systems, Logic, and Meta-Logic

Let us pause here to discuss, in a philosophical sense, exactly what we are trying to do. We are considering the process of attaching additional true statements (theorems) to a consistent mathematical system. We deduce these mathematical theorems using a process commonly called logic. (That is, logic is the tool used to "manufacture" mathematics.) We wish to assess carefully which logical processes we will accept. In order to do this, we need to examine a list of valid arguments. In examining this list of valid arguments, we must enter into some discussion. A discussion requires the existence of a language. The language used to discuss logic is called *meta-language*. In order to carry out sensible discussions using the meta-language, it must be the case that there is a "meta-logic." We therefore wish to apply meta-logic to "derive" additional valid arguments (logic theorems) to a given list of valid arguments. Perhaps the diagram in Figure 2.1 will clarify this discussion.

It is clear that any attempt to finalize this process of rising up to meta-logic to examine the logic we are using; to meta-meta-logic to examine the meta-logic; etc., would be useless. We hope, however, that we can reach a stage at which the difference between the thinking processes of any two given people is extremely small. In fact, we strive to rise to a sufficiently primitive level

107

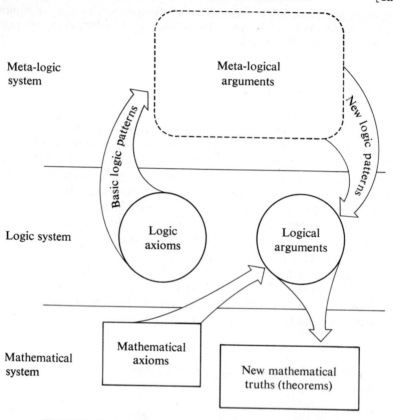

FIG. 2.1 By reasoning about the logic we use, we build a large logic system. In turn this system is used to deduce new mathematical truths (theorems). In reasoning about logic, we make use of "meta-logic."

so that there is no difference whatsoever in the associated "meta" type logic. It is, of course, impossible to determine whether this can be done.

In describing the thinking (logical) processes used to deduce theorems (more valid inference patterns) about our logic, we do not intend to formalize to any extent. We shall be content merely to show some proofs, along with scant descriptions of what we are doing. We hope that the process is sufficiently primitive that nearly all intelligent beings would agree that we have deduced new valid arguments.

Conditionalizing and Discharging a Premise

An essential part of any working logical process is the concept of *conditionalizing* and *discharging* a premise. This consists of temporarily assuming a fact, then using in an argument that fact, along with other true statements. We then indicate, in the final results, that they were obtained by assuming the first fact. The following one-line diagram illustrates this idea.

$$p*$$
$$\cdot$$
$$\cdot$$
$$\cdot$$
$$\frac{q}{p \Rightarrow q}*$$

The $p*$ indicates that p is an assumed premise and the diagram indicates that by using in a legitimate way other known facts, one has arrived at q. The statement "p implies q" is arrived at as a final result; the $*$ on the line indicates that the assumed premise "p" has been "discharged." This "conditionalizing and discharging" process is an extremely important process by which we shall deduce additional valid arguments.

Multi-Line Diagram Proofs of Logic Theorems

We wish to describe informally the process by which we will deduce and prove logic theorems. The process is primarily one of implication type thinking, combined with some primitive notions of step by step processes.

A *multi-line diagram* derivation (proof) will consist of:

1) A *major line* above which is listed a collection of sentences (premises).

2) A "tree type" structure below the major line consisting of "branches" connected together as a result of some previously accepted inference pattern (or as a result of discharging some temporarily assumed premise).

3) The trunk, or final sentence, which is considered to be a valid result deducible from the collection of sentences above the line.

4) The collapsing of the diagram and the acceptance of the new pattern as being a new valid inference. We will shortly clarify this with some examples, but first we note some "rules of deduction." In the construction of such a proof, the following rules must be carefully observed.

a) Any top branch (first statement listed below the major line) must either come from the list above the major line or be appropriately marked as a temporarily assumed premise.

b) Any statement derived as a result of other statements must be a result of some already known inference pattern (be in the list of logic axioms or known theorems), or be a result of discharging some temporary premise.

c) Any temporarily assumed premise must be discharged at some point in the diagram.

Example:
$$\frac{p \Rightarrow q, \; q \Rightarrow r}{p \Rightarrow r}$$

109

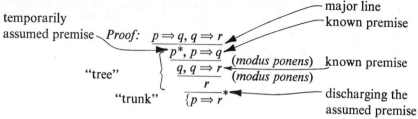

Since the sentences p, q, r were not specified, it is considered that a new inference pattern is the result of the above construction; namely,

$$\frac{p \Rightarrow q,\, q \Rightarrow r}{p \Rightarrow r}.$$

Notice that each statement in the proof below the major line was introduced as a result of one of the following:

a) It was one of the statements above the major line.

b) It was a temporary premise (properly marked) to be discharged later.

c) It was a result of connecting one or more statements with a single line inference pattern which was already accepted.

d) It was the result of properly discharging a temporary premise.

Notice also that each temporary premise ("p" in this case) was discharged.

Example:
$$\frac{p \Rightarrow q}{\sim q \Rightarrow \sim p}$$

Proof:
$$\frac{\dfrac{p \Rightarrow q}{\dfrac{\sim q^*,\, p \Rightarrow q}{\sim p}} \quad (modus\ tolens)}{\sim q \Rightarrow \sim p}^*$$

Remark: The implication "$\sim q \Rightarrow \sim p$" is called the *contrapositive* of the implication "$p \Rightarrow q$."

Example:
$$\frac{(\sim p)\ \text{or}\ q}{p \Rightarrow q}$$

Proof:
$$\frac{\dfrac{(\sim p)\ \text{or}\ q}{q\ \text{or}\ (\sim p)}\ (LA\ 11.),\ \dfrac{p^*}{\sim(\sim p)}\ (DD\ 1.)}{\dfrac{q}{p \Rightarrow q}^*}\ (LA\ 4.)$$

In making derivations of this sort, there are some important things that we have not yet had a chance to illustrate clearly. They are:

1) The major premises (statements above the major line) may be used as often as necessary. (They don't get used up.)

2) A temporary premise may be used more than once, but after it has been discharged it cannot be used again (unless it is again assumed, in which case it must be re-discharged).

3) Several different temporary premises may be marked differently so one can clearly see where each is discharged.

4) The p, s, and q, etc., in the axioms and theorems are pattern space holders and not actual sentences (*i.e.*, they are "sentential variables").

Some Logic Theorems

The following is a list of useful logic theorems which can be deduced using the logic axioms and multi-line diagrams. It is helpful (though not necessary) to prove them in the order in which they are given. This will enable you to take advantage of the fact that one is allowed to use previously proved theorems. Some of them have been proved in the examples above. Several of these logic theorems have been given names, which we indicate below. (These names are not especially important in themselves, however.)

T 1. $\dfrac{q}{p \text{ or } q}$

T 2. $\dfrac{p \text{ and } q}{q}$

T 3. $\dfrac{p \Rightarrow q}{\sim q \Rightarrow \sim p}$ (*rule of contraposition*)

T 4. $\dfrac{p \Rightarrow q,\ q \Rightarrow r}{p \Rightarrow r}$ (*syllogism*)

T 5. $\dfrac{p \Rightarrow \sim q}{q \Rightarrow \sim p}$

T 6. $\dfrac{\sim p \Rightarrow q}{\sim q \Rightarrow p}$

T 7. $\dfrac{\sim p \Rightarrow \sim q}{q \Rightarrow p}$

T 8. $\dfrac{q,\ \sim q}{p}$ (*rule of contradiction*)

Proof:
$$
\begin{array}{cl}
q,\ \sim q & \\
\hline
q & \\
\hline
\sim p \Rightarrow q,\ \sim q & \text{(LA 7.)} \\
\hline
\sim\sim p & \text{(LA 9.)} \\
\hline
p & \text{(LA 2.)}
\end{array}
$$

Remark: This theorem shows why mathematicians are concerned about their systems being consistent (*i.e.*, not containing as true sentences both q and $\sim q$). Thus if a system contains a contradiction, *any* statement in the system is a theorem, and the whole system reduces to trivia.

111

T 9. $\dfrac{\sim p \Rightarrow p}{p}$

T 10. $\dfrac{(\sim p \Rightarrow q), (\sim p \Rightarrow \sim q)}{p}$ (*proof by contradiction*)

Proof:

$$\cfrac{\cfrac{\cfrac{\sim p \Rightarrow q, \ \sim p \Rightarrow \sim q}{\sim p \Rightarrow \sim q}}{\cfrac{\sim p \Rightarrow q, \quad q \Rightarrow p}{\cfrac{\sim p \Rightarrow p}{p}}}}{}$$

(T 7.)
(T 4.)
(T 9.)

T 11. $\dfrac{p \Rightarrow q, \ p \Rightarrow \sim q}{\sim p}$

T 12. $\dfrac{p \Rightarrow q, \ \sim p \Rightarrow q}{q}$ (*proof by cases*)

T 13. $\dfrac{p \text{ or } q, \ p \Rightarrow r, \ q \Rightarrow r}{r}$ (*dilemma*)

T 14. $\dfrac{p \Rightarrow (q \Rightarrow r)}{(p \text{ and } q) \Rightarrow r}$ (*importation*)

T 15. $\dfrac{(p \text{ and } q) \Rightarrow r}{p \Rightarrow (q \Rightarrow r)}$ (*exportation*)

T 16. $\dfrac{p \Rightarrow q}{\sim p \text{ or } q}$

T 17. $\dfrac{\sim p \text{ or } q}{p \Rightarrow q}$

T 18. $\dfrac{p \Rightarrow (q \text{ and } \sim q)}{\sim p}$

There are many more inference patterns which are valid results of the simple patterns with which we started. We do not wish to spend the entire course studying logic, so we will hope that the patterns we already have, along with the intuitive feeling about implications you have developed, will suffice. Occasionally throughout the text we will elaborate on certain important points of logic. When it is convenient, we shall give a one-line diagram which indicates the primary inference pattern used. Where it might be helpful to the student, we have included a multi-line diagram indicating the structure of a proof, along with the proof itself.

Exercises 2.2

1. Prove the logic theorems given above in the order in which they are given.
2. Show that LA 7. could be derived from the other axioms, using the described method of proof.

3. Prove the following logic patterns:

a) $\dfrac{(p \text{ and } q) \text{ and } r}{p \text{ and } (q \text{ and } r)}$

d) $\dfrac{p \text{ and } (q \text{ and } r)}{(p \text{ and } q) \text{ and } (p \text{ and } r)}$

b) $\dfrac{p \text{ and } (q \text{ or } r)}{(p \text{ and } q) \text{ or } (p \text{ and } r)}$

e) $\dfrac{p \text{ or } (q \text{ or } r)}{(p \text{ or } q) \text{ or } (p \text{ or } r)}$

c) $\dfrac{p \text{ or } (q \text{ and } r)}{(p \text{ or } q) \text{ and } (p \text{ or } r)}$

4. Investigate (prove or disprove). Which of the following are valid inference diagrams?

a) $\dfrac{(p \Rightarrow q) \text{ and } \sim q}{\sim p}$

e) $\dfrac{p \Rightarrow r}{(p \text{ or } q) \Rightarrow r}$

b) $\dfrac{(p \text{ and } q) \Rightarrow r}{p \Rightarrow r}$

f) $\dfrac{\sim (p \Rightarrow r)}{p \text{ and } r}$

c) $\dfrac{p \Rightarrow r}{(p \text{ and } q) \Rightarrow r}$

g) $\dfrac{\sim (p \Rightarrow r)}{p \text{ or } r}$

d) $\dfrac{(p \text{ or } q) \Rightarrow r}{p \Rightarrow r}$

5. Show that if a statement can be proved using the axioms and a number of "new truths" (theorems) derived from the axioms, then it can be derived directly from the axioms alone.

6. State and prove De Morgan's Laws.

2.3 More About Quantifiers

In Section 1.5 we discussed informally the use of the quantifiers "for all" ($\forall$) and "for some" ($\exists$). We would like to formally introduce the accepted logic patterns for proving and applying sentences which contain quantified variables. From there, we shall prove some fairly elaborate inference patterns which can be used in mathematical arguments.

Proving and Applying a Generalization "$\forall x \in S, p(x)$"

The pattern for proving a statement "$\forall x \in S, p(x)$," where S is some set, is as follows.

2.3-1 Logic Axiom: (The test pattern principle) (Universal generalization)

113

Assume $a \in S^*$ (arbitrary a, fixed but unspecified)

.

. $\left\{\begin{array}{l}\text{arguments which use no special} \\ \text{properties of } a, \text{ except that } a \in S\end{array}\right\}$

.

$$\dfrac{p(a)}{\forall x \in S,\, p(x)}^*$$ (discharge the assumption)

The pattern for applying a generalization is given in what follows. The concept is sometimes verbalized by saying "each instance is a consequence of the generalization."

2.3-2 Logic Axiom: $\dfrac{\forall x \in S\, p(x),\; a \in S}{p(a)}$ (*Universal instantiation*)

Proving and Applying an Existence Statement
"$\exists x \in S\; p(x)$"

2.3-3 Logic Axiom: $\dfrac{p(a),\; a \in S}{\exists x \in S,\, p(x)}$ (*Existential generalization*)

This axiom states the simple fact that if you have found one object a with a given property, then it is possible to relax the statement involving "a" explicitly and merely assert that such an object exists.

The next inference pattern is slightly more subtle. This pattern asserts that if we know the existence of some element such that p is true (possibly more than one), then we may assume that we can "select" one such element (give it a name) and proceed from there.

2.3-4 Logic Axiom: $\dfrac{\exists x \in S,\, p(x)}{p(a) \text{ and } a \in S}$ (*Existential specification*)

Very often in applying these inference patterns, a subscripted letter is used instead of shifting between a's and x's. This procedure can be observed in the proof of the following inference pattern.

2.3-5 Logic Theorem: $\dfrac{\forall x \in S \quad \forall y \in T \quad p(x, y)}{\forall y \in T \quad \forall x \in S \quad p(x, y)}$

Proof: $\underline{\forall x \in S \quad \forall y \in T\, p(x, y)}$

$$\dfrac{y_1 \in T^*,\; \dfrac{x_1 \in S^+,\; \forall x \in S \quad \forall y \in T \quad p(x, y)}{\forall y \in T \quad p(x_1, y)}}{\dfrac{p(x_1, y_1)}{\dfrac{\forall x \in S \quad p(x, y_1)}{\forall y \in T \quad \forall x \in{}^* S \; p(x, y)}}} \qquad \square$$

Perhaps the above proof seems a bit dull, since the fact is so obvious. We shall soon prove some facts which are not so obvious. Moreover, some patterns which appear "obvious" are not even true. (These are known as "student theorems.") The next theorem is one which will often prove useful. Perhaps even more important is the knowledge that the converse is a "student theorem."

2.3-6 Logic Theorem: $\dfrac{\exists x \in S \ \ \forall y \in T\, p(x, y)}{\forall y \in T \ \ \exists x \in S\, p(x, y)}$

Proof:
$$\dfrac{\dfrac{\dfrac{\dfrac{\exists x \in S \ \ \forall y \in T\, p(x, y)}{y_1 \in T^* \ \ \ \forall y \in T\, p(x_1, y)}}{p(x_1, y_1)}}{\exists x \in S\, p(x, y_1)}}{\forall y \in T \ \ \exists x \in S\, p(x, y)}{}^*$$ $\Box$

Exercise: Try to prove the pattern $\dfrac{\forall y \in T \ \ \exists x \in S\, p(x, y)}{\exists x \in S \ \ \forall y \in T\, p(x, y)}$. This pattern is not valid and if you succeed in "proving" it, then you should search your proof for some bad reasoning. You should also note that this is indeed the *converse* of the preceding theorem.

2.3-7 Logic Theorem: $\dfrac{\forall y \in T \ \forall x \in S\, p(x) \text{ and } q(y),\ T \neq \varnothing,\ S \neq \varnothing}{\forall x \in S\, p(x) \text{ and } \forall y \in T\, q(y)}$

Proof:
$$\dfrac{\dfrac{\dfrac{x_1 \in S^*,\ \forall x \in S \ \ \forall y \in T \ \ p(x) \text{ and } q(y)}{\forall y \in T \ \ p(x_1) \text{ and } q(y)} \quad \dfrac{T \neq \varnothing}{y_1 \in T}}{p(x_1) \text{ and } q(y_1)}}{\dfrac{p(x_1)}{\forall x \in S \ \ p(x)}{}^*}$$

$$\dfrac{\dfrac{\dfrac{\begin{array}{l} S \neq \varnothing, \\ x_2 \in S \\ y_2 \in T^{\ddagger}, \end{array} \quad \forall x \in S \ \ \forall y \in T\, p(x) \text{ and } q(y)}{\forall y \in T\, p(x_2) \text{ and } q(y)}}{p(x_2) \text{ and } q(y_2)}}{\dfrac{q(y_2)}{\forall y \in T \ \ q(y)}{}^{\ddagger}}$$

Connecting both these branches together, we have

$$\dfrac{\forall x \in S\, p(x), \qquad \forall y \in T\, q(y)}{\forall x \in S\, p(x) \text{ and } \forall y \in T\, q(y)} \qquad \Box$$

As we see in the above proof, it is often the case that ordinary size paper does not allow enough room for the entire tree diagram. Inasmuch as butcher paper is too bulky to carry to class, it is usually the policy to write out proofs in paragraph form, using hints as to how the tree fits together. It is also common to indicate an inference pattern by implication notation ($\Rightarrow$).

2.3-8 Logic Theorem: $\forall x \in S\, p(x)$ or $\forall x \in S\, q(x) \Rightarrow \forall x \in S\, p(x)$ or $q(x)$.

Proof: Let $x_1 \in S$ and assume not-$p(x_1)$. Therefore

$$\text{not-}\forall x \in S\, p(x) \quad (\textit{See exercise 7.})$$

115

From which $\quad\quad \forall x \in S\, q(x)$ (*Theorem hypothesis*)

and so $\quad\quad\quad\quad\quad\quad q(x_1).$

Therefore $\quad\quad\quad$ if not-$p(x_1)$, then $q(x_1)$

from which $\quad\quad\quad p(x_1) \quad$ or $\quad q(x_1).$

Hence $\quad\quad\quad \forall x \in S \;\; p(x) \quad$ or $\quad q(x).$ ☐

2.3-9 Logic Theorem: $\dfrac{\text{not-}\exists x \in S\, p(x)}{\forall x \in S\, \text{not-}p(x)}$

Proof: $\quad\quad \dfrac{\text{not-}\exists x \in S\, p(x)}{a \in S^*, \quad\quad\quad p(a)^{\ne}}$ (*Existential generalization*)

$$\dfrac{\exists x \in S\, p(x) \quad\quad \text{not-}\exists x \in S\, p(x)}{\exists x \in S\, p(x) \text{ and not-}\exists x \in S\, p(x)} \text{ (LA 5.)}$$

$$\dfrac{p(a) \Rightarrow \exists x \in S\, p(x) \text{ and not-}\exists x \in S\, p(x)}{}{}^{\ne} \text{ (T 18.)}$$

$$\dfrac{\text{not-}p(a)}{\forall x \in S\, \text{not-}p(x)}{}^{*} \text{ (*Universal generalization*)} \;☐$$

2.3-10 Logic Theorem: $\dfrac{\text{not-}\forall x \in S\, p(x)}{\exists x \in S\, \text{not-}p(x)}$

Proof:

$$\dfrac{\text{not-}\forall x \in S\, p(x)}{\text{not-}\exists x \in S\, \text{not-}p(x)*} \text{ (2.3-9)}$$

$$\dfrac{}{\forall x \in S\, \text{not-not-}p(x)} \text{ (*Double denial*)}$$

$$\dfrac{\forall x \in S\, p(x) \quad\quad \text{not-}\forall x \in S\, p(x)}{\forall x \in S\, p(x) \text{ and not-}\forall x \in S\, p(x)} \text{ (LA 5)}$$

$$\dfrac{[\text{not-}\exists x \in S\, \text{not-}p(x)] \Rightarrow [\forall x \in S\, p(x) \text{ and not-}\forall x \in S\, p(x)]}{\text{not-not-}\exists x \in S\, \text{not-}p(x)}{}^{*} \text{ (T 18.)}$$

$$\dfrac{}{\exists x \in S\, \text{not-}p(x)} \text{ (*Double denial*)} \;☐$$

Theorems 2.3-9 and 2.3-10 are the facts discussed earlier concerning negation of quantified sentences.

Exercises 2.3

1. Write out the proof of Logic Theorem 2.3-8 in "line diagram" form.

2. Try to prove the converse of Logic Theorem 2.3-6. (Be sure to fail, but be able to "pin point" the step at which one might use faulty logic and accidentally "succeed." This is a *very popular* "student theorem.")

3. Prove each of the following:

   a) $\forall x \in S\, p(x)$ and $\forall x \in S\, q(x) \Leftrightarrow \forall x \in S\, p(x)$ and $q(x)$

   b) $\exists x \in S\, p(x)$ or $\exists x \in S\, q(x) \Leftrightarrow \exists x \in S\, p(x)$ or $q(x)$

   c) $\exists x \in S\, p(x)$ and $\exists x \in S\, q(x) \Leftarrow \exists x \in S\, p(x)$ and $q(x)$

4. Does the converse of (3c) hold?

5. Investigate (prove or disprove). Which of the following are valid patterns?

a) $$\dfrac{\forall x\, \forall y\ \ p(x) \Rightarrow q(y)}{\forall x\, p(x)\ \ \Rightarrow\ \ \forall y\, q(y)}$$

c) $$\dfrac{\forall x\, \exists y\ \ p(x) \Rightarrow q(y)}{\forall x\, p(x)\ \ \Rightarrow\ \ \exists y\, q(y)}$$

b) $$\dfrac{\exists x\, \exists y\ \ p(x) \Rightarrow q(y)}{\exists x\, p(x)\ \ \Rightarrow\ \ \exists y\, q(y)}$$

d) $$\dfrac{\exists x\, \forall y\ \ p(x) \Rightarrow q(y)}{\exists x\, p(x)\ \ \Rightarrow\ \ \forall y\, q(y)}$$

6. Decide "valid" or "invalid" for each of the following inference patterns.

a) $$\dfrac{A \subset B,\, B \subset D}{\forall x\ \ \text{if } x \in A, \text{ then } x \in D}$$

e) $$\dfrac{A \cap B = \varnothing,\, \exists x\ \ x \notin B}{A \neq \varnothing}$$

b) $$\dfrac{A \cap D \neq \varnothing,\, D \subset B}{\exists x\ \ x \in B}$$

f) $$\dfrac{A \neq \varnothing,\, \forall x \in A\ \ x \in B \text{ and } x \in H}{\exists x \in B\ \ x \in H}$$

c) $$\dfrac{\exists x\ \ x \in B \cap A,\, A \subset D}{B \subset D}$$

g) $$\dfrac{\exists x\ \ x \in B \text{ and } x \in H,\, \exists x \in B\ \ x \in R}{\exists x \in B\ \ x \in H \text{ and } x \in R}$$

d) $$\dfrac{\forall x\ \ x \in A \Rightarrow x \in B,\, B \neq \varnothing}{A \neq \varnothing}$$

h) $$\dfrac{a \in B,\, m \in A}{\exists x\ \ x \in B}$$

7. Show that the following is a valid pattern.

$$\dfrac{\exists x \in S\ \ \text{not-}p(x)}{\text{not-}\forall x \in S\, p(x)}$$

2.4 Order Relations and Ordered Sets

A great deal of mathematics deals with the examination of various structural patterns and properties of some universe U under consideration. It is useful in the description and examination of such properties to pay special attention to certain sub-collections of the two universes $U \times U$ (the set of all ordered pairs whose components are elements from U) and 2^U (the collection of all subsets of U). In this chapter, we deal with a few special sub-collections from $U \times U$ and 2^U and discuss the structure on U which is being studied in each case.

Order Relations

We begin by studying a type of relation on U^* which seems to describe the concept of order. We wish to lay down some rule or method to decide

---

* When a relation is between a set A and itself it is usually called a "relation on A" rather than saying a "relation in $A \times A$" or a "relation between A and A."

when we have one element of U "before" another; that is, when we can "line up" all the things in a universe U. We want this done in such a way that every element in the set is in the "line-up," and also so that there is only one such line-up. Further, we wish to avoid a line which meets itself at some point.

2.4-1 Definition: A relation $< \subset U \times U$ is called an *order relation* on U, or simply an *ordering* of U (sometimes also called a *linear order*)† iff

a) $\forall x, y \in U$ if $x \neq y$, then $(x, y) \in <$ or $(y, x) \in <$
(totality property)

b) $\forall x, y \in U$ if $(x, y) \in <$ and $(y, x) \in <$, then $x = y$
(antisymmetric property)

c) $\forall x, y, z \in U$ if $(x, y) \in <$ and $(y, z) \in <$, then $(x, z) \in <$
(transitive property)

Using a standard notation for relations, these properties are stated as:

a) $\forall x, y \in U$ if $x \neq y$, then $x < y$ or $y < x$
b) $\forall x, y \in U$ if $x < y$ and $y < x$, then $x = y$
c) $\forall x, y, z \in U$ if $x < y$ and $y < z$, then $x < z$

(It is common and useful to define "$x > y$" to mean "$y < x$.")

Example: Let $U = \{a, b, c\}$ where a, b, c are all distinct. Let

$$< = \{(a, c), (a, b), (c, b)\}.$$

Then $<$ is an order relation on U. (Verify that conditions *a)*, *b)*, and *c)* are satisfied.)

Example: Let $S = \{$Gurnie, Glenda$\}$, and let $<$ be described by

Gurnie $<$ Gurnie

Glenda $<$ Glenda

Gurnie $<$ Glenda.

Then $<$ is an order relation on S. (Verify this!)

Questions: a) What are the ordered pairs in $<$ in this example?

b) What is another ordering of the set $S = \{$Gurnie, Glenda$\}$?

Graphically, we think of an ordered set as possessing a "line up", according to the particular ordering.

Example: Let $S = \{1, 3, 7\}$. Describe an order relation which "lines up" the elements in S as follows:

1   7   3

Solution: Let $< = \{(1, 7), (1, 3), (7, 3), (3, 3)\}$.

Question: Can you find a different order relation which "lines up" S the same way?

† See G. Birchoff "Lattice Theory" 2nd ed., New York, Amer. Math. Society (Colloquium Publications, Vol. 25), 1948.

Let us examine some relations which look somewhat like order relations, but are *not*.

Example: Let $S = \{a, b, c, d\}$ all distinct. If $<_1 = \{(a, b), (c, d)\}$, we have the graphical interpretation.

$$a \qquad \qquad b$$

$$c \qquad \qquad d$$

Since $a \neq c$ and neither $a <_1 c$ nor $c <_1 a$, we have not satisfied the first condition for an order relation.

If $<_2 = \{(a, b), (b, c), (c, d), (a, c), (a, d), (b, d), (d, b), (b, b), (c, b)\}$, the graphical situation is given as follows.

$$d$$

$$c$$

$$a$$

$$b$$

Note that $d <_2 b$ and $b <_2 d$ but $b \neq d$, so property (2) is not satisfied.

2.4-2 Definition: If $<$ is an ordering of S such that $(x < y \Rightarrow x \neq y)$, then we say that $<$ is a *strict ordering* of S.

Example: $S = \{5, 3, 6\}$ is ordered by

$$<_1 = \{(5, 3), (5, 6), (3, 6)\},$$

and also by

$$<_2 = \{(5, 3), (5, 6), (3, 6), (3, 3), (5, 5)\}.$$

Note that $<_1$ is a strict ordering of S, whereas $<_2$ is not.

If U is ordered by some ordering $<$, then certain ideas naturally arise concerning subsets of U.

2.4-3 Definition: Let U be ordered by $<$, and let $S \subset U$. If $b \in U$ and $\forall x \in S, x \leq b$, then b is called an *upper bound for S*. (*S* is said to be *bounded above by b*.) ($x \leq b$ means $x < b$ or $x = b$.)

2.4-4 Definition: Let p be an upper bound for S. If $\forall b \in U$, b an upper bound for $S \Rightarrow p < b$ or $p = b$, then p is called a *least upper bound for S*.

Example: Let $U = \{$pig, horse, cow$\}$ be ordered by:

$$\text{pig} < \text{horse}$$

$$\text{pig} < \text{cow}$$

$$\text{horse} < \text{horse}$$

$$\text{horse} < \text{cow}$$

119

then $S = \{$pig, horse$\}$ is bounded above by cow. S also is bounded above by horse. In this case, horse is a least upper bound.

A theorem which we will find useful later is the following.

2.4-5 Theorem: Consider $S \subset U$, where U is an ordered set. If p_1 is a least upper bound for S, and if p_2 is a least upper bound for S, then $p_1 = p_2$.

Proof: Both p_1 and p_2 are upper bounds, and so from the definition of a least upper bound,

$$p_1 \leq p_2 \quad \text{and} \quad p_2 \leq p_1.$$

By the properties for an order relation,

$$p_1 = p_2. \quad \square$$

The uniqueness of the least upper bound (if the least upper bound exists) leads to the following notation definition.

2.4-6 Notation Convention: If $S \subset U$ has a least upper bound p, then we write "$p = l.u.b.(S)$" or "$p = $ supremum (S)" or "$p = $ sup (S)."

We have not asserted that a set which is bounded above *has* a least upper bound. In fact, we shall see later that some sets can be bounded above and not have a least upper bound.

Exercise: Make similar definitions for the *lower bound* of a set and for the *greatest lower bound* (called "$g.l.b.(S)$," "infimum (S)," "inf (S)"). Also prove a similar theorem for the uniqueness of $g.l.b.(S)$.

2.4-7 Definition: If a set S is bounded both above and below, then we say that S is *bounded*.

Exercises 2.4

1. Let $S = \{1, 5, 9\}$.

   a) Let $< = \{(5, 1), (5, 9), (1, 9)\}$. Show that $<$ is an order relation. Graphically line up the elements in S according to $<$.

   b) Let $< = \{(5, 1), (5, 9), (1, 9), (1, 1), (9, 9)\}$. Show that $<$ is an order relation. Line up the elements in S according to $<$.

2. Let $S = \{a, b, 4, 7\}$. List the ordered pairs in some order relation which lines up S as follows.

How many order relations on S line up S as above?

3. Let $S = \{a, b, c\}$ all distinct. How many relations on S are there? How many order relations? How many strict orderings?

4. *a)* Show that if $<$ is an order relation on S, then $<^* = \; < - \{(x, x): x \in S\}$ is also an order relation. (*I.e.*, any non-strict order relation can be made into a strict ordering by removing some of the pairs.)

   b) If T is a strict ordering, what can you say about $\overline{T}$?

5. *a)* Is the relation $<$ on R with which you are familiar an order relation? What about $\leq$? What about $>$ and $\geq$?

b) Verify that $\overline{<} = \geq$.

6. Let $U = \{a, b, c, d, e\}$, where

$a < c$	$c < d$	$d < b$
$a < d$	$c < e$	$e < b$
$a < e$	$c < b$	$b < b$
$a < b$	$d < e$	

Show that $<$ is an ordering of U. Let $S = \{a, c, d\}$. List all upper bounds for S. Does sup (S) exist? List all lower bounds for S. What can you say about inf (S)?

7. Show that if S and T are subsets of some ordered set U, if sup (S) exists and sup (T) exists, and if $S \subset T$, then sup $(S) \leq$ sup (T). Moreover, inf $(T) \leq$ inf (S) (when they exist).

8. Determine the *inf* and *sup* (if it exists) of each of the following sets of real numbers. Indicate in each case whether it is in the set.

a) $(2, 5]$ *c)* $[1, 5]$ *e)* $(-8, 7]$

b) $(0, 1)$ *d)* $(2, \infty)$ *f)* $(0, \pi]$

9. Give the set of ordered pairs which is a strict linear ordering on $S = \{a, b, c, d, e\}$ where the order is given by the following diagram.

$$c \nearrow^{a} \searrow \ _e \nearrow^{b} \searrow \ d$$

10. Suppose $A = \{a, b, c\}$ and $U = 2^A$. Let $\subset$ be the usual set inclusion relation. Is $\subset$ an order relation on U? Is it a strict ordering of U? Does $\{\{a, b\}\}$ have an upper bound? Does $\{\{a, b\}\}$ have a *l.u.b.*?

11. Consider R under the usual ordering $\leq$. Determine the supremum and infimum of each of the sets below if they exist. Decide whether they are in the sets. If they are in the sets they are called the *maximum* and the *minimum*, respectively.

a) $\{2, 8, 6, 3/4, -3, 16\}$ *e)* $[(1/3, 12/5) \cup (5, 7)] \cap (1, 6]$

b) $\{x: 5 < x \leq 8\}$ *f)* $\{.3, .33, .333, .3333, \ldots\}$

c) $\{x: x \leq -5 \text{ or } 0 < x\}$ *g)* $\{x: x = 1 - 1/n \text{ where } n \in N\}$

d) $\{x: x = 1/n \text{ where } n \in N\}$ *h)* $\{-.5, -.55, -.555, -.5555, \ldots\}$

2.5 Index Sets and Set Operations

Index Sets

We are now in a position to make use of the function concepts we have studied thus far. We shall first introduce the useful concept of "index sets."

You should note that this idea is closely associated with the notion of *1-1* correspondences and counting, which we discussed previously.

2.5-1 Definition: Let I be some non-empty set and let χ be a collection of sets. If $f: I \xrightarrow[onto]{} \chi$, then we say that χ is *indexed by the index set I* through the function f.

In making use of this definition, one usually makes no specific reference to the function f. If $A \in \chi$ and $f(\alpha) = A$ (where $\alpha \in I$), then A is (by convention) denoted by A_α. Thus, the collection may be specified by $\{A_\alpha\}_{\alpha \in I}$ (read "the collection of sets indexed by I"). The set I serves merely as a collection of names for the sets in $\chi = \{A_\alpha\}_{\alpha \in I}$. The fact that f is a *function* guarantees us that no name is given to two different sets, although it might be the case that some sets have more than one name.

Example: Let $I = \{a, b, c, d\}$ all distinct. Let $\chi = \{D, B, C\}$, all distinct sets. Let $f: I \to \chi$ be described by

$$f(a) = D \qquad f(b) = B \qquad f(c) = C \qquad f(d) = C.$$

This could be denoted by

$$A_a = D \qquad A_b = B \qquad A_c = C \qquad A_d = C,$$

and by $\{A_\alpha\}_{\alpha \in I}$ we mean the collection $\{A_a, A_b, A_c, A_d\}$ which is, of course, the collection $\{D, B, C\}$.

Example: Consider the set $\mathcal{F}$ of sets

$$\mathcal{F} = \{\{1\}, \{1, 2, 7\}, \{5, 43, \pi\}, R\}.$$

$\mathcal{F}$ can be indexed by the set $\theta = \{4, 5, 5.5, 5.55\}$ as follows:

set #4 is $\{1\}$ $\qquad\qquad$ set #5 is $\{1, 2, 7\}$

set #5.5 is $\{5, 43, \pi\}$ $\qquad$ set #5.55 is R.

In this case, the indexing function is a *1-1* correspondence. Note that this is certainly not the only way in which to establish a *1-1* correspondence between $\mathcal{F}$ and θ. For example, we might have taken the *1-1* correspondence described by

$$\{(4, \{1, 2, 7\}), (5.5, \{1\}), (5.55, R), (5, \{5, 43, \pi\})\},$$

or by any other *1-1* and *onto* function in $\theta \times \mathcal{F}$.

The reader saw in the example above that $\mathcal{F}$ was taken to be a set of sets. Recall that there are practically no restrictions on the kind of objects that can serve as elements of sets.‡ In particular, it is perfectly acceptable to consider a set whose elements also happen to be sets. We will, in fact, have occasion to make a great use of sets whose elements are sets.

Example: Suppose $\mathcal{F}$ is the set of intervals $[n, n + 1)$ for $n \in N$, and suppose the index set is taken to be N. A "natural" way to index $\mathcal{F}$ would be to use the function

‡ In order to avoid contradictions such as the Russell paradox, we may not allow a set to be a member of itself.

$$\{(n, [n, n + 1))\},$$

so that interval #1 in $\mathfrak{F}$ is $[1, 2)$, and in general $S_k = [k, k + 1)$, where "S_k" stands for "interval number k."

The use of the label "S_k" above, to denote the interval corresponding to the number k in the index set N, is a convenient device. Usually, in making use of the index set concept, the index set is chosen so as to have some connection with the sets being indexed. Although this is not necessary, it is essentially the thing that makes the idea useful.

Example: Let $I = N$ (the natural numbers). Suppose that

$$\forall n \in N \quad A_n = [0, n] = \{x \in R: 0 \leq x \leq n\}.$$

Then
$$\{A_n\}_{n \in N} = \{[0, 1], [0, 2], [0, 3], \ldots\}.$$

Example: Let $A_n = [0, 1/n]$ for each $n \in N$.

Then
$$\{A_n\}_{n \in N} = \{[0, 1], [0, 1/2], [0, 1/3], \ldots\}.$$

Example: $\forall \alpha \in R$ let $B_\alpha = (0, \alpha)$. Then, for example,

$$B_{1/2} = (0, 1/2) \qquad B_\pi = (0, \pi) \qquad B_{-1} = (0, -1) = \varnothing.$$

Also,
$$\{B_\alpha\}_{\alpha \in R} = \{\varnothing, (0, 1/3), (0, 2\pi), \ldots\}.$$

Note that $\{B_\alpha\}_{\alpha \in R}$ contains a great number of elements!

Set Operations

In this section we define and investigate the set operations union ($\cup$) and intersection ($\cap$). We shall see that one of the interesting properties of these operations is that they may operate on many sets at a time, in distinction with the ordinary *binary* operations on numbers (addition and multiplication). We have already seen these set operations as binary operations, but, as you shall see, this restriction is entirely unnecessary. We make use of an index set in each case to indicate the sets entering into the operation.

Recall that if $\mathfrak{F}$ is a collection of sets indexed by a set θ, we can always make use of the labeling convention discussed above so as to be able to refer to the elements of $\mathfrak{F}$ by the names F_α (where $\alpha \in \theta$). In what follows, we assume this has been done.

2.5-2 Definition: Let $\mathfrak{F}$ be a set of sets $\{F_\alpha\}$ indexed by a set θ. The *union* of the members of $\mathfrak{F}$ is defined by

$$\bigcup_{\alpha \in \theta} F_\alpha = \{x: x \in F_\alpha \text{ for at } least one \ \alpha \in \theta\}$$

$$= \{x: \exists \alpha \in \theta, x \in F_\alpha\}.$$

Note that the union of the sets in $\{F_\alpha\}_{\alpha \in \theta}$ is in turn a *set*.

123

Example: Suppose $\mathfrak{F} = \{\{0, 2\}, \{0, 3\}\}$, and that the index set θ is the set $\{1, 2\}$. Suppose the labeling scheme associated with the particular "indexing" function we choose assigns

$$F_1 = \{0, 2\} \quad \text{and} \quad F_2 = \{0, 3.\}$$

Now
$$\bigcup_{\alpha \in \{1,2\}} F_\alpha = \{x: x \in F_1 \text{ or } x \in F_2\}$$

$$= \{x: x \in \{0, 2\} \text{ or } x \in \{0, 3\}\}$$

$$= \{0, 2, 3\}. \quad (\text{Why?})$$

The union of *two* sets, as you recall, is usually written in the form

$$\bigcup_{\alpha \in \{1,2\}} F_\alpha = F_1 \cup F_2.$$

Similarly, the union of three sets may be written $F_1 \cup F_2 \cup F_3$, and similarly for four, five, or any other "small" number of sets (*i.e.*, for any case in which $\#(\theta)$ is small).

Example: Suppose $\mathfrak{F}$ is the set of intervals of the form $[i - 1, i)$ for $i \in N$, and suppose N is the index set and that

$$F_i = [i - 1, i).$$

Then
$$\bigcup_{i \in \{4,5,7\}} F_i = F_4 \cup F_5 \cup F_7$$

is the set of all numbers in at least one of the sets F_4, F_5, F_7. This set is graphed on the real number line in Figure 2.2.

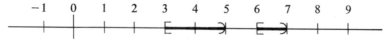

FIG. 2.2 The shaded segments together form the graph of $\bigcup_{i \in \{4,5,7\}} F_i$.

Note that $5 \notin \bigcup_{i \in \{4,5,7\}} F_i$ and similarly for the "end point" 7.

Remark: $\bigcup_{i \in N} F_i = [0, \infty) = \{x \in R: x \geq 0\}$,

since every nonnegative real number is in at least one of the F_i's, and since each of the F_i's contain only nonnegative real numbers.

Examples: (*A*) Let us sketch a graph of $F = [1, 2] \times \{-3\}$. A few of the members of F are: $(1, -3)$, $(1\ 1/2, -3)$, and $(1\ 7/8, -3)$. Of course it is impossible to describe F by a list (why?), but we can *graph* F, as in Figure 2.3. (*B*) A graph of $G = [1, 2] \times [-3, -2]$ is shown in Figure 2-4.

Note that $G = \bigcup_{\alpha \in [-3,-2]} ([1, 2] \times \{\alpha\})$. In terms of the graph of G, we see that this simply states that the square region can be viewed as a union of horizontal line segments (one of which is graphed in part (*A*) above). Thus in this case, the notion of graphs of product sets, and of Venn diagrams for unions, are closely associated.

124

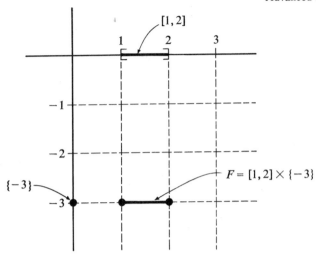

FIG. 2.3

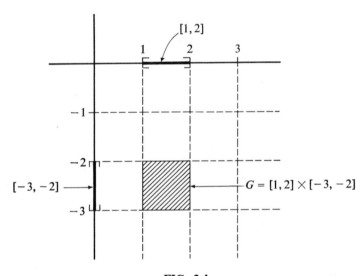

FIG. 2.4

2.5-3 Definition: Under the above notation conventions for indexing, the *intersection* of the F_α's is defined by

$$\bigcap_{\alpha \in \theta} F_\alpha = \{x : x \in F_\alpha \, for \, all \, \alpha \in \theta\} = \{x : \forall \alpha \in \theta, \, x \in F_\alpha\}.$$

The intersection of sets is a *set:* the set of all elements common to all of the F_α's.

125

Example: For the set $\mathfrak{F}$ in which $\mathfrak{F} = \{F_1, F_2\}$ where $F_1 = \{0, 2\}$ and $F_2 = \{0, 3\}$, we have

$$\bigcap_{\alpha \in \{1,2\}} F_\alpha = \{x : x \in F_1 \text{ and } x \in F_2\}$$
$$= \{x : x \in \{0, 2\} \text{ and } x \in \{0, 3\}\}$$
$$= \{0\}.$$

We could have alternatively denoted this intersection by

$$F_1 \cap F_2$$

with a similar convention for other cases in which the index set θ is "small."

Example: For the sets defined by $F_i = [i - 1, i)$, $i \in N$, note that $F_4 \cap F_5 \cap F_7 = \bigcap_{i \in \{4,5,7\}} F_i = \varnothing$, since there are no real numbers that are in all three of the intervals F_4, F_5, and F_7. In fact, we note that

$$F_i \cap F_j = \varnothing$$

(for any unequal integers i and j) where $F_i = [i - 1, i)$. Such sets having no elements in common are called *"disjoint,"* or *"pairwise disjoint."*

Example: Suppose $\mathfrak{A}$ consists of the intervals $A_i = [0, 1/i]$ for each $i \in N$. Thus, for example, A_6 is the interval $[0, 1/6]$. Then

$$\bigcap_{i \in \{1,4,7,10\}} A_i = [0, 1/10],$$

since each real number between 0 and $1/10$ is in each of the intervals $[0, 1]$, $[0, 1/4]$, $[0, 1/7]$, and $[0, 1/10]$. Moreover, there are no other real numbers that are in all four of these intervals.

Note that $\bigcap_{i \in N} A_i = \{0\}$, since 0 is in *every* A_i, but no other real number is in *all* of the A_i's.

Example: Consider the two functions

$$F_1 = \{(x, y) : y = -1\}, \qquad F_2 = \{(x, y) : y = x\}$$

in $R \times R$. The graphs appear as in Figure 2.5.

Note that the graphs intersect in a single point, its coordinates being $(-1, -1)$. Thus we can say that

$$F_1 \cap F_2 = \{(-1, -1)\}.$$

Note that this is closely associated with the Venn diagram interpretation of the intersection of two sets as discussed earlier.

Question: If $F_k = \{(x, y) : y = kx + 1\}$ for each $k \in Z$, what is $\bigcup_{k \in Z} F_k$ and what is $\bigcap_{k \in Z} F_k$?

Let us next consider some interesting relationships between certain unions and intersections of sets.

2.5-4 Theorem: $\forall \alpha \in I$, $F_\alpha \subset \bigcup_{\beta \in I} F_\beta$.

2.5-5 Theorem: $\forall \alpha \in I$, $\bigcap_{\beta \in I} F_\beta \subset F_\alpha$.

Corollary: $\bigcap_{\alpha \in I} F_\alpha \subset \bigcup_{\alpha \in I} F_\alpha$.

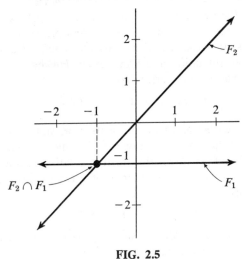

FIG. 2.5

Since these proofs are quite similar, we give only the proof of Theorem 2.5-5, leaving the other proofs as exercises.

Proof (of 2.5-5 Theorem): We must show that for any particular F_α, the elements of the set $\bigcap_{\beta \in I} F_\beta$ are also in F_α. We shall make use of the "test pattern principle" discussed earlier. Suppose then that we fix our attention on a particular F_α. Now suppose x is an element in $\bigcap_{\beta \in I} F_\beta$. (If $\bigcap_{\beta \in I} F_\beta = \varnothing$, the conclusion is vacuously true.) Since

$$x \in \bigcap_{\beta \in I} F_\beta$$

x must be in all of the F_β's, including the particular one, F_α. Thus

$$\forall x \quad x \in \bigcap_{\beta \in I} F_\beta \Rightarrow x \in F_\alpha$$

so, by definition

$$\bigcap_{\beta \in I} F_\beta \subset F_\alpha.$$

But this argument will be the same, regardless of which particular F_α is used, so the conclusion holds for every $\alpha \in I$. $\square$

2.5-6 Theorem: $F_\alpha \subset A \ \forall \alpha \in I \Rightarrow \bigcup_{\alpha \in I} F_\alpha \subset A.$
Proof left as an exercise.

Note: By Corollary 2.5-5 and the "transitive property of set inclusion", it immediately follows that

$$\bigcap_{\alpha \in I} F_\alpha \subset A.$$

That is, $(\bigcap F_\alpha \subset \bigcup F_\alpha$ and $\bigcup F_\alpha \subset A) \Rightarrow (\bigcap F_\alpha \subset A).$

127

Remark: Since the particular function from I onto $\mathfrak{F}$ that is used to set up the labeling convention is usually more or less picked at "random," it might appear at first that the use of another index set, J (say), to index $\mathfrak{F}$ would lead to a different union and intersection. However, upon close inspection, the reader can readily verify that

$$\bigcap_{\alpha \in I} F_\alpha \quad \text{and} \quad \bigcap_{\beta \in J} F_\beta$$

both represent the intersection of the elements of $\mathfrak{F}$, and thus are the same set. Note in particular that the concept of *order* in which sets enter into union or intersection is absent, in distinction to the situation encountered in the Cartesian product sets, where the order is of great importance. Thus the statements of the form

$$``A_1 \cap A_2 = A_2 \cap A_1"$$

are trivial inasmuch as both sides of such equations refer to the same set ($\bigcap_{i \in \{1,2\}} A_i$ in this particular case).

De Morgan's Laws

Recall the logic laws called De Morgan's Laws and their set theoretic analogue.

$$\overline{A \cup B} = \overline{A} \cap \overline{B} \quad \text{and} \quad \overline{A \cap B} = \overline{A} \cup \overline{B}$$

These two results are also valid in the more general case.

2.5-7 Theorem: (*De Morgan's Laws*)

$$a) \ \overline{\bigcap_{i \in I} A_i} = \bigcup_{i \in I} \overline{A_i}$$
$$b) \ \overline{\bigcup_{i \in I} A_i} = \bigcap_{i \in I} \overline{A_i}$$

Proof: a) $x \in \overline{\bigcap_{i \in I} A_i} \Leftrightarrow x \notin \bigcap_{i \in I} A_i \Leftrightarrow x \notin A_i$ for some $i \in I \Leftrightarrow x \in \overline{A_i}$ for some $i \in I \Leftrightarrow x \in \bigcup_{i \in I} \overline{A_i}$.

b) $x \in \overline{\bigcup_{i \in I} A_i} \Leftrightarrow x \notin \bigcup_{i \in I} A_i \Leftrightarrow x \notin A_i$ for each $i \in I \Leftrightarrow x \in \overline{A_i}$ for each $i \in I \Leftrightarrow x \in \bigcap_{i \in I} \overline{A_i}$. $\square$

Exercises 2.5

1. Simplify (*i.e.*, express each union or intersection as an interval, if possible):
   a) Let $A_n = (0, 1 + 1/n) \quad \forall n \in N$
   $$\bigcap_{n \in N} A_n = \underline{\hspace{2cm}} \qquad \bigcup_{n \in N} A_n = \underline{\hspace{2cm}}$$
   b) Let $B_n = [0, 1/n) \cup [n, n + 20]$
   $$\bigcap_{n \in N} B_n = \underline{\hspace{2cm}} \qquad \bigcup_{n \in N} B_n = \underline{\hspace{2cm}}$$

  c) $\bigcap\limits_{n \in N} [n, n + 2] =$ _____ $\bigcup\limits_{n \in N} [n, n + 2] =$ _____

  d) Let $A_\alpha = [0, \alpha) \cap Q \quad \forall \alpha \in R$

  $\bigcap\limits_{\alpha \in R} A_\alpha =$ _____ $\bigcup\limits_{\alpha \in R} A_\alpha =$ _____

2. For convenience, mathematicians often define $\bigcup_{\alpha \in \varnothing} A_\alpha$ to be the empty set. If this is done, what is the consistent way in which to define $\bigcap_{\alpha \in \varnothing} A_\alpha$? (*Hint:* Apply De Morgan's Law.)

3. Prove Theorem 2.5-4.

4. Prove Corollary 2.5-5.

   (*Hint:* One could use standard "element-tracer" argument, but it is more easily done using the "transitive property" of set inclusion together with Theorems 2.5-4 and 2.5-5.)

5. Investigate (prove or disprove):

   a) $I \subset J \Rightarrow \bigcap_{i \in I} F_i \subset \bigcap_{j \in J} F_j$

   b) $I \subset J \Rightarrow \bigcup_{i \in I} F_i \subset \bigcup_{j \in J} F_j$

   c) $A \subset F_i$ for all $i \in I \Rightarrow A \subset \bigcap_{i \in I} F_i$

   d) $F_i \subset A$ for all $i \in I \Rightarrow \bigcap_{i \in I} F_i \subset A$

6. What is the distinction between a "lemma," a "theorem," and a "corollary"?

7. a) Prove that $[1, 2] \times [5, 6] = \bigcup_{\alpha \in [5,6]} ([1, 2] \times \{\alpha\})$.

   b) Show that this can also be written as $\bigcup_{\beta \in [1,2]} (\{\beta\} \times [5, 6])$.

   c) Interpret a) and b) graphically.

2.6 Partitions and Equivalence Relations

In preceding sections, we indicated that many mathematical ideas concerning a universe U can be examined by looking at universes 2^U (the collection of all subsets of U) and $2^{U \times U}$ (the collection of all relations on U). In this section, we will develop an important and useful result which makes a direct connection between 2^U and $2^{U \times U}$ with respect to a certain structural concept on U. That is, we shall show that a certain fundamental structural concept can be studied by either looking at 2^U or by $2^{U \times U}$, whichever appears convenient in the specific problem under examination.

Partitions

We have defined an operation (complementation) which associates with a subset A of U another subset $\overline{A}$ of U with the following properties:

1) $A \cap \overline{A} = \varnothing$
2) $A \cup \overline{A} = U$.

Thus A and $\bar{A}$ constitute a "non-overlapping division of U" into two parts. This type of "division" of U into two disjoint subsets can be generalized to a division into various numbers of subsets. Such a division is called a "partition."

2.6-1 Definition: A class of *non-empty* sets, $\{A_i\}_{i \in I}$, is called a *partition* of the set U provided that:

1) $\forall i \in I \quad A_i \subset U$
2) $\forall i, j \in I$ if $i \neq j$, then $A_i \cap A_j = \varnothing$ or $A_i = A_j$
3) $\bigcup_{i \in I} A_i = U$

Example: Let $U = \{1, 5, 6, 11\}$. Then $\{\{1\}, \{5\}, \{6, 11\}\}$ is a partition of U. Also $\{\{1, 5, 6\}, \{11\}\}$ is a partition of U. But $\{\{1, 5\}, \{6\}\}$ is not, since $\{1, 5\} \cup \{6\} \neq U$. Also $\{\{1, 5\}, \{6\}, \{6, 11\}\}$ is not, since $\{6\} \cap \{6, 11\} \neq \varnothing$ and $\{6\} \neq \{6, 11\}$.

Question: How many partitions of $U = \{1, 5, 6, 11\}$ are there?

Example: Let $S = \{a, b, c\}$, a, b, and c all distinct. Then $\{\{a\}, \{b\}, \{c\}\}$ is a partition of S. Also $\{\{a, b, c\}\}$ is a partition. But $\{\{a, b\}, \{b\}, \{b, c\}, \{a\}\}$ is not. (Why?)

Remark: The condition (2) in the definition is described verbally by saying "the distinct sets in $\{A_i\}$ are pairwise disjoint." The word "pairwise" refers to the fact that the intersection of condition (2) involves only two members of the class $\{A_i\}_{i \in I}$ of partition subsets at a time. This is, of course, quite different from merely insisting that the intersection of all of the sets in $\{A_i\}_{i \in I}$ be empty.

Example: If $A = \{1, 3, 2\}$, then $\mathcal{F} = \{\{1, 3\}, \{2\}\}$ is a partition but $\mathcal{I} = \{\{1, 3\}, \{3, 2\}, (1, 2)\}$ is not. Note that the intersection of all sets in $\mathcal{I}$ is empty, but that they are not "pairwise" disjoint.

Example: In general, there are many distinct partitions of a non-empty set U. For example, if $U = \{0, 1, 2\}$, then all possible partitions of U are:

1) $\{U\}$　　　　3) $\{\{0\}, \{1, 2\}\}$　　　　5) $\{\{2\}, \{1, 0\}\}$
2) $\{\{0\}, \{1\}, \{2\}\}$　4) $\{\{1\}, \{0, 2\}\}$

Equivalence Relations

We now define yet another special class of relations, and show that they are very closely associated with partitions of the universal set. This interesting turn of events forms an important fundamental concept which is of great use in mathematics.

2.6-2 Definition: A relation E in $U \times U$ is an *equivalence relation* provided that the ordered pairs in E satisfy the following three conditions:

1) (*Reflexive property*) $a \in U \Rightarrow (a, a) \in E$.

2) (*Symmetric property*) $(a, b) \in E \Rightarrow (b, a) \in E$.

3) (*Transitive property*) $(a, b) \in E$ and $(b, c) \in E \Rightarrow (a, c) \in E$.

Remark: This definition could be stated more briefly as: a reflexive, symmetric, and transitive relation in $U \times U$ is called an equivalence relation.

Remark: Using the alternate notation of relations, the above definition can be stated as: a relation "$\sim$" defined on U is an equivalence relation, provided that

1) $\forall a \in U$, $a \sim a$ (read: "a is equivalent with a")

2) $a \sim b \Rightarrow b \sim a$

3) $a \sim b$ and $b \sim c \Rightarrow a \sim c$.

Note that if "$\sim$" is interpreted as the ordinary equal sign ($=$), then the three properties of an equivalence relation are satisfied. Thus "$=$", $\{(a, b):$ $a = b\}$ is an equivalence relation. In fact, historically, it was an attempt to examine the abstract properties of equality that lead to the notion of the equivalence relation. The equivalence relation does not completely characterize equality, however, as we shall see in the examples that follow. Note also that the reflexive property insures that if E is an equivalence relation in $U \times U$, then $D_E = R_E = U$.

Example: Let $U = \{a, b, c\}$ where a, b, and c are all distinct. Then $\sim$ $= \{(a, a), (a, b), (b, a), (b, b), (c, c)\}$ is an equivalence relation on U (*i.e.*, $a \sim a$, $a \sim b$, $b \sim a$, $b \sim b$, $c \sim c$).

Example: Let S be the set of all lines in the plane and define two lines m and t to be equivalent "$m \sim t$" iff they are parallel. Then it is easily seen that "$\sim$" is an equivalence relation in $S \times S$, provided we use the convention that a line is parallel to itself (*i.e.*, "$\sim$" is an equivalence relation on S).

Example: Define a relation K in $Z \times Z$ by $(a, b) \in K$ iff $a - b$ is a multiple of 3. (That is, $(a, b) \in K$ iff $a - b = 3n$ for some $n \in Z$.) Thus $(1, 4)$, $(-7, -13)$, $(42, 0)$ are all members of K. We prove that K is an equivalence relation by showing that it is reflexive, symmetric, and transitive, as follows:

K Is a Reflexive Relation

Proof: For any integer $m \in Z$ we have $m - m = (0) \cdot 3$, so that $m - m$ is a multiple of 3 and (by definition) $(m, m) \in K$. Thus we have shown that $m \in Z \Rightarrow (m, m) \in K$. ▯

K Is a Symmetric Relation

Proof: Suppose $(a, b) \in K$. Then $a - b = (n) \cdot 3$ for some n. But then $b - a = -(a - b) = (-n) \cdot 3$, so $b - a$ is also a multiple of 3, and $(b, a) \in K$. Thus, $(a, b) \in K \Rightarrow (b, a) \in K$. ▯

K Is a Transitive Relation

Proof: Suppose $(a, b) \in K$ and $(b, c) \in K$. Then $a - b = (n) \cdot 3$ and $b - c = (m) \cdot 3$. This implies in turn that

$$a - c = (a - b) + (b - c) = n \cdot 3 + m \cdot 3 = (n + m) \cdot 3$$

so $a - c$ is a multiple of 3, and $(a, c) \in K$. Thus, $(a, b) \in K$ and $(b, c) \in K \Rightarrow (a, c) \in K$. $\square$

Example: Let U be the set of points in the plane, and define the equivalence of any two points p and q as follows: $p \sim q$ iff p and q are at equal distances from the origin. The student should verify that this relation satisfies the three conditions of the equivalence relation.

Equivalence Classes

An interesting aspect of an equivalence relation on U is that it naturally gives rise to certain subsets of U. Indeed, we shall show that they form a partition of U! We make this precise by the following definition and theorem.

2.6-3 Definition: Let $\sim$ denote an equivalence relation in $U \times U$. Then for any element $a \in U$, *the equivalence class* C_a (with respect to $\sim$) is the set defined by

$$C_a = \{x \in U : x \sim a\}.$$

Remark: Note that $C_a \subset U$, and that the reflexive property ensures that $a \in C_a$. Thus we know that for each element a in the universe, C_a is a nonempty subset of the universe. We will be interested in examining these sets in more detail after looking at some specific examples.

Example: Let $U = \{a, b, d\}$ where a, b, and d are all distinct. Let $\sim$ be given by: $a \sim b$, $b \sim a$, $a \sim a$, $b \sim b$, $d \sim d$. Then

$$C_a = \{a, b\} \qquad C_b = \{b, a\} \qquad C_d = \{d\}.$$

Notice that $C_a = C_b$ and that $\{C_a, C_d\}$ is a partition of U.

Example: Let $S = \{1, 2, 3, 4\}$ and let $\sim$ be given by:

$$1 \sim 1, 2 \sim 2, 3 \sim 3, 4 \sim 4, 1 \sim 2, 2 \sim 1, 3 \sim 4, 4 \sim 3.$$

Now $C_1 = \{1, 2\}, \qquad C_2 = \{2, 1\}, \qquad C_3 = \{3, 4\}, \qquad C_4 = \{4, 3\}.$

Notice that the collection of equivalence classes forms a partition of S. Also note that $C_1 = C_2$ and that $C_3 = C_4$ which was a result of the fact that $1 \sim 2$ and $3 \sim 4$.

Example: For the equivalence relation of a previous example in which parallel lines are equivalent, the equivalence classes are sets of parallel lines, (sometimes called "families" of lines). To be more precise, suppose α denotes the line in the plane described by the equation $y = 0$. Then $C_\alpha = \{$horizontal lines in the plane$\}$. Note that in this case there are infinitely many distinct equivalence classes, and that each equivalence class in turn contains infinitely many lines. Notice again that many equivalence classes turn out to be identical. On the other hand, if two classes are distinct then they are disjoint (have no elements in common). In fact this "all or nothing in common" aspect of equivalence classes is true, in general. That is, as we shall prove, any two given equivalence classes are either disjoint or equal. This leads us naturally to the following theorem.

2.6-4 Theorem: If $\sim$ is an equivalence relation on U, then

$$\{C_\alpha\} \quad \text{(where } \forall \alpha, \ C_\alpha = \{x: x \sim \alpha\})$$
$$\alpha \in U$$

is a partition of U (*i.e.*, the collection of all equivalence classes *induced* by $\sim$ forms a partition of U).

Proof: We know that for each element $\alpha \in U$, C_α is a non-empty subset of U. Further, for any $i, j \in U$ either

$$C_i = C_j \quad \text{or} \quad C_i \cap C_j = \varnothing$$

because if $i \sim j$, $C_i = C_j$ and if $i \neq j$, then $C_i \cap C_j = \varnothing$ (see Exercise 15). Clearly, $\bigcup_{i \in U} C_i = U$ since each $i \in U$ is in C_i. $\square$

We see then that if $\sim$ is an equivalence relation on U, then there is a partition $\mathcal{P}_\sim = \{C_\alpha\}$ induced on U by $\sim$. We shall now show that if $\mathcal{P}$ is *any* partition on U, then in a natural way there is also an equivalence relation $\sim_\mathcal{P}$ *induced* on U. In fact, we do even better; we show that if one looks at the equivalence classes in turn induced by $\sim_\mathcal{P}$, then he is looking at $\mathcal{P}$ itself!

2.6-5 Theorem: Let $\mathcal{P}$ be a partition of U. The relation $\sim_\mathcal{P}$, defined by $\forall x, y \in U \ x \sim_\mathcal{P} y$ iff $x, y \in A$ for some $A \in \mathcal{P}$, is an equivalence relation (*i.e.*, x, y are equivalent, provided they appear in the same set in the partition $\mathcal{P}$).

Proof: 1) If $x \in U$, then $x \sim_\mathcal{P} x$, since x appears in the same set as itself.

2) $x \sim_\mathcal{P} y$ implies x, y are in the same set and therefore $y \sim_\mathcal{P} x$.

3) $x \sim_\mathcal{P} y$ and $y \sim_\mathcal{P} z \Rightarrow x, y \in A$ and $y, z \in A$. Therefore $x, z \in A$ and so $x \sim_\mathcal{P} z$. $\square$

2.6-6 Theorem: If $\sim$ is an equivalence relation on U and $\mathcal{P}_\sim$ is the partition induced by $\sim$, then $\sim_{\mathcal{P}_\sim} = \sim$.

Proof: $x \sim_{\mathcal{P}_\sim} y$ iff $x, y \in C$ where $C \in \mathcal{P}_\sim$. But $\mathcal{P}_\sim$ is nothing more than the set of equivalence classes determined by $\sim$. Therefore

$$x, y \in C_x = C_y \Leftrightarrow x \sim y. \ \square$$

Remark: The preceding two theorems together can be restated as follows:

Corollary: For *any* partition $\mathcal{P}$ of U, there is an equivalence relation $\sim_\mathcal{P}$ in

$U \times U$ such that the class of distinct equivalence classes with respect to $\sim_{\mathcal{P}}$ is the partition $\mathcal{P}$.

Example: Let $S = \{0, 1, 2\}$, and $0 \sim 0$, $1 \sim 1$, $2 \sim 2$, $0 \sim 1$, $1 \sim 0$.

Then $$\mathcal{P}_{\sim} = \{\{0, 1\}, \{1, 0\}, \{2\}\} = \{\{0, 1\}, \{2\}\}$$

and the equivalence relation induced by this partition is

$$\sim_{\mathcal{P}_{\sim}} = \{(0, 0), (1, 1), (2, 2), (0, 1), (1, 0)\} = \sim.$$

Example: Consider the equivalence relation on Z defined by

$$a \sim b \Leftrightarrow a - b = 3n \text{ for some } n \in Z.$$

There are exactly three distinct equivalence classes, which can be represented by C_0, C_1, C_2. The reader should verify that these classes can be described by the following lists:

$$C_0 = \{\ldots, -6, -3, 0, 3, 6, 9, \ldots\} = \{x: x = 3n \text{ where } n \in Z\}$$
$$C_1 = \{\ldots, -5, -2, 1, 4, 7, \ldots\} = \{x: x = 3n + 1 \text{ where } n \in Z\}$$

and

$$C_2 = \{\ldots, -4, -1, 2, 5, 8, \ldots\} = \{x: x = 3n + 2 \text{ where } n \in Z\}.$$

The collection of subsets of Z, $\{C_0, C_1, C_2\}$, partitions Z into three sets. Notice that the numbers in each class all leave the same remainder when divided by 3.

Remark: The preceding theorems show, among other things, that equivalence relations are quite plentiful if U has many elements. For example, if U has only 3 distinct elements, there are 5 possible distinct partitions of U. Thus, according to the preceding theorems, there are exactly 5 distinct equivalence relations that can be defined in $U \times U$. Note that the number of ways in which U can be partitioned increases rapidly as the number of elements in U increases. For example, if U contains 4 elements there are 15 ways to partition U, and hence 15 distinct equivalence relations in $U \times U$.

Question: How many equivalence relations are there on U if U contains 5 distinct elements?

Exercises 2.6

1. *a)* Determine all possible partitions of the set $\{0, 1\}$ and give the corresponding equivalence relations induced by each partition.

   b) Do the same for $\{a, b, c\}$ where a, b, and c are all distinct.

2. *a)* Prove that cardinal equivalence of sets is an equivalence relation. (Be sure to define the domain and range of this relation.)

   b) Find equivalence classes in 2^S for $S = \{1, 2, 3, 4\}$ with respect to the cardinal equivalence relation.

3. Verify that "$=$" is an equivalence relation.

4. Prove that if E is an equivalence relation in $U \times U$, then $D_E = R_E = U$.

5. Determine the equivalence classes (partition) induced on Z by the definition

$$x \sim y \Leftrightarrow x - y = 5n \text{ for } n \in Z.$$

6. List the ordered pairs in the equivalence relation induced by the following partition of $\{0, 1, 2, 3\}$: $\{\{0, 1\}, \{2\}, \{3\}\}$.

7. Give the partition induced by the following equivalence relation on $\{0, 1, 2, 3\}$

$$\sim = \{(0, 0), (1, 1), (2, 2), (3, 3), (0, 1), (1, 0)\}$$

8. *a*) Construct the "smallest" equivalence relation on $\{2, 4, 9\}$ which contains at least the ordered pair $(2, 4)$.

b) Construct the corresponding partition.

9. Give graphical interpretations in $R \times R$ of:
a) reflexive condition
b) symmetric condition
c) transitive condition

10. Suppose $U = R \times R$ and we define two points on this plane to be equivalent iff they are the same distance from the origin $(0, 0)$.

a) Argue that this is an equivalence relation.

b) Determine the equivalence classes of this relation.

c) Argue that the set of these equivalence classes forms a partition of U.

11. For the given set and relation below, determine which define equivalence relations:

a) U is the set of all people in the world today, $a \sim b$ if a and b have an ancestor in common.

b) U is the set of all people in the world today, $a \sim b$ if a lives within 100 miles of b.

c) U is the set of all people in the world today, $a \sim b$ if a and b have the same father.

d) U is the set R, $a \sim b$ if $a = \pm b$ (*i.e.*, $a = b$ or $a = -b$).

e) U is the set Z, $a \sim b$ if both $a > b$ and $b > a$.

f) U is the set of all people in the world, $a \sim b$ if a and b live in the same house.

12. Give an example of a relation which is symmetric and reflexive but not transitive.

13. Give an example of a relation which is reflexive and transitive, but not symmetric.

14. Give an example of a relation that is symmetric and transitive, but not reflexive, or show that such an example does not exist.

15. Let $\sim$ be an equivalence relation on S, and $a, b \in S$. Let C_a, C_b be the equivalence classes containing a and b, respectively.

a) Show that if $a \sim b$, then $C_a = C_b$.

b) Show that if $a \sim b$, then $C_a \cap C_b = \varnothing$.

16. What is wrong with the following "proof" that a symmetric and transitive relation T must be reflexive?

Suppose $(a, b) \in T$. Then $(b, a) \in T$ (why?). But $(a, b) \in T$ and $(b, a) \in T$ implies that $(a, a) \in T$ by the transitivity of T. Thus T is reflexive.

17. Suppose A and B are two non-empty subsets of the universe U such that
   a) $A \cap B = \varnothing$, and
   b) $A \cup B \neq U$.

Prove that there is an extension $\mathfrak{I}^*$ of the class $\mathfrak{I} = \{A, B\}$ which is a partition of U.

18. Interpret a partition of U in terms of Venn diagrams.

19. How many distinct partitions are there of a set U containing five elements?

20. Show that $A \subset U, B \subset U \Rightarrow \mathcal{P}$ is a partition of U where

$$\mathcal{P} = \{\overline{A \cup B}, A - B, A \cap B, B - A\}$$

(assume that the four subsets of U are non-empty).

21. Show that pairwise disjointedness of the sets F_α in a class $\mathfrak{F} = \{F_\alpha : \alpha \in I\}$ implies that

$$\bigcap_{\alpha \in J} F_\alpha = \varnothing,$$

where J is any subset of the index set I containing at least two elements (*i.e.*, "pairwise" disjointedness $\Rightarrow$ "n-wise" disjointedness).

2.7 Sub-universes and Closure Under Set Operations, Minimal Extension to Accommodate Closure

Closure

In our consideration of binary operations on a set, we have discussed the notion of a subset which is *closed* with respect to a given operation. We wish now to consider a similar notion of closure under set operations in certain sub-collections of the universe 2^U.

Example: Let $U = \{1, 2, 3\}$. Then

$$2^U = \{\varnothing, \{1\}, \{2\}, \{3\}, \{1, 2\}, \{1, 3\}, \{2, 3\}, U\}.$$

The collection $V = \{\{1\}, \{2\}, \{1, 2\}\}$ is said to be closed under the set operation of arbitrary unions, since the union of any collection of sets in V is again an element of V. However, V is not closed under intersections, since $\{1\} \cap \{2\} = \varnothing$ is not again in V.

It happens in some mathematical discussions that one is particularly interested in a collection of subsets of U which does not include all subsets of

U. This class of sets, which is of particular interest, is often called "the universal class of sets under consideration." Such universal classes are known by various names such as "topologies," "measurable sets," "σ-algebras," "event spaces," "Cauchy nests," etc., depending on certain properties possessed by the collection. Among the most common properties used to determine interesting universal classes of sets is closure with respect to one or more set operations.

Example: Let $U = \{a, b, c, d\}$ all distinct. Then the class $\mathfrak{J} = \{\varnothing, U, \{a\}, \{b\}, \{a, b\}\}$ is closed under unions and intersections. (*Do you agree?*)

Example: Let $U = \{1, 2, 3, 4, 5\}$, $\mathfrak{S} = \{\{1, 2\}, \{3\}, \{1\}, \{2\}\}$. $\mathfrak{S}$ is closed under distinct relative complementation. That is, the set difference of any pair of distinct sets in $\mathfrak{S}$ is again in $\mathfrak{S}$. However, $\mathfrak{S}$ is not closed under unions and intersections, nor is it closed under arbitrary relative complementation (why?).

2.7-1 Definition: A class $\mathfrak{J}$ of subsets of a universe U is said to be *closed under an operation* $\mathfrak{o}$ provided that performing that operation on elements of $\mathfrak{J}$ results in "answers" that are also elements in $\mathfrak{J}$. More precisely, $R_{\mathfrak{o}|\mathfrak{J}} \subset \mathfrak{J}$.

Remark: You should compare this definition with that given for closure of a set A under a *binary* operation φ (1.12-6).

The major contribution of this restriction of our attention to sets in $\mathfrak{J}$ is that of allowing us to consider special *types* of sets. Thus the objects with which we are working in a certain context (that is, the elements of a certain universal class $\mathfrak{J}$) may have additional interesting properties—properties that we cannot expect *all* subsets of the universal set U to have. In fact, a partition $\{A_1, A_2, \ldots, A_n\}$ of U is an example of a useful type of universal class. In this case, the A_i's satisfy certain properties discussed in the preceding section.

Extension to Accommodate Closure

In some studies such as statistics, topology, and analysis, one is dealing with a universal class of subsets which he knows to be closed under certain set operations. However, he may not immediately know the full extent of such a class. It may be the case that he has some limited information concerning the elements in the class, and from this he might be able to determine at least a "minimal" subset of the universe for which closure holds.

Suppose, for example, that the universal set U is the set of one-digit natural numbers, and that the universal class $\mathfrak{J}$ is the set of subsets containing exactly one number from U. That is,

$$U = \{1, 2, 3, \ldots, 9\},$$

and
$$\mathfrak{J} = \{\{1\}, \{2\}, \{3\}, \ldots, \{9\}\}.$$

In this case, the objects under consideration are the *singleton* subsets of U.

This represents a strong restriction from the class of *all* subsets of U. In order to make the system more interesting, we may add an *operation* to the system— for example, the operation "$-$" (*relative complementation*). A difficulty soon arises, however, with our small universal class $\mathfrak{I}$. The problem is, by taking relative complements of elements of $\mathfrak{I}$, we don't necessarily obtain an answer! For example, consider the following:

a) $\{1\} - \{3\} = \{1\}$.

In this case, an answer $\{1\}$ in $\mathfrak{I}$ is obtained.

b) $\{1\} - \{1\}$ is not defined. More precisely, the resulting set $\varnothing$ is not in our universal class $\mathfrak{I}$. Since $\mathfrak{I}$ is precisely the set of objects we are considering, and since our candidate $\varnothing$ for the answer is not in $\mathfrak{I}$, we have to assert that

$$\{1\} - \{1\}$$

is not defined for the universal class $\mathfrak{I}$. That is, "$-$" is not a binary operation in $\mathfrak{I}$.

Briefly, it appears that our universal class of singleton subsets of U is not "large" enough to accommodate the operation we have in mind. We might consider extensions of (that is, the addition of more subsets of U to) the class $\mathfrak{I}$ which will admit the relative complementation operation.

One could define a new universal class $\mathfrak{I}^*$ containing the original class $\mathfrak{I}$ and additional subsets of U in such a way that the operation could always be performed. For example, one could take $\mathfrak{I}^*$ to be the class of *all* subsets of U. (Do you agree that such a class is closed under relative complementation operations?) There is a less "drastic" extension $\mathfrak{I}^*$ of $\mathfrak{I}$ which will accommodate the operation, however. This is to take $\mathfrak{I}^*$ to be $\mathfrak{I} \cup \{\varnothing\}$. (Add the empty set to the list of members of the universal class.) In this case we would have

$$\mathfrak{I}^* = \{\varnothing, \{1\}, \{2\}, \ldots, \{9\}\}.$$

The student should verify the following statements concerning the system composed of U, $\mathfrak{I}^*$, and the relative complementation operation:

1) $\mathfrak{I}^*$ is large enough to accommodate the difference operation. (That is, closed under "$-$", so that

$$A \in \mathfrak{I}^* \quad \text{and} \quad B \in \mathfrak{I}^* \Rightarrow A - B \in \mathfrak{I}^*.)$$

2) $\mathfrak{I}^*$ is an extension of $\mathfrak{I}$. (That is, $\mathfrak{I} \subset \mathfrak{I}^*$.)

3) $\mathfrak{I}^*$ is a *minimal* extension of $\mathfrak{I}$ admitting the relative complementation operation. (That is, if $\mathfrak{I}^{**}$ is any class of subsets of U satisfying 1) and 2) above, then $\mathfrak{I}^* \subset \mathfrak{I}^{**}$.)

In what follows, we shall be interested in making sure that our universal classes are large enough to accommodate the operations we have in mind.

Example: Let $U = \{0, 5, 9\}$, $\mathcal{S} = \{\{0\}, \{5\}\}$.

Question: What is the smallest collection of subsets of U which contains all the elements of $\mathcal{S}$ and is closed under unions?

Answer: $S^* = \{\{0\}, \{5\}, \{0, 5\}\}$ is the smallest such collection. There are other collections with the stated properties, but any such collections will contain S^* as a subset.

Example: Let $U = \{0, 5, 6, 7\}$, $S = \{\{0\}, \{5\}\}$. What is the smallest collection which contains S as a subset and which is closed under unions and relative complements?

Answer: $S = \{\{0\}, \{5\}, \{0, 5\}, \emptyset\}$. (You should verify this.)

2.7-2 Definition: If S is a collection of subsets of some universe U (*i.e.,* $S \subset 2^U$) and $*$ is some set operation, then $S \subset 2^U$ is called the *"set generated from S under the operation $*$"* or "the smallest set containing S which is closed under $*$" provided:

    a) $S \subset S$
    b) S is closed under $*$
    c) If $S \subset \mathfrak{I}$ and $\mathfrak{I}$ is closed under $*$, then $S \subset \mathfrak{I}$.

S is also called "the minimal extension of S to accommodate $*$." Note that by "smallest" (or "minimal"), we mean in terms of set inclusion. (See Problem 10, 2.4.)

Example: Let $U = \{2, 4, 6, 8\}$, $S = \{\{2, 4\}, \{6\}\}$. What is the minimal extension of S which will accommodate intersections?

Answer: $S = \{\{2, 4\}, \{6\}, \emptyset\}$. (Verify this!)

What is the minimal extension of S which will accommodate both intersections and unions?

Answer: $\{\{2, 4\}, \{6\}, \emptyset, \{2, 4, 6\}\}$.

Exercises 2.7

1. Let $U = \{1, 2, 3, 4, 5\}$ and $S = \{\{1, 2\}, \{3\}, \{5\}\}$. Find the minimal extension of S to accommodate

    a) unions
    b) intersections
    c) relative complements
    d) distinct relative complements
    e) complementation in U
    f) union and intersection
    g) intersection and complementation in U

2. Find a non-minimal extension of U which is not the entire power set of U (2^U) which accommodates the operations in Exercise 1, taking U and S as in Exercise 1.

3. Prove that for any set A, the power set 2^A is closed under

    a) intersections   *c)* differences
    b) unions   *d)* complementation (with respect to A)

4. Show that Z is the minimal extension of N so that the resulting system is closed under subtraction. (*Hint:* You have two things to show:

1) That Z contains N and is closed under subtraction, and

2) That *any* other set K which contains N and is closed under subtraction *must necessarily* also contain Z.)

5. Let $U = R$ and $S = \{(0, 1/n): n \in N\}$.

   a) Is S closed under finite intersections?

   b) Is S closed under arbitrary intersections?

   c) Is S closed under unions?

   d) Is S closed under relative complementation?

6. Is $\varnothing$ closed for any operation? Vacuously perhaps?

7. A topology on U is a universal class of subsets of U which

   i) is closed under finite intersections.

   ii) is closed under arbitrary unions.

   iii) has $\varnothing$ and U as elements.

   If $U = \{1, 2, 3, 4, 5\}$, then find the smallest topology which contains S where:

   a) $S = \{\{1\}, \{2\}\}$ *c*) $S = \{\{1, 3\}, \{1, 5\}\}$

   b) $S = \{\{1, 2\}\}$ *d*) $S = \{\{3\}, \{5\}, \{3, 5\}\}$

8. A σ-algebra on U is a universal class of subsets of U which

   i) is closed under countable unions. (A countable union is a union which can be indexed by N.)

   ii) is closed under relative complementation.

   iii) has U as an element.

   Find the smallest σ-algebra generated by S where $U = \{1, 2, 3, 4, 5\}$ and

   a) $S = \{\{1\}, \{2\}\}$ *c*) $S = \{\{1, 3\}, \{1, 5\}\}$

   b) $S = \{\{1, 2\}\}$ *d*) $S = \{\{3\}, \{5\}, \{3, 5\}\}$

9. Let $\mathfrak{I}$ be the set of all finite subsets of N.

   a) Show that each element of $\mathfrak{I}$ has a *l.u.b.*

   b) Show that $\mathfrak{I}$ is closed under finite unions and intersections.

   c) Show that $\mathfrak{I}$ is closed under arbitrary intersections but not under arbitrary unions.

   d) Is $\mathfrak{I}$ closed under complementation?

2.8   n-tuples and Product Spaces, Functions of Several Variables

Cross Products

Recall that the cross product operation between sets is *not* an associative operation. An element of $A \times (B \times C)$ is an ordered pair whose second component is again an ordered pair while an element of $(A \times B) \times C$ is an ordered pair whose first component is an ordered pair.

Example: Let $A = \{a, b\}$, $B = \{2\}$, and $C = \{\alpha, \beta\}$. Then

$$A \times (B \times C) = \{(a, (2, \alpha)), (a, (2, \beta)), (b, (2, \alpha)), (b, (2, \beta))\},$$

$$(A \times B) \times C = \{((a, 2), \alpha), ((a, 2), \beta), ((b, 2), \alpha), ((b, 2), \beta)\}.$$

We see that by taking sets into products several times results each time in a set of ordered pairs, whose components are, of course, themselves ordered pairs, etc. It is useful to extend this concept introducing some truly different objects. We shall call them "ordered triples," "ordered four-tuples," "ordered n-tuples," etc. We do this by making use of index sets and functions.

2.8-1 Definition: Let A_1, A_2, and A_3 be non-empty sets. Then

$$\mathop{\times}_{i \in \{1,2,3\}} A_i$$

$$= \{f : f \text{ is a function, } D_f = \{1, 2, 3\} \text{ and } f(1) \in A_1, f(2) \in A_2, f(3) \in A_3\}.$$

The functions in this product set are called ordered 3-tuples.

Example: Let $A_1 = \{a, b\}$, $A_2 = \{1\}$, $A_3 = \{\alpha, \beta\}$

$$\mathop{\times}_{i \in \{1,2,3\}} A_i = \{f_1, f_2, f_3, f_4\},$$

where

$$f_1 = \{(1, a), (2, 1), (3, \alpha)\}, \qquad f_2 = \{(1, b), (2, 1), (3, \alpha)\},$$

$$f_3 = \{(1, a), (2, 1), (3, \beta)\}, \qquad f_4 = \{(1, b), (2, 1), (3, \beta)\}.$$

Each function can be indicated more simply as an ordered triple in which the functional values are given in the appropriate position, 1st, 2nd, or 3rd. Thus f_1 above could be denoted by the ordered triple $(a, 1, \alpha) = (f_1(1), f_1(2), f_1(3))$. Thus, for the preceding example, we could write

$$\mathop{\times}_{i \in \{1,2,3\}} A_i = \{(a, 1, \alpha), (b, 1, \alpha), (a, 1, \beta), (b, 1, \beta)\}.$$

This concept can be extended to four-tuples etc., and in fact for arbitrary index sets I.

2.8-2 Definition: Let $\{A_i\}_{i \in I}$ be a collection of sets indexed by I. Then

$$\mathop{\times}_{i \in I} A_i = \{f : f \text{ is a map, } D_f = I \text{ and } \forall i \in I \ f(i) \in A_i\}.$$

If I is finite (with n elements), the functions in $\times_{i \in I} A_i$ are called ordered n-tuples and can be listed in the "ordered tuple" form as discussed above.

Example: $\forall i \in R$, let $A_i = (i, \infty)$. Then $\times_{i \in R} A_i$ is the collection of all functions whose domain is R and such that for each function, each number is mapped onto some larger number. Note that there is a large "number" of functions in this product set!

Example: $\forall i \in N$, let $A_i = R$. $\times_{i \in N} A_i$ is the collection of all functions whose domain is N and have functional values in R. (Such functions are called sequences of real numbers.) Sequences are a natural extension of the concept of n-tuples and hence are often denoted by $(x_1, x_2, x_3, x_4, \ldots)$ where $f(1) = x_1$

etc. Occasionally you may see a sequence called an "infinite-tuple." We shall return to these functions later.

Example: Let $S = \{1, 2, 3, 4, 5\}$ and $\forall i \in S \, A_i = R$. Then $\times_{i \in S} A_i$ is the collection of all functions from S into R. That is, $\times_{i \in S} A_i$ is the collection of all 5-tuples of real numbers. For example, $(2, \pi, 3/4, 1, 0)$ and $(12, 6, \pi/2, 2\pi, 5)$ are such functions, where the position in the tuple gives the functional value. (These values are often called components.)

Remark: Note that the Cartesian product $A_1 \times A_2$ defined previously as the set of all ordered pairs (a_1, a_2) such that $a_1 \in A_1$ and $a_2 \in A_2$, can be written in the "index set" notation as $\times_{i \in \{1,2\}} A_i$. Note also that the use of the "ordered tuple" notation requires that we view the product as taking the sets A_i in a *specific order*. This should be contrasted with our use of index sets in arbitrary unions and intersections.

In the mathematician's effort to construct models of our universe, he finds it convenient to interpret the "three dimensional world" he lives in as the set of all 3-tuples of real numbers. Each point in space can be thought of as being a 3-tuple (that is, a function which takes on a first component (value at 1), a second component (value at 2), and a third component (value at 3)). This then is the space in which he lives. Due to the mathematical similarity between the collection of 3-tuples and the collection of 4-tuples, 5-tuples, . . . , infinite-tuples, and even more complicated collections of functions given as a product, one finds it convenient to call these collections "spaces" and give various *geometric* names and interpretations to certain sub-collections.

2.8-3 Definition: Let $S = \{1, 2, \ldots, n\}$ and $E_i = R$ for each i in S. Then $\times_{i \in S} E_i$ (usually denoted by E^n) is called *Euclidean n-space*.

Note that R is itself such a space, $R = E^1$.

2.8-4 Definition: If $x = (x_1, x_2, \ldots, x_n)$ and $y = (y_1, y_2, \ldots, y_n)$ are elements of E^n (Euclidean n-space), then the *distance from x to y, $d(x, y)$,* is defined as follows:

$$d(x, y) = \sqrt{(x_1 - y_1)^2 + (x_2 - y_2)^2 + \ldots + (x_n - y_n)^2}.$$

(Does this agree with your concept of distance on a line or a plane?) (*Hint:* Use the Pythagorean theorem.)

Example: $(2, 3, 5, 1)$ and $(1, 2, 0, 3)$ are elements of 4-space, and the distance between them is

$$\sqrt{(2 - 1)^2 + (3 - 2)^2 + (5 - 0)^2 + (1 - 3)^2} = \sqrt{1 + 1 + 25 + 4} = \sqrt{31}.$$

Functions of Several Variables

Very often one deals with functions whose domains are product spaces. Such functions are commonly called *functions of several variables.*

Example: Let $f: E^3 \to R$ given by $\forall\, (x, y, z) \in E^3$

$$f((x, y, z)) = 2x + y + 3z.$$

Then, for example, $f((1, 2, 4)) = 2 \cdot 1 + 2 + 3 \cdot 4 = 16,$

and $f((2, 1, 1)) = 2 \cdot 2 + 1 + 3 \cdot 1 = 8.$

In discussing and denoting functional values for such functions, it is convenient to eliminate one set of parentheses when the domain value is given in terms of an n-tuple.

Example: Let $f: E^4 \to R$ given by $\forall(x, y, z, v) \in E^4$

$$f((x, y, z, v)) = 2x^2 + y + 3z + v.$$

This description is usually given simply as

$$f(x, y, z, v) = 2x^2 + y + 3z + v$$

since the elimination of the parenthesis is supposed to result in no confusion whatsoever.

2.8-5 Definition: A function from E^n to R is called a *real valued function of n real variables.*

Note that an ordinary function $f: R \to R$ is a real valued function of one real variable.

Let us now consider some characteristics of a function $f: E^n \to R$. f is a collection of ordered pairs whose first component is an n-tuple and whose second component is a real number.

Example: Let $f: E^3 \to R$ be given by $f(x, y, z) = x + y + 2z$. Then some typical elements of f are:

$$((1, 1, 2), 6), \qquad ((2, 1, 1), 5), \qquad ((1, 2, 1), 5).$$

It is common practice to identify such elements with corresponding 4-tuples and hence interpret f as a subset of four space.* Thus, for example,

$$((1, 1, 2), 6) \text{ is identified with } (1, 1, 2, 6),$$

and $((2, 1, 1), 5)$ is identified with $(2, 1, 1, 5).$

Hence, in general, if $f: E^n \to R$, then f can be considered to be a particular subset of E^{n+1}. This concept is especially useful in graphing a function of two variables. That is, a function $f: E^2 \to R$ can be thought of as a subset of E^3. E^3 is in turn thought of as a Euclidean 3-dimensional coordinate system, with three mutually perpendicular axes. An element in E^3 is a 3-tuple (x, y, z) and is located in space by measuring x, y, z, respectively, on each axis. (See Figure 2.6.)

Example: Let $f: E^2 \to R$ given by $f(x, y) = -2x - y + 3$. Then f can be interpreted graphically as a set of points in E^3. We have, in general

$$f = \{(x, y, z): z = f(x, y)\},$$

---

* See "Elementary Topology," by D. Hall and G. Spencer. John Wiley and Sons, Inc., 1955, p. 144.

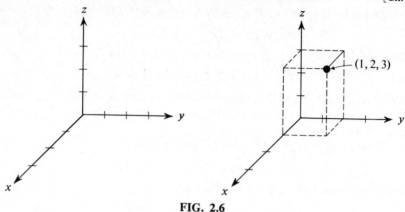

FIG. 2.6

and in this special case

$$f = \{(x, y, z): z = -2x - y + 3\}.$$

Graphically, f is thought of as some sort of "surface" in E^3 provided f has certain "nice" properties. In this case, the graph of f is a plane, as shown in Figure 2.7.

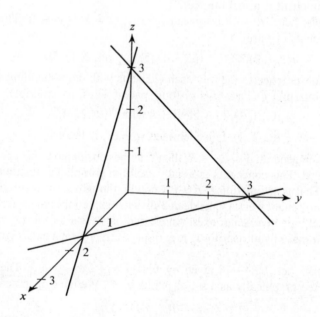

FIG. 2.7

Graphing functions of two variables as subsets of E^3 is, in general, very difficult and will not be considered in detail. It is the case, however, as for functions in $R \times R$, that one can gather much information simply by plotting
points (*i.e.*, evaluating the function at numerous points in E^2 and locating
the resulting point in E^3).

Exercises 2.8

1. If $A_1 = \{a, b, c\}$, $A_2 = \{x, y\}$, $A_3 = \{p, q\}$, list all elements in
   a) $A_1 \times (A_2 \times A_3)$
   b) $(A_1 \times A_2) \times A_3$
   c) $\times_{i \in \{1,2,3\}} A_i$

2. Let $A_i = [i, i + 1]$ for all $i \in N$. Determine which of the following are elements
   of $\times_{i \in N} A_i$.
   a) $f: R \to R$ given by $f(x) = 2x$
   b) $f: N \to R$ given by $f(n) = n$
   c) $f: N \to R$ given by $f(n) = 1/2 + n$
   d) $f: N \to R$ given by $f(n) = 1 + n$
   e) $f: N \to R$ given by $f(n) = 2 + n$
   f) $f: N \to R$ given by $f(n) = 2n$

3. List 6 elements of $\times_{i \in \{1,2,3,4\}} A_i$ where $A_1 = A_2 = A_4 = N$ but $A_3 = Z - N$.

4. Find the distance from x to y in the appropriate n-space where:
   a) $x = (2, 1, 3)$, $y = (1, 1, 4)$
   b) $x = (3, 1, 1, 4)$, $y = (5, 2, 1, 3)$
   c) $x = (3, 3, 3, 2, 2, 2)$, $y = (5, 5, 2, 4, 1, 1)$

5. a) Evaluate f at $(2, 1, 1, 4)$ and $(4, 5, 3, 1/3)$ where $f: E^4 \to R$ is given by
   $f(x, y, z, v) = 2x + 3y + z^2 + 3v$.
   b) Find two points in E^5 which would be considered as points of the function
   as it is graphically interpreted in E^5.

6. By plotting points and using your intuition, graph $f: E^2 \to R$ as a collection of
   points in E^3 where:
   a) $f(x, y) = 2x^2 + y$ c) $f(x, y) = 2x$
   b) $f(x, y) = -x + 2y$ d) $f(x, y) = 2 - y$

7. Explain how the distance function $d(x, y)$ for E^2 utilizes our convention of taking
   the axes to be perpendicular. (*Hint:* Think about the Pythagorean theorem.)

8. Let $f: E^3 \to E^2$ be given by $f(x, y, z) = (x + y, z + 1)$ and let $g: E^2 \to R$ be
   given by $g(x, y) = x - y$. Determine:
   a) $f(3, 4, 1)$ and $g(f(3, 4, 1))$
   b) $f(-2, 1, 0)$ and $g \circ f(-2, 1, 0)$

145

  c) $f(5, -1, 3)$ and $g \circ f(5, -1, 3)$

  d) $f(a, b, c)$ and $g(f(a, b, c))$

9. Let $f: R \to E^2$ be given by $f(x) = (2x + 1, x - 2)$. Determine the distance between:

  a) $f(1)$ and $f(3)$

  b) $f(2)$ and $f(0)$

  c) $f(-3)$ and $f(6)$

3

NUMBER SYSTEMS

3.1   The Natural Numbers and the Principle of Induction

In this section we would like to examine intuitively the concept of counting, and then state two axioms which seem to characterize the counting process. From these axioms and some well-motivated definitions we will then deduce various formal properties of the natural numbers.

The concept of counting seems to be innate and somehow basic to our world. Animals of very low intelligence can be taught to count. Experiments indicate that crows seem to be able to count as high as four.* Children at a very young age learn to count objects, in the usual fashion by making a one-one correspondence between objects of some set and a set of sounds, and later the set of symbols 1, 2, 3, ... Glenda Gibson could count the twelve buildings in Eagle Beak when she was only fourteen years old. (It was clear from the beginning that she was college material.) With very little formalization we seem to feel convinced that, given any two intelligent beings, they have essentially the same concept of counting discrete objects. We feel sufficiently convinced of the naturalness of the counting concept to believe other intelligent beings in the universe, if they exist, would have the same basic feeling about counting as we do.†

* For a discussion of the counting ability of animals and people in various cultures, see "Counting" by Levi Conant, *The World of Mathematics*, J. R. Newman (ed.), (New York: Simon and Schuster, 1956), Vol. 1, pp. 432–41.

† Thus, in sending signals into space for reception by other intelligent life in the universe, it has been suggested that signals be used which are easily recognized (by us) as being associated with counting and simple arithmetic operations on counting numbers. *Interstellar Communications*, A. G. W. Cameron (ed.), New York (1963), pp. 141, 163, 268, 302.

The Approach

There are two distinctly different approaches that we can take in developing the natural numbers. One way is to construct a collection of objects, doing the construction in such a way that the basic properties we desire are built into the set. The authors feel that such a construction is highly superficial, and that the properties which must be built into the collection are the things of primary interest. The second approach, and the one we shall take, is axiomatic. In this approach, we assert the existence of a collection of objects (with no concern as to what sort of material the objects are made from) and then list as axioms some basic properties that we feel the set should have in relation to a particular function on the set.

Let us note some very special properties of the natural number system $N = \{1, 2, 3, \ldots\}$ (sometimes also called the "counting numbers" or "positive whole numbers"). First, we feel there are lots of them, in fact, an "unboundedly" large amount of them. On the other hand, we feel that given any one natural number, we could begin counting 1, 2, 3,—and if given sufficient time, we could count all the way to that number. Another important concept or feeling which is involved with the idea of counting is that, by continually counting, we could never return to any previously counted number.

In the process of trying to decide exactly what is meant by counting, one realizes that the fundamental concept involved is the concept of "increasing from one number to the next number." Let us formalize this concept by the following axiom.

3.1-1 Axiom: There exists a function $\varphi: N \to N$ with the following properties:
   1) φ is 1-1;
   2) There exists a unique element y in N such that $\forall n \in N,\ \varphi(n) \neq y$.
   Remark: Note that φ is *1-1* but not *onto*. We call φ the "counting function" or "successor function" and call $\varphi(n)$ the "successor of n." The unique y of condition 2) is called the "first element in N" or simply "one," and is usually denoted by "1."

Names are given to other members of N as well. The following is a partial list of such names.

$$\varphi(1) = 2$$
$$\varphi(\varphi(1)) = \varphi(2) = 3$$
$$\varphi(\varphi(\varphi(1))) = \varphi(\varphi(2)) = \varphi(3) = 4$$
$$\varphi(4) = 5$$
$$\varphi(5) = 6$$
$$\varphi(6) = 7$$

.

.

.

The Romans denoted the first element by "I" and had the following partial list of names.

$$\varphi(I) = II$$
$$\varphi(\varphi(I)) = \varphi(II) = III$$
$$\varphi(III) = IV$$
$$\varphi(IV) = V$$
$$\varphi(V) = VI$$
$$\varphi(VI) = VII$$

.

.

.

For the sake of familiarity, let us denote $\varphi(n)$ by $n + 1$. Later we shall extend the concept of "addition" to all natural numbers. (For now assume we know how to add 1, but nothing further about addition is known.) From the concept of the successor function, one becomes aware of an important property known as the "induction property." Let us elaborate upon this property.

We feel confident that if we first take 1 and then take $1 + 1 = 2$ and then $2 + 1 = 3$ and continue successively to add 1 to our result in this fashion (which is merely what we had in mind for the counting process), we could eventually reach any given natural number. In fact, we feel that if p is some property possessed by the number 1, and that when given any natural number n it can be shown that if n has property p then $\varphi(n) = n + 1$ also has property p, then p is some property possessed by every natural number.

Example: You are given a book and the following information:

1) For any natural number n, if you find a page numbered n, then turn the leaf and you will find a page numbered $n + 1$. (That is, if you find page 1000, then turn the leaf and you will find page 1001; if you find page 111, then turn the leaf and you will find page 112, etc.)

2) You have found a page numbered 1.

Conclusion: This is a very large book. At least it is, if it is not somehow "circular" and has more than one number per page. We can be sure, however, that, given any natural number, there is a page numbered with that number.

Let us formalize this process (called "mathematical induction").

3.1-2 Definition: Let $H \subset N$. H is a *hereditary set* if $\forall k \in N$

$$k \in H \Rightarrow k + 1 \in H.$$

3.1-3 Induction Axiom: If $S \subset N$, $1 \in S$, and S is hereditary, then $S = N$.

We will find numerous opportunities to apply this principle; however, in making an application, it is common to use a slightly different form which we shall prove follows from the induction axiom.

3.1-4 Theorem: Let $p(x)$ be a statement form over N. (That is, for any given natural number n, $p(n)$ is a sentence and is therefore either true or false.)

149

If   i) $p(1)$ is true

   ii) $\forall k \in N \quad p(k)$ is true $\Rightarrow p(k + 1)$ is true,

then $\forall n \in N \quad p(n)$ is true.

Proof: Let $H = \{x \in N: p(x)\}$, $1 \in H$ since $p(1)$ is true by hypothesis. Let $k \in N$ and assume $k \in H$.

Therefore, $p(k)$ is true (by def. of H),

   $p(k + 1)$ is true (by hypothesis),

   $k + 1 \in H$ (by def. of H),

   $k \in H \Rightarrow k + 1 \in H$ *(discharge assumption)*,

   $\forall k \in N \quad k \in H \Rightarrow k + 1 \in H$ *(generalization (test pattern))*.

Hence H is hereditary, and by the induction axiom $H = N$. Therefore, $\forall n \in N \quad p(n)$ is true. $\square$

Until now, we have discussed only two ways of proving a generalization about a universe. (That is, a statement of the form $\forall x \in U \, p(x)$.) One way, of course, is simply to test $p(x)$ for every $x \in U$. This is effective only if we have a very small universe. The other way is to use the test pattern principle. (Recall this very important concept of logic allows us to make a proof using an arbitrary element.) We survey the proof, and note that no particular property for the element was used. We then conclude that the same proof could be used for *any* element. We have now a new and entirely different method for making proofs, where our universe is the natural number set N. This is the principle of induction. We will encounter other universes for which proofs can also be made by induction. Proof by induction is an extremely important and useful device, and should be thoroughly mastered.

A property of the natural number system, which distinguishes it from other "inductive systems" which we encounter later, is the property of having a unique "starting place." One sees the significance of this in the example where the book would be very thick if it were not "circular." In turning the pages of a circularly-constructed book, one could eventually get to each page regardless of where he started. This is not the kind of counting we had in mind for counting with the natural numbers.

The fact that this "starting place" property is built into the axioms is clarified by the following discussion. If all that is known about a set S of natural numbers is that S is hereditary and $k \in S(k \neq 1)$, then it cannot be deduced that $S = N$. For example, we cannot show that $1 \in S$, since we have at our disposal only the notion of placing an element in S if it is the successor of some element in S. But 1 is not the successor of any element in N; hence we *cannot* deduce that $1 \in S$. Thus we see that in order to claim that a set of natural numbers is the entire set N, we need to know independently that 1 is in the set. We shall later encounter number systems for which this is not true.

In our very informal discussion of the natural numbers, we introduced the notion of "adding 1" to a number to obtain the "next" number. We would like to elaborate on the concept of adding any two arbitrary natural numbers. We wish to assign to a pair of numbers m, n another natural number $m + n$ in a way which is consistent with the concept of counting the elements in a set $A \cup B$, where A has m elements and B has n elements, under the condition that $A \cap B = \varnothing$. We would like to say that $A \cup B$ has $m + n$ elements. In order to do this, we shall utilize a very important principle: *the inductive definition*. We also introduce at this time a very special and useful class of functions.

3.1-5 Definition: Any function f from the natural numbers into a set S, $f: N \to S$, is called a *sequence of elements from S*.

Remark: Note that a sequence of elements from S is a function whose domain is N and whose range is contained in S. A common notation is to label the image of a number n by f_n rather than $f(n)$ as we have been doing. A sequence is sometimes described by a list as

$$f = \{f_1, f_2, f_3, \ldots, f_n, \ldots\} \quad \text{or} \quad \{f_n\},$$

rather than using the ordered pair list

$$f = \{(1, f_1), (2, f_2), \ldots, (n, f_n), \ldots\}.$$

Example: The successor function φ is a sequence in which the image φ_n of the number n is $n + 1$.

3.1-6 Theorem: (*Recursive definition theorem*) Let S be a set, and $g: S \to S$ and $\alpha \in S$. Define $f \subset N \times S$ by

$$f(1) = \alpha \quad (i.e., (1, \alpha) \in f)$$

and
$$\forall n \in N$$

$$f(n + 1) = g(f(n)) \quad (i.e., s \in S \text{ and } (n,s) \in f \Rightarrow (n + 1, g(s)) \in f).$$

Then f is a sequence of elements from S.

Proof: We need to argue that f is defined for each number and that the value as described is unique. That is, we need to argue that $\forall m \in N$ $f(m)$ is uniquely determined. By induction,

i) $f(1)$ is uniquely determined since 1 is not a successor (*i.e.*, $\forall n$ $n + 1 \neq 1$).

ii) Let k be arbitrary and assume $f(k)$ is uniquely determined. By definition, $f(k + 1) = g(f(k))$; and since g is a function and $f(k)$ is uniquely determined, it follows that $g(f(k))$ is also uniquely determined.

Hence $\forall k$, if $f(k)$ is unique, then $f(k + 1)$ is unique. By the induction axiom we conclude the statement we need. $\square$

We are now in a position to define addition of any two natural numbers in terms of adding 1, that is, in terms of the successor or counting function.

Let us first define a class of sequences using the recursive definition principle.

3.1-7 Definition: Let $P_m: N \rightarrow N$, $m \in N$, be defined by

1) $P_m(1) = m + 1 = \varphi(m)$
2) $\forall k \in N, P_m(k + 1) = P_m(k) + 1 = \varphi(P_m(k))$.

As a result of the recursive definition principle, we know that this truly does define a sequence of elements from N. Now let us define addition in general for natural numbers.

3.1-8 Definition: $\forall m, n \in N, m + n = P_m(n)$. ($m + n$ is called the *sum of m and n*. Note that we are defining a binary operation on N.)

This may seem like a very complicated definition, but all it says intuitively is: in order to add n to m, you begin at m and count n more things. Perhaps the student will feel that we have overly complicated a very simple concept, but it is our aim to logically deduce some further results about the natural number system. Therefore, it is necessary to decide carefully what we have in mind about a given concept, and to express this concept in some precise language which will admit logical examination. The above definition, although seemingly overly involved, can be used to examine carefully certain facts about the numbers, Let us restate our definition in more familiar terms, that is, in terms of the symbol "+" itself. The two assertions of definition 3.1-7 express the following facts:

1) $\forall m \quad m + 1 = m + 1$ (*i.e.*, $m + 1 = \varphi(m)$),

and

2) $\forall m \, \forall k \quad m + (k + 1) = (m + k) + 1$.

That is, to add 1 to a natural number m, one takes the successor of m; and to add $k + 1$ to m, one takes the successor of $m + k$.

Exercises 3.1

1. What is the successor of:
   a) 65   b) 102   c) 165

2. What is:
   a) $\varphi(16)$ b) $\varphi(\varphi(29))$ c) $\varphi(\varphi(\varphi(62)))$

3. Describe some subsets of N which are hereditary and some which are not.

4. a) Show that $\varnothing$, the empty set, is hereditary. Does this show that $\varnothing = N$?
   b) Let $S = \{1\}$. Note that $1 \in S$. Does this show that $S = N$?
   c) What *two* things must one verify in order to show that a set $S \subset N$ is the whole collection of natural numbers?

5. Compute:
   a) $P_5(1)$ c) $P_5(3)$ e) $P_5(5)$ g) $P_6(4)$
   b) $P_5(2)$ d) $P_5(4)$ f) $P_4(3)$

6. *a*) Use the definition of P_m (3.1-7) and show by induction that

$$\forall n \in N \quad P_n(1) = P_1(n).$$

b) What does this say with respect to addition?

7. "Checkerboard Jimmy" is a robot located on a very large checkerboard. Jimmy can be programmed to understand any function $f: N \rightarrow \{L, R, F, B, S\}$. (*L*—one step left, *R*—right, *F*—forward, *B*—back, *S*—stop.) He has a very clear understanding of N, the successor function φ, and the inductive definition principle. Describe a function (inductively, if necessary) so that Jimmy will:

a) walk forward forever.

b) walk to the left forever.

c) walk three steps to the right and then remain still.

d) walk two steps back and then walk to the left forever.

8. What do you suppose is meant by the dot, dot, dot (. . .) in the following set description? $\{5, 6, 7, 8, 9, \ldots\}$

9. What is a sequence? Is a subset of a sequence, a sequence?

10. Prove: $\forall m \in N \quad \varphi(m) \neq m$. (*Hint:* Use induction.)

11. Let $f \subset N \times N$ such that $f(1) = \varphi(\varphi(1))$

$$f(n + 1) = \varphi(f(n)).$$

a) Is f a sequence of elements in N?

b) Prove: $\forall m \in N \quad f(n) = \varphi(\varphi(n))$.

c) Is the range of f hereditary?

3.2 Properties of Addition and Multiplication

Associative Law

A well-known property of addition in the number system N is the "associative law", $\forall x, z, y \ (x + y) + z = x + (y + z)$. This law is a natural result of the counting concept from which we define addition. Recall that the binary operation "$+$" was defined recursively by the following:

1) $\forall m \quad m + 1 = \varphi(m) \qquad$ (*the counting function*),

2) $\forall m, k \quad m + (k + 1) = (m + k) + 1$.

The associative law is given directly from the definition if $z = 1$. To extend the law to all z, we use induction.

3.2-1 Theorem: (*Associative law for addition of natural numbers*) $\forall m, p, n$
$(m + p) + n = m + (p + n)$.

Proof: Using induction on n, we have

1) $(m + p) + 1 = m + (p + 1)$ *(recursive definition of* $+$*)*.

2) Assume $(m + p) + k = m + (p + k)$.

Now $(m + p) + (k + 1) = ((m + p) + k) + 1$ *(recursive definition of* $+$*)*

$\qquad\qquad\qquad\qquad = (m + (p + k)) + 1$ *(induction hypothesis)*

$\qquad\qquad\qquad\qquad = m + ((p + k) + 1)$ *(recursive definition of* $+$*)*

$\qquad\qquad\qquad\qquad = m + (p + (k + 1))$ *(recursive definition of* $+$*)*

Hence, by induction the theorem follows. □

Notice that the above theorem was a triple generalization. Two parts were proved by test pattern and one by induction.

As a result of the associative law for addition, many grouping symbols can be omitted. Addition is a binary operation, so we know only how to add two numbers together at one step. If someone wrote "$2 + 3 + 5$", a question which arises is whether to compute "$(2 + 3) + 5 = 5 + 5 = 10$" or to compute "$2 + (3 + 5) = 2 + 8 = 10$." As a result of the associative law, we find that it doesn't matter since we always get the same number.

The Commutative Law

Let us now prove the famous "commutative law" for the addition of natural numbers.

3.2-2 Theorem: (Commutative law) $\forall m, n \quad n + m = m + n$.

Proof: We use induction on m.

1) $n + 1 = 1 + n$ (Problem 6, 3.1).

2) Assume $n + k = k + n$.

Now $n + (k + 1) = (n + k) + 1$ (Theorem 3.2-1)

$\qquad\qquad\quad = (k + n) + 1$ (inductive hypothesis)

$\qquad\qquad\quad = k + (n + 1)$ (Theorem 3.2-1)

$\qquad\qquad\quad = k + (1 + n)$ (Problem 6, 3.1)

$\qquad\qquad\quad = (k + 1) + n$ (Theorem 3.2-1).

Hence

$$n + k = k + n \Rightarrow n + (k + 1) = (k + 1) + n$$

and the theorem immediately follows by induction. □

Question: Induction was used on m. How do we conclude the "for every n" part of the theorem?

The Big Σ

We next use the recursive definition theorem to define a very useful multiple addition process.

3.2-3 Definition: Let $g: N \rightarrow N$. Then

  1) $\sum_{i=1}^{1} g(i) = g(1)$

and

  2) $\sum_{i=1}^{k+1} g(i) = \sum_{i=1}^{k} g(i) + g(k+1)$ for every $k \in N$.

($\sum_{i=1}^{n} g(i)$ is read "the sum of $g(i)$ as i varies from 1 to n." n is called the *upper index* of the sum, and 1 is called the *lower index*.)

Recall that the recursive definition theorem allows us to define a sequence of elements from some set S which depends on a function $g: S \rightarrow S$. In the definition above, we are letting $S = N$ and leaving g arbitrary. Actually, we have defined a whole collection of sequences of natural numbers, one for every function $g: N \rightarrow N$. The $\sum$ notation for the sequence we have defined may seem a bit strange at first, but it is used because it suggests the sum of the first n terms of the sequence $\{g_n\}$.

Example: Let $g: N \rightarrow N$ be defined by $\forall n \; g(n) = n + 1$. Then, by expanding,

$$\sum_{i=1}^{3} g(i) = \sum_{i=1}^{2} g(i) + g(3)$$

$$= \sum_{i=1}^{1} g(i) + g(2) + g(3) = g(1) + g(2) + g(3)$$

$$= (1+1) + (2+1) + (3+1) = 9.$$

Example: Suppose $g(i) = 3$ for all i. Then

$$\sum_{i=1}^{5} g(i) = g(1) + g(2) + g(3) + g(4) + g(5)$$

$$= 3 + 3 + 3 + 3 + 3 = 15.$$

Note: In "expanding" a $\sum$, it does not matter whether one thinks of summing from "1 up to n" or summing from "n down to 1."

It is extremely useful to use in place of $g(i)$ the expression which tells how to compute the value of g at the point i.

Example: If $g(i) = i + 2$, then $\sum_{i=1}^{4} g(i)$ is written $\sum_{i=1}^{4} (i + 2)$, and $\sum_{i=1}^{4} (i + 2) = (1 + 2) + (2 + 2) + (3 + 2) + (4 + 2) = 18$.

Example: $\sum_{i=1}^{4} 2 = 2 + 2 + 2 + 2 = 8$.

Here the "2" indicates that the function $g: N \rightarrow N$ is the constant function which takes the value 2 at each point.

The "i", as used in all of our examples so far, means nothing special and clearly other symbols would serve as well.

Example: $\sum_{m=1}^{3} (3 + m) = (3 + 1) + (3 + 2) + (3 + 3) = 15$.
$\sum_{n=1}^{6} n = 1 + 2 + 3 + 4 + 5 + 6 = 21$.

155

Multiple Addition

When Grant Gibson was in the fifth grade, he learned about "multiplication" or "times"; and his teacher insisted that everyone learn the "times table." Grant felt, however, that there was no need for him to memorize the "table" because he could always "figure it out" if he felt he needed it very badly. He explained to the teacher that if he wanted to know 6×4, he would add 4 to itself 6 times. That is, $6 \times 4 = 4 + 4 + 4 + 4 + 4 + 4$. "After all," he explained, "multiplication is nothing but a fast way to do multiple-addition." He also noted that $4 \times 6 = 6 + 6 + 6 + 6$ and that so far, whenever he interchanged the order in which he multiplied two numbers together, he always got the same answer.

The Multiplication Operation

From the concept of "multiple addition" arises the concept of a new binary operation on N, that of multiplication denoted by "$\times$."

3.2-4 Definition: $\forall m, n \in N$, $m \times n = \sum_{i=1}^{m} n$. $m \times n$ is called the *product* of n by m.

Remark: We often use the common notation of a dot "$\cdot$" or simply juxtaposition to indicate the operation of multiplication. Thus, $m \times n = m \cdot n = mn$. One of the most fundamental facts we immediately notice concerning the new operation "$\times$" is that

$$1 \cdot m = \sum_{i=1}^{1} m = m$$

and

$$m \cdot 1 = \sum_{i=1}^{m} 1 = m \quad \text{(see Problem 7 (a))}.$$

Thus multiplying an element of N on either side by 1 "does not change anything." We will recall this fact later. (Do you think that 1 is the only element in N with this property?)

Another useful property, which we leave as an exercise in induction, is the following:

3.2-5 Theorem: (Commutative law for multiplication)

$$\forall m, n \quad m \times n = \sum_{i=1}^{m} n = \sum_{i=1}^{n} m = n \times m.$$

Remark: Due to the commutative law for multiplication, it is common to refer to "$m \cdot n$" as the "product of m *and* n" rather than the "product of n by *m*," as we have been doing. Of course, "*m* and *n*" is the same as "*n* and *m*."

As a result of having noticed that "$+$" is an associative operation, we might conjecture that "$\times$" also is associative. However, before investigating this, it is convenient to establish a very useful and important theorem which connects addition and multiplication. We shall use a convention concerning the "grouping" in an expression involving "$+$" and "$\times$," as follows: if not specifically indicated otherwise, "$\times$" is to be performed before "$+$." Thus the symbol "*nm* $+$ 1" means "(*nm*) $+$ 1," and "$2 \times 3 + 4 + 6 \times 3$" means "$(2 \times 3) + 4 + (6 \times 3)$." (By the *associative law for addition*, we may take the latter sum in any order.)

3.2-6 Theorem: (*Distributive law*) $\forall m, n, p \quad m(n + p) = mn + mp$.

Proof: We use induction on *m* as follows:

1) $1(n + p) = n + p = 1 \cdot n + 1 \cdot p$.
2) Assume $k(n + p) = kn + kp$. Now

$$(k + 1)(n + p) = \sum_{i=1}^{k+1} (n + p) = \sum_{i=1}^{k} (n + p) + (n + p)$$
$$(Definition\ 3.2\text{-}3)$$
$$= k(n + p) + (n + p) = kn + kp + (n + p)$$
$$(induction\ hypothesis)$$
$$= kn + n + kp + p$$
$$(associative\ and\ commutative\ laws\ for\ addition)$$
$$= \sum_{i=1}^{k} n + n + \sum_{i=1}^{k} p + p$$
$$= \sum_{i=1}^{k+1} n + \sum_{i=1}^{k+1} p \quad (Why?)$$
$$= (k + 1)n + (k + 1)p. \quad (Why?) \quad \square$$

Remark: It immediately follows from the *commutative law* that

$$(n + p)m = nm + pm.$$

This is called the *right distributive law*.

Now we are in a position to prove that "$\times$" is associative.

3.2-7 Theorem: (*Associative law for multiplication*)

$$\forall m, n, p \quad (m \times n) \times p = m \times (n \times p)$$

Proof: We use induction on *n*.

1) $(m \times 1) \times p = m \times p$ (see *remark* following *Definition* 3.2-4)
                $= m \times (1 \times p)$ (see *remark* following *Definition* 3.2-4)

2) Assume $(mk)p = m(kp)$. Now

$$\begin{array}{ll} (m(k + 1))p = (mk + m)p & (distributive\ law) \\ = (mk)p + mp & (right\ distributive\ law) \\ = m(kp) + mp & (induction\ hypothesis) \\ = m(kp + p) & (distributive\ law) \\ = m((k + 1)p) & (right\ distributive\ law). \end{array}$$

Hence by induction the theorem follows. $\square$

Remark: We can easily extend the distributive law to such expressions as

$$m(k + p + n) = mk + mp + mn.$$

In fact, in the problems you are asked to prove by induction that the following holds in general.

3.2-8 Corollary: $\forall m, n \in N \ \ n \sum_{i=1}^{m} f(i) = \sum_{i=1}^{m} nf(i)$
for all functions $f: N \to N.$

3.2-9 Corollary: $\forall m \ \sum_{i=1}^{m} (f(i) + g(i)) = \sum_{i=1}^{m} f(i) + \sum_{i=1}^{m} g(i)$ for all sequences f and g in N.

Let us recall, as a review, some of the properties we have established for the natural numbers with respect to the operations "$+$" and "$\times$." These properties are a result of our laying down some simple axioms about the natural numbers and stating some well-motivated definitions.

For all natural numbers m, n, and p, we have the following "laws" for addition and multiplication:

Commutative
laws $: m + n = n + m; m \times n = n \times m$

Associative
laws $: (m + n) + p = m + (n + p); (m \times n) \times p = m \times (n \times p)$

Distributive
law $: m \times (n + p) = m \times n + m \times p$

Identity element
for $: 1 \times m = m$
multiplication

These are all well-known properties which we henceforth use liberally without making specific reference.

Exercises 3.2

1. Evaluate:

    a) $\sum_{i=1}^{5} 1$ *d)* $\sum_{m=1}^{3} (m + m)$ *g)* $\sum_{i=1}^{9} 2$

    b) $\sum_{m=1}^{4} (1 + m)$ *e)* $\sum_{i=1}^{7} 1$ *h)* $\sum_{n=1}^{m} m$

    c) $\sum_{m=1}^{3} 2$ *f)* $\sum_{i=1}^{m} a$

2. Evaluate:

    a) $\sum_{i=1}^{4} 2i$ *c)* $\sum_{i=1}^{5} i(2 + i)$ *e)* $\sum_{i=1}^{5} i$

    b) $\sum_{i=1}^{7} 6(i + 1)$ *d)* $2 \sum_{i=1}^{4} i$ *f)* $2 \sum_{i=1}^{7} (i + 1)$

3. Determine $f(5)$ where

   a) $f(1) = 2$ and $\forall k \quad f(k+1) = 2f(k)$

   b) $f(1) = 3$ and $\forall k \quad f(k+1) = f(k)$

   c) $f(1) = 4$ and $\forall k \quad f(k+1) = f(k) + 2$

   d) $f(1) = 6$ and $\forall k \quad f(k+1) = 3 + 2f(k)$

4. Find $f(4)$ where

   a) $f(n) = \sum_{i=1}^{n} 2i$

   c) $f(n) = \sum_{i=1}^{2n} i$

   b) $f(n) = \sum_{i=1}^{n} (i + 2)$

   d) $f(n) = 2 \sum_{k=1}^{3} n$

5. If $f(i) = 3i$ for all i, then find

   a) $\sum_{i=1}^{3} f(i)$

   b) $\sum_{i=1}^{4} (2f(i) + 1)$

6. a) Compare $2 \sum_{i=1}^{5} i$ with $5(5+1)$.

   b) Show by an intuitive argument that $2 \sum_{i=1}^{n} i = n(n+1)$.

   c) Show by induction that $2 \sum_{i=1}^{n} i = n(n+1)$.

   d) Don't ever forget that $2 \sum_{i=1}^{n} i = n(n+1)$.

   e) Compute $2 \sum_{i=1}^{20} i$.

7. Establish (prove):

   a) $\forall m \in N \quad \sum_{i=1}^{m} 1 = m$ (Hint: Induction on m.)

   b) $\sum_{i=1}^{m} (f(i) + g(i)) = \sum_{i=1}^{m} f(i) + \sum_{i=1}^{m} g(i)$ (Note: This is Corollary 3.8-9.)

   c) $\forall m, n \quad \sum_{i=1}^{m} n = \sum_{i=1}^{n} m$

   d) $\forall m, n, p$ if $m + p = n + p$, then $m = n$. (This is called "the cancellation law for addition.")

   e) $\forall m, n \quad n \sum_{i=1}^{m} f(i) = \sum_{i=1}^{m} nf(i)$

8. Investigate (prove or disprove):

   a) $\forall n \quad \sum_{i=1}^{2n} i = n(2n + 1)$

   b) $\forall n \quad \sum_{i=1}^{n} 2i = n(n + 2)$

   c) $\forall n \quad 6 \sum_{i=1}^{n} i \cdot i = n(n + 1)(2n + 1)$

   d) $\forall n \quad \sum_{i=1}^{2n} (i + 1) = n(2n + 1) + 2n$

9. Solve each of the following equations in N. That is, find all natural numbers n which satisfy the equation:

   a) $3 + n = 5$ c) $3n + 5 = 16$ e) $7 + n = 4$

   b) $2n + 4 = 10$ d) $5n + 1 = 16$ f) $2n + 3 = 8$

10. Does every equation $ax + b = c$ have a solution in N where a, b, c are natural numbers? (That is, is $N \cap \{x: ax + b = c\}$ always non-empty for $a, b, c \in N$?)

11. Compute the first five values of the sequence defined recursively by:

   a) i) $s_1 = 5$

      ii) $s_{k+1} = s_k + 4$

   c) i) $s_1 = 3$

      ii) $s_{k+1} = 2s_k + 1$

   b) i) $s_1 = 1$

      ii) $s_{k+1} = s_k + 2k$

   d) i) $s_1 = 2$

      ii) $s_{k+1} = 2s_k$

159

12. *a*) Using 11. *a*), show that $\forall n \; s_{n+1} = 5 + 4n$.

    b) Using 11. *b*), show that $\forall n \; s_{n+1} = 1 + \sum_{i=1}^{n} 2i$.

13. Prove Corollary 3.2-8.

3.3 The Π Notation, Exponents, Factorial, and Order

Let us now define a function which acts the same with respect to products as "$\sum$" does with respect to sums.

3.3-1 Definition: If $f: N \to N$, then

1) $\Pi_{i=1}^{1} f(i) = f(1)$

2) $\forall k, \Pi_{i=1}^{k+1} f(i) = f(k+1) \cdot \Pi_{i=1}^{k} f(i)$.

Example: $\Pi_{i=1}^{3} 2i = (2 \cdot 3) \, \Pi_{i=1}^{2} 2i = (2 \cdot 3)(2 \cdot 2) \, \Pi_{i=1}^{1} 2i$

             $= (2 \cdot 3)(2 \cdot 2)(2 \cdot 1) = 48$.

Example: $\Pi_{i=1}^{5} (i+1) = (1+1)(2+1)(3+1)(4+1)(5+1)$

                $= 2 \cdot 3 \cdot 4 \cdot 5 \cdot 6 = 720$.

Recall that "$\sum$" distributes over "$+$." That is, (*Corollary* 3.2-9)

$$\sum_{i=1}^{n} (f(i) + g(i)) = \sum_{i=1}^{n} f(i) + \sum_{i=1}^{n} g(i).$$

In a similar way, "Π" distributes over multiplication.

3.3-2 Theorem: If $f: N \to N$ and $g: N \to N$, then

$$\forall n \; \prod_{i=1}^{n} f(i)g(i) = \prod_{i=1}^{n} f(i) \prod_{i=1}^{n} g(i),$$

Proof: By induction.

1) $\Pi_{i=1}^{1} f(i)g(i) = f(1)g(1) = \Pi_{i=1}^{1} f(i) \, \Pi_{i=1}^{1} g(i)$

2) $\Pi_{i=1}^{k+1} f(i)g(i) = f(k+1)g(k+1) \, \Pi_{i=1}^{k} f(i)g(i)$ (*Definition* 3.3-1)

        $= f(k+1)g(k+1) \, \Pi_{i=1}^{k} f(i) \, \Pi_{i=1}^{k} g(i)$

                                 (*induction hypothesis*)

        $= (f(k+1) \, \Pi_{i=1}^{k} f(i))(g(k+1) \, \Pi_{i=1}^{k} g(i))$

        $= \Pi_{i=1}^{k+1} f(i) \, \Pi_{i=1}^{k+1} g(i)$. $\square$

Notice in the above proof that the induction hypothesis was never specifically stated as having been assumed. This is because in any case where the reader clearly understands proof by induction, he will know what the induction hypothesis says without having it stated. Notice also that we should have had the final statement read $\forall k$, if

$$\prod_{i=1}^{k} f(i)g(i) = \prod_{i=1}^{k} f(i) \prod_{i=1}^{k} g(i),$$

then

$$\prod_{i=1}^{k+1} f(i)g(i) = \prod_{i=1}^{k+1} f(i) \prod_{i=1}^{k+1} g(i).$$

But once again it was assumed that the reader would understand the method sufficiently well to make it unnecessary to include these details. It is important in a study of mathematics to understand how such details fit, even though they are not included. It may seem that the omission of details would make things more difficult to understand; but you will see, as discussions become more involved, that if all the details were included, then the important information would be lost in the maze of details. This is, of course, not intended to belittle the importance of such details, but rather to emphasize the importance of gaining a clear understanding of such details since they will be omitted in so much of your reading.

Exponents and Factorials

Using the product notation, we can define the commonly used "exponent" notation, which is a sort of "multiple multiplication."

3.3-3 Definition: If k, n are natural numbers, then

$$k^n = \prod_{i=1}^{n} k.$$

Example: $4^6 = 4 \cdot 4 \cdot 4 \cdot 4 \cdot 4 \cdot 4.$

Remark: It follows immediately from Theorem 3.3-2 that

$$(k \cdot m)^n = k^n \cdot m^n.$$

Another common notation is the "factorial," which is a second type of "special product."

3.3-4 Definition: $\forall n \quad n! = \prod_{i=1}^{n} i.$

Example: $5! = 5 \cdot 4 \cdot 3 \cdot 2 \cdot 1$

Question: Which is larger, n^n or $n!$? Can you prove your assertion? What does one mean by "larger"?

There are many useful and interesting results which can be obtained concerning general products and their relation to special products involving exponents and factorials.

Example: $\forall n \quad (2n + 1)! = 2^n n! \prod_{i=1}^{n} (2i + 1).$

Proof: By induction.

1) $(2 \cdot 1 + 1)! = 3 \cdot 2 = 6$ and $2^1 \cdot 1! \prod_{i=1}^{1} (2i + 1) = 2 \cdot 1 \cdot (2 \cdot 1 + 1) = 6.$

161

2) Once again, we do not specifically mention the induction hypothesis. What is it? What statement do we wish to deduce?

$$
\begin{aligned}
(2(k+1)+1)! &= (2(k+1)+1) \times ((2(k+1))!) && \textit{(definition of !)}\\
&= (2(k+1)+1) \times ((2k+2)!) && \textit{(distributive law)}\\
&= (2(k+1)+1) \times (2k+2) \times ((2k+1)!)\\
&&& \textit{(definition of !)}\\
&= (4k(k+1)+2k+4(k+1)+2)2^k k! \ \Pi_{i=1}^{k}(2i+1)\\
&&& \textit{(multiplication and induction hypothesis)}\\
&= (4k^2+4k+2k+4k+4+2)2^k k! \ \Pi_{i=1}^{k}(2i+1)\\
&= (4k^2+10k+6)2^k k! \ \Pi_{i=1}^{k}(2i+1)\\
&= (2k^2+5k+3)2\cdot 2^k k! \ \Pi_{i=1}^{k}(2i+1)\\
&= (2k+3)2\cdot 2^k(k+1)k! \ \Pi_{i=1}^{k}(2i+1)\\
&= 2^{k+1}(k+1)!(2(k+1)+1) \ \Pi_{i=1}^{k}(2i+1)\\
&= 2^{k+1}(k+1)! \ \Pi_{i=1}^{k+1}(2i+1). \ \square
\end{aligned}
$$

Order and The Natural Numbers

Another concept which is intuitively connected with the idea of counting is the concept of "order." We feel that certain natural numbers "precede" others, and that it can be determined for any two distinct natural numbers which one "precedes" the other. The idea of counting leads naturally to the graphical representation of the numbers lying along a line in the order in which they occur in the counting process.

$$
\begin{array}{ccccccccc}
1 & 2 & 3 & 4 & 5 & 6 & 7 & 8 & 9 \\
\bullet & \bullet & \bullet & \bullet & \bullet & \bullet & \bullet & \bullet & \bullet
\end{array}
$$

We wish to define an order relation which reflects this idea. We wish to say that one number is larger than the other if we can count from the smaller to the larger. We formalize this concept by the following definition.

3.3-5 Definition: The relation "$<$" in $N \times N$ is defined as follows:

$$\forall m, n \quad (m, n) \in < \quad \text{iff} \quad m + p = n \text{ for some } p \in N.$$

Remark: The definition can be restated as

$$m < n \quad \text{iff} \quad m + p = n \text{ for some } p \in N.$$

($m < n$ is read "*m* is less than *n*.")

Remark: It follows immediately from the definition that $n < n + 1$ for every n.

Question: Do you feel that this definition properly reflects the concept of counting from a smaller number to a larger one?

The first useful property we establish for this relation is similar to the cancellation law for addition.

3.3-6 Theorem: $\forall m, s, n$ if $m + s < n + s$, then $m < n$.

Proof: Assume $m + s < n + s$. Then

$$m + s + p = n + s \qquad \text{for some } p, \text{ so}$$
$$m + p = n \qquad (cancellation\ law).$$

Therefore $m < n$ (Definition 3.3-5). □

We next establish the fact that $<$ is an order relation. Let us first show that $<$ is a transitive relation.

3.3-7 Theorem: (*Transitive law for* $<$) $\forall m, n, q$ if $m < n$ and $n < q$, then $m < q$.

Proof: If $m < n$ and $n < q$, it follows that

$$m + p_1 = n$$

and

$$n + p_2 = q.$$

Hence

$$(m + p_1) + p_2 = q.$$

Therefore

$$m + (p_1 + p_2) = q$$

and hence $m < q$. □

Remark: As a result of the transitive law, it is customary to write $a < b < c$ to mean $a < b$ and $b < c$.

The fact that $<$ is a bonafide order relation follows immediately from the transitive law and the following very important result.

3.3-8 Theorem: (*Trichotomy law*) $\forall m, n$ exactly one of the following is true:

a) $m = n$
b) $m < n$
c) $n < m$

We postpone the proof of this theorem until the next chapter. The proof is not difficult, but it is lengthy and detailed.

Remark: It easily follows that $<$ is an order relation. Recall that a relation $<$ in $N \times N$ is an order relation provided that:

1) for every two distinct natural numbers n and m,
   $(n, m) \in\ <$ or $(m, n) \in\ <$;
2) if $m \neq n$ and $(m, n) \in\ <$, then $(n, m) \notin\ <$; and
3) $(n, m) \in\ <$ and $(m, s) \in\ < \Rightarrow (n, s) \in\ <$.

Conditions 1) and 2) above are implied by the trichotomy law, and condition 3) is the transitive law.

Notation Convention: We shall use the following common notational devices in examining and discussing properties of the $<$ ("less than") relation.

163

a) $m > n$ iff $n < m$,
b) $m \leq n$ iff $m < n$ or $m = n$,
c) $m \geq n$ iff $m > n$ or $m = n$,
d) $m < n < p$ iff $m < n$ and $n < p$ and similarly for $\leq, >, \geq$.

Warning: Expressions of the form $m < n > p$ or $m > n < p$ are meaningless.

Preservation of Order Under Operations

We have established the fact that the natural numbers are ordered in a natural fashion and have denoted this order by "$<$." We wish now to develop some useful results concerning the preservation of order between two numbers when both are subjected to some operation.

3.3-9 Theorem: If $m < s$, then

$$\forall n \quad m + n < s + n.$$

Proof: $m < s \Rightarrow m + p = s$. This implies that

$$m + p + n = s + n$$
$$(m + n) + p = s + n$$
$$m + n < s + n. \ \square$$

3.3-10 Theorem: If $m < s$, then

$$\forall n \quad m \cdot n < s \cdot n$$

(where, as usual, the universal set is N, so that $m, s, n \in N$).

Proof: $m < s \Rightarrow m + p = s$ implies that

$$(m + p)n = sn$$
$$mn + pn = sn$$
$$mn + p' = sn$$
$$\therefore mn < sn. \ \square$$

3.3-11 Theorem: If $m < s$ and $n < q$, then $mn < sq$ $(m, n, s, q \in N)$.

Proof: $m + p_1 = s$ and $n + p_2 = q$ implies that

$$(m + p_1)(n + p_2) = sq$$
$$mn + (p_1n + mp_2 + p_1p_2) = sq$$
$$mn + p' = sq$$
$$\therefore mn < sq. \ \square$$

3.3-12 Theorem: If $m < s$, then $\forall n \quad m^n < s^n$ $(m, n, s \in N)$.

Proof: By induction.

1) $m^1 < s^1$ by hypothesis.
2) If $m^k < s^k$, then by (Theorem 3.3-11)

$$m^k m < s^k s$$

and therefore $m^{k+1} < s^{k+1}$. The result follows immediately. $\square$

These theorems are important results which should be remembered as later they will be extended in a limited way to other number systems.

Exercises   3.3

1. Evaluate:

    a) $\prod_{i=1}^{3} (i + 1)$ b) $\prod_{i=1}^{5} 2$ c) $\prod_{i=1}^{2} 3i$ d) $\prod_{i=1}^{3} i^2$

2. Find $f(4)$ where:

    a) $f(n) = \prod_{i=1}^{n} 2i$ c) $f(n) = \prod_{i=1}^{2n} (1 + i)$

    b) $f(n) = 2 \prod_{i=1}^{n} i^2$ d) $f(n) = \prod_{i=1}^{n} (2i + 1)$

3. If $f(i) = 2i$ and $g(i) = i + 1$, compute:

    a) $f(4)$ e) $\prod_{i=1}^{3} (f(i) + g(i))$ i) $\sum_{k=1}^{3} f(2k + 2)$

    b) $g(7)$ f) $\prod_{i=1}^{3} f(i)g(i)$ j) $\prod_{k=1}^{3} (f \circ g)(k)$

    c) $\sum_{i=1}^{3} f(i)$ g) $\sum_{k=1}^{2} f(k + 1)$ k) $\sum_{i=1}^{3} (g \circ f)(i)$

    d) $\prod_{i=1}^{3} f(i)$ h) $\sum_{k=1}^{2} g(2k)$

4. Rewrite each of the following, using "$\sum$" notation.

    a) $2 + 4 + 6 + \cdots + 2n$
    b) $1^2 + 2^2 + 3^2 + \cdots + n^2$
    c) $3^3 + 5^3 + 7^3 + \cdots + (2n + 1)^3$

5. Find all $x \in N$ such that

    a) $2x < 12$ b) $3x < 16$ c) $4x + 7 < 14$ d) $x^2 < 24$

6. a) Find $g(4)$ if $\forall k \; g(k) = 2k + 1$.
    b) Find $h(3)$ if $\forall i \; h(i) = 3i^2 + 2$.
    c) Find $f(7)$ if $\forall k \; f(k + 1) = kf(k)$ and $f(1) = 2$.
    d) Find $g(6)$ if $\forall k \; g(k + 1) = g(k)$ and $g(1) = 9$.

7. Rewrite each of the following using "$\prod$" notation.

    a) $1^2 \cdot 2^2 \cdot 3^2 \cdot 4^2 \cdot 5^2$
    b) $2^3 \cdot 2^4 \cdot 2^5 \cdot 2^6 \cdot 2^7 \cdot 2^8$
    c) $(1 + 1)(1 + 2)^2(1 + 3)^3(1 + 4)^4(1 + 5)^5$
    d) $(2 + 2 \cdot 1)^2(2 + 2 \cdot 2)^3(2 + 2 \cdot 3)^4 \cdots (2 + 2n)^{n+1}$

8. Expand:

a) $\prod\limits_{i=1}^{5} f(i)g(i)$

c) $\prod\limits_{i=1}^{3} [f(i) + g(i)]$

b) $\left(\prod\limits_{i=1}^{5} f(i)\right) \times \left(\prod\limits_{i=1}^{5} g(i)\right)$

d) $\prod\limits_{i=1}^{3} f(i) + \prod\limits_{i=1}^{3} g(i)$

e) Why aren't c) and d) the same?

9. Is there a natural number between 7 and 8? How do you know? What do you suppose is meant by "between"?

10. Establish (prove):

a) $\prod\limits_{i=1}^{n} 3i = 3^n n!$

b) If $m > n$, then $\forall k \in N \quad m + k > n$.

c) If $m > k + n$, then $m > k$.

d) $\leq$ is an order relation. (See Section 2.4.)

e) If $n < m$, then $n + 1 \leq m$.

f) Prove that for every $n \in N$, there is no natural number k such that $n < k < n + 1$.

(*Hint:* Recall that $\forall n$ if $n + p_1 = n + p_2$, then $p_1 = p_2$ (*cancellation law for addition*).) Deduce that if $n < m$, then there is a unique p such that $n + p = m$.

g) $k^{m+n} = k^m \cdot k^n$.

11. Graph the following sets as points along a line.

a) $\{n \in N : 3 < n < 10\}$
b) $\{n \in N : n < 7\}$
c) $\{n \in N : n \geq 6\}$
d) $\{n \in N : 3n \leq 12\}$
e) $\{n \in N : 15 \leq n + 5 < 21\}$
f) $\{n \in N : 7 < 2n + 5 \leq 13\}$

12. Investigate (prove or disprove):

a) $\forall m, n, k \in N$ if $m < n$, then $\sum\limits_{i=1}^{k} m < \sum\limits_{i=1}^{k} n$

b) $\forall m, n, k \in N$ if $m < n$, then $\prod\limits_{i=1}^{k} m < \prod\limits_{i=1}^{k} n$

c) If $\forall i \quad f(i) < g(i)$, then $\forall k \sum\limits_{i=1}^{k} f(i) < \sum\limits_{i=1}^{k} g(i)$

d) $\prod\limits_{i=1}^{n} 3^i = 3^{n+1}$

e) $2^n < n!$

f) $\forall x \in N \quad m < n \Rightarrow x^n < x^m$

13. Simplify each of the following:

$a)\ \dfrac{8!}{11!}$
$\qquad$
$c)\ \dfrac{3! + 5!}{3!}$
$\qquad$
$e)\ \dfrac{5!}{6!(5)!}$

$b)\ \dfrac{5!3!}{6!}$
$\qquad$
$d)\ \dfrac{(n + 1)!(n + 2)!}{(n!)^2}$
$\qquad$
$f)\ \dfrac{5!}{3!(2)!}$

14. $\forall x \in N$, define $f(x) = 2^x$, $g(x) = 5^x$.

$a)$ Graph f and g.

$b)$ What is happening to the values of f and g as larger and larger numbers are substituted for x?

$c)$ Look at Theorem 3.3-12. What can you say about the graph of f as compared to the graph of g?

3.4 Zero, the Division Theorem, and Base Names

Attaching the Zero

We notice a rather significant fact about the multiplication operation on N, which is immediately obvious, but whose full significance must have gone unnoticed for centuries. We have the element "1" with the property that $\forall n \in N$, $1 \cdot n = n$. That is, "1" is an identity element for the operation of multiplication. Indeed, this is not a startling fact, but it should make us wonder whether we have the same sort of element in our system for addition. That is, is there a $y \in N$ such that $\forall x \in N$, $x + y = x$? It is clear that the answer is "no." Let us then consider the possibility of extending our number system to include such an element. We are going to attach to the set of natural numbers an element not already in N, and call this element "zero."‡ (We denote zero by "0.") We wish to extend the operations of addition and multiplication to include 0, doing this in such a way that they remain the same on the nonzero numbers.

3.4-1 Definition: (Addition of zero) Let $N_0 = N \cup \{0\}$, where $0 \notin N$. $\forall n \in N_0$, $n + 0 = 0 + n = n$; otherwise, define addition in N_0 the same as in N.

It might appear that in order to extend multiplication to include multiplication on zero, we could perhaps define multiplication by zero in any way we wish. However, recall that multiplication was defined as multiple addition, and that if we extend this definition, then

‡ Do you agree that given a set S there always exists some element not in S? That is, is it always possible to make the universal set under consideration larger?

167

$$n \cdot 0 = \sum_{i=1}^{n} 0 = 0 + 0 + \cdots + 0 = 0.$$

Since we wish to retain the commutative law for multiplication, we see that we must define $0 \cdot n = 0$ even though $\sum_{i=1}^{0} n$ is not defined. Further, we see that if we use the definition $\forall m, n \in N_0\, m < n$ iff $\exists p \in N\, m + p = n$, then $\forall n \in N\, 0 < n$.

To summarize: We have attached an element "0" to our set N ($0 \notin N$) and extended "$+$," "$\times$," and "$<$" to the new set $N_0 = N \cup \{0\}$ so that the following properties hold:

a) $\forall n \in N_0 \quad n + 0 = 0 + n = n$
b) $\forall n \in N_0 \quad n \times 0 = 0 \times n = 0$
c) $\forall n \in N \quad 0 < n$

For reasons which may not seem clear at the moment, we make the following definition, allowing us to use zero as an exponent.

3.4-2 Definition: If $n \in N$, then $n^0 = 1$ and $0! = 1$. (0^0 is not defined.)

It is easily shown that "$<$" (as extended) is an order relation on N_0, and also that the trichotomy law holds. The following is a list of useful properties which could be proved at this stage. You should be familiar with these results, and in each case should convince yourself that they are true. (You should even attempt to prove some of them!) Note that the universal set is N_0, and that the quantifiers have been omitted in several of the statements.

1) The associative, commutative, and distributive laws hold for "$+$" and "$\times$" on N_0.
2) $\forall m, n \in N_0$ if $mn = 0$, then $m = 0$ or $n = 0$.
3) $\forall m, n \in N_0$ if $m < n$, then $\forall p \in N \quad mp < np$.
4) $\forall m, n, p \in N_0$ if $mp < np$, then $m < n$.
5) If $m + n = m$, then $n = 0$.
6) $m + n = m + p$ iff $n = p$.
7) $m \neq 0$ and $mn = mp \Rightarrow n = p$.
8) $m = n \Rightarrow pm = pn$.
9) If $p \neq 0$ and $mp = p$, then $m = 1$.
10) $ms < mp \Rightarrow s < p$.
11) $s < p$ and $m \neq 0 \Rightarrow ms < mp$.

The Division Theorem

Historically, the idea of having a zero was very long in developing. It was one of the major mathematical breakthroughs, since it made possible the construction of our "base naming" system (or "position principle") for numbers. Of course, this principle is extremely useful for computation as compared to other systems, such as Roman numerals. Keep in mind that basically all we know about a given natural number is that it has a successor different from itself, and that if it isn't 1 then it is itself a successor. We know that the collection of natural numbers is a very large one, and we would like to give each number a name. We would like these names to be organized in some convenient fashion so that if "a" and "b" are named members of N, then we could rather quickly decide which name is assigned to the numbers "$a + b$" and "$a \times b$." You are familiar with such a naming system, called the "base ten system" or the "decimal system" or the "base ten position system." You are perhaps even familiar with similar naming systems in which bases other than ten are used.

All of the base naming systems are possible as a result of the following very important theorem. Notice that we could not have proved a similar theorem on N without the zero.

3.4-3 Theorem: (*Division theorem*) If $b \in N$, then $\forall n \in N_0 \, \exists q \in N_0 \, \exists r \in N_0$ $n = qb + r$ where $0 \le r < b$. Further, if $n = q_1 b + r_1$ where $0 \le r_1 < b$ and $n = q_2 b + r_2$ where $0 \le r_2 < b$, then $q_1 = q_2$ and $r_1 = r_2$.

Remark: This shows that the existing q, called the *quotient*, and the existing r, called the *remainder*, are unique. b is called the *base*.

Proof: Existence (by induction on n). Let $b \in N$.

1) $[P(1)]$ Case 1. $b = 1$
$$1 = 1 \cdot 1 + 0 \text{ and } 0 \le 0 < b.$$

   Case 2. $1 < b$
$$1 = b \cdot 0 + 1 \text{ and } 0 \le 1 < b.$$

2) $[P(k) \Rightarrow P(k + 1)]$ Assume that
$$k = bq + r \qquad \text{where} \qquad 0 \le r < b.$$

Now $k + 1 = bq + r + 1.$

   Case 1. $b = r + 1.$
$$\begin{aligned} k + 1 &= bq + b \\ &= b(q + 1) \\ &= bq' + 0 \text{ and } 0 \le 0 < b \text{ where } q' = q + 1. \end{aligned}$$

   Case 2. $r + 1 < b.$
$$\begin{aligned} k + 1 &= bq + (r + 1) \\ &= bq + r' \text{ and } 0 \le r' < b \text{ where } r' = r + 1. \end{aligned}$$

(*Question:* What about the third possibility that $b < r + 1$?) Hence by induction $\forall n \, \exists q \exists r \; n = bq + r$ where $0 \le r < b$, $n \in N$, and q, $r \in N_0$. How about $n = 0$?

Next let us establish the *uniqueness*. Assume
$$n = bq_1 + r_1 = bq_2 + r_2 \text{ where } 0 \le r_1 < b \text{ and } 0 \le r_2 < b.$$

   Case 1. $r_1 = r_2.$ Then
$$bq_1 = bq_2$$
$$q_1 = q_2.$$

Case 2. $r_1 \neq r_2$. *WLOG* (without loss of generality) assume
$r_1 < r_2$ (why?). Therefore, $r_1 + p = r_2$ for some $p \in N$

$$bq_1 + r_1 = bq_2 + r_1 + p$$
$$bq_1 = bq_2 + p$$
$$bq_2 < bq_1$$
$$q_2 < q_1$$

and so $q_2 + p' = q_1$ for some $p' > 0$.

Now substituting into the original equation, we have

$$b(q_2 + p') + r_1 = bq_2 + r_2.$$

Therefore

$$bq_2 + bp' + r_1 = bq_2 + r_2$$

and by cancellation

$$bp' + r_1 = r_2.$$

If $p' = 1$, then

$$b + r_1 = r_2.$$

If $r_1 = 0$, then

$$b = r_2,$$

and if $r_1 \neq 0$, then $b < r_2$ which contradicts $r_2 < b$. If $p' \neq 1$, then $p' = k + 1$ for some $k > 0$ and so

$$bk + b + r_1 = r_2.$$

Clearly

$$bk + r_1 > 0$$

and since

$$b + (bk + r_1) = r_2$$

it follows that $b < r_2$, again a contradiction. Hence we must return to the case $r_1 = r_2$; and as we have seen, it then follows that $q_1 = q_2$. $\square$

Example: Find the unique q and r such that

$$25 = 6q + r \quad \text{where} \quad 0 \le r < 6.$$

Answer: $25 = 6 \times 4 + 1$.

Example: Find the unique q and r such that

$$256 = 10q + r \quad \text{where} \quad 0 \le r < 10.$$

Answer: $256 = 10 \times 25 + 6$.

Notice how easy it is to answer such questions when the base b is the number 10. Why is this so?

The Base Place Principle

Perhaps you have noticed that the names you use for the natural numbers are very closely related to the number 10 and the Division Theorem. A similar system for names can be based on any natural number. Such naming systems are possible due to the following theorem, which is a direct consequence of the Division Theorem.

3.4-4 Theorem: (*The base place principle*) (*the radix representation theorem*) Let $b > 1$ and $n \in N$. There exists a unique sequence

$$r_0, r_1, r_2, r_3, \ldots$$

of elements from N_0 and a unique $p \in N_0$ such that

a) $r_p \neq 0$
b) $r_i = 0$ if $i > p$
c) $\forall m \, 0 \leq r_m < b$
d) $n = \sum_{i=0}^{p} b^i r_i$ $\quad (\sum_{i=0}^{p} f(i) = f(0) + \sum_{i=1}^{p} f(i))$

(*i.e.*, $n = r_0 + b r_1 + \cdots + b^p r_p$, keeping in mind that $b^0 = 1$).

Proof: Existence by induction on n.

i) Let $b > 1$.
$$1 = b \cdot 0 + 1$$
and $r_0 = 1, r_1 = 0, r_2 = 0, r_3 = 0, \cdots$

(The uniqueness follows from the division theorem.)

ii) Assume the theorem holds for the fixed but unspecified element k. Now

$$k + 1 = \sum_{i=0}^{p} b^i r_i + 1$$
$$= \sum_{i=1}^{p} b^i r_i + r_0 + 1.$$

Case 1. $r_0 + 1 < b$. We define the sequence which works for $k + 1$ by
$$r_0' = r_0 + 1, \qquad r_1' = r_1 \qquad r_2' = r_2 \cdots$$

Case 2. $b = r_0 + 1$. If $r_1 + 1 < b$, then we define
$$r_0' = 0, \qquad r_1' = r_1 + 1, \qquad r_2' = r_2, \qquad r_3' = r_3 \cdots$$

In general, let r_j be the last remainder such that $r_j + 1 = b$. (How do we know there is one?) Then the sequence

$$r_0' = 0, \quad r_1' = 0, \cdots, \quad r_j' = 0, \quad r_{j+1}' = r_{j+1} + 1, \quad \text{and} \quad r_{j+2}' = r_{j+2} \cdots$$

will be the sequence which works. We leave the uniqueness argument for (ii) for the student to establish. $\square$

This theorem allows us to name every element in N_0 by using only the limited set of symbols $\{0, 1, 2, 3, 4, 5, 6, 7, 8, 9\}$, using position to denote multiplication of one of these numbers by a power of ten.

Example: $5642 = 10^3 \times 5 + 10^2 \times 6 + 10 \times 4 + 2$.

Example: $46{,}010 = 10^4 \times 4 + 10^3 \times 6 + 10^2 \times 0 + 10 \times 1 + 0$.
On the other hand, we could use some other number for the base.

Example: $964 = 5^4 \cdot 1 + 5^3 \cdot 2 + 5^2 \cdot 3 + 5 \cdot 2 + 4$.

So in base 5 radix representation, the number would be written 12324.

Example: $768 = 6^3 \cdot 3 + 6^2 \cdot 3 + 6 \cdot 2 + 0$.

Therefore, in base 6 place representation, the number would be written 3320.

Exercises   3.4

1. Write 364 in the form

$$9q + r \quad \text{where} \quad 0 \le r < 9$$

(*Hint:* Divide by 9.)

2. Find the unique quotient and remainder which satisfies the division theorem in each case for the given base.

a) $542 = 15q + r$ d) $2000 = 48q + r$

b) $9812 = 30q + r$ e) 643 where $b = 12$

c) $24 = 19q + r$ f) 962 where $b = 10$

3. a) Write 9642 as a sum which satisfies the radix representation theorem for $b = 13$.

(That is, $9642 = r_0 + 13r_1 + 13^2r_2 + 13^3r_3 + 13^4r_4 + \cdots$ where $0 \le r_i < 13$ $i = 1, 2, 3, \cdots$.)

b) Do the same for 1263 where $b = 19$.

c) For 649 where $b = 26$.

d) For 67,432 where $b = 10$.

4. How would you represent 6794 in base 5 notation?

5. Explain how the well-known algorithm for "long division" works in terms of radix representation and the division theorem.

6. We can easily extend our $\sum$ and $\prod$ notation to include sums and products "beginning" at 0. Compute:

a) $\sum_{i=0}^{3} (2i + 1)$ b) $\prod_{i=0}^{3} (2i + 1)$ c) $\sum_{i=0}^{5} f(i)$ where $f(i) = 3i + 2$

7. Investigate (prove or disprove):

a) $\prod_{i=0}^{n} 2i = 0$ for any $n \in N_0$.

b) If $\sum_{i=0}^{n} f(i) = 0$ for all $n \in N_0$, then $f(i) = 0$ for all $i \in N_0$.

c) If $\prod_{i=0}^{n} f(i) = 0$ for some $n \in N_0$, then $\forall i \in N_0 \ f(i) = 0$.

8. Recall "Checkerboard Jimmy", the robot (Problem 7, 3.1). Jimmy has learned to understand any well-defined function $f: N_0 \to \{R, L, F, B, S\}$.

a) Define a function that will program Jimmy to first go right, then left, and to continue in this fashion alternating from right to left. (*Hint:* Explicitly define $f(0)$ and $f(1)$, and then use an inductive definition. Note that $2 = 1 \times 2, 4 = 2 \times 2$, $6 = 3 \times 2 \cdots$, and that $3 = 1 \times 2 + 1, 5 = 2 \times 2 + 1, 7 = 3 \times 2 + 1 \cdots$.)

b) Program Jimmy to go $L, F, R, F, L, F, R, F, \cdots$, etc.

9. Outline the logic used in the proof of Theorem 3.4-3.
   (*Hint:* Verify that Case 2 is of the form

$$\left.\frac{r_2 < b,\ r_1 \neq r_2 \Rightarrow r_2 \not< b}{\therefore\ r_1 = r_2}\cdot\right)$$

3.5 Subtraction of Natural Numbers, and the Integers

Subtraction of Natural Numbers

At a very early stage in our experience with natural numbers the concept of "take away" was developed. That is, we developed the idea of subtracting a smaller number from a larger one and arriving at an answer. Being students of elementary mathematics in this modern "after the 0" age, we also allowed subtraction of a number from itself. But, at first, we did not believe in taking larger numbers away from smaller ones.

Let us define precisely how this "take away" operation maps some members of $N_0 \times N_0$ into N_0.

3.5-1 Definition: If $m, n \in N_0$ and $m \leq n$, then the unique§ $p \in N_0$ such that $m + p = n$ is called the difference between n and m, denoted by $n - m$.

Remark: This asserts that if $m \leq n$, then $n - m \in N_0$ and that $m + (n - m) = n$. Note, however, that at this stage we cannot arbitrarily select numbers p and q and speak of $p - q$, since the existence of $p - q$ depends on having $q \leq p$.

There are some useful results which we can derive concerning this "partial binary operation" on N_0. The first is a sort of associative law.

3.5-2 Theorem: For any $m, n \in N_0$ $(m + n) - m$ is defined, and if $m \leq n$, then $(m + n) - m = m + (n - m) = n$.

Proof: $m \leq m + n$ for any $m, n \in N_0$. (Why?) Therefore the difference is defined. By definition, $m + ((m + n) - m) = m + n$, and by the cancellation law $(m + n) - m = n$. On the other hand, if $m \leq n$, then by definition $m + (n - m) = n$. $\square$

Example: $6 < 11$ and therefore $6 + (11 - 6) = 11$. (In fact, $6 + 5 = 11$; therefore, $11 - 6 = 5$.) But $6 < 6 + 11$ and

$$(6 + 11) - 6 = 11$$

since

$$6 + ((6 + 11) - 6) = 6 + 11$$

§ Do you agree that p exists and is unique? See Problem 13, 3.3.

Recall that in elementary arithmetic you had a method for checking subtraction. You added the answer to the smaller number and if the sum was the larger number, you concluded that you had subtracted correctly. Does this correspond with our definition of subtraction?

Trying to Extend Subtraction

We have now that $m - n$ exists if and only if $n \leq m$. It seems natural to hope that we can extend this partial operation to include subtraction of any two numbers in either order. (That is, we wish to have both $a - b$ and $b - a$ defined for any a, b in our number system so that "$-$" is a full-fledged operation.) For example, consider the following "extension by commutativity."

We know now that if $m, n \in N_0$, then $m - n$ or $n - m$ is defined. It might be possible to make the decision to define $m - n = n - m$. (We would extend subtraction in such a way that it is commutative.)

But let us hesitate for a moment to see if perhaps there isn't some property which we consider to be more important than making subtraction a commutative operation. We recall that if $m - n$ is defined, then it is the number p such that

$$n + p = m.$$

That is, $n + (m - n) = m$. Further, we showed that $(n + m) - n$ exists and is equal to m. We wish to consider the possibility of keeping the property $n + (m - n) = (n + m) - n$. However, doing so and still allowing $m - n = n - m$ would introduce a contradiction into the system, as we will see.

Remark: It is important that attention be given to the process of introducing new definitions. Hopefully, a definition will do two things. First, it should introduce into the system a new concept; second, it should introduce no contradiction of properties we wish to retain.

Example: Show that we cannot define $m - n = n - m$ for arbitrary natural numbers, and at the same time retain the property that $n + (m - n) = (n + m) - n = m$.

Solution: Suppose $n < m$, that $n - m = m - n$, and we allow the property that $\forall a, b \in N, a + (b - a) = (a + b) - a = b$. We know that $m = n + (m - n)$. Now add $n - m$ to both sides (can we do this?) so that

$$m + (n - m) = n + (m - n) + (n - m).$$

It then follows that

$$m + (n - m) = [(n + m) - n] + (n - m) = m + (n - m) = n.$$

Hence $m + p = n$ for some p and $m \leq n$. But this contradicts the assumption $n < m$. We see that if we insist upon making the commutativity definition, we are going to be forced into either removing our "trichotomy law" or the result that $a + (b - a) = (a + b) - a = b$ and perhaps many other "desirable" properties.

Let us then agree not to make the definition that $m - n = n - m$, but go back and examine the property which determined our ability to subtract. That is, $m - n$ is defined if and only if $n \leq m$, in which case $n + (m - n) = m$. In the case $m < n$, there is no number $p \in N_0$ such that $n + p = m$. Let us then introduce such a number by once again extending the number system to include some new numbers. We begin by examining the concept of the zero element, concentrating on numbers whose difference is zero. We notice that $0 + 0 = 0$; but given any natural number $n \in N$, there is no element $p \in N_0$ such that $n + p = 0$.

The Negative Integers

One day Gurnie Gibson was explaining to his brother, Guy, how much money he had. "I have $300 in the sugar bowl; and if I add the $1,000 worth of grain in the barn, it would be $1,300. Then if I add the $1,300 I owe the bank, I have nothing." Guy explained that what he should say is "subtract $1,300." But Gurnie explained in return, "When I add 'owed money', I mean to subtract 'real money'." Probably neither Gurnie nor Guy realizes the full mathematical significance of the resultant "nothing" they are talking about, but it seems clear from their discussion that the extension of subtraction will be related to addition in some way. Also it indicates that we may want to attach additional numbers to our system to account for the concept of "owed money" in this discussion which is a different kind of thing than "real money."

We attach additional numbers to N_0 by the following.

3.5-3 Definition: Let N^- be a set which can be placed in *one-one* correspondence with N, and such that $N_0 \cap N^- = \varnothing$.|| Denote the correspondence by $\eta \colon N \to N^-$. η is called the *negation function* or the *negating function*.

3.5-4 Definition: Let $Z = N \cup \{0\} \cup N^-$. Z is called the set of *integers*.

Note: If $x \in Z$, then exactly one of the following is true: $x \in N^-, x = 0, x \in N$. (Why?)

Graphically, we wish to attach additional numbers to our system so that the negation of a number is a reflection across the zero.

Example:

$$\xleftarrow{\hspace{3em}} \overset{\eta(3)}{\bullet} \quad \overset{\eta(2)}{\bullet} \quad \overset{\eta(1)}{\bullet} \quad \overset{0}{\bullet} \quad \overset{1}{\bullet} \quad \overset{2}{\bullet} \quad \overset{3}{\bullet} \xrightarrow{\hspace{3em}}$$

Before we discuss the extension of our operations to the negative integers, let us extend the negation function to Z so that elements in N^- are reflected across the zero back to where they came from under η.

|| Do you agree that there exists such a set?

3.5-5 Definition: $\eta(0) = 0$ and if $a \in N^-$, then $\eta(a) = b$ where $b \in N$ and $\eta(b) = a$. (That is, any element in N^- is the image of some element in N, and we extend η to N^- by mapping this image back.)

Graphically, we have

$$\eta(3) \quad \eta(2) \quad \eta(1) \quad 0 = \eta(0) \qquad 1 \qquad 2 \qquad 3$$

$$\eta(\eta(1)) \qquad \eta(\eta(3))$$

3.5-6 Theorem: $\forall x \in Z \ \eta(\eta(x)) = x$.

Proof: If $x = 0$, then $\eta(\eta(0)) = \eta(0) = 0$. If $x \in N^-$, then for some $b \in N$, $\eta(x) = b$ where $\eta(b) = x$ by definition. Therefore

$$\eta(\eta(x)) = \eta(b) = x.$$

If $x \in N$, then $\eta(x) \in N^-$, and therefore by definition $\eta(\eta(x)) = x$. □

Ordinarily, the negating function η is designated with a minus sign, "$-$." Using this notation, the above theorem says that for every integer n, $-(-n) = n$.

One of the things that seems to cause some confusion with beginners in mathematics is the fact that we use here the same mark "$-$" to indicate negation as we did previously for subtraction. There is no essential reason for confusion, since negation is a function which is applied to only one number (the pre-image), whereas subtraction is a function applied to two numbers (an ordered pair pre-image). We shall see later, after we have extended our operations "$+$", "$\times$", "$-$" to the entire set of integers, that there are some nice properties which relate subtraction and negation in such a way that we are very happy that we used the same symbol for both.

Extending the Operations

We wish now to extend our operations to include the new numbers which we attached. We could do this by defining in all possible cases exactly how to multiply, add, and subtract. Then we could check to see if we had introduced any undesirable properties into the system. Instead, let us take a "back door" approach. Let us insist on retaining all the nice properties that we have grown to so much admire, and then investigate axioms for extending addition and multiplication to Z.

3.5-7 Axioms: Addition "$+$" and multiplication "$\times$" (or "$\cdot$") are binary operations on Z such that:

1) $\forall x, y \in N_0 \ \ x + y$ and $x \cdot y$ are the same as previously defined.
2) $\forall x \in Z \ \ x + (-x) = 0$ (*i.e.*, $x + \eta(x) = 0$).
3) Addition and multiplication are associative.

4) Addition and multiplication are commutative.

5) $\forall x \in Z \quad x + 0 = x$ and $x \cdot 1 = x$ (*identity laws*).

6) Multiplication distributes over addition (*i.e.*, $\forall x, y, z \in Z \quad x \cdot (y + z) = x \cdot y + x \cdot z$).

It can be shown that these axioms are consistent (*i.e.*, introduce no contradictions into the system) and, further, that there is only one pair of binary operations which satisfies these properties. (Thus, these axioms uniquely determine addition and multiplication of integers.) A proof of the existence of such operations would be gained by defining binary operations on Z (functions from $Z \times Z$ to Z), verifying that they satisfy the axioms. The problem with beginning in this fashion is that although we have a fairly clear idea about how we want addition to be extended, we do not have a clear idea as to how we want to define multiplication. After we examine various properties about any pair of operations which satisfy the axioms, then we will be in a better position to define some operations which satisfy the axioms. We leave this as an exercise at the end of the section, along with a description of how to define the operations. To show the uniqueness of such a pair of operations is not difficult; and we leave this also as an exercise with liberal hints given as to the method used.

Number Rings

Let us notice in particular that Z is a collection of numbers, along with two binary operations $+$ and $\cdot$ which satisfy the following properties.

3.5-8   (Axioms for a Number Ring)

1) *a*) $\forall x, y, z \quad (x + y) + z = x + (y + z)$
   b) $\forall x, y, z \quad (xy)z = x(yz)$
2) *a*) $\forall x, y \quad x + y = y + x$
   b) $\forall x, y \quad xy = yx$
3) *a*) $\exists y \quad \forall x \quad x + y = x$ (This y is called 0.)
   b) $\exists y \quad \forall x \quad xy = x$ (This y is called 1.)
4) $\forall x \quad \exists y \quad x + y = 0$ (We denote this y by $(-x)$ and call it the additive inverse for x.)
5) $\forall x, y, z \quad x(y + z) = xy + xz$

It is easy to show that in a number ring there is no more than one identity element for each operation, and hence justify the use of the particular names

In the literature, one usually finds this called a "commutative ring with a multiplicative identity element." This is due to the detailed step-by-step approach taken in abstract algebra in the study of binary operations. For simplicity, and for at least an attempt to conform with standard usage, we have chosen to call such a structure a "number ring."

0 and 1. Further, the uniqueness of additive inverses can be shown, which justifies a functional designation of that number by saying that if $x + y = 0$, then $y = -x$. In any arbitrary number ring, we can define the operation of subtraction and the function of negation by the following.

3.5-9 Definition: Let D be a number ring.

　1) Negation: $\forall x \in D$　$-x$ is that unique $y \in D$ such that $x + y = 0$.
　2) Subtraction "$-$": $\forall x, y \in D$　$x - y = x + (-y)$.

As we shall see, the "arbitrary" subtraction defined in the number ring Z gives the same result as our previously defined "limited" subtraction when it is restricted to the limited case (that is, to the particular pairs of natural numbers for which "limited" subtraction was previously defined). We would be terribly unhappy with our extended subtraction if this were not the case.

Natural questions which the student should ask at this point are: "Why study number rings as an abstract structure? Why not simply stick to the integers, since they are the things we wish to consider at present?" These are good questions and deserve good answers. Later, we shall encounter some unfamiliar structures which we wish to investigate. It will be possible in some cases to quickly establish the fact that we are dealing with a number ring, so that we will know immediately that the given structure is a great deal like some number systems with which we are familiar. Thus, we save a great deal of time that would otherwise have been spent duplicating work which we have essentially already done. Also, it turns out that many properties of the integers can be discovered and studied more easily when non-essential structure is swept away or ignored. In this section, we shall study results which can be applied to *any* (arbitrary) number ring, and in particular to the integers. It will prove useful to collect mentally some of the critical results which can be quickly applied in future situations to produce more general results.

Right now, let us satisfy ourselves that our general definition for subtraction will not "disturb" our previously defined subtraction.

3.5-10 Theorem: Let $m, n \in N_0$ such that $m \leq n$. Then

　1) $n + \eta(m) \in N_0$
　2) $m + (n + \eta(m)) = n$.

(Equivalently, $n + (-m) \in N_0$ and $m + (n + (-m)) = n$.)

　Proof (of 1): Since $m \leq n$, then there is some $p \in N_0$ such that

$$m + p = n.$$

Hence

$$n + (-m) = (m + p) + (-m)$$

and by liberally applying the associative and commutative laws, we have

$$n + (-m) = (m + (-m)) + p.$$

Since

$$m + (-m) = 0$$

the additive identity, we have

$$n + (-m) = p$$

which is in N_0.

Proof (of 2): $m + (n + (-m)) = (m + (-m)) + n$
$$= 0 + n = n. \;\square$$

Some Fundamental Properties of a Number Ring and in Particular of the Integers

The first three properties which we prove have already been anticipated, but you would feel uncomfortable if we did not actually give a proof.

3.5-11 Theorem: Let D be a number ring. Let $y_1, y_2 \in D$ such that

$$\forall x \in D \quad x + y_1 = x$$

and

$$\forall x \in D \quad x + y_2 = x.$$

Then

$$y_1 = y_2.$$

Proof: $y_2 \in D$. Therefore, from the first generalization, $y_2 + y_1 = y_2$, $y_1 \in D$. Therefore, from the second generalization, $y_1 + y_2 = y_1$. But from the commutative law

$$y_1 + y_2 = y_2 + y_1.$$

Therefore

$$y_1 = y_2. \;\square$$

This theorem tells us that there is only one additive identity element. As we mentioned previously, we call it "zero" denoted by "0."

The next theorem tells us the same thing about the multiplicative identity which we call "one" denoted by "1."

3.5-12 Theorem: If D is a number ring and $y_1, y_2 \in D$ such that

$$\forall x \in D \quad xy_1 = x$$

and

$$\forall x \in D \quad xy_2 = x,$$

then

$$y_1 = y_2.$$

Proof: This proof is similar to the proof of the preceding theorem. The only difference is that here we use multiplicative commutativity instead of additive. $\square$

3.5-13 Theorem: If D is a number ring, if $x \in D$, and if $y_1, y_2 \in D$ such that

$$x + y_1 = 0$$

179

and

$$x + y_2 = 0,$$

then

$$y_1 = y_2.$$

Proof: Now $y_1 = y_1 + 0$, and since $0 = x + y_2$,

$$y_1 = y_1 + (x + y_2)$$
$$= (y_1 + x) + y_2 \qquad \text{(Why?)}$$
$$= (x + y_1) + y_2 \qquad \text{(Why?)}$$
$$= 0 + y_2 = y_2. \quad \square$$

This theorem verifies that for each given x there is only one y such that $x + y = 0$, and hence verifies that the negation function is truly a function. That is, $\forall x \in D \ \eta(x) = -x$ is the unique number in D which gives 0 when added to x.

The next few theorems are useful results used in computations with numbers in number rings. They are also useful in solving equations whose solutions are in number rings. (In these theorems, it is understood that all elements are in some number ring.)

3.5-14 Theorem: (The cancellation law for addition) If $x + y = x + z$, then $y = z$.

Proof: $x + y = x + z \Rightarrow (x + y) + (-x) = (x + z) + (-x)$; and after liberal use of the associative and commutative laws, we have

$$(x + (-x)) + y = (x + (-x)) + z$$

and

$$0 + y = 0 + z.$$

Therefore

$$y = z. \quad \square$$

3.5-15 Theorem: $0x = 0$.

Proof: $x + 0 = x$ and

$$x + 0x = 1 \cdot x + 0x = (1 + 0)x$$
$$= 1 \cdot x = x$$

and therefore by Theorem 3.5-11

$$0x = 0. \quad \square$$

3.5-16 Theorem $(-1)x = -x$.

Proof: $x + (-x) = 0$ and

$$x + (-1)x = 1 \cdot x + (-1)x$$
$$= (1 + (-1))x$$
$$= 0x = 0.$$

Therefore by Theorem 3.5-13

$$(-1)x = -x. \quad \square$$

3.5-17 Theorem: $(-x)y = -(xy) = -xy.$ $(-(xy) = -xy$ by notational convention.)

Proof: $xy + (-xy) = 0.$ Also
$$xy + (-x)y = (x + -x)y$$
$$= 0y = 0.$$
Therefore
$$(-x)y = -xy. \quad \text{(Why?)} \quad \square$$

3.5-18 Theorem: $(-x)(-y) = xy.$

Proof: $-xy + xy = 0$ and
$$-xy + (-x)(-y) = (-x)y + (-x)(-y) \quad \text{(Why?)}$$
$$= (-x)(y + -y)$$
$$= (-x) \cdot 0 = 0.$$
Therefore
$$(-x)(-y) = xy. \quad \square$$

Recall that subtraction in a number ring is defined by $x - y = x + (-y)$. Recall also that we promised to justify using the same symbol for subtraction as for negation. The following theorems involving subtraction and negation should convince you that this was a good idea.

3.5-19 Theorem: $-(-x) = x.$

Proof: $-x + x = 0$ and
$$-x + (-(-x)) = 0. \quad \text{(Why?)}$$
Therefore
$$-(-x) = x. \quad \text{(Why?)} \quad \square$$

3.5-20 Theorem: $(-x)(y - z) = -xy + xz.$

Proof: $\quad (-x)(y - z) = (-x)(y + (-z))$
$$= (-x)y + (-x)(-z)$$
$$= -xy + xz. \quad \square$$

3.5-21 Theorem: $-(x - y) = y - x.$

Proof: $x - y + -(x - y) = 0$ and
$$x - y + (y - x) = x + (-y) + y + (-x)$$
$$= 0.$$

The result follows from Theorem 3.5-13. $\square$

There are many more useful theorems which are immediate consequences of the above theorems, along with the axioms for a number ring. You are perhaps familiar with many of them from previous equation solving experiences.

Exercises: List 10 theorems that we have not already given which you think can be proved about number rings.

Natural Number Exponents

In any number ring D, we can define x^n where $n \in N_0$ and $x \in D$.

3.5-22 Definition: Let $x \in D$, a number ring, and let $n \in N_0$. Then

$$x^0 = 1 \qquad \text{(the multiplicative identity in } D\text{)}$$

$$x^n = \prod_{i=1}^{n} x \quad \text{if } n \in N \qquad \text{(products being multiplication in } D\text{)}.$$

Recall that we defined Π by recursive definition, so all we need in order to define this kind of sequence in a set S is for multiplication to be defined in S. Thus, if $f: N \to S$ is any sequence in S,

$$\prod_{i=1}^{1} f(i) = f(1)$$

and

$$\forall n > 1, \prod_{i=1}^{n} f(i) = f(n) \cdot \prod_{i=1}^{n-1} f(i).$$

In particular, we can use Z for the (number ring) S. A similar statement can be made for $\sum$.

Exercises 3.5

1. Simplify each of the following. (Keep in mind that Z is a number ring. Use only number ring properties!)

   a) $-2(5 - 12)$

   b) $(3 - 4)(5 + (-1))$

   c) $-3(-7)(5 - 4)$

   d) $(4 - 3)(-7)$

2. When possible, find an integer x such that:

   a) $5x(3 - 1) = 4$

   b) $2x - 3x = 1$

   c) $7x = 15 - 1$

   d) $3x - 4 = 2$

3. Compute:

   a) $(-1)(-5)(4)(-3)$

   b) $\prod_{i=1}^{4} (-2)$

   c) $\prod_{i=1}^{5} (-3)$

   d) $(-7)^3$

   e) $\prod_{i=0}^{4} (-2)i$

   f) $\prod_{i=1}^{3} 2(i)$

4. Write out the details of the proof of Theorem 3.5-12.

5. Compute:

a) $\sum_{i=1}^{3} 2(i)$

c) $\sum_{i=1}^{7} (-3 + i)$

e) $\sum_{k=1}^{4} k^k$

b) $\sum_{i=0}^{4} (-2)i$

d) $\sum_{i=1}^{5} (-2i + 3(-i))$

6. Suppose that we define $+$ and $\cdot$ on Z by the following:

Addition:

Case 1. $m, n \in N_0$.

$$m + n = m + n$$

(That is, in this case the operation gives the same result as previously defined on N_0.)

Case 2. $m \in N^-, n \in N_0$.

$$m + n = n - (-m) \quad \text{if} \quad -m < n$$
$$m + n = -(-m - n) \quad \text{if} \quad n < -m$$

Case 3. $m \in N_0, n \in N^-$.

$$m + n = -(-m + (-n))$$

Multiplication:

Case 1. $m, n \in N_0$.

$$m \cdot n = mn$$

Case 2. $m \in N^-, n \in N_0$.

$$m \cdot n = -(-m \cdot n)$$

Case 3. $m \in N_0, n \in N^-$.

$$m \cdot n = -(m(-n))$$

Case 4. $m, n \in N^-$.

$$m \cdot n = (-m)(-n)$$

Verify that $+$ and $\cdot$ satisfy the axioms for a number ring.

7. Let $+$ and $\cdot$ be operations on Z which satisfy the axioms for a number ring, and let $\oplus$ and $\odot$ be operations on Z which also satisfy the axioms for a number ring. Assume in addition that $\forall x \in Z \quad x + \eta(x) = 0$ and $x \oplus \eta(x) = 0$. Show that $\forall a, b \in Z \quad a + b = a \oplus b$ and $a \cdot b = a \odot b$.

8. Establish (prove) $\forall x, y, z \in Z$:
   a) $-x(-y - z) = xy + xz$
   b) $(x - y)(x + y) = x^2 - y^2$
   c) $(x - y)(x^2 + xy + y^2) = x^3 - y^3$
   d) $\forall n \in N \quad x^{n+1} - y^{n+1} = (x - y) \sum_{i=0}^{n} x^{n-i} y^i$

9. a) Extend the $\sum$ and $\prod$ notation to include expressions with possibly negative numbers for upper and lower limits. (*Hint:* Give the definitions in terms of $f: Z \to Z$, with limits $a < b$.)

b) Compute:

i) $\sum_{i=-3}^{0} 2i$

iii) $\prod_{i=-2}^{2} (i^2 - 1)$

ii) $\sum_{i=-4}^{-1} -i$

iv) $\prod_{i=-1}^{3} (3 + i)$

10. Investigate (prove or disprove).

a) $\sum_{i=0}^{4} i = \sum_{i=1}^{5} i - 1$.

b) For any function $f: Z \to Z$, $\sum_{i=2}^{7} f(i) = \sum_{i=1}^{6} f(i + 1)$ and $\sum_{i=2}^{7} f(i) = \sum_{i=3}^{8} f(i - 1)$. Can you generalize this?

c) $\prod_{i=-3}^{12} f(i) = 0$ implies that for some $n \in Z$ $f(n) = 0$.

d) $\forall n \in N$ $\forall x, y \in Z$ $(x - y)^n = x^n - y^n$.

e) $\sum_{i=a}^{b} f(i) = \sum_{i=a+n}^{b+n} f(i - n)$ $\forall n \in Z$, where $a \leq b$.

3.6 The Integers an Ordered Ring, Finite Cardinality, and Variations on Induction

We have developed the idea of the natural numbers being an ordered set in correspondence with points lying along a line. We have attached to N a zero and an extra collection N^-. We have a negation function which we feel reflects numbers in the line across the zero. Let us then extend our order relation in a way which orders all the elements in Z, and which corresponds with this negating or reflecting concept.

We notice that, as was the case for natural numbers, when we add 1 to a negative number, it "moves" a space to the right.

Example: -3 -2 -1 0 1 2 3

$-3 \to (-3 + 1)$

We thus define the ordering on Z in a way similar to that used for N. It should be obvious from our definition that we have extended the ordering to Z and have not changed it on N.

3.6-1 Definition: $\forall a, b \in Z$, $a < b$ iff $\exists p \in N$ $a + p = b$.

To prove that we have an order relation, we could establish the order properties in much the same way as we did for the set N. We leave this as an exercise, since the similarity is so strong.

The following properties are important in that they give us insight into order properties with respect to the operations in Z. Later, in developing order for the rational numbers, we shall look back on this characterization of order and pattern our definition from it.

3.6-2 Theorem:

1) $\forall x \in Z$, if $x \neq 0$, then $x \in N$ or $-x \in N$, but not both.
2) $\forall x, y \in Z$, if $x \in N$ and $y \in N$, then $x + y \in N$.
3) $\forall x, y \in Z$, if $x \in N$ and $y \in N$, then $xy \in N$.

Proof: 1) This follows directly from the fact that $N^- \cap N = \emptyset$ and that $Z = N_0 \cup N^-$.

2) and 3) follow directly from the definition of addition and multiplication in N. $\square$

3.6-3 Theorem: If $x, y \in Z$, then $x < y$ iff $y - x \in N$.

Proof: $x < y \Leftrightarrow x + p = y$ and $p \in N$
$\qquad\quad \Leftrightarrow p = y - x$ and $p \in N$
$\qquad\quad \Leftrightarrow y - x \in N$. $\square$

Corollary: (*The Trichotomy law*) $\forall x, y \in Z$ exactly one of the following is true:

$$x = y \qquad \text{or} \qquad x < y \qquad \text{or} \qquad y < x$$

Let us notice now an algebraic property of Z which cannot be deduced from the general properties of a number ring. Later, we shall encounter number rings which do not have this property. However, we shall be very interested in number rings which have this property and shall encounter many such structures.

3.6-4 Theorem: $\forall x, y \in Z$, if $x \neq 0$ and $y \neq 0$, then $xy \neq 0$.

Proof: Case 1. $x, y \in N$, therefore $xy \in N$.

Case 2. $x, y \in N^-$, then $(-x), (-y) \in N$, and therefore

$$(-x)(-y) = xy \in N.$$

Case 3. $x \in N, y \in N^-$, therefore $-y \in N$ and so

$$x(-y) = -(xy) \in N$$

but then

$$xy \in N^-.$$

Case 4. (Similar to Case 3.) $\square$

Corollary: $\forall x, y \in Z$ ($x \neq 0$), if $xy = 0$, then $y = 0$. $\square$

Corollary: $\forall x, y \in Z$, if $xy = 0$, then $x = 0$ or $y = 0$. $\square$

3.6-5 Definition: If D is a number ring such that

$$xy = 0 \Rightarrow x = 0 \text{ or } y = 0$$

we say that D is an *integral ring*.

185

Perhaps you recognize this as the property that makes it possible to solve certain equations by factoring. Thus, for an equation in the form $(x - a)(x - b) = 0$, it follows that $x - a = 0$ or $x - b = 0$.

Example: Find all $x \in Z$ such that

$$x^2 - 7x + 10 = 0.$$

Since $x^2 - 7x + 10 = (x - 2)(x - 5)$,

$$x - 2 = 0 \quad \text{or} \quad x - 5 = 0.$$

Hence $\{5, 2\}$ is the solution set for the equation.

Counting, Countable Sets, Finite Sets

Later in this section we wish to discuss an extension of the method of making proofs and definitions by induction to certain subsets of Z other than the set N of natural numbers. To this end, we define some special subsets of Z which will also be used in discussing countability.

3.6-6 Definition: Let $k, m \in Z$, $k < m$. Then

1) $\{k, \cdots, m\} = \{n \in Z: k \leq n \leq m\}$
2) $\{k, \cdots, \infty\} = \{n \in Z: k \leq n\}$
3) $\{-\infty, \cdots, k\} = \{n \in Z: n \leq k\}$

Since the natural numbers were originally conceived as the things with which we count the number of discrete objects in a set, let us formalize what is meant by such common statements as "there are five elements in the set," "the set is finite," and "the set is countable."

3.6-7 Definition: A non-empty set S is said to have *finite cardinality n* if it can be placed in *one-one* correspondence with the set $\{1, \cdots, n\}$. That is, for some ψ, $\psi: S \xrightarrow[onto]{1\text{-}1} \{1, \cdots, n\}$. We then define $\#S = n$. We define $\#\emptyset = 0$.

3.6-8 Definition: A set is said to be *countable* if it can be placed in *one-one* correspondence with some subset of the natural numbers N.

Recall that we defined two sets to be cardinally equivalent if there exists a *one-one* correspondence between the sets. (Recall also that cardinal equivalence is an equivalence relation.) Let us now develop some useful cardinality theorems for both finite and infinite sets. (A set is said to be finite if it has finite cardinality, and infinite otherwise.)

3.6-9 Theorem: If $m \leq n$, then $\#\{m, \cdots, n\} = n - m + 1$.

Proof: Define $\psi: \{m, \cdots, n\} \to N$ as follows:

$$\forall k \in \{m, \ldots, n\}, \quad \psi(k) = k - m + 1.$$

We need to show that $\psi \colon \{m, \cdots, n\} \xrightarrow[\text{onto}]{1\text{-}1} \{1, \cdots, n - m + 1\}$

1) *Into:* If $k \in \{m, \cdots, n\}$, then $m \leq k \leq n$, so that

$$m - m + 1 \leq k - m + 1 \leq n - m + 1$$

thus

$$1 \leq k - m + 1 \leq n - m + 1$$

and hence

$$\psi(k) \in \{1, \cdots, n - m + 1\}.$$

2) *One-one:* If $\psi(k_1) = \psi(k_2)$, then

$$k_1 - m + 1 = k_2 - m + 1$$

which implies that $k_1 = k_2$.

3) *Onto:* Let $p \in \{1, \cdots, n - m + 1\}$ so that $1 \leq p < n - m + 1$. Then

$$1 + m - 1 \leq p + m - 1 \leq n - m + 1 + m - 1$$

so that

$$m \leq p + m - 1 \leq n.$$

Since

$$\psi(p + m - 1) = p + m - 1 - m + 1 = p$$

the map is *onto.* $\square$

Corollary: If $n - m = p - k \in N$, then $\#\{m, \cdots, n\} = \#\{k, \cdots, p\}$. $\square$

3.6-10 Theorem: $\#N = \#Z$.

Proof: Define $\psi \colon Z \to N$ as follows: if $n \leq 0$, $\psi(n) = 2(-n) + 1$; and if $n > 0$, $\psi(n) = 2n$. We leave it for the reader to convince himself that $\psi \colon Z \xrightarrow[\text{onto}]{1\text{-}1} N$. $\square$

Variations on Induction

We now prove several useful versions of the principle of mathematical induction which apply to subsets of integers not necessarily the natural numbers.

3.6-11 Theorem: If S is a hereditary subset of Z and $m \in S$, then $\{m, \cdots, \infty\} \subset S$. (A hereditary set is one in which $k \in S \Rightarrow k + 1 \in S$.)

Proof: Select p such that $m - p = 1$. Let $H = \{x - p \colon x \in S\}$. Clearly, $H \cap N$ is a hereditary subset of N since S is hereditary. Also, $1 \in H \cap N$ since $m \in S$. It follows by the induction principle for N that $H \cap N = N$ and therefore $N \subset H$. Now suppose $n \in \{m, \cdots, \infty\}$. We know that $1 = m - p \leq n - p$. (Why?) Also, $n - p \in N$ since $N = \{x \in Z \colon x \geq 1\}$; so it follows that $n - p \in H$. (Why?) Therefore $n - p = x - p$ for some $x \in S$.

(Why?) Therefore $n = x \in S$. Hence $n \in \{m, \cdots, \infty\} \Rightarrow n \in S$, showing that $\{m, \cdots, \infty\} \subset S$. ☐

This theorem says that if $p(x)$ is a property of some integer m, and if

$$\forall k \geq m, \qquad p(k) \Rightarrow p(k + 1)$$

then $p(x)$ is a property of m and every integer to the right of m as well. Recall that previously it was necessary to "start" the induction at $m = 1$.

We leave as an exercise for the reader the proof of the following useful variation of induction which, intuitively speaking, says that induction works in the negative direction also.

3.6-12 Theorem: If m is an element of some subset S of Z, and if $\forall k \leq m$, $k \in S \Rightarrow k - 1 \in S$, then $\{-\infty, \cdots, m\} \subset S$. The proof is left for the reader.

With very little difficulty, we can make the same generalization concerning recursive definitions. Thus one does not have to start at any particular place in making recursive definitions, and also one can define recursively "to the left."

Example: We are able to extend the summation and product notation (see Problem 9, 3.5) to include such expansions as:

$$\sum_{i=5}^{7} (2 \cdot i) = 2 \cdot 5 + 2 \cdot 6 + 2 \cdot 7$$

$$\prod_{i=3}^{8} i = 3 \cdot 4 \cdot 5 \cdot 6 \cdot 7 \cdot 8$$

Remark: We agree to keep the top number (the "upper limit") of our summation and product notation at least as large as the bottom one ("lower limit"). Thus we shall not define such expressions as

$$\sum_{i=7}^{5} (2 \cdot i) \qquad \text{and} \qquad \prod_{i=8}^{3} i$$

Trivial Induction and Dot, Dot, Dot

Very often mathematical arguments and proofs are given which require the principle of induction, but for which no mention is made of this fact. This is usually what amounts to a "trivial induction." This is a case in which it is obvious that the induction can be started and that it "will continue." on the other hand, many non-trivial induction arguments are given in terms of a "dot, dot, dot," illustrative argument. This is an acceptable proof only if the reader truly sees how it all fits together, and is confident that a routine (but rigorous) induction argument could be given.

Example: Recall the theorem $2 \sum_{i=1}^{n} i = n(n+1)$. An illustrative "dot, dot, dot" inductive proof would be as follows:

$$\sum_{i=1}^{n} i = 1 + 2 + \cdots + n$$

Add this to itself.

$$\sum_{i=1}^{n} i + \sum_{i=1}^{n} i \begin{cases} = & 1 + & 2 & + \cdots + & n \\ & + n + & n-1 & + \cdots + & 1 \\ = (n+1) + & (n+1) + & \cdots & + (n+1) \end{cases}$$

We note that we have n, $(n+1)$'s, and therefore $2 \sum_{i=1}^{n} i = n(n+1)$.

Although such an argument is not as rigorous as going through the inductive steps, it is often more satisfying since one develops an intuitive feel for the theorem, as a result of having seen patterns which would not have been given in a rigorous proof.

Example: $k \sum_{i=1}^{n} f(i) = \sum_{i=1}^{n} kf(i)$ because

$$k \sum_{i=1}^{n} f(i) = k(f(1) + f(2) + \cdots + f(n))$$
$$= kf(1) + kf(2) + \cdots + kf(n)$$
$$= \sum_{i=1}^{n} kf(i).$$

We shall consider an even more subtle form of induction in the next chapter.

Exercises 3.6

1. Graph as points along a line all integers n such that:
   a) $3 < n < 9$ c) $-4 < n^2 < 27$
   b) $1 \leq 2n < 7$ d) $6 < 2n - 1 \leq 34$

2. Determine the cardinality of each of the following sets:
   a) $\{-3, \cdots, 10\}$ e) $\{2, \cdots, 4\} \cup \{3, \cdots, 6\}$
   b) $\{4, \cdots, 36\}$ f) $\{-4, \cdots, 5\} \cap \{7, \cdots, 12\}$
   c) $\{-11, \cdots, 26\}$ g) $\{-4, \cdots, 5\} \cup \{7, \cdots, 12\}$
   d) $\{2, \cdots, 4\} \cap \{3, \cdots, 6\}$

3. Show that if $m < n$, then
   a) if $k \in N$, then $km < kn$
   b) if $k \in N^-$, then $km > kn$
   c) if $k = 0$, then $km = kn$

4. a) If $\#A = m$ and $\#B = n$, then can you say $\#(A \cup B) = m + n$? Why?
   b) Show that $\#(A \cup B) = m + n - \#(A \cap B)$.

5. Let $S = Z \times Z$.

    a) Is S countable?

    b) Prove your assertion.

6. *a)* Show that if S is finite and if $A \subset S$, then A is finite.

    b) Show that if S is countable and if $A \subset S$, then A is countable.

7. Compute $f(2)$ and $f(-2)$ where

    a) $\forall x \in Z \quad f(x) = \sum_{i=-2}^{3} (x^2 + i)$

    b) $f(x) = \sum_{i=0}^{3} x$ if $x \geq 0$ and $f(x) = \Pi_{i=-2}^{2} (x + i)$ if $x < 0$

8. Investigate (prove or disprove):

    a) $\forall n \in N \quad 2^n \geq n!$

    b) $\forall n \in N \quad n^2 \geq n!$

    c) $\forall n \in N \quad 2 + 2^2 + \cdots + 2^n = \sum_{i=1}^{n} 2^i = 2^{n+1} - 2$

    d) $\forall n \in N \quad \sum_{i=1}^{n} (4i - 2) = 2n^2$

9. Find a, if $\sum_{j=1}^{5} (a + j) = 25$.

10. Find p and q if $\sum_{j=1}^{4} (pj + q) = 28$ and $\sum_{j=2}^{5} (pj + q) = 44$.

11. *a)* Show that if $\#S \in N$, $A \subset S$, and $\#A = \#S$, then $A = S$.

    b) Indicate why this is not true if any of the three premises is omitted.

12. For each of the following, find

    i) $\{x : f(x) = 0\}$

    ii) $\{x : f(x) \geq 0\}$

    iii) $\{x : f(x) \leq 0\}$

    where the universal set is Z:

    a) $f(x) = x^2 + x - 6$

    b) $f(x) = 5x - 2$

    c) $f(x) = x^3 + 2x^2 - 5x - 6$

    (*Hint:* Factor f into a product of terms of the form $(x - a)$.)

3.7 Some Elementary Number Theory Results and Applications to Arithmetic

A branch of mathematics known as "number theory" deals, at its elementary level, primarily with properties of the integers. We shall develop in this section some elementary number theoretic results which are necessary for the further development of our number systems.

We have already seen a fundamental and historically important number theory result, in the radix representation theorem. This theorem allows us to name positive integers systematically with a very limited collection of symbols by taking advantage of a simple "place principle." This principle also applies to the negative numbers, since essentially a negative number is named in terms of its positive counterpart. Due to the very strong connection between negative numbers and their positive number reflections, we find the following definition very useful.

3.7-1 Definition: (*The absolute value function*) $||: Z \rightarrow N_0$ is described by

$$||(n) = \begin{cases} n & \text{if } n \in N_0 \\ -n & \text{if } n \in N^- \end{cases}$$

Remark: We usually denote the image of n under the absolute value function by $|n|$ rather than $||(n)$ as would be done for most functions.

Example: $|5| = 5, |0| = 0, |-3| = -(-3) = 3, |-6| = --6 = 6.$

The absolute value of a number indicates how far away from 0 the given number is, that is, the number of counting steps it takes to get to the number, disregarding the direction one counts. Roughly speaking, one can think of the absolute value as folding the left side of the line over into the right, but leaving the right side fixed.

Divisors, Multiples, and Prime Numbers

3.7-2 Definition: Let $a, b \in Z$. If $\exists p \in Z$ $a = bp$, then we say that p is a *divisor of* a. (Written $p|a$, "p divides a" or "p is a factor of a.")

Example: $6 = 2 \cdot 3$. Therefore $2|6$ and $3|6$. Note that 1 is a divisor for each number in Z, and that 0 is not a divisor for any number in $Z - \{0\}$. Also note that every number is a divisor of itself.

3.7-3 Definition: If $a = nb$ for some $n \in Z$, where $a, b \in Z$, then we say that a *is a multiple of* b.

3.7-4 Definition: Let $a \in Z$. If a is a multiple *of 2* (*i.e.*, $a = 2b$ for some $b \in Z$), then we call a an *even integer*; otherwise, we call a an *odd integer*. (0 is even since $0 = 2 \cdot 0$.)

3.7-5 Theorem: 1 is odd.

Proof: (By contradiction) Assume that 1 is even, so that $1 = 2b$ for some $b \in Z$.

Case 1. $b = 0$. Then $1 = 2 \cdot 0 = 0$, which is a contradiction.

Case 2. $b \in N$. Then $1 = (1 + 1)b = b + b$. If $b = 1$, then 1 is a successor of itself. If $b \neq 1$, then

$$1 = b + (c + 1) = (b + c) + 1$$

for some $c \in N$; and hence 1 is a successor of some number in N, a contradiction in either situation.

191

Case 3. $b \in N^-$. Then $b = -b'$ for some b' in N. Therefore

$$1 = 2(-b') = (1 + 1)(-b') = -b' + -b' = -(b' + b')$$

But $b' + b' \in N$, and $-(b' + b') \in N^-$. That is, $1 \in N^-$, which is a contradiction. In every possible case we arrive at a contradiction, so we must conclude that 1 is not even. That is, 1 is odd. []

3.7-6 Theorem: Let $a \in Z$. a is odd if and only if $a = 2b + 1$ for some $b \in Z$.

Proof: ($\Rightarrow$) Assume a is odd.
Now $a = 2q + r$, where $0 \le r < 2$, by the division property. That is, $r = 0$ or $r = 1$. If $r = 0$, then a is even; therefore we must conclude that $r = 1$.
($\Leftarrow$) Assume that $a = 2b + 1$ for some $b \in Z$. Also assume that a is not odd (*i.e.*, a is even). Then $a = 2(b')$ for some $b' \in Z$. It follows that $2(b') = 2b + 1$ from which we deduce that $1 = 2(b') - 2b = 2(b' - b)$. This contradicts the fact that 1 is odd. Hence our assumption that a is even leads to a denial of known facts. We conclude then that a is odd. []

3.7-7 Definition: A number $p \in N$, $p > 1$, is called a *prime number* iff the only divisors of p in N are 1 and p. (Any natural number which is not prime is called *composite*.)

Example: $5 = 5 \times 1 = 1 \times 5$, but there are no other divisors of 5. It follows that 5 is prime.

Example: $7 = 7 \times 1 = 1 \times 7$, but once again there is no other way to factor 7, and hence 7 is a prime number.

Example: $9 = 3 \times 3$, and therefore 9 is a composite number.
In the examples above for 5 and 7, how do we know for sure that the numbers have no other divisors? We have not tried every possible combination of $m, n \in N$ to see if $m \times n = 5$. (Indeed, this is not possible.) The question leads us to observe the following theorem.

3.7-8 Theorem: If $b, n \in N$ and $b|n$, then $b \le n$.

Proof: Assume $bm = n$. Clearly $m \in N$, since $b, n \in N$. If $m = 1$, then $b = n$, in which case $b \le n$. If $m > 1$, then $m = p + 1$ for some $p \in N$. It follows that $b(1 + p) = n$. Therefore

$$b + bp = n$$

and hence $b \le n$ since $bp \in N$. []

Corollary: If $b, a \in Z$ and $b|a$, then $|b| \le |a|$.
It follows that if we test, as possible divisors, all natural numbers less than a given natural number, then we will be able to determine whether it is prime. There are more refined tests available, but we shall not develop them in this short section on number theory.
One of the most fundamental and useful facts concerning natural numbers is the fact that they can essentially be factored in only one way. By "essen-

tially factorable in only one way", we mean that if you ignore the fact that $a \times b$ and $b \times a$ are in a sense slightly different, and keep in mind that 1 is not considered to be prime, then any given natural number n, $n \neq 1$, can be expressed as a product of primes in exactly one way. This fact, known as the *Fundamental Theorem of Arithmetic* is the highlight of this section. The proof requires some preliminary results, and a method of induction which we have not yet introduced. For these reasons, we state the theorem now, but postpone its proof until Chapter IV.

3.7-9 Theorem: (The *unique factorization theorem*), (The *fundamental theorem of arithmetic*) For each $n \in N$, there exist prime natural numbers $p_1, p_2, \cdots, p_r$ such that

$$n = p_1 \cdot p_2 \cdots p_r.$$

Moreover, if

$$n = q_1 \cdot q_2 \cdots q_h$$

where $q_1, q_2, \cdots, q_h$ are prime, then there is a *1-1* correspondence f,

$$f: \{p_1, p_2, \cdots, p_r\} \xrightarrow[onto]{1\text{-}1} \{q_1, q_2, \cdots, q_h\}$$

such that $f(p_i) = p_i$, $i = 1, 2, \cdots, r$. (That is, the q's are the same as the p's in some order. It follows immediately that $h = r$.)

Roughly speaking, this asserts that "the factorizations of n into primes are the same, except possibly for some commutative shuffling."

Example: $24 = 4 \times 6 = (2 \times 2) \times (3 \times 2) = 2 \times 2 \times 3 \times 2$ and also $24 = 3 \times 8 = 3 \times (2 \times 4) = 3 \times 2 \times (2 \times 2) = 3 \times 2 \times 2 \times 2$.

Example: $26 = 2 \times 13 = 13 \times 2$
$48 = 6 \times 8 \; = (2 \times 3)(2 \times 2 \times 2)$
$ = 3 \times 16 = 3 \times (2 \times 2 \times 2 \times 2).$

We include some simple theorems and definitions which are useful in number theoretic discussions.

3.7-10 Theorem: Let a, b, $p \in Z$. If $p|a + b$ and $p|a$, then $p|b$.

Proof: Assume $pm = a + b$ and $pm' = a$.

$$b = pm - pm' = p(m - m'). \; \square$$

Keep in mind throughout this development that if $a|b$, a, $b \in Z$, then $-a|-b$, $-a|b$, and $a|-b$. As a result, it is possible to extend many results concerning divisibility to the entire set of integers, although the result was proved only for N.

Greatest Common Divisors

3.7-11 Definition: Let a, $b \in Z$. If $d|a$ and $d|b$, then d is said to be a *common divisor* for a and b.

3.7-12 Definition: If a and b are not both zero, if $d > 0$ is a common divisor for a and b, and if $d'|a$ and $d'|b \Rightarrow d'|d$, then d is called a *greatest common divisor* of a and b (written $gcd(a, b)$).

In the next chapter, we show that there exists at least one $gcd(a, b)$. It seems intuitively clear that this is the case. We can, however, establish its uniqueness.

3.7-13 Theorem: If d is a $gcd(a, b)$, and c is a $gcd(a, b)$, then $d = c$.

Proof: $d|c$ and $c|d$. (Why?) Therefore $nd = c$ and $mc = d$ for some $n \geq 0$ and $m \geq 0$, since $d > 0$ and $c > 0$. By substitution, $d = m(nd)$, from which $mn = 1$ (as $d \neq 0$). Therefore $m = 1$ and $n = 1$. Hence $d = c$. $\square$

We leave it as an exercise for you to show that the $gcd(a, b)$ really is the "greatest" common divisor of a and b.

Example: $gcd(9, 6) = 3$, $gcd(-4, 14) = 2$, $gcd(0, -5) = 5$. Do you think the symbol "$gcd(0, 0)$" has meaning?

One way to determine the greatest common divisor for two numbers is to first factor each into prime factors. Any common prime factor then can be included in the prime factorization of the gcd.

Example: $gcd(62, 36) = gcd(2 \cdot 3 \cdot 7, 2 \cdot 2 \cdot 3 \cdot 3) = 2 \cdot 3 = 6$.

Example: $gcd(2^3 \cdot 3^2 \cdot 5, 2^2 \cdot 3 \cdot 5^2) = 2^2 \cdot 3 \cdot 5$. (Explain!)

Relatively Prime Numbers and Least Common Multiples

We find it useful to define a concept related to primeness, but which deals with two numbers.

3.7-14 Definition: If $a, b \in Z$ and $gcd(a, b) = 1$, then we say that a and b are *relatively prime* or *prime to each other*.

Example: 35 and 6 are prime to each other, and 3 and 14 are relatively prime. However, 6 and 9 are not relatively prime since $gcd(6, 9) = 3$.

3.7-15 Theorem: If p is prime and $a \in Z$ and $p \nmid a$ ($\sim(p|a)$), then $gcd(p, a) = 1$.

Proof: Suppose $gcd(p, a) = d$. Then $d|p$, and hence $d = 1$ or $d = p$. Since $d|a$ and $p \nmid a$, it follows that $d = 1$. $\square$

Related to the concept of greatest common divisors is the idea of "least common multiples."

3.7-16 Definition: Let $a, b \in Z$. The *least common multiple* of a and b, $lcm(a, b)$, is the non-negative integer m such that:

1) m is a multiple of both a and b. (That is, $m = n_1 a$ and $m = n_2 b$.)
2) If k is a multiple of both a and b, then k is a multiple of m. (That is, any common multiple of a and b is a multiple of $lcm(a, b)$.)

Example: $lcm(5, 3) = 15$, $lcm(6, 9) = 18$,

$$lcm(2^2 \cdot 3^3 \cdot 5, \ 2^3 \cdot 3 \cdot 5^2) = 2^3 \cdot 3^3 \cdot 5^2.$$

3.7-17 Theorem: $m = lcm(a, b)$ if and only if $m \geq 0$ and satisfies the following two conditions:

1) $a|m$ and $b|m$.
2) If $a|k$ and $b|k$, then $m|k$.

Proof: ($\Rightarrow$) Assume $m = lcm(a, b)$. By definition, $m = n_1 a$ and $m = n_2 b$, which is equivalent to $a|m$ and $b|m$. Also, by definition, if $k = m_1 a$ and $k = m_2 b$, then $k = m_3 m$, which clearly is equivalent to 2).

The converse follows, since both conditions of the theorem were equivalent to the corresponding condition in the definition of lcm. $\square$

Exercises   3.7

1. *a)* $|9| = $ _____   *c)* $|6| = $ _____   *e)* $|--2| = $ _____
   b) $|-7| = $ _____   *d)* $|-11| = $ _____   *f)* $|a| = $ _____

2. Find all the integral divisors of:
   a) 6   *b)* 12   *c)* -15 *d)* 84

3. Decide in each case whether the number given is prime or composite:
   a) 9   *c)* 7   *e)* 17   *g)* 101   *i)* 41
   b) 31   *d)* 2   *f)* 69   *h)* 116   *j)* 29

4. *a)* Make a list of all even primes.
   b) Make a list of all primes which are divisible by 3.

5. Select all possible pairs of relatively prime numbers from the following list: 24, 30, 16, 17, 8, 15.

6. Factor each of the following into a product of prime factors:
   a) 24   *b)* 36   *c)* 52   *d)* 75   *e)* 53   *f)* 71

7. Find:
   a) $gcd(24, 9)$ *b)* $gcd(238, 142)$ *c)* $gcd(611, 314)$

8. List all divisors of 100 by first factoring 10 as a product of primes and then writing 10^2 as a product of primes.

9. Show that if $d|a$ and $d|b$, then $d \leq gcd(a, b)$. Assume $(a, b) \neq (0, 0)$. (*Hint:* If $m|n$, then $|m| \leq |n|$.)

10. Show that if $d|a$ and $d|b$, then $d|a + b$.

11. Show that if $d|a$, then $d|ax$ for any $x \in Z$.

12. Find all common divisors of the following pairs:
    a) 6, 4   *b)* 12, 16   *c)* 14, 31

13. Find:

    a) $lcm(24, 9)$ *c)* $lcm(611, 314)$

    b) $lcm(162, 324)$ *d)* $lcm(238, 142)$

14. Show that $gcd(a, b) \mid lcm(a, b)$.

15. *a)* Use the fundamental theorem of arithmetic to show that if p is prime and $p|ab$, then $p|a$ or $p|b$.

    b) Now deduce that if $p|a^2$, then $p|a$ where p is prime.

16. Find all prime numbers between 1 and 100. (*Note:* Once a prime $p < 100$ is found, you can eliminate as candidates all multiples of p.)

17. Investigate (prove or disprove):

    a) $\forall n \in N$ $3^{2n} - 1$ is a multiple of 8.

    b) $\forall n \in N$ $2^{n+2} - 1$ is a multiple of 7.

    c) $\forall n \in N$ $2n^3 + 3n^2 + n$ is a multiple of 6.

    d) $\forall n \in N$ $n^2 + n$ is a multiple of 2.

    e) $\forall n \geq 2$ $n^3 - n$ is a multiple of 3.

    f) $\forall n \geq 1$ n^5 is a multiple of 5.

18. Show that:

    a) $\forall m, n \in Z$ $|mn| = |m| \, |n|$.

    b) $\forall m, n \in Z$ $|m + n| \leq |m| + |n|$.

    c) $\forall m \in N$ $\forall n \in Z$ $|n| \leq m$ iff $-m \leq n \leq m$.

3.8 Rational Numbers

    In the process of making a list of some of the basic algebraic properties of the integers (see the definition of number ring), we notice a certain symmetry between additive properties and multiplicative properties. Both addition and multiplication are associative operations and both are commutative. We have an identity element for addition and one for multiplication. We note also that each element has an additive inverse. That is, given any integer x, there is a $y \in Z$ such that $x + y = 0$. We observe, however, that this is not true with regard to multiplication and the multiplicative identity element. In fact, we observe that the only element which possesses a multiplicative inverse is the multiplicative identity element itself. (That is, $1 \cdot 1 = 1$, but if $x \in Z$ and $x \neq 1$, then $\forall y \in Z, xy \neq 1$.) We wonder about the possibility of introducing new numbers into the system to provide for multiplicative inverses, as we did previously to provide for additive inverses. We also wonder if doing so makes our number system more useful. We will find that by introducing multiplicative inverses, we introduce into our number system the numbers commonly called the "fractions."

    Let us examine what happens if we try, as we did with the natural numbers, to extend our number system by simply attaching an additional set of numbers, and then properly defining multiplication and addition.

Question: Is it possible for every integer to have a multiplicative inverse and still retain the familiar properties of the integers?

Answer: No! If there is some number x such that $x \cdot 0 = 1$, we would have $n = 1 \cdot n = (x \cdot 0)n = x(0 \cdot n) = x \cdot 0 = 1$ for every integer n. Therefore we cannot expect 0 to have a multiplicative inverse.

Question: If we attach inverse elements for each non-zero integer, will we then need even more numbers in order to arbitrarily add and multiply in the new system in accordance with the ring properties?

Answer: Yes! For example, if $x \cdot 3 = 1$, then $2x$ cannot be an integer, for if $2x = n$ for some $n \in Z$, then $3(2x) = 3(x2) = (3x)2 = 1 \cdot 2 = 2$ and therefore $3n = 2$. This would imply that $n > 0$ but $2 < 3$; therefore $2 < 3n$, a contradiction.

We could, if we wished, continue in this fashion, deciding where we need extra elements, and making decisions as to how they should be added and multiplied. However, let us again take a "back door" approach. We know the additional property we want our new system to have, so let's insist that we have this new property, and also that we retain the old properties. We examine this new system, beginning with the following definition of an abstract algebraic structure known as a "field."

3.8-1 Definition: (*Field axioms*) A set F with two binary operations (called addition "$+$" and multiplication "$\cdot$") is called a *field* iff the following properties hold:

1) $\forall x, y, z$ $(x + y) + z = x + (y + z)$ and $(xy)z = x(yz)$
2) $\forall x, y$ $x + y = y + x$ and $xy = yx$
3) $\exists 0 \forall x$ $x + 0 = x$ and $\exists 1 \forall x$ $x \cdot 1 = x$
4) $\left\{ \begin{array}{l} \forall x \exists y \quad x + y = 0 \\ (y \text{ is called } -x) \end{array} \right\}$ and $\left\{ \begin{array}{l} \forall x \neq 0 \;\; \exists y \;\; xy = 1 \\ (y \text{ is called } x^{-1} \text{ or } 1/x) \end{array} \right\}$
5) $\forall x, y, z$ $x(y + z) = xy + xz$
6) $1 \neq 0$

Notice that a field is a number ring where $1 \neq 0$ and all non-zero elements have multiplicative inverses. Let us hesitate for a moment to make a short study of fields, as we did previously for number rings. First, the 1 and the 0 and the additive inverses are unique because, in particular, a field is a number ring. We have anticipated the uniqueness of multiplicative inverses, but nevertheless let us show it to be true.

3.8-2 Lemma. (*A field is an integral ring*) If x and y are in a field F, if $xy = 0$ and $x \neq 0$, then $y = 0$.

Proof: Since $x \neq 0$, then $\exists z \; xz = 1$. Therefore

$$(xy)z = 0z = 0 \quad \text{(Why?)}$$

and

$$(xz)y = 0.$$

Therefore $1 \cdot y = 0$ (*i.e.*, $y = 0$). $\square$

3.8-3 Theorem: If $x \neq 0$ and $xy = 1$ and $xz = 1$, then $y = z$.

Proof: $xy = xz \Rightarrow xy - xz = 0 \Rightarrow x(y - z) = 0 \Rightarrow x = 0$ or $y - z = 0$. But since $x \neq 0$, it follows that $y - z = 0$ (*i.e.*, $y = z$). $\square$

For convenience, let us define an "inverse operation" for multiplication as we did for addition.

3.8-4 Definition: Let x, $y \in F$, a field. If $y \neq 0$, then $x \div y = xy^{-1} = x(1/y) = x/y$.

We wish now to state a definition of the rational numbers, keeping in mind what we were trying to do previously. We wanted to attach enough elements to the set of integers to provide for multiplicative inverses, and to attach enough more to accommodate arbitrary addition and multiplication. We wanted to make sure we had done both in such a way as to maintain all of the nice algebraic properties we had for the integers. Further, we wished to attach only elements which were needed, either for new inverses or for new addition or multiplication results.

We begin by assuming that there exists a field F which contains Z as a subring, that is, $Z \subset F$ and when addition and multiplication are restricted to Z, we have the familiar ring of integers. (There are constructions which bear out the existence of such structures.**)

3.8-5 Definition: Let F be a field such that $Z \subset F$. The *rational number system* is the smallest subset of F, which is a field, and which contains the ring Z. We denote this number system by Q.

Perhaps the word "smallest" in this definition needs clarification. What is meant here is that if H is a field and if $Z \subset H$, then $Q \subset H$. That is, we could not construct a field by starting with Z and attaching elements without generating at least all the rational numbers. Thus, Q is "smallest" in the sense of set inclusion. We shall see later that there are indeed larger fields which contain Z.

Let us now prove a very important result which gives us information about the rational numbers.

3.8-6 Theorem: Let $Q^* = \{m/n : m, n \in Z, n \neq 0\}$. (Since we are assuming that $Z \subset F$ where F is a field, this is possible.) Then $Q^* = Q$.

Proof: Clearly any field which contains Z must also contain Q^*. (Why?) Therefore $Q^* \subset Q$. To show that $Q \subset Q^*$, it suffices to show that Q^* is a field, because we have assumed that Q is the smallest field containing Z, and Q^* contains Z (why?). Thus we need to show that Q^* is a field. Note that we need not show associativity, commutativity, nor the distributive law since Q^*

** See *Set Theory, the Structure of Arithmetic*, by N. Hamilton and J. Landin (Boston: Allyn and Bacon, Inc., 1961).

is contained in some field. (Why?) Also note that $0 \in Q^*$ and $1 \in Q^*$. We know that $\forall x \in Q^*$ $x + 0 = x$ and $\forall x \in Q^*$ $x \cdot 1 = x$, because we are assuming Q^* to be contained in a field. Clearly $1 \neq 0$, so all we need to establish is the following:

a) $\forall x \in Q^*$ $\exists y \in Q^*$ $x + y = 0$
b) $\forall x \in Q^*$ if $x \neq 0$ $\exists y \in Q^*$ $xy = 1$

along with the fact that "$+$" and "$\times$" are binary operations on Q^* (that is, Q^* is closed under addition and multiplication).

a) Let $m/n \in Q^*$ Then $-m/n \in Q^*$, and

$$m/n + -m/n = mn^{-1} + (-m)n^{-1}$$
$$= (m + (-m))n^{-1}$$
$$= 0n^{-1} = 0.$$

(Keep in mind that the big field F is also a number ring, and hence we can use any established result for number rings.)

b) Suppose $m/n \in Q^*$ such that $m/n \neq 0$. Then $m \neq 0$ and $n \neq 0$. Therefore m^{-1} and n^{-1} exist, so

$$(m/n)(n/m) = mn^{-1}m^{-1}n = mm^{-1}nn^{-1}$$
$$= 1 \cdot 1 = 1.$$

Now let m/n and $a/b \in Q^*$.

$$m/n + a/b = (m/n) \cdot 1 + (a/b) \cdot 1$$
$$= (m/n) \cdot bb^{-1} + (a/b) \cdot nn^{-1}$$
$$= mn^{-1}bb^{-1} + ab^{-1}nn^{-1}$$
$$= (mb)(n^{-1}b^{-1}) + an(n^{-1}b^{-1})$$
$$= (mb + an)b^{-1}n^{-1}$$
$$= (mb + an)(bn)^{-1} \quad \text{(See Exercise 2, 3.8.)}$$
$$= (mb + an)/bn$$

which is in Q^*. Therefore Q^* is closed under addition. Now

$$(m/n)(a/b) = mn^{-1}ab^{-1}$$
$$= man^{-1}b^{-1}$$
$$= ma(nb)^{-1} \quad \text{(See Exercise 2, 3.8.)}$$
$$= ma/nb.$$

Therefore Q^* is closed under multiplication. $\square$

What we have done, then, is to characterize the rational numbers as the set of all possible quotients of integers. This is useful in discussing the rational numbers Q in situations in which Q is contained in a larger field. Keep in mind that a number is rational if and only if it is the quotient of two integers.

Note that the representation of a rational number as the quotient of two integers is not unique. The following theorem is useful in that it gives for any non-zero rational number a unique representation as the quotient of two integers.

199

3.8-7 Theorem: If $q \in Q$ and $q \neq 0$, then $q = m/n$ where $gcd(m, n) = 1$; and further if $q = s/k$ where $gcd(s, k) = 1$, then $|m| = |s|$ and $|n| = |k|$. (When q is represented in such a fashion, we say that q has been reduced to simplest form.")

Proof: (Existence) Let $q = m/n$. Now $|m|$, $|n| \in N$, and therefore

$$|m| = p_1 p_2 \cdots p_h$$

($|m|$ uniquely factored into prime factors). Similarly,

$$|n| = p_1' p_2' \cdots p_r'.$$

Let δ be the product of all p_i's and p_{ℓ}''s that appear in common in the factorization. Then

$$|m| = \alpha \cdot \delta \quad \text{and} \quad |n| = \beta \cdot \delta$$

where $gcd(\alpha, \beta) = 1$. Now

$$\alpha/\beta = (\alpha/\beta)(\delta/\delta) = (\alpha \cdot \delta)/(\beta \cdot \delta) = \frac{|m|}{|n|}.$$

(*Uniqueness*) If $m/n = s/k$, both reduced to lowest form, then

$$|m| \, |k| = |s| \, |n|$$

where $|m|$ and $|n|$ have no common prime factors. It follows that $|m| = |s|$ since the number can be factored only one way into prime factors. Then it follows that $|n| = |k|$. □

Exercises 3.8

1. Each of the following assume that x, y, z are rational numbers (non-zero where necessary). Use the field properties and notational conventions to reduce the expression to a simpler form.

a) $\dfrac{xy^{-1}}{x^2 y} + \dfrac{3y}{x}$

c) $x^{-1}(xy + xz^{-1})$

b) $\dfrac{1}{x} yxy^{-1} - x^2 y(x^2)^{-1}$

d) $x^{-1}y^{-1}\left(\dfrac{1}{x} - \dfrac{x^2}{y}\right)$

2. Show that $1/m \cdot 1/n = 1/mn$ where $m, n \in Z$ $m \neq 0$ and $n \neq 0$. That is, show that $m^{-1}n^{-1} = (mn)^{-1}$. (*Hint:* Show that $(mn)(m^{-1}n^{-1}) = 1$.)

3. Is it possible for a field to consist of only the two identities 0 and 1?

4. Use the field properties (and only the field properties) to compute:

a) $2/3 + 5/8$

b) $9/7 + (2 + 3)/9$

c) $5/6 + (2 + 1/2)(3 - 1/4)$

d) $\dfrac{2 + 5/8}{1/2 + 1/3} - \dfrac{7 + 2}{1/2 + 3/4}$

5. Use the field properties to solve the following equations.

   a) $3x + 1 = 5$ *c)* $6 + (5x - 1)/2 = 2x$

   b) $(2/3)x - 3/4 = 7$

6. Show that every equation $ax + b = 0$ $a, b \in Q, a \neq 0$ has a solution in Q. Was this true for Z?

7. Investigate (prove or disprove): $\forall x, y, z \in Q$ (non-zero where necessary)

   a) $x^{-1}y^{-1}z^{-1} = (xyz)^{-1}$

   b) $(1/x)^{-1}yx^{-1} = y$

   c) $\dfrac{xyz}{(xyz)^{-1}} = x^2y^2z^2$

   d) $\dfrac{\left(\dfrac{1}{x} - x^2\right)^{-1}}{x - x^{-1}} = \dfrac{1}{1 - x^3} - (1 - x)$

   e) $\dfrac{\left(\dfrac{x^{-1}}{y} - \dfrac{x}{y^{-1}}\right)^{-1}}{(x - y)x} = (x - y)^{-1}(y^{-1} - x^2y)^{-1}$

   f) $\dfrac{x^{-1}y}{(x^{-1} - xy^{-1})^{-1}} = x^{-1}y^{-1} - 1$

8. We have been using subtraction on Q, but made no special definition. How can we do this?

9. Simplify:

   a) $(xy \div x^{-1}y)xy^{-1}$ *c)* $\dfrac{x}{y} - (x \div y) + (x^{-1} \div y)$

   b) $\dfrac{xy \div yz^{-1}}{(x - y)^{-1}}$

10. How many rational numbers are there? (*Hint:* It is possible to describe a function $f: N \xrightarrow[\text{onto}]{1\text{-}1} Q$. Can you find such an f? See, for example, *Mathematics: the Man-Made Universe*, by S. K. Stein (San Francisco: W. H. Freeman & Co., 1963), pp. 248–252.)

11. Show in detail that $a/b + c/d = (ad + bc)/bd$.

12. State five theorems about rational numbers which you think can be deduced from the field axioms. (*Example:*

$$\forall x, y \quad \frac{(x^{-1} - y^{-1})^2}{x^{-1}y^{-1}} = \frac{y}{x} - 2 + \frac{x}{y}$$

provided x and y are both non-zero.)

13. Reduce each of the following fractions to simplest form.

   a) $236/921$ *b)* $72/80$ *c)* $-100/654$

14. Investigate (prove or disprove):

   a) $\exists x, y \in Q \quad xy = 10$

   b) $\exists x, y \in Q \quad xy = 5/8$

c) $\exists x, y \in Q \quad xy = 2/3$

d) $\exists x, y \in Q \quad xy = 35/6$

15. Let $x \in Q \left(i.e., x = \dfrac{m}{n} \text{ where } m, n \in Z \right)$. Prove:

a) $-x = -\left(\dfrac{m}{n}\right) = \dfrac{(-m)}{n} = \dfrac{m}{(-n)}$

b) $\dfrac{m}{n} = \dfrac{(-m)}{(-n)}$

16. Write each of the following in the form $\dfrac{m}{n}$ where $n \in N$ and $m \in Z$:

a) $-\dfrac{-3}{2}$ b) $-\dfrac{2}{-5}$ c) $-\dfrac{-5}{-7}$ d) $\dfrac{-3}{-11}$

3.9 Order and the Rational Numbers

We now have the rational number system Q, which possesses all the algebraic properties (the field properties) which make equation solving and computation such a pleasure. We also have $Z \subset Q$ such that the operations on Q, when restricted to Z, yield the operations which we previously developed for Z. The integers Z, however, are ordered; and as yet we have not given an ordering for Q. We would like to order Q in such a way that when the ordering is restricted to Z, we obtain the ordering we already have on Z. Furthermore, due to our previous experience, most of us have in mind for Q a certain order which makes it a very useful number system in physical applications involving measurements of length. Certainly we do not wish to attempt to make a list showing where each number fits with respect to every other. When we described the ordering on Z in Section 3.6, we noted that the order and the operations were connected through a particular decomposition of Z into the sets $N^- \cup \{0\} \cup N$. Let us model our ordering for Q on this property, and then verify that it gives the order we have in mind. We can then use our definition to deduce further properties of order which we may find useful in physical and theoretical applications.

3.9-1 Definition: $Q^+ = \{m/n : m, n \in N\}$. Note that $N \subset Q^+$, $0 \notin Q^+$, and that if $m \in N^-$, then $m \notin Q^+$. Define $Q^- = Q - (Q^+ \cup \{0\})$, so that $Q = Q^- \cup \{0\} \cup Q^+$ and the three sets in the decomposition are pairwise disjoint.

The following theorem is an immediate consequence of the definition for Q^+.

3.9-2 Theorem: 1) $\forall x \in Q$, if $x \neq 0$, then $x \in Q^+$ or $-x \in Q^+$, but not both.

2) $\forall x, y \in Q$, if $x, y \in Q^+$, then $x + y \in Q^+$ and $xy \in Q^+$.

Proof: 1) If $x \in Q$ and $x \neq 0$, then $x = m/n$ where $m, n \in Z - \{0\}$. If $m, n \in N$, then $x \in Q^+$ by definition. If $m, n \in N^-$, then $m/n = -m/-n$ where $-m, -n \in N$, so that $x \in Q^+$. If $m \in N^-$, $n \in N$, then $-x = -(m/n) = -m/n$ and is therefore in Q^+. The case for $m \in N$, $n \in N^-$ is similar. Now if $x \in Q^+$ and $-x \in Q^+$, then $x = m/n$ where $m, n \in N$. Further

$$-x = p/q, \quad \text{where} \quad p, q \in N.$$

Therefore

$$-(m/n) = p/q$$

and so

$$-(mq) = np$$

but this is contradictory, since we know that $-(mq) \in N^-$ and $np \in N$. Hence we know that not both x and $-x$ can be elements of Q^+.

2) Left as an exercise for the reader. $\square$

3.9-3 Definition: $\forall x, y \in Q$ $x < y$ iff $y - x \in Q^+$.
(This should not be a surprising definition in view of Theorem 3.6-3, since clearly our new ordering must be an extension of the ordering on Z. Why?)

3.9-4 Theorem: The relation $<$ as defined above is an ordering of Q.

Proof: 1) If $x, y \in Q^+$ and $x \neq y$, then $y - x \in Q^+$ or

$$-(y - x) = x - y \in Q^+.$$

Therefore

$$x < y \quad \text{or} \quad y < x.$$

2) If $x \neq y$ and $x < y$, it follows that $y - x \in Q^+$, but we know then that $-(y - x) = x - y \notin Q^+$. Therefore $y \not< x$.

3) If $x < y$ and $y < z$, then $y - x \in Q^+$ and $z - y \in Q^+$. Therefore $(y - x) + (z - y) \in Q^+$. Then

$$z - x \in Q^+$$

and therefore

$$x < z. \quad \square$$

We would not be happy with the way we have ordered Q if this ordering did not correspond with certain elementary physical applications concerning the order of fractions. For example, we know that it should be true that $0 < 1/2 < 1$, $1/2 < 3/4 < 9/10$, and that many other familiar fractional inequalities hold. Let us establish a few of these in order to set our minds at ease that we have ordered the rationals in the familiar fashion.

Example: a) $1/2 < 3/4$ because $3/4 - 1/2 = 3/4 - 2/4 = 1/4 \in Q^+$ since $1, 4 \in N$.

b) $5/8 < 9/10$ because $9/10 - 5/8 = 72/80 - 50/80 = 22/80 \in Q^+$ since $22, 80 \in N$.

Let us also test a few inequalities involving negative rational numbers (*i.e.*, elements of Q^-).

Example: a) $-(7/5) < -(1/10)$ because $-(1/10) - -(7/5) = -(1/10) + 7/5 = -(1/10) + 14/10 = 13/10 \in Q^+$ since $13, 10 \in N$.

b) $-5 < 1/3$ because $1/3 - (-5) = 1/3 + 5 = 16/3 \in Q^+$ since $16, 3 \in N$.

It is obvious that $0 < a$ iff $a \in Q^+$ and that $a < 0$ iff $a \in Q^-$. Let us establish some other interesting and useful properties of the order relation.

3.9-5 Theorem: If $a < b$ and $c > 0$, then $ac < bc$.

Proof: $b - a \in Q^+$ and $c \in Q^+$. Therefore

$$bc - ac = (b - a)c \in Q^+$$

and hence

$$ac < bc. \ \square$$

3.9-6 Theorem: If $a < b$ and $c < d$ and if $a, d \in Q^+$, then $ac < bd$.

Proof: From the preceding theorem $ad < bd$ and $ac < ad$, so by the transitive property of $<$, $ac < bd$. $\square$

Example: $5/3 < 11/2$ and $1/2 > 0$. Therefore

$$1/2 \times 5/3 < 1/2 \times 11/2$$

that is,

$$5/6 < 11/4.$$

Example: $7/8 < 22/23$ and $1/3 > 0$. Therefore

$$1/3 \times 7/8 < 1/3 \times 22/23$$

and

$$7/24 < 22/69.$$

Example: $1/2 < 3/4$ and $-2 < 1/2$. Therefore

$$-2 \times 1/2 < 3/4 \times 1/2$$

that is,

$$-1 < 3/8.$$

Example: $1/5 < 1$ and $6 < 10$. Therefore

$$6 \times 1/5 < 1 \times 10$$

that is,

$$6/5 < 10.$$

3.9-7 Theorem: If $a < b$, then $-a > -b$.

Proof: $b - a \in Q^+$ and therefore

$$b - a = - -b - a \in Q^+$$
$$-a - (-b) \in Q^+$$
$$-b < -a. \ \square$$

3.9-8 Theorem: If $a < b$ and $c < 0$, then $ac > bc$.

   Proof: $a < b$ and $-c > 0$. Therefore

$$-ac < -bc$$

and by the previous theorem,

$$bc < ac. \; \square$$

   Example: $5 < 6$. Therefore $-6 < -5$.

   Example: $-1/2 < 3/4$. Therefore $-3/4 < 1/2$.

   Example: $-12 < -1/2$. Therefore $1/2 < 12$.

   Example: $1/2 < 5/8$ and $-2 < 0$. Therefore

$$-2 \times 1/2 > -2 \times 5/8$$

that is,

$$-1 > -5/4.$$

   Example: $-2 < 3/4$ and $-5 < 0$. Therefore

$$(-2) \times (-5) > -5 \times 3/4$$

that is,

$$10 > -(15/4).$$

The Absolute Value Function on Q

   We wish now to extend the absolute value function, $||$, to include all elements in Q. Since we have ordered Q, we have a built-in concept for the points in Q to be lying along a line. This line leaves Z ordered as before, with the fractions "sprinkled in between."

   Recall that on Z, the absolute value of an integer described in some sense how far the number was away from zero. We wish to describe a similar function on Q. It is probably not surprising that we model our definition after the definition of absolute value for an integer.

3.9-9 Definition: $||: Q \to Q^+ \cup \{0\}$ such that $\forall x \in Q$,

$$\text{if } x \geq 0 \text{ then } |x| = x$$
$$\text{if } x < 0 \text{ then } |x| = -x.$$

   Example: $|3/4| = 3/4 \quad |-(2/3)| = - -(2/3) = 2/3 \quad |-(1/4)| = 1/4$.

   It is of interest in many applications to look at certain sets of rational numbers which are described in terms of the absolute value function. That is, we wish to find solutions to certain equations and inequalities involving absolute values.

Example: $S_1 = \{x \in Q: |x| = 5\} = \{-5, 5\}$
$S_2 = \{x \in Q: |x| < 5\} = \{x \in Q: -5 < x < 5\}$.

Graphed on the rational number line, S_1 looks as follows:

S_2 looks as follows:

(The curved brace at the end indicates that the end point is not in the set.)

It helps in thinking of such solutions to use verbal descriptions such as "$|x| < 5$ iff x lies within 5 units of the zero." "$\{x \in Q: |x| > 6\}$ is the set of all numbers whose distance from the origin is larger than 6." (Zero is often called "the origin.")

Example: Graph the set $\{x \in Q: |x| \leq 2\}$.

It is clear that $|x| \leq 2$ provided $x \leq 2$ and $-2 \leq x$ (why?). Thus we are interested in $\{x: -2 \leq x \leq 2\}$. This is graphed as follows:

(The squared brace at an end indicates graphically that the end point is included in the set.)

Let us now consider some slightly more difficult inequalities.

Example: Find all $x \in Q$ such that $|x - 5| \leq 2$.

We know that $|x - 5| \leq 2$ iff $x - 5 \leq 2$ and $-2 \leq x - 5$. (Consider $|y| \leq 2$ where $y = x - 5$.) Then $x \leq 7$ and $3 \leq x$ (*i.e.*, $3 \leq x \leq 7$). This is graphed as follows:

Notice that this is "the set of all points within two units of the number 5."

Example: Graph on the rational number line all x such that $|x - 2| > 4$. Now $|x - 2| > 4$ if and only if

$$x - 2 > 4 \quad \text{or} \quad x - 2 < -4.$$

(Why "or" here, instead of "and"?)
That is,

$$x > 6 \quad \text{or} \quad x < -2$$

Notice that $|x - 2| > 4$ provided x is more than four units away from 2.

The following are useful and important results concerning absolute values.

3.9-10 Theorem: $\forall x, y \in Q$ $|xy| = |x| \, |y|$. The proof is left as an exercise.

Example: Graph all x, where $|2x - 3| \leq 7$. The following are all equivalent inequalities:

$$|2| \, |x - 3/2| \leq 7$$
$$|x - 3/2| \leq 7/2$$

Hence the graph appears as follows:

Example: Find all x such that $|2x + 4| > 10$.

$$|2| \, |x + 2| > 10$$
$$|x + 2| > 10/2 = 5$$
$$|x - (-2)| > 5$$

Therefore

$$x > 3 \quad \text{or} \quad -7 > x.$$

Example: Find the set of all x such that $(x - 2)(x + 3) \leq 0$.
$(x - 2)(x + 3) \leq 0$ iff

$$(x - 2) \leq 0 \quad \text{and} \quad (x + 3) \geq 0$$

or

$$(x - 2) \geq 0 \quad \text{and} \quad (x + 3) \leq 0$$

that is, iff

$$(x \leq 2 \quad \text{and} \quad x \geq -3)$$

or

$$(x \geq 2 \quad \text{and} \quad x \leq -3)$$

Thus the set under consideration is $\{-3 \leq x \leq 2\} \cup \emptyset = \{-3 \leq x \leq 2\}$, the set of rational numbers between -3 and 2, inclusive.

Example: Find the set of all x such that $(x - 2)/(x + 3) \leq 0$.

$(x - 2)/(x + 3) \leq 0$ iff the conditions of the preceding example are satisfied, *and we insist that* $x \neq -3$ (why?). Thus the set is described as $\{-3 < x \leq 2\}$.

3.9-11 Theorem: (The triangle inequality)†† $\forall x, y \in Q$

$$\left| |x| - |y| \right| \leq |x - y| \leq |x| + |y|.$$

The proof is left as an exercise.

Corollary: $\forall x, y \in Q \; \left| |x| - |y| \right| \leq |x + y| \leq |x| + |y|.$

Exercises   3.9

1. Show that $\forall x, y, z \in Q$ if $x < y$, then $x + z < y + z$.

2. Solve and graph the solution set for each of the following inequalities:

    a) $2x - 3 < 0$ *d)* $5x + 2 \leq 2x + 1$
    b) $x + 2 > 0$ *e)* $12x + 1 \leq 4 - 2x$
    c) $7x - 3 > 0$ *f)* $16x + 13x \leq 4x - 1$

†† The use of the word "triangle" will be justified when we extend this notion to complex numbers.

3. Graph the set of rational numbers x which have the following properties:

   a) $2x < 3$ and $x > -2$

   b) $x < 3/2$ and $x > -2$

   c) $2x - 3 > 0$ and $x + 2 < 0$

   d) $2x > 3$ or $x < -2$

   e) $-1 \le 3x$ or $x < -2/3$

   f) $-(1/3) \le x$ and $3x < -(2/3)$

4. Solve and graph:

   a) $(x + 2)/(x - 3) > 0$

   b) $(x + 3)/(2x + 4) \le 0$

   c) $x^2 - 4x + 3 > 0$

5. Prove that $\forall x, y \in Q \quad |xy| = |x|\,|y|$.

6. Solve and graph:

   a) $|x| \le 4$

   b) $|x| > 1$

   c) $|x| = 6$

   d) $|x| \le 5/3$

   e) $|2x| \le 8$

   f) $|3x| \le 19$

7. Solve and graph:

   a) $|x - 2| \le 7$

   b) $|x + 3| > 4$

   c) $|2x + 4| \le 8$

   d) $|3x - 9| = 14$

   e) $|(2/3)x + 7| > 4$

   f) $|(5/8)x - 1/2| < 3/4$

8. Show that if $x > 0$, then $x^{-1} > 0$. (*Hint:* Assume otherwise and deduce that $-1 > 0$, a contradiction.)

9. Show that:

   a) $\forall x \in Q \quad \forall y \in Q^+ \quad |x| < y \Leftrightarrow -y < x < y$

   b) $\forall x \in Q \quad \forall y \in Q^+ \quad |x| > y \Leftrightarrow x > y$ or $x < -y$

   (This result can, in a sense, be viewed as the fundamental theorem of absolute value.)

10. Solve and graph:

    a) $|(x - 1/2)(x + 2/3)| \le 0$

    b) $-3 < |x^2 + 7x + 12|$

11. Show that if $x < y$, then $x < \dfrac{x + y}{2} < y$. (This shows that there is a rational number between any two rational numbers.)

12. Prove the triangle inequality, considering all possible cases for x and y being negative and non-negative.

13. Define a sequence of rational numbers S_n as follows: $S_n = \dfrac{1 + n}{n^2}$.

    a) Compute the first five values of S_n (*i.e.*, the images of $1, 2, \cdots, 5$).

    b) Show that $\forall n \quad S_{n+1} < S_n$.

14. Define a sequence a_n by $a_n = \dfrac{1}{2^n}$. Define S_n by $S_n = \sum_{i=1}^{n} a_i$.

    a) Compute the first five values of S_n.

    b) Show that $\forall n \quad S_{n+1} > S_n$.

    c) Show that $\forall n \quad S_n < 1$.

15. Show that if $a \in Q$, then $a^2 \geq 0$.

16. Prove Theorem 3.9-10.

3.10 Exponents and Rational Numbers

Integral Exponents

Recall that in the set of natural numbers, we defined a special kind of multiplication called "exponentiation." We can choose any $n \in N_0$ and any $m \in N$ and have determined (in N) a number called m^n (m to the nth power). Using the same type of definition, we can extend this concept to allow the base number m to come from an extended number system. Thus, for $x \in Q$ and for any $n \in N$, x^n is defined recursively as before. We noted in N_0 the following three rather useful properties:

a) $(x^m)^n = x^{mn}$
b) $x^{m+n} = x^m \cdot x^n$
c) $(xy)^m = x^m y^m$

In keeping with the spirit of our development so far, we would like to know if it is possible to extend the domain from N_0 in such a way that we can choose exponents in Z. In making such an extension, we would like to retain the two properties $(x^m)^n = x^{mn}$ and $x^{m+n} = x^m \cdot x^n$. Thus we make the following definition. (Notice that we could not make this extension with bases restricted to Z since we make use of multiplicative inverses.)

3.10-1 Definition: $\forall x \in Q$ $(x \neq 0)$ and $\forall m \in N^-$ $x^m = 1/x^{-m}$. (Recall that $-m \in N$ and so x^{-m} is defined, and that $x^0 = 1$.) Define $x^m = 0$ for $x = 0$ and $m \in N \cup N^-$.

We now have x^m defined for any $x \in Q$ and $m \in Z$.‡‡ Let us now show that the properties we had hoped to retain are still available.

3.10-2 Theorem: $\forall x \in Q \ \forall m, n \in Z$

1) $(x^m)^n = x^{mn}$
2) $x^{m+n} = x^m x^n$
3) $(xy)^m = x^m y^m$

We prove only parts of 1) and 2), and leave 3) entirely for the reader's enjoyment.

---

‡‡ With the exception of 0^0. This restriction will hereafter be understood, and not explicitly stated.

Proof: Case 1. $m, n \in N$(same as proof in N).

Case 2. $m, n \in N^-$

$$(x^m)^n = \frac{1}{(x^m)^{-n}} = \frac{1}{(1/x^{-m})^{-n}}$$

$$= \frac{\frac{1}{1-n}}{(x^{-m})^{-n}} = \frac{1}{\frac{1}{x^{mn}}} = x^{mn}$$

and

$$x^{m+n} = \frac{1}{x^{-(m+n)}} = \frac{1}{x^{-m-n}} = \frac{1}{x^{-m}x^{-n}}$$

$$= \frac{1}{x^{-m}} \cdot \frac{1}{x^{-n}} = x^m x^n.$$

The cases in which $(m \in N^-$ and $n \in N)$ and $(n \in N^-$ and $m \in N)$ are proved similarly, and are left for the reader. The cases in which m or n are zero are trivial since $x^0 = 1$. ∎

Example: $5^{-2} = 1/5^2 = 1/25$
$\qquad 5^{-2+3} = 5^1 = 5$ $\quad$ and $\quad$ $5^{-2+3} = 5^{-2}5^3 = 5^3/5^2 = 5.$

Example: $(3/4)^{6+(-2)} = (3/4)^4$
$\qquad (3/4)^{6+(-2)} = (3/4)^6(3/4)^{-2} = (3/4)^6/(3/4)^2 = (3/4)^4.$

Example: $((1/2)^3)^2 = ((1/2)\cdot(1/2)\cdot(1/2))^2$
$\qquad\qquad = (1/2)\cdot(1/2)\cdot(1/2)\cdot(1/2)\cdot(1/2)\cdot(1/2) = (1/2)^6.$

Let us now establish the following inequation properties for exponents.

3.10-3 Theorem: $\forall n \in N$ if $x > 1$, $x^n > 1$.

Proof: By induction.

1) $x^1 > 1$ by hypothesis.

2) Assume $x^k > 1$. Using this fact, and the hypothesis that $x > 1$ along with Theorem 3.9-6, we have

$$x^k \cdot x > 1 \cdot 1.$$

Therefore

$$x^{k+1} > 1.$$

Hence by induction, $x^n > 1$ for all $n \in N$. ∎

Corollary: If $x > 1$ and $m < n$ $\quad m, n \in Z$, then $x^m < x^n$.

Proof: $n - m \in N$. Therefore

$$x^{n-m} > 1$$

that is $x^n/x^m > 1$, and since $x^m > 0$ it follows that

$$\frac{x^n}{x^m}(x^m) > x^m.$$

Thus $x^n > x^m$. ∎

3.10-4 Theorem: If $0 < x < 1$ and $m < n$, then $x^m > x^n$. The proof is left as an exercise.

We have established that if $x > 1$, then x^n "grows larger" as n "grows larger", and if $0 < x < 1$ then x^n "grows smaller" as n "grows larger". This is for all integers n, both positive and negative.

Example: $5^1 = 5$, $5^2 = 25$, $5^3 = 125$, etc.

$$(1/5)^1 = 1/5, \qquad (1/5)^2 = 1/25, \qquad (1/5)^3 = 1/125, \qquad \text{etc.}$$

Example: $4^{-2} = 1/16$, $4^{-1} = 1/4$, $4^0 = 1$, $4^1 = 4$, $4^2 = 8$, etc., and $(1/4)^{-2} = 16$, $(1/4)^{-1} = 4$, $(1/4)^0 = 1$, $(1/4)^1 = 1/4$, $(1/4)^2 = 1/16$, etc.

Roots

Let us now entertain the idea of extending the exponents we use to include all rational numbers. As before, we wish to retain the properties $(x^a)^b = x^{ab}$ and $x^{a+b} = x^a x^b$. Let us see, then, what kind of numbers we would obtain in making such an extension. If $x \in Q$, then $x^{1/4}$ must be a number such that $(x^{1/4})^4 = x^{4/4} = x$. So we ask ourselves the question, "Given $x \in Q$, does there exist a unique number y such that $y^4 = x$?" We know that in some cases such a number exists, although it is not unique.

Example: $2^4 = 16$; however $(-2)^4$ is also 16.

In order to discuss the problem more intelligently, let us establish some language tools.

3.10-5 Definition: If $x \in Q$ and $n \in N$ and if $y^n = x$, then we say that y is an *nth root* of x.

Example: $3^2 = 9$. Therefore 3 is a 2nd root of 9 (usually called a "square root").

Example: $(-5)^3 = -125$. Therefore -5 is a 3rd root of -125 (usually called a "cube root").

Let us list some very simple facts concerning roots.

3.10-6 Theorem: Let $n \in N$, n even (so that $n = 2m$ for some m), and let $x \in Q$, $x \neq 0$. If x has an nth root, then x has exactly two nth roots, one positive and the other negative.

Proof: $y^n = x$ (i.e., $y^{2m} = x$). Therefore

$$(-y)^{2m} = ((-y)^2)^m = (y^2)^m = y^{2m}.$$

Now if $z^n = x$ and $y^n = x$, then $z^n - y^n = 0$. Therefore $z^n = y^n$, from which $|z|^n = |y|^n$. Applying the result obtained in Exercise 8(d), 3.5, we have

$$(|z| - |y|) \sum_{i=0}^{n-1} |z|^{n-1-i} |y|^i = |z|^n - |y|^n = 0.$$

Since neither y nor z can be zero and since the sum and product of positive numbers are positive, it follows that

$$|z| - |y| = 0$$

that is, $|z| = |y|$ so that $z = y$ or $z = -y$. ▯

3.10-7 Theorem: Suppose x is a rational number and n is an odd positive integer. If x has an nth root, it is unique.

The proof is left as an exercise.

We have some information regarding roots, *provided they exist*. We note that, in general, roots for rational numbers do not exist (in Q). In particular, -1 has no square root since the square of any rational number is nonnegative. We know that some positive numbers have nth roots, however. We shall show in the next section that not all positive rational numbers have arbitrary nth roots. We shall "cure" this problem by making another extension, so let us establish some notation conventions which we shall continue to use after we make the extension.

3.10-8 Definition: If $x > 0$ and $y^n = x(i.e.,$ y is an nth root of x), then $x^{1/n}$ denotes the unique positive number y such that $y^n = x$. ($x^{1/n}$ is also denoted by $\sqrt[n]{x}$.)

Note that $y^n = x \Rightarrow \sqrt[n]{x} = |y|$. In particular, note that $\sqrt{x}$ is positive if x has a square root, even though $-\sqrt{x}$ is also a square root. Hence $\sqrt{x^2}$ does not necessarily equal x.

Example: $\sqrt{(-2)^2} = \sqrt{4} = 2$.

We see, then, that if we were working in a field in which every positive number had a unique nth root, then it would be possible to define exponents for all rational numbers. In the next section we develop such a field.

Let us further anticipate this extension by developing a formula with which we can solve many equations of the form $ax^2 + bx + c = 0$ where $a \neq 0$. The important thing to note in the development of this formula (the quadratic formula) is that, until the very last stage, we use nothing more sophisticated than field theorems. *This points out that in any field, we could develop the same result up to the last step.* The last step, however, depends on the existence of square roots.

"Completing the Square" and the "Quadratic Formula"

The process known as "completing the square" is useful in many mathematical disciplines where one needs to recognize certain formula forms (for example, in analytic geometry, differential equations, and probability theory). We use it here to develop the "quadratic formula."

Consider an equation $ax^2 + bx + c = 0$ where a, b, c are elements of some field containing Z (for example, the rational numbers). Assume that $a \neq 0$, so that we have the equivalent equation

$$x^2 + \frac{b}{a}x + \frac{c}{a} = 0.$$

We would like to have an equivalent equation in the form

$$(x + p)^2 = q$$

or equivalently

$$x^2 + 2px + p^2 = q$$

from which it would follow that $2p = b/a$ gives the desired p. To find q, we use an equation equivalent to the original equation. Thus, comparing the two equations

$$x^2 + \frac{b}{a}x = -\frac{c}{a}$$

and

$$x^2 + 2px = q - p^2 = q - \frac{b^2}{4a^2}$$

we immediately see that

$$q = \frac{b^2}{4a^2} - \frac{c}{a} = \frac{b^2 - 4ac}{4a^2}.$$

We now have an equation in the desired form,

$$\left(x + \frac{b}{2a}\right)^2 = \frac{b^2 - 4ac}{4a^2}.$$

Our ability to solve this equation depends on finding square roots for $\dfrac{b^2 - 4ac}{4a^2}$ or, in particular, for $b^2 - 4ac$ since $\dfrac{1}{4a^2}$ has a square root. (See Exercise 13.)

We thus have the following theorem.

3.10-9 *Theorem:* (*The quadratic formula*) Let F be any field containing Z. If a, b, $c \in F$, $a \neq 0$, then the equation $ax^2 + bx + c = 0$ has a solution in F provided $b^2 - 4ac$ has a square root in F. Further $\forall S$ such that $S^2 = b^2 - 4ac$, $x = \dfrac{-b + S}{2a}$ is a solution. (The number $b^2 - 4ac$ is called the *discriminant* of the equation.) □

Question: If $b^2 - 4ac$ is a positive rational number with a square root, then how many numbers S have the property $S^2 = b^2 - 4ac$? (See Theorem 3.10-6.)

Exercises 3.10

1. Compute:
    a) $(5^2)^3$
    b) $(-1)^{5+1}$
    c) $(-1/4)^3(-1/4)^2$
    d) $4^2 \cdot 5$

2. Simplify where $x, y, z \in Q$:

    a) $(xy)^{-2}/x^4y^2$

    b) $\dfrac{xy^{-3} + (xy)^{-2}}{x^{-1}(yz)^2}$

    c) $\dfrac{x^{-2}(yz)^2 + (xy)^{-2}z^{-5}}{x(yz)^{-2}}$

    d) $\dfrac{xy + xz^{-1}}{x^{-2}y}$

    e) $\dfrac{x(yz)^{-3}}{xy^{-3} + yz^{-2}}$

3. Complete the proof of Theorem 3.10-2.

4. Prove:

$$\forall n \in N \quad \forall y_i \in Q \quad \left| \prod_{i=1}^{n} y_i \right| = \prod_{i=1}^{n} |y_i|$$

5. Complete the square (*i.e.*, express each of the following in the form $(x + p)^2 + r$).
    a) $x^2 + 3x + 2$
    b) $x^2 - 2x + 4$
    c) $x^2 - x - 1$
    d) $x^2 + 4x + 3$

6. Express each of the following in the form $a(x + p)^2 + r$. (*Hint:* Factor out the leading coefficient and proceed as in Exercise 5.)
    a) $6x^2 + 3x + 1$
    b) $2x^2 - x + 4$
    c) $5x^2 - 3x - 2$
    d) $5x^2 + 5x - 2$

7. Express each of the following in the form $(ax + p)^2 + r$.
    a) $9x^2 + 7x - 1$
    b) $16x^2 - 2x + 3$
    c) $4x^2 - x + 1$
    d) $25x^2 - 3x - 5$

8. Can you tell which of the following equations will have solutions in Q? (*Hint:* Look at the discriminant.)
    a) $3x^2 - 2x + 7 = 0$
    b) $x^2 + 1/4 - 3/8 = 0$
    c) $4x^2 + 7x - 4 = 0$
    d) $x^2 + 1 = 0$

9. Solve the following equations if they have solutions in Q.
    a) $x^2 + (5/4)x - 3/2 = 0$
    b) $x^2 + 5x + 4 = 0$
    c) $8x^2 + (13/3)x - 7/3 = 0$
    d) $3x^2 + (1/2)x - 1 = 0$

10. Show that if $x > 0$ and $y^n = z^n = x$ where $y, z > 0$, then $y = z$. (*Hint:* Apply Theorem 3.10-6.)

11. Show that if $S^2 = b^2 - 4ac$, then

$$ax^2 + bx + c = a\left(x - \frac{-b + S}{2a} \right)\left(x - \frac{-b - S}{2a} \right).$$

12. Solve the following equations (if they don't have solutions in Q, the solution set is $\emptyset$):

    a) $|x^2 - 2x - 15| = 9$ *c*) $|2x^2 + 3x - 2| = 6$

    b) $|x^2 - 3| = 6$

13. Let $x, y \in Q$ such that $\sqrt{x}, \sqrt{y} \in Q$. Investigate:

    a) $\sqrt{\dfrac{x}{y}} = \dfrac{\sqrt{x}}{\sqrt{y}}$

    b) $\sqrt{xy} = \sqrt{x} \cdot \sqrt{y}$

    c) $\sqrt{x + y} = \sqrt{x} + \sqrt{y}$

14. Compute:

    a) $\sqrt{4}$ *b*) $\sqrt{36/9}$ *c*) $\sqrt{9 + 16}$

15. Prove Theorem 3.10-4.

16. Prove Theorem 3.10-7.

3.11 The Real Numbers

In viewing the rational numbers geometrically or graphically, we think of them as lying along a line which extends indefinitely in both directions. If $x < y$, then we usually think of x being to the left of y on the line.§§

We find this number system to be very useful for recording and computing physical lengths. The natural numbers N are not entirely satisfactory for length measurements, since there simply are not "enough" of them. As they are placed in position along the line, there is always some space in which there are no numbers. This appears not to be a weakness of the rational numbers since we know that $\forall a, b \in Q$ if $a < b$, then $\exists x \in Q$ $a < x < b$ (see Exercise 11, 3.9). That is, between any two rational numbers there is another rational number (in fact, infinitely many of them).

Example: $1/2 < 9/16$ and

$$1/2 < (1/2 + 9/16)(1/2) < 9/16.$$

At first, it seems that there should be a rational number at each point on the line (as a line is interpreted in geometry). For centuries it was thought that this was the case. It was discovered by the Pythagoreans that there are not enough rational numbers to completely cover the line.

§§ It is interesting to note that a race which is predominantly right handed usually places larger numbers to the right, instead of to the left. There is no mathematical reason for interpreting the order relation in this fashion.

A Geometric Proof of the Pythagorean Theorem

The famous Pythagorean theorem states that if x, y, z are numbers which represent the lengths of the two legs and the hypotenuse, respectively, of a right triangle, then $x^2 + y^2 = z^2$.

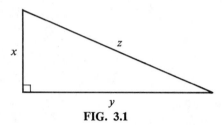

FIG. 3.1

One of the earliest proofs of this theorem is as follows:

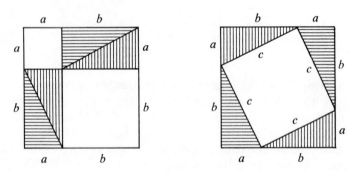

FIG. 3.2

Consider a square whose side has length $a + b$ cut two different ways, as shown above. The length of the hypotenuse of a right triangle with legs a and b is given by c. The area of the square is independent of the way in which it is

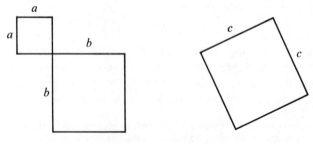

FIG. 3.3 $a^2 + b^2 = c^2$

cut. Let us then remove equal areas in each case and compare areas of what remains.

Clearly then, $a^2 + b^2 = c^2$.

As a result, the right triangle with legs of length 1 has a hypotenuse whose length, when squared, should be 2.

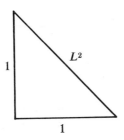

FIG. 3.4 $1^2 + 1^2 = L^2 = 2$.

If there are rational numbers at each point on the line, then there should be some rational number r whose square is 2.

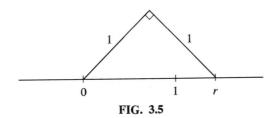

FIG. 3.5

We shall show that there is no such rational number.

There Is No Rational Square Root for 2

3.11-1 Theorem: $\forall x \in Q \; x^2 \neq 2$.

Proof: Assume $x \in Q$, $x^2 = 2$. Therefore $x = a/b$ where $a, b \in Z$, and $\left(\dfrac{a}{b}\right)^2 = 2$, where $gcd(a, b) = 1$ (3.8-7). But then

$$a^2 = 2b^2$$

so 2 divides a^2, and hence divides a (see Exercise 15, 3.7). Thus

$$a = 2c$$

so that

$$a^2 = (2c)^2 = 4c^2 = 2b^2$$

and hence $2c^2 = b^2$. It follows that 2 divides b^2, and hence divides b. But we

217

assumed that $gcd(a, b) = 1$, so we have arrived at a contradiction, namely that 2 divides a and 2 divides b. □

Remark: The format of this proof is as follows: Either $\sqrt{2} \in Q$ or $\sqrt{2} \notin Q$. But if $\sqrt{2} \in Q$, then a contradiction results. Since mathematics is consistent (?) (no contradictions), it must not be the case that $\sqrt{2} \in Q$.

The Completion

Once again we have become unhappy with the number system we have developed. We have dealt with this kind of situation before by attaching extra things to our set and then extending our operations and relations in such a way that we obtained the kind of number system we had in mind.

We now wish to attach extra numbers (wherever needed) in order to fill the "holes" that exist in the number line. In previous extensions of our number system, we made "algebraic extensions." That is, we extended our system in order to accommodate and complete some algebraic operation. However, at this point we are quite satisfied with the algebraic structure we have. One could not hope for a much nicer algebra than a field. In this case, we make what is called a "topological" extension. We are simply going to "fill in all the holes", and then extend our operations to the new elements in R in such a way that we retain all the nice algebraic properties that we had in Q.

Before we begin, let us recall some definitions and theorems from Section 2.4 which concern subsets of an ordered set R.

Definition: If $S \subset R$ and $\exists b \in R \; \forall x \in S$, $x \le b$, then we say that S is *bounded above* by b. b is called an *upper bound* for S.

Definition: Let S be bounded above by p. If $(\forall b \quad b$ an upper bound for $S \Rightarrow p \le b)$, then p is called a *least upper bound* for S.

Theorem: If p is a least upper bound for S and q is a least upper bound for S, then $p = q$.

Definition: If p is the least upper bound for S, then we denote p by "*l.u.b. S*" or by "*supremum S*" or "*sup S*".

A similar collection of statements holds for *lower bounds*. A *greatest lower bound* for a set S (if it exists) is called "*g.l.b. S*" or "*infimum S*" or "*inf S*".

3.11-2 Axioms for the Set R

Let R be an ordered set with a strict ordering $<$ such that:

1) $Q \subset R$, and $<$, when restricted to Q, is the familiar ordering of Q.
2) If $S \subset Q$, $S \ne \varnothing$, and S is bounded above by $q \in Q$, then sup S exists in R.

3) If $x \in R$, then $S_x = \{r \in Q : r < x\}$ is non-empty and is bounded above by some $q \in Q$. Further, sup $S_x = x$.

Note: Throughout this and the next two sections, we generally use variables r, q, p to denote rational numbers and x, y, z for arbitrary elements of the extended system R. (The elements of R will be called *real numbers.*)

We shall hypothesize the existence of such an ordered set R. There are various constructions which guarantee its existence.‖ ‖ What we have done here is attach exactly enough things to Q to allow every non-empty subset of Q which is bounded above to have a least upper bound. Axiom 2) gives the existence of the desired least upper bounds, while axiom 3) eliminates everything not needed for an upper bound.

Existence and Location of Irrational Numbers

In the next section, we are going to extend our operations of addition and multiplication to include the extra elements which are in R but not in Q. At this point the bright student, being properly belligerent, should want to know for certain that there are indeed extra things around before going through any fancy extensions of the operations.

3.11-3 Theorem: There exist subsets of Q which are non-empty and bounded above, but for which there is no least upper bound in Q.

We postpone the proof of this theorem temporarily. We would, however, like to outline the method of proof in order to familiarize ourselves with some of the processes with which we must deal. Let $S = \{r \in Q : r^2 \leq 2\}$. We know that S is bounded above by a rational number. We also know that by increasing r we increase r^2. It seems reasonable that if S has a least upper bound in Q, then the square of that number would be equal to 2. However, we know that 2 has no rational square root, and therefore sup S would necessarily be in $R - Q$.

Being satisfied now that there are things in R which are not in Q, we would like to give them a name. We call the elements in $R - Q$ the *irrational numbers.*

At this point, we have the ordered set R which contains Q (still ordered as before), but we have not given any rules for adding or multiplying with the newly attached irrational points. We are not even sure how many irrational numbers we have attached, only that they must be "sprinkled" somewhere in among the rational numbers.

The results which follow enlighten us somewhat as to the location of the irrational points on the line.

3.11-4 Theorem: If $x \in R$, then $\exists p \in Q \quad x < p$.

‖ ‖ See *Set Theory, the Structure of Arithmetic*, by N. Hamilton and J. Landin (Boston: Allyn and Bacon, Inc., 1961).

Proof: $x = \sup S_x$ where $S_x = \{r \in Q : r < x\}$, and S_x is bounded above by $q \in Q$ (axiom 3). Therefore $x \leq q$. But $q < q + 1$, and hence $x < q + 1$. $\square$

From this theorem, we know that there is no irrational number which is larger than all rational numbers.

3.11-5 Theorem: Between any two real numbers there is a rational number. That is, if $x < y$, then $\exists q \in Q \; x < q < y$.

Proof: Let $S_x = \{r \in Q : r < x\}$ and $S_y = \{r \in Q : r < y\}$. We know $x = \sup S_x, y = \sup S_y$. (Why?) Now for some $q \in S_y$, $x < q$, for if not, then x is an upper bound for S_y which implies that $\sup S_y \leq x$, a contradiction of $x < y$. Hence $x < q < y$ since $q \in S_y$. $\square$

Corollary: If $x < y, x, y \in R$, and $n \in N$, then there exists $q_1, q_2, \cdots, q_n$ such that

$$x < q_1 < q_2 < \cdots < q_n < y.$$

It is also true that between any two real numbers there is an irrational number. We will show this after we have extended our operations to include the new points (see Exercise 4, 3.12).

The next two theorems characterize 2) and 3) in Axioms 3.11-2 in terms of lower bounds and greatest lower bounds.

3.11-6 Theorem: If $S \subset Q$, $S \neq \varnothing$, and S is bounded below by $q \in Q$, then inf S exists.

Proof: Let $S' = \{t \in Q : t \leq r \; \forall r \in S\}$. $S' \neq \varnothing$ because $q \in S'$. S' is bounded above since $S \neq \varnothing$. Hence we let $\alpha = \sup S'$, and show also that $\alpha = \inf S$. Now any member of S is an upper bound for S'. Therefore $\alpha \leq r$ for all r in S since α is the least upper bound of S'. Hence α is a lower bound for S. Now if $\alpha < \beta$ and β is also a lower bound for S, then a rational number p, where $\alpha < p < \beta$, would also be a lower bound for S, and hence an element of S'. But if $p \in S'$, then $p \leq \alpha$, a contradiction. Hence α is the greatest lower bound of S. $\square$

3.11-7 Theorem: If $x \in R$ and $B_x = \{r \in Q : x < r\}$, then $B_x \neq \varnothing$ and B_x is bounded below by a rational number. Further inf $B_x = x$.

Proof: $S_x = \{r \in Q : r < x\}$ is bounded above by $q \in Q$. Therefore $q + 1 \in B_x$, so that $B_x \neq \varnothing$. Since $S_x \neq \varnothing$, B_x is bounded below by a rational number. Clearly, x is a lower bound for B_x. If b is a lower bound for B_x, then $b \leq x$ (for if $x < b$, then $\exists p \in Q \; x < p < b$, and b would not be a lower bound). Hence x is no smaller than any arbitrary lower bound (*i.e.*, x is the greatest lower bound for B_x). $\square$

Extending Negation

Before we attempt to extend our operations to R, let us extend the negation function η in such a way that it behaves as before, namely, it reflects a number across the zero point on the number line.

Example: Let $S = \{1, 1.9, 1.99, 1.999, \cdots\}$.

We are familiar with the fact that sup $S = 2$. Consider what happens with the set

$$S' = \{-1, -1.9, -1.99, -1.999, \cdots\}.$$

We see that S' "clusters" toward -2 from above.

Example: Recall the method for computing square roots. Using this method, one finds a collection of rational numbers which he believes gets "closer and closer" to the desired root. For example, in the computation for $\sqrt{2}$, one looks at the set $S = \{1, 1.4, 1.41, 1.414, \cdots\}$. No member of S, when squared, gives 2. But we know that if the computation is carried further and further, the result, when squared, will be very close to 2. That is, we want $\sqrt{2} = \sup S$. Where, then, do we expect $-\sqrt{2}$ to be on the line? We look at the set

$$S' = \{-1, -1.4, -1.41, -1.414, \cdots\} \text{ for the answer.}$$

Again we see that S' "clusters" toward $-\sqrt{2}$ from the right.

Thus, we see that we want the following definition for the negating function η. (The uniqueness of greatest lower bounds guarantees the single-valuedness of η.)

3.11-8 Definition: If $x \in R$, then

$$\eta(x) = \inf \{-r \colon r \leq x \quad \text{and} \quad r \in Q\}$$

or equivalently

$$\eta(x) = \inf \{r \colon -r \leq x \quad \text{and} \quad r \in Q\}.$$

(Keep in mind here that negation is defined in Q and is denoted by "$-$.")

As always when making an extension of this sort, we would not be very pleased if the restriction to the old set did not yield the same results which we had before. We want to be sure we made an extension, and did not define an entirely new function.

3.11-9 Theorem: If $q \in Q$, then $\eta(q) = -q$.

Proof: By definition,

$$\eta(q) = \inf \{-r \colon r \leq q, r \in Q\}.$$

Now $-q \in \{-r \colon r \leq q\}$. Therefore $-q \geq \eta(q)$. On the other hand, if $r \leq q$, then $-r \geq -q$. Hence $-q$ is a lower bound for the set. Therefore $-q \leq \eta(q)$, since $\eta(q)$ is the greatest lower bound. It follows from the order properties that

$$-q = \eta(q). \quad \square$$

Corollary: $\eta(0) = 0$.

We can now denote this function on R by the standard minus sign "$-$." Being satisfied that our negation is truly an extension, we would like to show that most of the familiar properties which hold on Q also hold on R.

3.11-10 Lemma: If $r \in Q$, $x \in R$, and if $r < x$, then $-x < -r$. Also, if $x < r$, then $-r < -x$.

Proof: $-x = \inf T_x$ where $T_x = \{-q: q \in Q, q \le x\}$. Now $r < x \Rightarrow r < p < x$ for some $p \in Q \Rightarrow -p < -r$. Also,

$$p < x \Rightarrow -p \in T_x \Rightarrow -x \le -p.$$

(Why?) But $-p < -r$. Therefore $-x < -r$. We leave the second case ($x < r \Rightarrow -r < -x$) as an exercise. $\square$

We can immediately replace $<$ in this result by $\le$. (Why?)

3.11-11 Theorem: $-(-x) = x$ for all $x \in R$.

Proof: We use the assumption that $<$ is a strict ordering of R.

Case 1. Suppose $-(-x) < x$. For some $q \in Q$, $-(-x) < q < x$, and therefore $-q \in \{-r: r \le x\}$. But

$$-x = \inf\{-r: r \le x\}.$$

Hence $-x \le -q$; and by the preceding lemma, $q \le -(-x)$. By transitivity, we have $-(-x) < -(-x)$, a contradiction.

Case 2. $x < -(-x)$. Again for some $q \in Q$ $x < q < -(-x)$, and by the lemma $-q < -x$. Therefore $q \in \{-r: r \le -x\}$. But $-(-x) = \inf\{-r: r \le -x\}$. Hence $-(-x) \le q$; and again by transitivity, $-(-x) < -(-x)$.

We conclude then that $-(-x) = x$. $\square$

3.11-12 Theorem: If $x < y$, then $-y < -x$.

Proof: If $x < y$, then $x < q < y$ for $q \in Q$. That is, $x < q$ and $q < y$; and by Lemma 3.11-10, $-q < -x$ and $-y < -q$. By transitivity, $-y < -x$. $\square$

Corollary: $\forall x \in R$, $x < 0$ iff $0 < -x$.

Corollary: Negation is a *one-one* and *onto* function from R into R.

Exercises   3.11

1. Graph on a number line the set $S = \{.5, .55, .555, .5555, \cdots\}$. Locate sup S and inf S.

2. Graph on a number line the sets
   a) $S = \{1.12, 1.1212, 1.121212, \cdots\}$.
   b) $S' = \{-1.12, -1.1212, -1.121212, \cdots\}$.
Locate sup S, inf S, sup S', inf S'.

3. *a)* Define $\forall n \in N$ $a_n = \sum_{i=1}^{n} i/n^2$.

Compute a_1, a_2, a_3, a_4, a_5. Graph the set $S = \{a_n : n \in N\}$. Locate on the number line sup S.

   b) Do the same for $b_n = \sum_{i=1}^{n} 1/n$.

4. Let $r_1 = .19$, $r_2 = .1919$, $r_3 = .191919$, $\cdots$ and $q_1 = .04$, $q_2 = .0404$, $q_3 = .040404$, $\cdots$.

   a) Graph sup $\{r_i\}$, sup $\{q_i\}$, sup $\{r_i + q_i\}$.

   b) Graph inf $\{-r_i\}$, inf $\{-q_i\}$, inf $\{-r_i + q_i\}$.

5. $\sqrt{2} = \sup \{1, 1.4, 1.41, 1.414, \cdots\}$ and $\pi = \sup \{3, 3.1, 3.14, 3.141, 3.1415, \cdots\}$.

   a) Graph $\sqrt{2}$, π.

   b) Where do you think $\sqrt{2} + \pi$ should be on the number line? Why?

6. *a)* Show that if $S_1 \subset S_2$ are subsets of Q, $S_1 \neq \varnothing$, S_2 is bounded above, then sup S_1 and sup S_2 exist, and sup $S_1 \leq$ sup S_2.

   b) Give an example of $S_1 \subset S_2$ where sup $S_1 <$ sup S_2. Give an example of $S_1 \subset S_2$ where sup $S_1 =$ sup S_2, but $S_1 \neq S_2$.

7. Let $S = \{1, 1/2, 1/3, 1/4, 1/5, \cdots\}$:

   a) sup $S =$ _____   *c)* sup $\{-x : x \in S\} =$ _____

   b) inf $S =$ _____   *d)* inf $\{-x : x \in S\} =$ _____

Graph S on the number line. Also graph the points asked for in *(a)*, *(b)*, *(c)*, *(d)*.

8. What is the "first" rational number to the right of zero on the real line? Is there such a thing? Why or why not? What is the "first" irrational number to the right of zero on the real line?

9. Show that $\{r : -r \leq x\} = \{-r : r \leq x\}$. (*Hint:* For rational numbers r, $-(-r), = r$.)

10. Complete the first five terms of the sequence:

   a) $S_n = (1 + 1/n)^n$ *c)* Show that $\forall n$ $(1 + 1/n)^n < 3$.

   b) $S_n = \sum_{i=1}^{n} \frac{i}{i!}$

11. Do you suppose $\{(1 + 1/n)^n : n \in N\}$ has a least upper bound?

12. If $H \subset Z$ bounded above and $H \neq \varnothing$, then show that sup $H \in H$.

13. Let $S \subset Q$, $S \neq \varnothing$, and be bounded below. Let $S' = \{t \in Q : t < r, r \in S\}$. Show that:

   a) $S' \neq \varnothing$.

   b) S' is bounded above.

   c) Every member of S is an upper bound for S'.

   d) Every member of S' is a lower bound for S.

   e) Inf $S =$ sup S'.

14. Let $S \subset Q$, $S \neq \varnothing$. Let $S' = \{r + q : r \in S\}$ where q is a positive rational number. Show that if $S' \subset S$, then S is unbounded. (*Hint:* Show that for any positive integer nq, $r + n \in S$. Then show that for any $b \in Q$ $\exists n$ such that $r + nq > b$.)

223

3.12   The Real Numbers: an Ordered Field

The Operations

We now have R as an ordered collection which contains Q as a subset. We interpret the elements of R as being points on a line and we have a function "η" or "$-$," which reflects points in R across the zero in Q. We would like to define the operations "$+$" and "$\times$" in a way which conforms to our intuitive idea about adding and multiplying lengths on the line, and also in such a way that when restricted to Q, we have the same operations as already defined on Q. Also, we would like to retain all the nice algebraic properties we have. In particular, we would be very happy if we again end up with a field. Before we state our definitions, let us examine some special examples.

Example: sup $\{.3, .33, .333, .3333, \cdots\} = 1/3$.

   sup $\{.6, .66, .666, .6666, \cdots\} = 2/3$.

$.3 + .6 = .9, .3 + .66 = .96, .33 + .6 = .93, .33 + .66 = .99, .33 + .666 = .996$, etc. Also, sup $\{.9, .93, .96, .99, .996, .9966, .999, \cdots\} = 1$. (Note also that $1/3 + 2/3 = 1$.)

We see that if we look at a set whose least upper bound is $1/3$ and a set whose least upper bound is $2/3$, and then add the elements in all possible ways (one number from each set), we get a set whose least upper bound is the sum of $1/3$ and $2/3$. These computations are in Q, but we expect the same thing to happen anywhere in R.

Example: sup $\{1, 1.4, 1.41, 1.414, \cdots\} = \sqrt{2}$.

   sup $\{3, 3.1, 3.14, 3.141, 3.1415, \cdots\} = \pi$.

Where should we find $\sqrt{2}\pi$ on the number line? If we consider products in the way we did sums above, then the "product set" S is

$$S = \{1 \times 3, 1 \times 3.1, 1.4 \times 3, 1.4 \times 3.1, 1.41 \times 3.14, \cdots\}$$
$$= \{3, 3.1, 3.34, 4.2, 4.4274, \cdots\}.$$

We have a set S of rational numbers which is bounded above, and the least upper bound is the number we wish to call $\sqrt{2}\pi$.

We are now prepared to extend our operations. Keep in mind that we "know how" to add and multiply rational numbers.

3.12-1 Definition: If $x, y \in R$, then

   $x + y = \sup \{r_1 + r_2 : r_1 \leq x \quad$ and $\quad r_2 \leq y, r_1, r_2$ in $Q\}$.

3.12-2 Definition: If $x, y \in R$, $x \geq 0$, $y \geq 0$, then

   $xy = \sup \{r_1 r_2 : 0 \leq r_1 \leq x$ and $0 \leq r_2 \leq y, r_1, r_2$ in $Q\}$.

If $x, y \in R$ are not both zero, then

Case 1. $x < 0, y \geq 0$

$$xy = -((-x)y).$$

(Note that $-x > 0$.)

Case 2. $x \geq 0, y < 0$

$$xy = -(x(-y)).$$

Case 3. $x < 0$ and $y < 0$

$$xy = (-x)(-y).$$

It can be shown that these operations, when restricted to Q, are the same addition and multiplication as already defined on Q. Further, it can be shown that R forms a field under these operations. We will not verify all the field properties, but will select some typical examples and prove them.

3.12-3 Theorem: If $x, y \in R$, then

$$x + y = y + x.$$

Proof: $x + y = \sup \{r_1 + r_2 : r_1 \leq x$ and $r_2 \leq y\}$.
  $y + x = \sup \{r_1 + r_2 : r_1 \leq y$ and $r_2 \leq x\}$.

Since addition is commutative in Q, the sets involved are the same, and therefore their least upper bounds are the same. (How do we know the sets are non-empty and bounded above?) □

3.12-4 Theorem: $\forall x \in R, x + -x = 0$.

Proof: $x + (-x) = \sup \{r_1 + r_2 : r_1 \leq x$ and $r_2 \leq -x\}$. If $r_1 \leq x$ and $r_2 \leq -x$, then

$$r_1 \leq x \qquad \text{and} \qquad x \leq -r_2.$$

Therefore $r_1 \leq -r_2$ so $r_1 + r_2 \leq 0$, and 0 is an upper bound for the set. Therefore $x + (-x) \leq 0$. However, if $x + (-x) = \alpha$ where $\alpha < 0$, then $\exists q \in Q, \alpha < q < 0$. Now $-q > 0$; therefore for some $r \leq x$ $r + (-q) > x$, otherwise $\{r + (-q) : r \leq x\} \subset \{S : S \leq x\}$ which would mean that $\{S : S \leq x\}$ is unbounded (see Exercise 14, 3.11). We thus have $r \leq x$ and $q - r < -x$. Therefore

$$r + q - r = q \in \{r_1 + r_2 : r_1 \leq x \qquad \text{and} \qquad r_2 \leq -x\}.$$

Hence $q \leq \alpha$. But this is a contradiction to $\alpha < q$. It follows then that $x + (-x) = 0$. □

3.12-5 Theorem: If $x > 0$, then $\exists y$ $xy = 1$.

Proof: Let $y = \sup \{r^{-1} : 0 < r < x\}$. □

3.12-6 Corollary: $\forall x \in R, x \neq 0, \exists y \in R$ $xy = 1$.

As previously for Q, we define subtraction by the following:

3.12-7 Definition: If $x, y \in R$, then

$$x - y = x + (-y).$$

We don't wish to burden the student here with too many of these difficult arguments. It is possible, in fact, that the proofs we have chosen to include are not intelligible to the novice. The important thing to keep in mind is that we have extended our operations in such a way that if a is "near" x and b is "near" y, then the sum $a + b$ will be "near" $x + y$ and the product ab will be "near" xy. This kind of extension is known as "extension by continuity." You will examine this in more detail in Chapter 5.

3.12-8 Theorem: If $x > 0$, then $\exists y$ such that $y^n = x$. That is, every positive real number has an nth root.

Proof: Let $A = \{r \geq 0: r^n \leq x\}$. $0 \in A$ and $\{s \geq 0: s \leq x\}$ is bounded by some $q \in Q$. Hence for each $r \in A$, r^n is bounded by q. By using the definition for multiplication, one can show that if $y = \sup A$, then $y^n = x$. We omit the details of this argument. □

We wish to mention here, again without proof, that we could prove a slightly more workable completeness property for R in which we need not restrict ourselves to sets of rational numbers bounded by rational numbers. That is, the following more general form also holds.

3.12-9 Theorem: Any non-empty subset of R which is bounded above (in R) has a least upper bound. The proof is given in Chapter 4.

We need not elaborate upon the algebraic properties of R, since we have already studied in some detail the properties of a field. Although in a sense R is a much more elaborate number system than Q, it is comforting to know that once we have established the field axioms, we immediately possess a vast storehouse of knowledge concerning the system.

R is an Ordered Field

The student should keep in mind that R forms a field, so we now have a field in which arbitrary nth roots for numbers larger than zero exist. There are still other numbers with which you may not yet be familiar.

Although we began with the assumption that R is ordered, let us note that we can separate R into three disjoint parts which have special properties and which relate the order relation to the algebra. (Recall that we had such a decomposition for Z and for Q; in fact, we used the structure to define these orderings. You will often encounter developments of R in which one begins with the algebra and then defines the order relation in terms of a special decomposition for the set, as we did with Q.)

3.12-10 Definition: Let $R^+ = \{x \in R: x > 0\}$ and $R^- = \{x \in R: x < 0\}$.

We know then that R can be decomposed into the union $R^- \cup \{0\} \cup R^+$ of the three disjoint sets (*i.e.*, $\{R^-, \{0\}, R^+\}$ forms a partition of R).

3.12-11 Theorem: 1) $\forall x \in R$, if $x \neq 0$ then $x \in R^+$ or $-x \in R^+$, but not both.

2) $\forall x, y \in R$, if $x, y \in R^+$ then $x + y \in R^+$ and $xy \in R^+$. The proof is left as an exercise.

This theorem, along with the next one, points out that we need not re-develop many of our order results since their proofs would be exactly the same as they were in the rational number system Q.

3.12-12 Lemma: If $x < y$ and $z \in R$, then $x + z < y + z$.

Proof: $\{r_1 + r_2: r_1 \leq x$ and $r_2 \leq z\} \subset \{r_1 + r_2: r_1 \leq y$ and $r_2 \leq z\}$. Therefore $x + z \leq y + z$. But since $\exists r_1 \in Q$ $x < r_1 < y$, it follows that $x + z < y + z$. $\square$

3.12-13 Theorem: If $x, y \in R$, then $x < y$ iff $y - x \in R^+$; that is,

$$x < y \quad \text{iff} \quad y - x > 0.$$

Proof: $(\Rightarrow)$. $x < y \Rightarrow x + (-x) < y + (-x) \Rightarrow y - x > 0$
$(\Leftarrow)$. $y - x > 0 \Rightarrow$
$$\sup \{r_1 + r_2: r_1 \leq y \text{ and } r_2 \leq -x\} > 0$$
$$\Rightarrow r_1 + r_2 > 0 \text{ for some } r_1 \leq y \quad \text{and} \quad r_2 \leq -x$$
$$\Rightarrow r_1 > -r_2$$

for some $r_1 \leq y$ and $x \leq -r_2$. That is, $x \leq -r_2 < r_1 \leq y \Rightarrow x < y$. $\square$

Any field which can be ordered by decomposing it according to Definition 3.12-10 is called an *ordered field*. We are thus familiar with two different ordered fields, R and Q. They are different because in R any non-empty set which is bounded above has a least upper bound, but in Q this is not true. Any ordered field which possesses least upper bounds for all non-empty subsets which are bounded above is called a *complete ordered field*. Although it is beyond the scope of this text to explore the full meaning of the following statement, it is worth mentioning. "Any complete ordered field is essentially the same as R, the real number field." We don't have the machinery to say what we mean by "essentially the same," but more or less it means that if you construct such a field, then mathematically it is the same as R, although the construction material for the elements in the set may be different. The property of possessing all least upper bounds is called the *completeness property*. The completeness property, and its exploitation in developing some powerful problem solving devices, makes up the heart of calculus.

Let us recall some order theorems which we proved in Q using only ordered field properties. Once again we find ourselves profiting from an abstraction. We have the following "free" results in R.

3.12-14 Theorem: 1) If $z > 0$ and $x < y$, then $xz < yz$.

2) If $x < y$, $u < v$, and $x > 0$, $v > 0$, then $xu < yv$.

3) If $z < 0$ and $x < y$, then $xz > yz$.

Remark: The absolute value function is extended to R by modeling the definition in Q. That is, $|x| = x$ if $x \geq 0$ and $|x| = -x$ if $x < 0$. As before, absolute value can be used to describe distance on the line.

Example: $\{x: |x| \leq 4\}$ is the set of real numbers not more than four units from zero, that is, the set $\{-4 \leq x \leq 4\}$.

Example: The solution set of the inequation $|x - 2| > 3$ is the set of real numbers more than three units from 2. This set is graphed on the number line as follows:

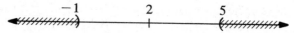

Example: The distance between -17 and -12 on the line is $|(-17) - (-12)| = 5$ units. (Note that this is the same as $|(-12) - (-17)|$.)

Exercises 3.12

1. *a)* Use the square root algorithm to find a rational number close to, but less than, $\sqrt{5}$. Do the same for $\sqrt{7}$.

   b) What is a rational number close to, but less than, $\sqrt{5} + \sqrt{7}$?

   c) What is a rational number close to, but less than, $1/3 + \sqrt{7}$?

2. *a)* Show that $x^2 = 2$, where $x = \sup \{\alpha: \alpha \geq 0 \text{ and } \alpha^2 \leq 2\}$.

   b) Conclude that irrational numbers exist.

3. *a)* Show that $2\sqrt{2}$ is irrational. (*Hint:* Assume otherwise and derive a contradiction.)

   b) Show that $q + \alpha$ and $q\alpha$ are irrational if α is irrational and q is rational $(q \neq 0)$.

4. Show that if p, $q \in R$ and $p < q$, then for some irrational number α, $p < \alpha < q$. (*Hint:* $p/\sqrt{2} < q/\sqrt{2}$.)

5. Investigate (prove or disprove):

   a) The sum of two irrational numbers is irrational.

   b) The product of two irrational numbers is irrational.

   c) The negation of an irrational number is irrational.

6. Find an irrational number larger than 16.

7. Investigate: We know now that between any two rational numbers there is an irrational. Also, between any two irrational numbers there is a rational. Can you use this to describe a *one-one* correspondence between the rational and irrational numbers? (*Hint:* Be careful!)

8. We know that $6 \times 8 = 48$. How near to 6 and 8 must x and y be (respectively) in order for you to conclude that xy is within $1/8$ of 48?

9. How near to 5 and 7 must x and y be (respectively) in order to conclude that $x + y$ is within $1/4$ of 12?

10. We know now that for every $x \in Q^+$, m, $n \in Z$ $(n \neq 0)$, $x^{m/n}$ exists in R since all nth roots exist in R. What do you suppose is meant, if anything, by $4^{\sqrt{2}}$?

11. Recall the quadratic formula (Theorem 3.10-9). In *any* field where $b^2 - 4ac$ has a square root, the equation $ax^2 + bx + c = 0$ has a solution $\dfrac{-b + S}{2a}$ for every S such that $S^2 = b^2 - 4ac$. In R we have considerably more square roots than in Q, and hence more of these equations have roots. Determine which of the following have solutions in R, and find all existing solutions:

a) $2x^2 + 3x - 4 = 0$

b) $x^2 - 3x + 1 = 0$

c) $2\pi x^2 - x - 1 = 0$

d) $x^2 - x + 3 = 0$

e) $5x^2 + 2x + 3 = 0$

f) $2x^2 - 12x + 18 = 0$

12. *a)* Graph each of the following sets:

    (*i*) $\{x:$ the distance from x to -5 is $3\}$

    (*ii*) $\{x:$ the distance from x to 4 is less than $2\}$

    (*iii*) $\{x:$ the distance from x to $1/2$ is greater than $7/2\}$

    b) Describe each of the sets above using absolute value notation.

13. Graph the solution set of each of the following:

a) $\sqrt{x - 5} = 6$

b) $\sqrt{2x + 7} = 8$

c) $\sqrt{2x^2 + 3x + 1} = 4$

d) $\sqrt{5x - 3} \geq 5$

e) $\sqrt{x^2 - 2x + 1} \leq 12$

f) $h(x) - 3 = 5$ where $h(x) = x^2 - 3$

g) $(k(x))^2 - 2x = 6$ where $k(x) = x - 1$

14. Write each of the following using rational exponents:

a) $\dfrac{3}{\sqrt{2}}$

b) $\dfrac{4\sqrt{2}}{\sqrt{6}}$

c) $\sqrt{3} + \dfrac{2}{\sqrt{6}}$

d) $\dfrac{\sqrt[3]{2}}{\sqrt[4]{6^3}}$

15. Find the distance between the pairs of points below:

a) $(2, 3)$ and $(5, 4)$

b) $(-2, 1)$ and $(-4, -2)$

16. Prove the following:

a) $\forall m \in N$, $\forall n \in R$, $n \sum_{i=1}^{m} f(i) = \sum_{i=1}^{m} n f(i)$, where $f: N \to R$.

b) $\forall m \in N$, $\sum_{i=1}^{m} (f(i) + g(i)) = \sum_{i=1}^{m} f(i) + \sum_{i=1}^{m} g(i)$, where f and g are sequences in R.

    c) Do parts (*a*) and (*b*) with "$\sum$" replaced by "$\prod$."

3.13   Exponents and Real Numbers,
A Discussion of Arithmetic

A General Discussion of Exponents

In the natural number system N, we successfully defined x^n for every $x \in N$ and every $n \in N$. In the number ring Z, we defined x^n for every $x \in Z$ and $n \in N$, but we needed to go to the extended system Q in order to successfully define arbitrary integral exponents. However, we then considered the possibility of defining x^q for all $x \in Q$ and all $q \in Q$, but we needed the existence of all natural number roots to solve the problem. We then considered the possibility of defining x^q for all $x \in Q^+$ and all $q \in Q$, but surprisingly we could not find all roots for positive rational numbers. We now have a number system in which all positive numbers possess nth roots for any $n \in N$. We can use this fact to extend the definitions of powers x^q for all $x \in R^+$ and $q \in Q$.

Properties of Rational Exponents

3.13-1 Definition: Let $x \in R^+$ and $n \in N$. $x^{1/n}$ is the unique element $y \in R^+$ such that $y^n = x$. $x^{1/n}$ is also denoted by $\sqrt[n]{x}$ and called the nth *root* of x.

3.12-2 Definition: $x^{m/n} = (x^{1/n})^m \; \forall m, n \in N$. $(x^{-1})^{m/n} = x^{-m/n}$ and $x^0 = 1$.

3.13-3 Theorem: If $x, y \in R^+$ and $q, r \in Q$, then

1) $x^{q+r} = x^q x^r$
2) $(x^q)^r = x^{qr}$
3) $(xy)^q = x^q y^q$

The proof is left as an exercise (for the talented student only).

Lemma: $\forall x \in R^+$ and $n \in N$,

$$\text{if } x < 1, \text{ then } x^{1/n} \geq x$$
$$\text{if } x = 1, \text{ then } x^{1/n} = x$$
$$\text{if } x > 1, \text{ then } x^{1/n} \leq x.$$

Proof: Case 1. $x < 1$

$$x = \sup \{r: 0 \leq r < x\} *$$

and

$$x^{1/n} = \sup \{r: r \geq 0, r^n \leq x\}.$$

---

* In this section, it is tacitly assumed that p, q, r are variables over Q unless stated to the contrary.

We know that if $0 < r < 1$, then $r^n \leq r$. Therefore

$$\{r: 0 \leq r < x\} \subset \{r: r \geq 0, r^n \leq x\}$$

(*i.e.*, $0 \leq r < x \Rightarrow 0 \leq r < 1 \Rightarrow 0 \leq r^n < r \Rightarrow 0 \leq r^n \leq x$). Therefore $x \leq x^{1/n}$. (Why?)

Case 2. $x = 1$. (trivial)
Case 3. $x > 1$.

Recall that if $r > 1$, then $r^n \geq r$. If $q \in \{r: r \geq 0, r^n \leq x\}$, then

i) if $0 \leq q < 1$, then $0 \leq q < x$ since $1 < x$;
ii) if $q \geq 1$, then $q \leq q^n \leq x$.

Therefore

$$q \in \{r: 0 \leq r < x\}.$$

Thus

$$\{r: r \geq 0, r^n \leq x\} \subset \{r: 0 \leq r < x\}.$$

Hence $x^{1/n} \leq x$. □

Lemma: $\forall x \in R^+$ and $n \in N$,

if $x < 1$, then $x^n \leq x$
if $x = 1$, then $x^n = x$
if $x > 1$, then $x^n \geq x$.

Proof: $x = \sup \{r: 0 \leq r < x\}$
and therefore

$$x^n = \sup \{r^n: 0 \leq r \leq x\}.$$

Case 1. $x < 1$.

Therefore $0 \leq p < x \Rightarrow 0 \leq p < 1 \Rightarrow 0 \leq p^n \leq p \Rightarrow 0 \leq p^n \leq x$. Therefore x is an upper bound for $\{r^n: 0 \leq r \leq x\}$, so $x^n \leq x$ (why?).

Case 2. $x = 1$. (trivial)
Case 3. $x > 1$.

We know that $1 < q < x$ for some $q \in Q$. Let $0 \leq p < x$. Now $p < 1 \Rightarrow p < 1 < q$, but $q \leq q^n$. Therefore $p \leq q^n$, where $q^n \in \{r^n: 0 \leq r \leq x\}$. Therefore $p \leq x^n$.

On the other hand, $p > 1 \Rightarrow p^n > p \Rightarrow p \leq x^n$. Thus x^n bounds the set $\{r: 0 < r < x\}$, and therefore $x \leq x^n$. (What about $p = 1$?) □

3.13-4 Theorem: $\forall x \in R^+$ and $r, q \in Q^+$ $(r < q)$,

if $x < 1$, then $x^r > x^q$
if $x = 1$, then $x^r = x^q$
if $x > 1$, then $x^r < x^q$.

Proof: $r = m/n$ and $q = k/n$, $m, n, k \in N$ and $m < k$. (Why can we use the same denominator for p and for q?)

Case 1. $x < 1 \Rightarrow x^{1/n} < 1$ (see Exercise 9, 3-13). Therefore

$$(x^{1/n})^m > (x^{1/n})^k$$

since $(x^{1/n})^{k-m} < 1$. (See Exercise 9, 3-13.) Then $x^{m/n} > x^{k/n}$ by definition.

Case 2. $x = 1$. (trivial)

Case 3. $x > 1 \Rightarrow x^{1/n} > 1$. Therefore

$$(x^{1/n})^m < (x^{1/n})^k$$

and therefore $x^{m/n} < x^{k/n}$. $\square$

Corollary: The result of Theorem 3.13-4 holds for all $r, q \in Q$. The proof is left as an exercise.

Real Number Exponents

In keeping with the spirit of contemporary mathematics, we now examine the possibility of extending our definitions to include exponentiation with all real number exponents. Let us first examine some special examples.

Example: $\sqrt{3} = \sup \{1, 1.7, 1.73, 1.732, 1.7320, \cdots\}$.

Where, then, on the number line do we expect to find $2^{\sqrt{3}}$? Each number 2^1, $2^{1.7}$, $2^{1.73}$, $2^{1.732}$, $\cdots$ is defined, and we know that as the rational exponents "grow larger," the power "grows larger." We then expect

$$2^{\sqrt{3}} = \sup \{2^1, 2^{1.7}, 2^{1.73}, 2^{1.732}, \ldots\}.$$

Similarly, where do we expect $(1/2)^{\sqrt{3}}$ to lie on the number line? Each of the numbers $(1/2)^1$, $(1/2)^{1.7}$, $(1/2)^{1.73}$, $(1/2)^{1.732}$, $\cdots$ are defined, but in this case the power grows smaller as the exponents grow larger. Hence we expect

$$(1/2)^{\sqrt{3}} = \inf \{(1/2)^1, (1/2)^{1.7}, (1/2)^{1.73}, (1/2)^{1.732}, \ldots\}.$$

Let us then make the following definition.

3.13-5 Definition: $\forall x \in R^+$ and $\alpha \in R$,

if $x < 1$, then $x^\alpha = \inf \{x^r : r \leq \alpha, r \in Q\}$

if $x \geq 1$, then $x^\alpha = \sup \{x^r : r \leq \alpha, r \in Q\}$.

It is fairly clear that the following theorem follows from the definition, and the corresponding properties for rational exponents.

3.13-6 Theorem: $\forall x \in R^+$ and $\alpha, \beta \in R(\alpha < \beta)$,

if $x < 1$, then $x^\alpha > x^\beta$

if $x = 1$, then $x^\alpha = x^\beta$

if $x > 1$, then $x^\alpha < x^\beta$.

Proof: $\{x^r : r \leq \alpha, r \in Q\} \subset \{x^r : r \leq \beta, r \in Q\}$. Recall that if $S \subset S'$, then

$$\inf S' \leq \inf S \quad \text{and} \quad \sup S \leq \sup S'$$

Equality in case $x \neq 1$ is impossible since $\exists p \in Q$ $\alpha < p < \beta$, and hence in case $x < 1$, then $x^\beta < x^p < x^\alpha$. In case $x > 1$, $x^\alpha < x^p < x^\beta$. Clearly if $x = 1$, then $x^\alpha = x^\beta$. $\square$

Let us review and emphasize the critical and important facts we have established. These will be used later in developing logarithm and exponential functions.

$\forall x > 0$ and $\forall \alpha \in R$, x^α is defined. If $0 < x < 1$, then x^α decreases as α increases. If $x > 1$, then x^α increases as α increases. If $x = 1$, then $x^\alpha = 1$.

A Discussion of Arithmetic

One of the critical developments made in mathematics, and in particular in arithmetic, was the development of zero and radix representation for natural numbers. This development allows the popular "Arabic numerals." That is, we have a name for every natural number in terms of the symbols 0, 1, 2, 3, 4, 5, 6, 7, 8, 9. This allows for some very nice computation algorithms, based on the fact that in radix representation the numeral just to the left of a given one is "worth 10 times as much" (in base 10 at least).

Example: 1023 represents the number computed from

$$1 \times 10^3 + 0 \times 10^2 + 2 \times 10 + 3$$

As you recall, the methods you learned for computing addition, multiplication, and division were based on this fact. The little arithmetical gimmicks of "borrowing," "carrying," etc., were available, due to the place position principle.

Since computation is so simple in such a naming system, it would be very convenient if we could devise a similar naming system for the positive real numbers. We shall show in Chapter 4 that each positive real number can be represented as the sum of $n \in N_0$ and $r \in R$, where $0 \le r < 1$. Therefore we need only hope that every real number between 0 and 1 can be represented in the form $b_1(1/10) + b_2(1/10^2) + \cdots + b_k(1/10^k)$, where $0 \le b_i \le 9$. (This is called decimal form.) Unfortunately, however, it turns out that this is not the case. In fact, there are rational numbers which cannot be represented in such a fashion. Due to the fact that our computational devices depend on such a representation, we often operate as if one existed. In this case, we compute with a number which is very near the number we wish to use, and we then end up with answers very near the answer we wish to have.

Example: $1/3 \neq .3333 = 3 \times 1/10 + 3 \times 1/10^2 + 3 \times 1/10^3 + 3 \times 1/10^4$ but it is very close. (How close?)

$$5/8 = .625 = 6 \times 1/10 + 2 \times 1/10^2 + 5 \times 1/10^3.$$

Further,

$$3 \times 1/10 + 3 \times 1/10^2 + 3 \times 1/10^3 + 3 \times 1/10^4$$
$$+ 6 \times 1/10 + 2 \times 1/10^2 + 5 \times 1/10^3$$
$$= 9 \times 1/10 + 5(1/10^2) + 8(1/10^3) + 3(1/10^4) = .9583.$$

This does not equal $1/3 + 5/8$, but it is very close, and so for many purposes serves as well.

Every positive real number α can be represented by $\alpha = n + r$, where $n \in N_0$, $0 \leq r < 1$ and $r \in R$. Therefore the "n" or "whole number" part can always be represented in base 10 numeration. For many rational numbers, the remainder can be represented by $r = b_1(1/10) + b_2(1/10^2) + \cdots + b_k(1/10^k)$ for some $k \in N$ and for $0 \leq b_i \leq 9$; and for these numbers, the base place representation can be extended provided some mark is used to indicate where the whole number representation ends and the remainder begins.

Example: If $\alpha = 6 \times 10^2 + 7 \times 10 + 2 \times 1 + 3 \times 1/10 + 4 \times 1/10^2$, then α is given the name 672.34.

Example: If $\alpha = 5 \times 10^3 + 3 \times 10^2 + 1 \times 10^1 + 2 \times 10^0 + 2 \times 10^{-1}$, then α is given the name 5312.2.

Although all numbers r, $0 \leq r < 1$ cannot be represented in the form $b_1 10^{-1} + b_2 10^{-2} + b_3 10^{-3} + \cdots + b_k 10^{-k}$, there is a theorem to the effect that one can come as close as he likes to any given number with some number of the above form. It is this theorem that makes it possible to use decimal representations for computational purposes in many applied problems. After all, in the physical world it is possible to make measurements only up to a certain precision; and as long as the final results of a computation are within the allowed margin of error, there is no need to compute a more precise number. However, this does not depreciate the need to use exact numbers in a theoretical analysis of a problem.

The algorithm for division can be used to either find the representation of a rational number (the quotient of two integers) in decimal form, or else to find closer and closer approximations which can be represented in decimal form.

Example: $7/8 = .875 = 8 \times 1/10 + 7 \times 1/10^2 + 5 \times 1/10^3$ is computed

```
        .875
   8)7.000
     6 4
     ───
      60
      56
      ──
      40
      40
      ──
```

Example: 2/3 $\cong$ .666. This is established by the following familiar computation. ("$\cong$" is read "approximately equal to.")

$$
\begin{array}{r}
.6666 \\
3\overline{)2.0000} \\
\underline{1\,8} \\
20 \\
\underline{18} \\
20 \\
\underline{18} \\
20 \\
\underline{18} \\
2
\end{array}
$$

Clearly the computation will not terminate, but one can find numbers as near 2/3 as desired by continuing the computation. That is,

$$2/3 = \sup \{.6, .66, .666, .6666, \cdots\} = \sup\left\{\sum_{i=1}^{n} \frac{6}{10^i} : n \in N\right\}.$$

It is easily seen that with a rational number m/n, either there exists a representation in decimal form, or at worst, the approximating numbers which are near m/n will be described by some "repeating process."

Example: 3/7 is approximated by the computation

$$
\begin{array}{r}
.42857142 \cdots \\
7\overline{)3.00} \\
\underline{2\,8} \\
20 \\
\underline{14} \\
60 \\
\underline{56} \\
40 \\
\underline{35} \\
50 \\
\underline{49} \\
10 \\
\underline{7} \\
30 \\
\underline{28} \\
20 \\
\cdot \\
\cdot \\
\cdot
\end{array}
$$

Although the process does not terminate, it begins to repeat. 3/7 = .428571428571428571 $\cdots$. (What are the next eight digits?)

235

This repetitive approximating process is often designated by placing a bar across the digits to be repeated.

Example: $.586\overline{586}$ means the number which can be approximated by $.586586$ and more nearly by $.586586586$, etc. That is,

$$.586\overline{586} = \sup \{.586, .586586, .586586586, \cdots\}$$

$$= \sup \left\{ \sum_{i=1}^{n} \frac{586}{(1000)^i} : n \in N \right\}.$$

The following theorem, which we shall state without proof, shows why decimal representations are useful.

3.13-7 Theorem: Every positive real number is the least upper bound for some collection of rational numbers which have decimal representations.

As we have pointed out, any rational number can be represented as a repeating decimal. The converse also is true, as the following illustration indicates.

Illustration: If $\alpha = .2364\overline{2364}$, then find a fractional representation for α·

Solution: $10000\alpha = 2364.2364\overline{2364}.$

Therefore

$$10000\alpha = 2364 + \alpha$$

so

$$\alpha = 2364/9999.$$

(Compare this with "dot, dot, dot" induction.)

The algorithm for extracting square roots operates in essentially the same way as the division algorithm. If the integer has an integral square root, it is obtained through the algorithm. Otherwise, the algorithm yields nearer and nearer decimal approximations of the square root.

Example:
$$\begin{array}{r} 2.\ 6\ 4 \\ \sqrt{7.0000} \\ \underline{4} \\ 46 | 3\ 00 \\ \underline{2\ 76} \\ 524 | \ \ 2400 \\ \underline{2096} \\ 304 \end{array}$$

By continuing the process, one finds decimal fractions which are very near $\sqrt{7}$, but which never actually are $\sqrt{7}$ (since $\sqrt{7}$ is irrational). Further, the process will never produce a repeating decimal because any repeating decimal is rational. (Explain!)

In later sections, we will discuss the concept of "limit" which is very closely related to the existence of least upper bounds. The limit idea is a fundamental one, and in its elementary form is very simple. As we have pointed out, you have been making use of it for years in your arithmetic.

Exercises 3.13

1. Find a decimal representation for each of the following rational numbers whenever it is possible. (If it is not possible, find a number which can be represented in decimal form and for which the difference between it and the given number is less than $1/1000$.)

a) $1/2$ c) $3/9$ e) $6/19$

b) $5/8$ d) $11/3$ f) $12/13$

2. Argue that $27/107$ can be expressed as a repeating decimal. (*Hint:* In the division process, how many possible distinct remainders can occur?)

3. Find a fractional representation for each of the following repeating decimals:

a) $.165165165\overline{165}$ c) $13.67143\overline{143}$

b) $.92929\overline{2}$ d) $6.43\overline{43}$

4. Write in decimal notation:

a) $\displaystyle\sum_{i=1}^{5} \frac{i}{10^i}$ c) $\displaystyle\sum_{i=3}^{6} \frac{2+i}{10^i}$ e) $\displaystyle\sum_{i=1}^{4} \frac{17}{10^i}$

b) $\displaystyle\sum_{i=4}^{7} \frac{2}{10^i}$ d) $\displaystyle\sum_{i=1}^{4} \frac{2}{10^i}$ f) $\displaystyle\sum_{i=1}^{5} \frac{23}{100^i}$

5. Find the supremum or infimum of each of the following sets, as indicated:

a) $\sup \{\sum_{i=1}^{n} 34/100^i : n \in N\}$

b) $\sup \{\sum_{i=1}^{n} 7/10^i : n \in N\}$

c) $\inf \{\sum_{i=1}^{n} - 83/100^i : n \in N\}$

d) $\inf \{\sum_{i=1}^{n} - 3156/10000^i : n \in N\}$

6. In each of the following, find a decimal representation for a rational number whose distance from the given number is less than $1/1000$:

a) $\sqrt{2} + \sqrt{7}$ c) $\sqrt{3} \cdot \pi$ where $\pi \cong 3.1415926535$

b) $\sqrt{5} + \pi$

7. Graph $1/3$ on the number line.

$1/3 = \sup \{.3, .33, .333, \cdots\}$.

Graph $2^{.3}$, $2^{.33}$, $2^{.333}$, $2^{.3333}$ on the line. Graph $2^{1/3}$ on the line.

8. Compute a four-decimal place rational approximation for $\sqrt{5}$. (Recall the square root algorithm.) Graph $2^{\sqrt{5}}$ on the number line.

9. Show that if $x \in R^+$ and $n \in N$, then

a) $x < 1 \Rightarrow x^n < 1$ and $x^{1/n} < 1$.

b) $x > 1 \Rightarrow x^n > 1$ and $x^{1/n} > 1$.

10. Show that if $x \in R^+$, then $x^n = \sup \{r^n : 0 \leq r \leq x\}$.

3.14 The Complex Number System

We now wish to develop the number system known as "the complex numbers." As we shall show rather quickly, the system is not "complex," as the name would lead one to believe.

Up to this point, we have avoided a constructional approach in defining our number systems. This is because in each of the preceding cases, a construction approach serves no essential purpose other than to guarantee the existence of such a system. In the case of the complex numbers, however, a construction approach provides us with a geometrical interpretation for the number system. This interpretation is useful, not only in gaining insight into the system, but also for suggesting how one might apply complex numbers to physical problems. We are going to define the complex numbers to be the points in $R \times R$, which we usually interpret geometrically as a plane. We then give rules for adding and multiplying these points or ordered pairs. We will see that it is possible to generate a very workable and familiar system which, it turns out, is an extension of R.

3.14-1 Definition: Let $\mathcal{C} = \{(x, y): x, y \in R\} = R \times R$. We define addition and multiplication in $\mathcal{C}$ as follows ($\mathcal{C}$ is called the *complex plane*):

$$(x, y) \oplus (a, b) = (x + a, y + b)$$
$$(x, y) \odot (a, b) = (xa - yb, ya + xb).$$

Example: $(2, 3) \oplus (5, 7) = (7, 10)$
$(1, 5) \odot (2, 6) = (-28, 16).$

It might seem that by defining this new number system, one would need to do a great deal of investigation in order to have a working knowledge of the algebra which governs it. The following theorem, however, makes it clear that you already know a great deal about the complex numbers.

3.14-2 Theorem: The complex number system is a field with $(0, 0)$ as the zero element and $(1, 0)$ as the multiplicative identity.

Remark: The proof of this theorem, for the most part, is left for the reader. We shall, however, verify that every non-zero element has a multiplicative inverse. This is done as follows: Let $(a, b) \in \mathcal{C}$ such that $(a, b) \neq (0, 0)$. Then

$$(a, b) \odot \left(\frac{a}{a^2 + b^2}, \frac{-b}{a^2 + b^2} \right) = (1, 0). \;\square$$

It follows that all the techniques for solving equations and performing computations in Q and in R are still applicable, since they were founded only on the field properties.

Let us examine a special subset of the complex numbers, the set of all complex numbers with a zero second component. Define

$$R^* = \{(x, 0): x \in R\}.$$

Notice that $(x, 0) \oplus (y, 0) = (x + y, 0)$ and $(x, 0) \odot (y, 0) = (xy, 0)$. We see that R^* acts just like the real numbers, so let us "identify" the complex number $(x, 0)$ with the real number x. That is, we denote by "x" the complex number "$(x, 0)$." We are taking the point of view that $R \subset \mathcal{C}$ and that complex numbers as points in the plane contain a special subset (a line) which is the real line.

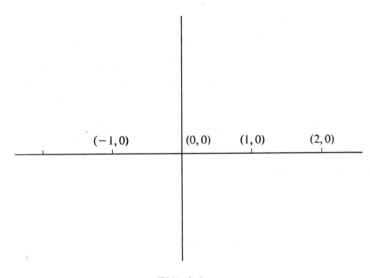

FIG. 3.6

Thus, we are eliminating the ordered pair notation for the particular set $R^* \subset \mathcal{C}$. The following observation will enable us to eliminate the ordered pair notation entirely. We shall then also drop the circle from our addition and multiplication. (We carried it temporarily to emphasize the fact that there really is a difference between real number addition and complex number addition.)

3.14-3 Theorem: Let $i = (0, 1)$ (i is called the *imaginary unit*).

$$\forall (a, b) \in \mathcal{C}, \qquad (a, b) = (a, 0) \oplus ((b, 0) \odot i.)$$

Proof: $(a, 0) \oplus ((b, 0) \odot (0, 1)) = (a, 0) \oplus (0, b) = (a, b).$ □

This enables us to denote every complex number in the form $a + bi$, where we have identified a with the complex number $(a, 0)$, and b with $(b, 0)$. For historical reasons, it is common to represent the elements of $\mathcal{C}$ without the ordered pair notation.

239

3.14-4 Definition: If $\alpha = a + bi$ is a complex number, then a is called the *real component* of α and b is called the *imaginary component* of α.

Example: Figure 3.7 is a graph of the complex numbers $2 + 3i$, $4 + i$, i, $3 - 2i$, $-2 - i$ in the complex plane:

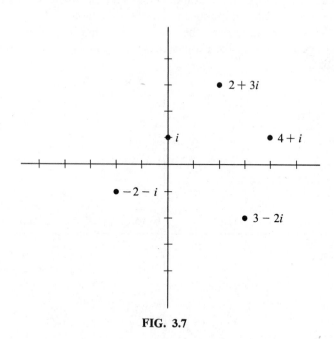

FIG. 3.7

We shall now prove the famous theorem which is the final step in eliminating the ordered pair notation for the complex numbers.

3.14-5 Theorem: $i^2 = -1$. (That is, $(0, 1) \odot (0, 1) = (-1, 0)$).

Proof: $(0, 1) \odot (0, 1) = (0 \cdot 0 - 1 \cdot 1, 1 \cdot 0 + 0 \cdot 1) = (-1, 0)$. ☐

From this point on, we will always designate complex numbers in the form $a + bi$ where a and b are considered to be real numbers. Keep in mind that $\mathcal{C}$ is a field, and hence all the problem solving and computational devices you already know carry over to $\mathcal{C}$. The only thing at all new at this point is the computation of inverses for non-zero numbers. Recall that $(a + bi)^{-1} = \dfrac{a}{a^2 + b^2} - \dfrac{b}{a^2 + b^2} i$.

Example: Solve for x.

$$(2 + 3i)x + 7i = 2 + 4i$$
$$(2 + 3i)x = 2 + 4i - 7i = 2 - 3i$$

$$x = \frac{(2 - 3i)}{2 + 3i} = (2 - 3i)(2 + 3i)^{-1}$$
$$= (2 - 3i)(2/13 - (3/13)i)$$
$$= 4/13 + (9/13)i^2 - (6/13)i - (6/13)i$$
$$= 4/13 - 9/13 - (12/13)i$$
$$= -(5/13) - (12/13)i$$

As you will see in the next example, there is no need to memorize this formula for reciprocals of complex numbers.

First, let us define a useful function from $\mathcal{C}$ to $\mathcal{C}$. This function is called *conjugation*, and the functional value is usually denoted by a bar over the number rather than by usual functional notation.

3.14-6 Definition: If $a + bi \in \mathcal{C}$, then

$$\overline{a + bi} = a - bi.$$

$\overline{a + bi}$ is called the *conjugate* of $a + bi$.

Notice the relative position in the complex plane of a complex number and its conjugate. We see that conjugation is merely a reflection across the real axis (x-axis). (This reflection occurs when we replace ordered pairs of the form (a, b) by ordered pairs of the form $(a, -b)$.)

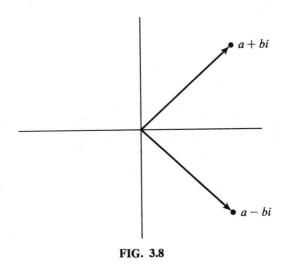

FIG. 3.8

Two rather useful and interesting facts about complex numbers are given by the following theorem.

3.14-7 Theorem: If $z_1, z_2 \in \mathcal{C}$, then

$$\overline{z_1 + z_2} = \overline{z_1} + \overline{z_2} \qquad \text{and} \qquad \overline{z_1 z_2} = \overline{z_1}\,\overline{z_2}.$$

241

Proof: Let $z_1 = a + bi$ and $z_2 = x + yi$. Then

$$\overline{z_1 + z_2} = \overline{a + bi + x + yi}$$
$$= \overline{a + x + (b + y)i}$$
$$= a + x - (b + y)i$$
$$= a - bi + x - yi$$
$$= \overline{a + bi} + \overline{x + yi}$$
$$= \overline{z_1} + \overline{z_2}.$$

Also,

$$\overline{z_1 z_2} = \overline{(a + bi)(x + yi)}$$
$$= \overline{(ax - by) + (ay + bx)i}$$
$$= (ax - by) - (ay + bx)i$$

and

$$\overline{z_1}\,\overline{z_2} = \overline{(a + bi)(x + yi)}$$
$$= (a - bi)(x - yi)$$
$$= (ax - by) + (-ay - bx)i$$
$$= (ax - by) - (ay + bx)i.$$

Therefore $\overline{z_1 z_2} = \overline{z_1}\,\overline{z_2}$. ☐

3.14-8 Corollary: For every complex number z, $z + \bar{z}$ is real, and $z\bar{z}$ is real and positive. The proof is left as an exercise.

Example: Find $(3 + 2i)^{-1}$.

$$(3 + 2i)^{-1} = \frac{1}{3 + 2i} = \frac{1}{3 + 2i} \cdot \frac{3 - 2i}{3 - 2i}$$

$$= \frac{3 - 2i}{3^2 + 2^2} = \frac{3}{13} - \frac{2}{13}\,i.$$

Example: Reduce to the standard "$a + bi$" form.

$$\frac{(6 + 3i)(2 - i)}{4 + 3i} = \frac{12 + 3 + (6 - 6)i}{4 + 3i}$$

$$= \frac{15}{4 + 3i} \cdot \frac{4 - 3i}{4 - 3i}$$

$$= \frac{60 - 45i}{16 + 9} = \frac{12}{5} - \frac{9}{5}\,i.$$

Exercises   3.14

1. Simplify (put in the form $a + bi$):

    a) $(3 + 2i) + (5 - 6i)$

    b) $(7 + 3i)(6 + 2i)$

    c) $(9 + i)(2 - 6i)$

    d) $\dfrac{2 - 4i}{3 + i}$

e) $\dfrac{5 + 2i}{6 - 3i}$

f) $(10 + 4i)^{-1}$

g) $\dfrac{(3 - 2i)(4 + 7i)}{3 + 7i}$

(h) $(1 + i)^2$

i) $(1 + i) \div (3 - i)$

j) $\dfrac{6 - 4i}{2 - 3i}$

k) $\dfrac{2 + 3i}{5 - 4i}$

2. Solve the following equations for z:

a) $3z + 2i = 5$

b) $16z + 3i = 4 - 7i$

c) $(4 + i)z + 7i - 1 = 28$

d) $14iz + 7i - z = 2i$

e) $iz + (2 - 10i)z = 3z + 2i$

3. Show that $\mathcal{C}$ is a field.

4. Prove Corollary 3.14-8.

5. Evaluate:

a) $i^2, i^3, i^4, i^5, i^6, i^7, i^8$

b) $i^{4n}, i^{4n+1}, i^{4n+2}, i^{4n+3}$

c) $i^{-1}, i^{-2}, i^{-3}, i^{-4}, i^{-5}, i^{-6}, i^{-7}, i^{-8}$

d) Show by induction that for any $n \in Z$, $i^{n+4} = i^n$.

6. Assume that $(a, b) \neq (0, 0)$. Deduce that if $(a + bi)(x + yi) = 0$, then $x = 0$ and $y = 0$.

7. Draw a graph representing each of the following complex numbers and its conjugate. Also graph the negative of each number.

a) $3 + 2i$

b) $7 - 2i$

c) $-3 - 4i$

d) i

e) 2

8. Prove that for any element $z \in \mathcal{C}$,

$$\overline{(\bar{z})} = z.$$

9. What can you deduce about a complex number z if $z = \bar{z}$?

10. Solve for z:

$$3z^2 + iz - 2 = 0$$

(*Hint:* Does the quadratic formula hold for $\mathcal{C}$?)

11. Solve for z:

$$z^2 + 4 = 0$$

Does this equation have solutions if the universal set is R?

3.15   Complex Numbers as Vectors

Since $\mathcal{C} = R \times R$, the complex numbers can be represented graphically as points in a plane, where we graph the complex number $a + bi$ as we did previously the ordered pair (a, b) in $R \times R$.

Example: a) $2 + 3i = (2, 3)$ b) $\pi + 2i = (\pi, 2)$

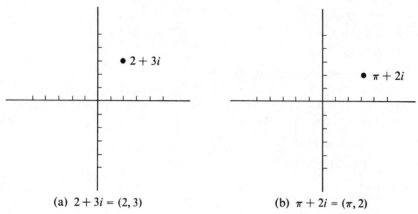

(a) $2 + 3i = (2, 3)$ (b) $\pi + 2i = (\pi, 2)$

FIG. 3.9

It is often useful to think of each complex number $x + iy$ as being an "arrow" or "vector", with "tail" at the point $(0, 0)$ and "head" at the point (x, y).

Example: a)   b)

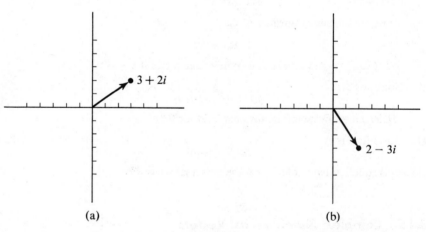

(a)   (b)

FIG. 3.10

Let us observe what happens graphically when we add the two complex numbers $3 + 2i$ and $3 + 5i$.

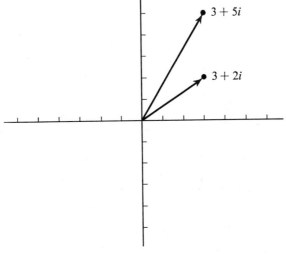

FIG. 3.11

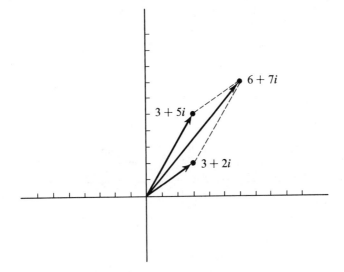

FIG. 3.12 $(3 + 2i) + (3 + 5i) = 6 + 7i$.

Notice that by some natural completions to our diagram, we have formed a parallelogram (dotted lines). This is a fact which makes complex numbers useful in certain physical applications.

Another way to graphically interpret addition of complex numbers is indicated by the following example.

Example: $(3 + i) + (2 + 2i) = 5 + 3i.$

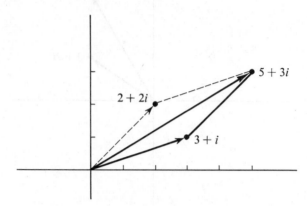

FIG. 3.13

By placing the tail of the second arrow at the head of the first, the sum of the two complex numbers is at the head of the second. We see, of course, that we have formed the same parallelogram as if we had drawn the diagram as in the previous example.

Example: $(5) + (2i) = (5 + 0i) + (0 + 2i) = 5 + 2i.$

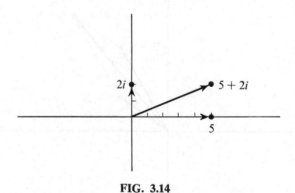

FIG. 3.14

Example: $(1 + 2i) + (2 - i) + (3 + 3i) + (-2 - 6i) = 4 - 2i.$
(Note our use of associativity for addition in $\mathbb{C}$ in this example.)

Length (Modulus) of a Complex Number

Since a complex number can be graphically represented as an arrow, it seems reasonable to discuss its length. Consider the complex number $x + iy.$

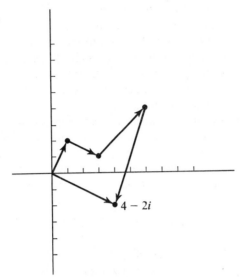

FIG. 3.15

The length of the arrow used to represent this number is determined by the Pythagorean theorem for right triangles. This length is $\sqrt{x^2 + y^2}$. As a result of this geometric property, we make the following definition.

3.15-1 Definition: If $z = x + iy \in \mathcal{C}$, then $\| \|: \mathcal{C} \to R$ where

$$\|(z) = |z| = |x + iy| = \sqrt{x^2 + y^2}.$$

$|z|$ is called the *modulus* or *absolute value* of z.

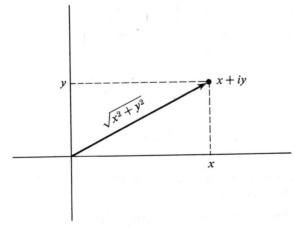

FIG. 3.16

Remark: Notice that if we choose a complex number x which is also real, $|x|$ is the same absolute value as defined for the reals. What we have done, then, is extend the absolute value function to the complex numbers. That is, we have enlarged the domain of the absolute value function in such a way that when restricted to the real numbers we have not changed its value. This is a familiar practice which will later be done with other functions whose domains are taken at first to be the real numbers.

Recall that the distance between two real numbers x and y on the real line was given by $|x - y|$. Let us examine this property to see if it extends to arbitrary complex numbers.

Consider $z_1 = x_1 + iy_1$ and $z_2 = x_2 + iy_2$. We see by Figure 3.17 and an application of the Pythagorean theorem, that the distance between z_1 and z_2 is given by

$$\sqrt{(x_1 - x_2)^2 + (y_1 - y_2)^2}.$$

Also notice that

$$
\begin{aligned}
|z_1 - z_2| &= |(x_1 + iy_1) - (x_2 + iy_2)| \\
&= |(x_1 - x_2) + (y_1 - y_2)i| \\
&= \sqrt{(x_1 - x_2)^2 + (y_1 - y_2)^2}.
\end{aligned}
$$

Thus, the concept of the distance between two numbers being given by the absolute value of their difference is also preserved in our extension of the absolute value function to a complex domain!

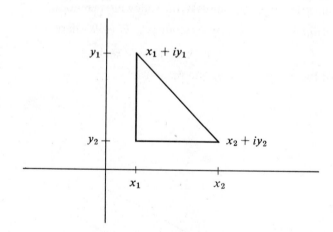

FIG. 3.17

Let us now examine some other properties of the absolute value function on the complex numbers.

3.15-2 Theorem: If z_1, $z_2 \in \mathbb{C}$, then $|z_1 \cdot z_2| = |z_1| \cdot |z_2|$.

Proof: Let $z_1 = x_1 + iy_1$ and $z_2 = x_2 + iy_2$. Then

$$|z_1 z_2| = |(x_1 + iy_1)(x_2 + iy_2)|$$
$$= |(x_1 x_2 - y_1 y_2) + (x_1 y_2 + x_2 y_1)i|$$
$$= [(x_1 x_2 - y_1 y_2)^2 + (x_1 y_2 + x_2 y_1)^2]^{1/2}$$
$$= [(x_1 x_2)^2 - 2x_1 x_2 y_1 y_2 + (y_1 y_2)^2 + (x_1 y_2)^2$$
$$\quad + 2x_1 y_2 x_2 y_1 + (x_2 y_1)^2]^{1/2}$$
$$= [(x_1 x_2)^2 + (y_1 y_2)^2 + (x_1 y_2)^2 + (x_2 y_1)^2]^{1/2}.$$

Also,

$$|z_1| \cdot |z_2| = |x_1 + iy_1| \cdot |x_2 + iy_2|$$
$$= (x_1^2 + y_1^2)^{1/2}(x_2^2 + y_2^2)^{1/2}$$
$$= [(x_1^2 + y_1^2)(x_2^2 + y_2^2)]^{1/2}$$
$$= [x_1^2 x_2^2 + y_1^2 y_2^2 + x_1^2 y_2^2 + y_1^2 x_2^2]^{1/2}$$
$$= [(x_1 x_2)^2 + (y_1 y_2)^2 + (x_1 y_2)^2 + (y_1 x_2)^2]^{1/2}$$

Hence

$$|z_1 \cdot z_2| = |z_1| \cdot |z_2|. \quad \square$$

Corollary: If $z \neq 0$, then

$$|z^{-1}| = |z|^{-1}$$

that is, $|1/z| = 1/|z|$.

   Proof: $1 = |1| = |zz^{-1}| = |z| \cdot |z^{-1}|$. Therefore

$$|z|^{-1} = |z^{-1}|. \quad \square$$

Corollary: $\left|\dfrac{z_1}{z_2}\right| = \dfrac{|z_1|}{|z_2|}.$

The Proof is left for the reader.

3.15-3 Theorem: If $z \in \mathcal{C}$, then

$$|\bar{z}| = |z|.$$

The Proof is left for the reader.

3.15-4 Theorem: If $z \in \mathcal{C}$, then

$$|z|^2 = |z\bar{z}| = z\bar{z}.$$

   Proof: Let $z = x + iy$. Then $z\bar{z} = (x + iy)(x - iy) = x^2 + y^2$
$$= |z|^2.$$

Note that $|z\bar{z}| = |x^2 + y^2| = x^2 + y^2 = z\bar{z}. \quad \square$

3.15-5 Theorem: (The *triangle inequality*) If z_1, $z_2 \in \mathcal{C}$, then

$$|z_1 + z_2| \leq |z_1| + |z_2|.$$

The analytic proof of this theorem is postponed for the time being, but the following geometric illustration is convincing, and motivates the name of the theorem as well.

   Let $z_1 = x_1 + iy_1$, $z_2 = x_2 + iy_2$. Using the parallelogram addition of two complex numbers, the number $z_1 + z_2$ is represented as the side of a triangle

249

having the other two sides represented by z_1 and z_2 (see Figure 3.18). The inequality $|z_1 + z_2| \leq |z_1| + |z_2|$ simply states the geometric property that a given side of a triangle can be no longer than the sum of the other two sides. In fact, equality will occur only if the triangle degenerates into a line segment.

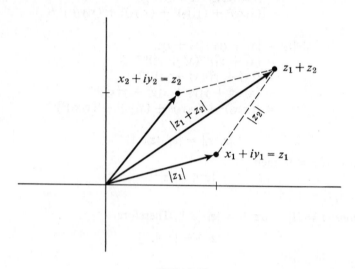

FIG. 3.18

As noted above, the distance between two complex numbers z_1 and z_2 is determined by $|z_1 - z_2|$. By Figure 3.19 we see that the distance between $a + bi$ and $c + di$ is determined from the Pythagorean theorem by computing $\sqrt{(b - d)^2 + (c - a)^2}$. But this is the same as $|(a + bi) - (c + di)|$.

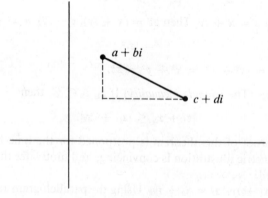

FIG. 3.19

Exercises 3.15

1. Compute
   a) $|6 + 3i|$ b) $|3 - 4i|$ c) $|-2 + i|$ d) $|1/(2 + 3i)|$

2. Show that $|(a + bi)/(b + ia)| = 1$ and graph each of the following pairs of complex numbers and their quotient (first divided by second):
   a) $2 + 3i, 3 + 2i$ c) $-2 - i, -1 - 2i$
   b) $1 + 4i, 4 + i$ d) $3 - 2i, -2 + 3i$

3. Determine what region in the plane represents each of the following sets:
   a) $\{x + iy: |x + iy| \leq 1\}$ c) $\{x + iy: |(x + iy) - (3 + 2i)| \leq 2\}$
   b) $\{x + iy: |x + iy| \geq 3\}$ d) $\{x + iy: |(x + iy) - (-2 - 4i)| \geq 5\}$

4. If the length of z, $|z|$, is 5, how long is z^{-1}?

5. Graph each of the following complex numbers (vectors) in the plane.
   a) $2 + i$ b) $(2 + i)^{-1}$ c) $3 - i$ d) $(2 + i)(3 - i)$

6. Let $f: \mathbb{C} \to \mathbb{C}$ be defined by $f(z) = 2z^2$. Graph z and $f(z)$ where $z =$
   a) $1 + i.$ b) $2 + i.$ c) $i.$ d) $2 - i.$ e) $-3 + 2i.$

7. Graph z and $1/z$ where $z =$
   a) $2 + i.$ c) $-3 + i.$ e) $i.$
   b) $1 - i.$ d) $-2 - 7i.$ f) $(1/\sqrt{2}) + (1/\sqrt{2})i.$

8. Let $C = \{z \in \mathbb{C}: |z| = 1\}$ (the unit circle).
   a) Show that if $z \in C$, then $1/z \in C$.
   b) Show that if z is "outside of" C, then $1/z$ is "inside" of C.
   c) Show that if z is "inside" of C, then $1/z$ is "outside."
   (*Hint:* If z is outside C what is $|z|$? If z is inside C, what is $|z|$?)

9. Establish (prove):
   a) $\forall n \in Z \quad \forall z \in \mathbb{C} \quad |z^n| = |z|^n$
   b) $\forall z \in \mathbb{C} \quad |z| = \sqrt{z\bar{z}}$
   c) $\forall u, v, z \in \mathbb{C} \quad |u - v| \leq |u - z| + |z - v|$

10. Show that $\mathbb{C}$ cannot be decomposed into three disjoint sets $\mathbb{C}^- \cup \{0\} \cup \mathbb{C}^+$ where
   a) $\forall x \neq 0 \quad x \in \mathbb{C}^+$ or $-x \in \mathbb{C}^+$ but not both.
   b) $\forall x, y$ if $x, y \in \mathbb{C}^+$, then $x + y \in \mathbb{C}^+$ and $xy \in \mathbb{C}^+$.

   (*Hint:* Look at the numbers $1, -1, i, -i$.)
   Note: This problem shows that $\mathbb{C}$ is not an ordered field.

11. Investigate (prove or disprove):
   a) $\forall u, v, z \in \mathbb{C} \quad ||u| - |v|| \leq |u - v|.$
   b) $z^2 = \bar{z}^2 \Rightarrow a = 0$ or $b = 0$. Assume $z = a + bi$.

251

12. Find a square root in $\mathcal{C}$ for

   a) -1 *b)* -2 *c)* -64 *d)* -36 *e)* -20 *f)* $-\pi$

13. $\mathcal{C}$ is a field with more square roots than we had in R or Q. Use the quadratic formula to solve the following equations.

   a) $2z^2 + 3z - 2 = 0$ *c)* $7z^2 - z - 1 = 0$
   b) $z^2 - 2z + 4 = 0$ *d)* $3z^2 + 5z + 7 = 0$

14. *a)* Do you think $1 + i$ has a square root in $\mathcal{C}$?
   b) Find two square roots for -1.
   c) Find two square roots for i.

15. Suppose f and g are sequences in $\mathcal{C}$. (That is, $f \colon N \to \mathcal{C}$ and $g \colon N \to \mathcal{C}$.)
   a) Define (inductively) what is meant by $\sum_{j=1}^{n} f(j)$.
   b) Same as *a)*, but for Π.
   c) Show that $\forall n$, $\sum_{j=1}^{n} (f(j) + g(j)) = (\sum_{j=1}^{n} f(j)) + (\sum_{j=1}^{n} g(j))$.
   d) Show that $\forall n$, $\Pi_{j=1}^{n} (f(j) \cdot (g(j))) = \Pi_{j=1}^{n} f(j) \cdot \Pi_{j=1}^{n} (g(j))$.
   (*Hint for c) and d):* You might be able to avoid repeating an inductive argument here by using previous proofs of these facts (for N) which used only algebraic properties enjoyed by $\mathcal{C}$.)

3.16   Operations on Functions

We have seen that one may view a function as a set of ordered pairs, or as a mapping device with a certain property (the "unique image" property). In this section we shall discuss how one can view functions simply as elements of a set of functions. (For historical reasons a set $\mathcal{F}$ of functions is often called a *function space* by mathematicians.) It will turn out that we can define "operations" (such as addition and multiplication) on certain classes of functions, and thus we could ask questions about the *closure* of a given subclass under the "operations" in question. We shall also investigate whether these operations are *commutative, associative*, etc. The point to remember, as we proceed in this section, is that we are considering functions to be (abstract) elements in a set, and that we are talking about adding, multiplying, etc., these elements to obtain other such elements. The reader should be very careful not to confuse, for example, the sum $f + g$ of the two functions f and g with the sum of the two images $f(x)$ and $g(x)$ (for a given x).

In order to avoid difficulties with notation and definitions, we shall restrict ourselves in this section to the class $\mathcal{R}$ of all functions from R into R. This very large class of functions contains many of the functions we will consider in later sections of the book, especially if we allow the domains to be subsets of R instead of necessarily the entire set of real numbers. Most of the definitions and theorems of this section can be easily generalized to functions having more abstract domains and ranges (such as $\mathcal{C}$).

Suppose two functions f and g are elements of $\mathfrak{R}$. If $f = g$ (*i.e.*, if *functions are equal*), they associate the same image with each pre-image, and have the same domain and range. That is,

$$f = g \Leftrightarrow f(x) = g(x) \quad \forall x \in R.$$

Note that if one views the functions f and g as sets of ordered pairs, then the statement

$$f = g$$

simply asserts the fact that the two sets f and g are equal sets. Of course, these notions of the equality of the functions f and g are the same.

We shall define several operations on the elements of $\mathfrak{R}$. In each case, we will be interested in giving a graphical interpretation of the operation, and in showing that the resulting object is again an element of $\mathfrak{R}$. (That is, we shall show that $\mathfrak{R}$ is closed under the operations being considered.)

3.16-1 Definition: Given two functions f and g in $\mathfrak{R}$, the sum $f + g$ is the function in $R \times R$ defined at each point x in R by

$$(f + g)(x) = f(x) + g(x).$$

This is sometimes called the *"pointwise"* sum of f and g.

It is clear that $f + g$ is a function in $R \times R$. (Is it clear that $f + g \in \mathfrak{R}$?) It might be pointed out that if $f \subset Q \times Q$ and $g \subset Q \times Q$, then $f + g \subset Q \times Q$. (That is, the subset of $\mathfrak{R}$ having elements which take on rational values at rational pre-images is closed under addition.)

3.16-2 Definition: a) The difference $f - g$ of two elements of $\mathfrak{R}$ is the function defined by

$$(f - g)(x) = f(x) - g(x) \quad \forall x \in R.$$

b) The product $f \cdot g$ of two elements of $\mathfrak{R}$ is the function defined by

$$(f \cdot g)(x) = f(x)g(x) \quad \forall x \in R.$$

c) If $0 \notin R_g$, the quotient f/g of two elements of $\mathfrak{R}$ is the function defined by

$$(f/g)(x) = f(x)/g(x) \quad \forall x \in R.$$

Note: If 0 is not in the range of g, then $1/g$ is defined. However, we cannot denote this by g^{-1}. (Why?)

Example: Suppose f is the function described by $f(x) = x$, and g is the function described by $g(x) = 3$. Then the sum, difference, product, and quotient functions are, respectively:

253

$$(f + g)(x) = x + 3 \qquad \forall x \in R$$
$$(f - g)(x) = x - 3 \qquad \forall x \in R$$
$$(f \cdot g)(x) = 3x \qquad \forall x \in R$$
$$(f/g)(x) = (1/3)x \qquad \forall x \in R.$$

Graphs of these functions, together with graphs of f and g are sketched below.

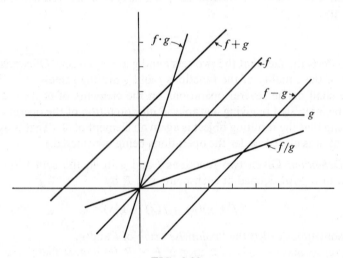

FIG. 3.20

Note that in this case $f, g, f + g, f - g, f \cdot g, f/g$ are all functions from R into R and that g/f is not defined. (Why?)

The graphical interpretation of the sum and of the difference of two functions is relatively straightforward. Given the graphs of f and g, we obtain

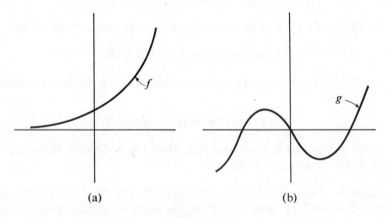

(a) (b)

FIG. 3.21

the graph of $f + g$, for example, by adding the heights of f and of g for each point x, and noting that this is the value $(f + g)(x)$. This procedure is sometimes described as "geometric addition." For example, in order to obtain the graph of $f + g$ for the function f and g whose graphs are as follows, we use geometric addition to obtain:

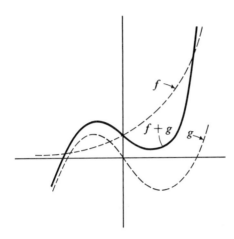

FIG. 3.22

Of course, there is a similar graphical interpretation of function subtraction. In this case, one subtracts the height to one graph from the height to the other at each pre-image point x.

Our definitions of operations on the elements of $\Re$ have so far been restricted to "pointwise" definitions; that is, at each point in R the sum, difference, product, and quotient of functions is defined according to the corresponding operations on real numbers. It is natural to expect that *some* of the properties of addition and multiplication of real numbers will thus be "inherited" by the corresponding operations on functions in $\Re$. For example, since $a + b = b + a$ $\forall a, b \in R$, we would expect

$$f + g = g + f \qquad \forall g, f \in \Re$$

since for each $x \in R$ this means that

$$f(x) + g(x) = g(x) + f(x).$$

Actually this does happen, and it is almost immediate that the operations of function addition and multiplication are commutative, associative, and distributive.

3.16-3 Theorem: $\forall f, g, h \in \Re.$

1) $f + g = g + f$ and $f \cdot g = g \cdot f$.
2) $(f + g) + h = f + (g + h)$ and $(f \cdot g) \cdot h = f \cdot (g \cdot h)$.
3) $f \cdot (g + h) = f \cdot g + f \cdot h$.

255

Proof: We have already shown that addition of functions is commutative. Let us now show that multiplication of functions is commutative. Let $f, g \in \mathcal{R}$. By definition, $\forall x \in R$,

$$(f \cdot g)(x) = f(x)g(x),$$

and $\qquad (g \cdot f)(x) = g(x)f(x).$

But $f(x)$ and $g(x)$ are numbers in R, and hence $f(x)g(x) = g(x)f(x)$. Since $f \cdot g$ takes the same value as $g \cdot f$ at each point in R, it follows that $f \cdot g = g \cdot f$.

We leave it for the reader to prove the associative laws. Let us now prove the distributive law for elements of $\mathcal{R}$.

$$\forall x \in R \quad f \cdot (g + h)(x) = f(x) \cdot (g + h)(x)$$
$$= f(x) \cdot (g(x) + h(x))$$
$$= f(x)g(x) + f(x)h(x) \qquad \text{(Why?)}$$
$$= f \cdot g(x) + f \cdot h(x)$$
$$= (f \cdot g + f \cdot h)(x).$$

Hence $f \cdot (g + h)$ takes on the same value at each point of R as does the function $(f \cdot g + f \cdot h)$, therefore

$$f \cdot (g + h) = f \cdot g + f \cdot h. \quad \square$$

Example: Let f and g be defined ($\forall x \in R$) by

$$f(x) = 2x + 1$$

and $\qquad g(x) = x - 3.$

Then $\forall x \in R, \qquad (f \cdot g)(x) = (2x + 1)(x - 3)$
$$= 2x^2 - 5x - 3.$$

We have included this material in the chapter on number systems because of the algebra which can be induced on a collection of functions, due to the existing algebra on the range set.

3.16-4 Definition: $\forall f \in \mathcal{R}$, $-f$ is the function defined by $\forall x \in R$

$$(-f)(x) = -f(x).$$

3.16-5: $\mathcal{R}$ is a number ring using the operations "$+$" and "$\cdot$" as defined.

Proof: We have already established the associative, commutative, and distributive laws. We need only establish the existence of an identity element for each operation, along with additive inverse elements. Let 0_f denote the function which takes on the value 0 at each point. That is, $\forall x \in R \;\; 0_f(x) = 0$. Similarly, $\forall x \in R \;\; 1_f(x) = 1$. Clearly 0_f is an identity element for the "adding functions" operation, and 1_f is an identity element for multiplication. Further, if $f \in \mathcal{R}$, then $-f$ is an additive inverse for f. $\square$

Notation Conventions

In many situations, we have a function which is described by a formula or expression which determines the functional values. In such cases, it is useful to become slightly sloppy in language usage and to use the formula as a name for the function. For example, in speaking about the function f, where

$$\forall x \in R \quad f(x) = 5x^2 + 1$$

we will often use, as a name for the function f, the expression $5x^2 + 1$. We could be consistent with the convention described above and use $(5x^2 + 1)_f$ to denote the function which takes the value $5x^2 + 1$ at each x. This would not correspond to common usage, however, and in most instances no confusion is created by not making the distinction. For instance, if $f(x) = 5x^2 + 1$ and $g(x) = 2x - 3$ for all $x \in R$, then we feel free to say "the function $5x^2 + 1$ when added to the function $2x - 3$ is equal to the function $5x^2 + 2x - 2$." In using this kind of language, it is traditional to employ an equal sign of the form "$\equiv$" rather than "$=$," in order to avoid some confusion which might otherwise arise.

Example: $x^2 + 2x^2 + 1 \equiv 3x^2 + 1$ means that the function f, where $\forall x$ $f(x) = x^2 + 2x^2 + 1$, is the same function as the function g, where $\forall x$ $g(x) = 3x^2 + 1$.

The sign "$\equiv$" is read "is identically equal to." It should be understood that this is not a different kind of equality, but merely a reminder that we are employing the language convention of using the same name for the function as for the value of the function at a point, and that by using "$\equiv$" we are designating equality of functions rather than equality of points in R.

3.16-6 Definition: Let $f: R \to R$ (i.e., $f \in \mathcal{R}$). We say that $a \in R$ is a *zero* of f provided $f(a) = 0$.

Example: Let $f(x) = 2x + 1$, then $-1/2$ is a zero of f.

Example: The function $5x^2 + 18x - 8$ has two zeros, $2/5$ and -4.

Example: The function $(x - a)(x - b)(x - c)(x - d)$ has as zeros, a, b, c, and d.

More Function Operations

Another operation that is frequently encountered is that of taking the "upper envelope" of two functions.

3.16-7 Definition: Given any two functions f and g in $\mathcal{R}$, $f \vee g$ is a function defined pointwise by

$(f \vee g)(x)$ is the largest of the real numbers $f(x)$ and $g(x)$.

(That is, $(f \vee g)(x) = \max \{f(x), g(x)\}$.)

It should be clear that

$$f \vee g: R \to R$$

so that $f \vee g \in \mathfrak{R}$. The graph of $f \vee g$ is interpreted as the graph formed by taking the highest point in the two graphs of f and g at each x. For example, using functions whose graphs were sketched previously, we obtain the graph of $f \vee g$:

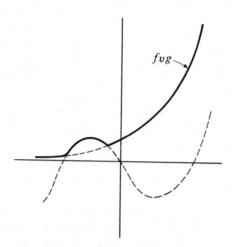

FIG. 3.23

One could, of course, analogously define the "lower envelope" $f \wedge g$ of two functions f and g (see Exercise 6).

We have already discussed the operation between functions known as composition of functions. Recall that $f \circ g$ (or sometimes simply "fg") is the function defined pointwise by $\forall x \quad (f \circ g)(x) = f(g(x))$. If $f \in \mathfrak{R}$ and $g \in \mathfrak{R}$, then $f \circ g \in \mathfrak{R}$. Recall, however, that composition is not a commutative operation.

Example: $\forall x \in R \quad f(x) = 2x + 1, g(x) = 5x - 1$.

Therefore $\quad f \circ g(x) = f(g(x)) = 2(5x - 1) + 1 = 10x - 1$.
$$g \circ f(x) = g(f(x)) = 5(2x + 1) - 1 = 10x + 4.$$

Note that the function h where $\forall x \in R \quad h(x) = x$ serves as an identity element for composition. For this reason, $h = x_f$ is usually called "the identity function."

Occasionally the convention of denoting a function by the expression which determines its functional value can lead to confusion. When this is the case, we shall then emphasize the fact that we mean a function by subscripting the expression with an f.

Example: 5_f means the constant function which maps all values to 5.
$\forall x \in R \quad 5_f(x) = 5; \forall x \in R \quad 0_f(x) = 0; \forall x \in R \quad x_f(x) = x$.

Hence *a*) 0_f (or simply 0, called the *zero function*) is the identity element for addition.

    b) 1_f (or simply 1, called the *unity function*) is the identity element for multiplication of functions.

    c) x_f (or simply x, called the *identity function*) is the identity element for composition of functions.

Exercises 3.16

1. Try to give a graphical interpretation for multiplication in $\Re$.

2. Find a formula which describes $f + g$, $f \cdot g$, $f \circ g$, and $g \circ f$ where $\forall x \in R$,
   a) $f(x) = 3x^2 - 1$ $g(x) = 5x + 2$
   b) $f(x) = 4x$ $g(x) = 4$
   c) $f(x) = x^2 + 4$ $g(x) = x^2 - 4$
   d) $f(x) = 3x^3$ $g(x) = x^6$

3. *a*) Add, *b*) multiply, *c*) subtract, *d*) divide, and *e*) compose the functions $6x^2 + 2x + 1$ and $x^2 + 1$.

4. *a*) Show that $\forall x$, $f(x) \leq (f \vee g)(x)$ and $g(x) \leq (f \vee g)(x)$.
   b) Show that $f \vee g = g \vee f$.

5. Show that:
   a) $f \vee f = f$
   b) $f + f = 2_f \cdot f$
   c) $f - f = 0_f$
   d) $f \cdot f = g \circ f$ where $g(x) = x^2$
   e) $f/f = 1_f$ provided $0 \notin R_f$
   f) $f \circ f^{-1} = x_f$ provided $f^{-1} : R \xrightarrow[\text{onto}]{1-1} R$

6. Define $f \wedge g = -(-f \vee -g)$.
   a) Interpret graphically.
   b) Show $(f \wedge g)(x)$ is the minimum of $f(x)$ and $g(x)$ $\forall x \in R$.

7. Define $f \geq g$ iff $f = f \vee g$.
   a) Is "$\geq$" an order relation on $\Re$?
   b) Show that $f \geq g$ iff $g = f \wedge g$.
   c) Show that $f \vee -f \geq 0_f$.

8. What are the zeros of the following functions?
   a) $f(x) = 2x + 1$
   b) $f(x) = 3x - 4$
   c) $f(x) = ax + b$
   d) $f(x) = 3x^2 + 2x - 5$

9. Investigate (prove or disprove):
   a) $f \circ (g + h) = f \circ g + f \circ h$
   b) $(g + h) \circ f = g \circ f + h \circ f$
   c) $f \wedge (g \vee h) = (f \wedge g) \vee (f \wedge h)$
   d) $f \vee (g \wedge h) = (f \vee g) \wedge (f \vee h)$
   e) $(f \vee g) \vee h = f \vee (g \vee h)$
   f) $(f \wedge g) \wedge h = f \wedge (g \wedge h)$

10. Graph $f \vee g$ and $f \wedge g$, where

$$f(x) = x^2 + 2 \qquad g(x) = -x^2 + 4.$$

11. Define "$f < g$" iff $f(x) < g(x)$ for all x in R. Show that "$<$" satisfies all of the order properties (see Definition 2.4-1) except the "totality" property. (This is what is known as a "partial ordering.")

4

NUMBER SYSTEMS—
ADVANCED TOPICS

Introduction

In this chapter we wish to continue on to some of the more sophisticated details which we bypassed in Chapter 3. Further, we would like to examine some specialized applications of concepts we introduced earlier with regard to induction and recursive definitions. We would also like to explore some special number systems which are not subsets of the complex field.

4.1 Some Topics on Induction and Sequences

Very often one is in the position of trying to establish a theorem in which several generalizations occur. We would like to discuss here the abstract distinction between certain inductive and non-inductive approaches to such problems.

Let $p(x, y)$ be a form statement in two variables over N (*i.e.*, for any pair of natural numbers, m and n, the statement $p(m, n)$ is either true or false). Consider the problem of trying to prove that $\forall x \ \forall y \ \ p(x, y)$. We have two methods for proving a generalization over N:

1) the test pattern principle
2) the principle of induction.

In order to prove $\forall x \ \forall y \ \ p(x, y)$, we need to show two generalizations. We could do both by the test pattern principle, we could do both by induction, or we could do one by induction and the other by test pattern. Recall that in *generalizations* we can interchange two universal quantifiers that are together. (That is, $\forall x \ \forall y \ \ p(x, y) \Leftrightarrow \forall y \ \forall x \ \ p(x, y)$.) If one is making a proof by inducting on one variable and "test patterning" the other, however, there may be considerable difference in the way the proofs go.

Example: If one were to prove $\forall x \ \forall y \ \ p(x, y)$ by test pattern on x and induction on y, the proof would be like the following.

Let x be arbitrary.

i) $p(x, 1)$
ii) $\forall k \ \ p(x, k) \Rightarrow p(x, k + 1)$

Therefore, by induction $\forall y \, p(x, y)$.
Hence, by test pattern, $\forall x \ \forall y \ \ p(x, y)$.

Example: If one were to prove $\forall x \ \forall y \ \ p(x, y)$ by inducting on x, the proof would go as follows.

i) $\forall y \ \ p(1, y)$
ii) $\forall k \ (\forall y \ \ p(k, y)) \Rightarrow (\forall y \ \ p(k + 1, y))$

Therefore, by induction, $\forall x \ (\forall y \ \ p(x, y))$, which is usually written without the extra parenthesis.

Example: Consider the process of proving $\forall x \ \forall y \ \ p(x, y)$ by inducting on both variables. The proof would go as follows.

i) j) $p(1, 1)$
jj) $\forall k \ \ p(1, k) \Rightarrow p(1, k + 1)$

Therefore, by induction, $\forall y \ \ p(1, y)$.

ii) $\forall k \ (\forall y \ \ p(k, y) \Rightarrow \forall y \ \ p(k + 1, y))$

Hence, by induction, $\forall x \ \forall y \ \ p(x, y)$.
We will soon have occasion to apply this process of "double induction."

Double Summations

In our definition for $\sum$ notation, it was assumed that some function $g: N \to N$ was given and that as a result $f: N \to N$ was defined by $f(n) = \sum_{i=1}^{n} g(i)$. We can in turn define a new function $h: N \to N$ by taking $h(n) = \sum_{i=1}^{n} f(i) = \sum_{i=1}^{n} (\sum_{j=1}^{i} g(j))$. An expression of this sort is called a *double summation*. Let us consider some simple examples of double summations.

Example: $\sum_{i=1}^{4} (\sum_{j=1}^{i} j) = \sum_{j=1}^{1} j + \sum_{j=1}^{2} j + \sum_{j=1}^{3} j + \sum_{j=1}^{4} j$
$\qquad = 1 + (1 + 2) + (1 + 2 + 3) + (1 + 2 + 3 + 4) = 20.$

To evaluate a double summation such as the one above, first expand the outer $\sum$ by replacing i first by 1 then by 2, etc. The variable on the outer $\sum$ might also appear inside the inner one as well as being the upper limit of the inner $\sum$.

Example: $\sum_{j=1}^{3} \sum_{i=1}^{j} (j + i) = \sum_{i=1}^{1} (1 + i) + \sum_{i=1}^{2} (2 + i) + \sum_{i=1}^{3}$
$(3 + i) = (1 + 1) + [(2 + 1) + (2 + 2)]$
$+ [(3 + 1) + (3 + 2) + (3 + 3)] = 24$

The following theorem is often very useful in dealing with double sums.

4.1-1 Theorem: If $f: N \times N \to R$, then $\forall n, m$ $\sum_{i=1}^{n} \sum_{j=1}^{m} f(i, j) = \sum_{j=1}^{m} \sum_{i=1}^{n} f(i, j)$. (That is, one can interchange the outer and inner summations, if the indices of the summations don't depend on each other.)

Proof: We use induction on n for an arbitrary m.

i) For $n = 1$ we need to show that

$$\sum_{i=1}^{1} \sum_{j=1}^{m} f(i, j) = \sum_{j=1}^{m} \sum_{i=1}^{1} f(i, j).$$

This is immediate, since either side of the equation reduces to

$$\sum_{j=1}^{m} f(1, j).$$

ii) Assume $\sum_{i=1}^{k} \sum_{j=1}^{m} f(i, j) = \sum_{j=1}^{m} \sum_{i=1}^{k} f(i, j)$.

Now

$$\sum_{i=1}^{k+1} \sum_{j=1}^{m} f(i, j) = \sum_{i=1}^{k} \sum_{j=1}^{m} f(i, j) + \sum_{j=1}^{m} f(k + 1, j)$$

$$= \sum_{j=1}^{m} \sum_{i=1}^{k} f(i, j) + \sum_{j=1}^{m} f(k + 1, j) \qquad \text{(\textit{inductive hypothesis})}$$

$$= \sum_{j=1}^{m} \left(\sum_{i=1}^{k} f(i, j) + f(k + 1, j) \right) \qquad \text{(Exercise 7(b), 3.2).} \ \square$$

In addition to double sums, one can describe sequences using double products or combinations of sums and products.

Example: $\sum_{i=1}^{3} \prod_{j=1}^{i} 2j = \prod_{j=1}^{1} 2j + \prod_{j=1}^{2} 2j + \prod_{j=1}^{3} 2j$
$= 2 \cdot 1 + 2^2 \cdot 2! + 2^3 \cdot 3! = 2 + 8 + 48 = 58$

Example: $\prod_{i=1}^{2} \sum_{j=1}^{2i} (i + j) = \left(\sum_{j=1}^{2} (1 + j) \right) \left(\sum_{j=1}^{4} (2 + j) \right)$
$= ((1 + 1) + (1 + 2)) ((2 + 1) + (2 + 2)$
$+ (2 + 3) + (2 + 4))$
$= 5 \times 18 = 90$

Question: Can summation and product be interchanged in a way similar to that for the double summations of Theorem 4.1-1?

Recursive and Explicit Definitions

One of the more exciting sports in the area of inductive definitions is that of finding an explicit description for a sequence which is given recursively.

Example: Let $S_1 = 2$ and $S_k = 2S_{k-1}$. What is an explicit expression for S_k? Let us compute some values so that we may see a pattern emerge. From this, we can determine an explicit formula.

$$S_1 = 2, \qquad S_2 = 2 \cdot S_1 = 2 \cdot 2, \qquad S_3 = 2 \cdot S_2 = 2 \cdot 2 \cdot 2, \qquad S_4 = 2^4, \ldots$$

Hence, for this sequence we see rather quickly that $\forall n \geq 1 \quad S_n = 2^n$.

Example: Let a sequence be given inductively by $S_1 = 1$, $S_{k+1} = 2^k S_k + 1$. Now

$S_1 = 1, S_2 = 2 \cdot 1 + 1,$
$S_3 = 2^2(2 + 1) + 1 = 2^3 + 2^2 + 1$
$S_4 = 2^3(2^3 + 2^2 + 1) + 1 = 2^6 + 2^5 + 2^3 + 1$
$S_5 = 2^4(2^6 + 2^5 + 2^3 + 1) + 1 = 2^{10} + 2^9 + 2^7 + 2^4 + 2^0$
$S_6 = 2^5(2^{10} + 2^9 + 2^7 + 2^4 + 2^0) + 1 = 2^{15} + 2^{14} + 2^{12} + 2^9 + 2^5 + 2^0$

After several pages of scratch paper, one notices that

$$\forall n \quad S_n = \sum_{i=1}^{n} 2^{\frac{n(n-1)}{2} - \frac{i(i-1)}{2}}.$$

Many recursively defined sequences can easily be given explicitly, while for others it is impossible. Like any other sport, this takes a great deal of practice in order to become proficient.

Subsequences

It is very often useful to consider a sequence derived from a given sequence by skipping some of the values. The new sequence derived in this fashion is called a "subsequence" of the original one.

Example: Let $S_n = n^2$ (*i.e.*, $S_1 = 1$, $S_2 = 4$, $S_3 = 9$, . . .). The sequence $a_m = m^4$ is a subsequence. Note that $a_1 = S_1 = 1$, $a_2 = S_4 = 16$, $a_3 = S_9 = 81$, ... Notice also that $a_m = S_m^2$.

4.1-2 Definition: Let $\{S_n\}$ be a sequence. If $\{a_m\}$ is a sequence given by $a_m = S_{f(m)}$, where f is a sequence of natural numbers such that $f(h) < f(h + 1)$, then $\{a_m\}$ is said to be a *subsequence* of $\{S_n\}$. (Subsequences are usually denoted by $\{S_{n_m}\}$, where n_m refers to the "increasing" sequence f in this definition.)

Example: Let $S_n = 2n + 1$.

$$S_1 = 3, \qquad S_2 = 5, \qquad S_3 = 7, \ldots$$

If $n_m = 3m$, then S_{n_m} yields the following values:

$$S_{n_1} = S_3 = 7, \qquad S_{n_2} = S_6 = 13, \qquad S_{n_3} = S_9 = 19, \ldots$$

Example: Find a formula for the values of S_{n_m}, where $S_n = n - 1$ and $n_m = 2m + 1$.

$$S_{n_1} = S_3 = 2, \qquad S_{n_2} = S_5 = 4, \qquad S_{n_3} = S_7 = 6$$

and $\forall m \quad S_{n_m} = S_{2m+1} = (2m + 1) - 1 = 2m$. Note that any sequence is a subsequence of itself where $n_m = m$.

Exercises 4.1

1. Evaluate $\sum_{j=1}^{5} (\sum_{i=1}^{j} (2 + i + j))$.

2. Evaluate:

a) $\sum_{i=1}^{3} \left(\sum_{j=1}^{i} 1 \right)$

b) $\sum_{i=1}^{4} \left(\sum_{j=1}^{i} j \right)$

3. Expand:

a) $\sum_{i=1}^{3} \left(\sum_{j=1}^{i} f(j) \right)$

c) $\sum_{i=1}^{3} \left(\sum_{j=1}^{3} (j + 1) \right)$

b) $\sum_{j=1}^{3} \left(\sum_{i=1}^{j} f(j) \right)$

d) $\sum_{j=1}^{2} \left(\sum_{i=1}^{3} (j + 1) \right)$

4. Expand $(\sum_{i=1}^{5} f(i))(\sum_{i=1}^{4} g(i))$, and compare with $\sum_{i=1}^{20} f(i) g(i)$.

5. Investigate (prove or disprove):

a) $\forall m, n \quad (\sum_{i=1}^{n} f(i))(\sum_{i=1}^{m} g(i)) = \sum_{i=1}^{nm} f(i) g(i)$.

b) If a, b are constant functions, then $\forall m, n$

$$\left(\sum_{i=1}^{n} a \right)\left(\sum_{i=1}^{m} b \right) = \sum_{i=1}^{nm} ab.$$

6. Let $\{S_n\}$ be a sequence such that $S_1 = 2$.

a) If $\forall n > 1 \quad S_n = 3S_{n-1}$, show that $S_n = 2 \cdot 3^{n-1}$.

b) If $\forall n > 1 \quad S_n = S_{n-1} + 5$, show that $S_n = 2 + 5(n - 1)$.

c) If $\forall n > 1 \quad S_n = (S_{n-1})^2$, show that $S_n = 2^{2^{n-1}}$.

d) If $\forall n > 1 \quad S_n = S_{n-1} + 2n$, show that $S_n = n(n + 1)$.

7. Evaluate or expand:

a) $\sum_{i=1}^{3} \left(\prod_{j=1}^{i} 2j \right)$

c) $\left(\prod_{i=1}^{3} f(i) \right)\left(\sum_{j=1}^{3} g(j) \right)$

b) $\prod_{i=1}^{3} \left(\sum_{j=1}^{i} 2j \right)$

d) $\sum_{j=1}^{3} \left(\prod_{i=1}^{3} f(i) \right) g(j)$

8. Simplify each of the following:

a) $8!/11!$

f) $\dfrac{n!}{(n - 1)!}$

b) $\dfrac{(n - 1)!(n + 1)!}{(n!)^2}$

g) $\dfrac{(n + 2)!}{(n - 1)!}$

c) $\dfrac{(10 + 3)!}{(12 - 1)!}$

h) $\dfrac{3! + 4!}{4!}$

d) $\dfrac{(n + 2)!}{n!}$

i) $\dfrac{5!}{(5 - 3)!3!}$

e) $\dfrac{3! + 5!}{5! - 3!}$

j) $\dfrac{8!}{(8 - 2)!2!}$

9. Determine an explicit formula for the following sequences given recursively.

   a) $S_1 = 1$, $S_k = 3S_{k-1}$
   b) $S_1 = 1$, $S_{k+1} = S_k + 1$
   c) $S_1 = 1/2$, $S_k = S_{k-1} + 2^{-k}$
   d) $S_1 = 3$, $S_{k+1} = 2^{S_k}$
   e) $S_1 = 1/3$, $S_k = 2kS_{k-1}$

10. Determine a formula for the values of the subsequence $\{S_{n_m}\}$ where

   a) $S_n = 3n + 1$ and $n_m = 2m$.
   b) $S_n = n^2$ and $n_m = 2m + 1$.
   c) $S_n = n^2 + 1$ and $n_m = 3m$.
   d) $S_n = 2n + 4$ and $n_m = m + 1$.

11. Show that the range set of a subsequence $\{S_{n_m}\}$ is a subset of the range set of the sequence $\{S_n\}$.

4.2 Proof for the Trichotomy in N, Strong Induction and the Well Ordering Principle

The Trichotomy in N

We would now like to present a proof of the trichotomy law for natural numbers which we stated without proof in Theorem 3.3-8. We shall include some logic diagrams which should help you understand the structure of the proof. One thing the student should do in reading a presentation of this sort is keep a sharp eye for cheating on the part of the writer. For example, make certain that no machinery is used in the proof which was developed from the theorem. To prove a theorem using results derived from itself would be very bad mathematics. (Why?)

In order to prove the theorem, we first establish a sequence of informative lemmas.

4.2-1 *Lemma:* $\forall m \in N$, $m + 1 \neq m$.

Proof: (By induction.)

1) $1 + 1 \neq 1$, because $1 + 1 = \varphi(1)$ by definition (where φ is the counting function), but by Axiom 3.1-1, 1 is not the successor of any natural number.

2) Assume $k + 1 \neq k$. Now if

$$(k + 1) + 1 = k + 1$$

then

$$k + 1 = k$$

by the cancellation law, which contradicts the induction hypothesis. Hence we conclude that

$$(k + 1) + 1 \neq k + 1.$$

Having established the two necessary results, we conclude by induction that the theorem is true. ☐

4.2-2 Lemma: $\forall n \in N$, if $n \neq 1$, then $1 < n$.

Proof: (By induction.)

1) "If $1 \neq 1$, then $1 < 1$" is true vacuously, since the hypothesis "$1 \neq 1$" is a false statement.

2) Assume that if $k \neq 1$, then $1 < k$. We wish to establish the implication if $k + 1 \neq 1$, then $1 < k + 1$.

We find an interesting thing happens in proving this implication: namely, that we do not need to use the hypothesis of the implication. In fact, we do not even need to use the induction hypothesis! The proof proceeds as follows:

$$1 + k = (k + 1)$$

and hence for some p (namely, $p = k$),

$$1 + p = (k + 1).$$

Thus, by definition $1 < k + 1$, and so we conclude that $\forall n$, if $n \neq 1$, then $1 < n$. ☐

The fact that we did not use the induction hypothesis in the above proof should indicate that perhaps we could make the proof without using induction. It can be done easily, and we leave it as an exercise for you to do so. (See Exercise 1.) But let us see what this means in terms of the axioms with which we began. A proof without induction leans heavily on the fact that there is only one element in N, namely 1, which is not a successor. We then wonder, since this proof could be done using induction, whether we had to state the uniqueness of the starting element in our axioms. It turns out that if we had made the induction axiom in terms of arbitrary elements which were not successors, then we could have proved that there was only one such element. Hence the uniqueness was unnecessary as an axiom. (See Exercise 2.)

Let us return to the work at hand.

4.2-3 Lemma: $\forall n \in N$, $n \not< 1$.

Proof: We use proof by contradiction. Assume $n < 1$. Then for some p, $n + p = 1$.

If $p = 1$, then $n + 1 = 1$ and this contradicts the fact that 1 is not a successor. If $p \neq 1$, then p is a successor, hence $p = k + 1$ for some k. Thus we have

$$n + (k + 1) = 1$$
$$(n + k) + 1 = 1$$

so again we have the contradiction that 1 is a successor. ☐

Logic diagram for Lemma 4.2-3: Define the following sentential variables.

$q =$ "$n < 1$," $r =$ "$n + p = 1$," $t =$ "$p = 1$," $s =$ "1 is not a successor."

$$\frac{\begin{array}{ll} q^{*1} \\ r \qquad t^{*2} \end{array}}{t \Rightarrow \text{not-}s}\ *2 \qquad\qquad \frac{\dfrac{\begin{array}{ll} q^{*1} \\ r \qquad \text{not-}t^{*3} \end{array}}{\dfrac{\text{not-}t \Rightarrow \text{not-}s}{\dfrac{\text{not-}s}{q \Rightarrow \text{not-}s}\ *1}}\ *3}{}$$

$$\frac{s \qquad\qquad\qquad\qquad q \Rightarrow \text{not-}s}{\text{not-}q}$$

4.2-4 Corollary: $\forall n \in N$, exactly one of the following is true:

$$1 = n, \qquad n < 1, \qquad 1 < n.$$

Proof: This follows directly from Lemmas 4.2-2 and 4.2-3. □

4.2-5 Lemma: $\forall n \in N \quad n \not< n$.

Proof: Let us show that $\forall p \forall n \quad n + p \neq n$. Let p be given and induct on n.

1) $1 + p \neq 1$, since 1 is not a successor.
2) Assume $k + p \neq k$. Now if

$$(k + 1) + p = k + 1$$

it follows that $k + p = k$, which contradicts the induction hypothesis. Therefore

$$(k + 1) + p \neq k + 1$$

and hence

$$\forall k \quad k + p \neq k \Rightarrow (k + 1) + p \neq k + 1.$$

It follows by induction that

$$\forall n \in N \quad n + p \neq n.$$

By test pattern logic, we have

$$\forall p \forall n \quad n + p \neq n.$$

Since the order of these two quantifiers can be exchanged, we have $\forall n \forall p$ $n + p \neq n$, which is equivalent with

$$\forall n \quad \text{not-}(\exists p \quad n + p = n)$$

which says $\forall n \quad \text{not-}(n < n)$, or equivalently, $\forall n \quad n \not< n$. □

Remark: Many of the details in the above proof would not ordinarily be printed, but would be left for the reader to work out himself.

4.2-6 Lemma: $\forall m, n \in N$ if $m \neq n$, then $m < n$ or $n < m$.

Proof: (By induction on n.)

1) If $m \neq 1$, then $1 < m$ (Lemma 4.2-2), from which it follows that if $m \neq 1$, then $1 < m$ or $m < 1$.

2) Assume that if $m \neq k$, then $k < m$ or $m < k$. Assume now that $m \neq k + 1$.

Case 1. $m = k$. We must have $m + 1 = (k + 1)$, and hence $\exists p \; m + p = k + 1$.

Therefore $m < k + 1$.

Case 2. $m \neq k$. By the induction hypothesis, $k < m$ or $m < k$. If $m < k$, then $m < k + 1$ by the transitive property. If $k < m$, then $k + p = m$ where $p \neq 1$. (Why?) Therefore, p is a successor for some q, and so

$$m = k + \varphi(q) = k + (q + 1) = (k + 1) + q.$$

That is, $(k + 1) + q = m$, and hence $k + 1 < m$. Hence $m \neq k \Rightarrow k + 1 < m$ or $m < k + 1$. We conclude by induction that the theorem is true. $\square$

4.2-7 Lemma: $\forall m, n \in N$, if $m < n$, then $n \not< m$.

Proof: (By contradiction.) Assume that $m < n$ and $n < m$. Then

$$m + p_1 = n \qquad \text{and} \qquad n + p_2 = m$$

so that

$$m + (p_1 + p_2) = m.$$

Therefore $m < m$, which contradicts Lemma 4.2-5. Hence we conclude that $m < n \Rightarrow n \not< m$. $\square$

We are now in position to prove the very important "Trichotomy Law."

4.2-8 Theorem: (Trichotomy Law) $\forall m, n \in N$, exactly one of the following is true:

a) $m = n$
b) $m < n$
c) $n < m$

Proof:

Case 1. $m = n$. By Lemma 4.2-5, $m \not< n$ and $n \not< m$.

Case 2. $m \neq n$. By Lemma 4.2-6, $m < n$ or $n < m$, and by Lemma 4.2-7, it follows that both cannot occur. $\square$

Logic diagram for trichotomy law:

Let $p = $ "$m = n$," $q = $ "$m < n$," $r = $ "$n < m$," $s = $ "exactly one of p, q, r."

$$\frac{p^{*1}}{p^{*1}, \text{not-}q \text{ and not-}r} \text{ (Lemma 4.2-5)} \qquad \frac{\text{not-}p^{*2}}{\text{not-}p^{*2}, q \text{ or } r, q \Rightarrow \text{not-}r} \text{ (Lemma 4.2-6)}$$

$$\frac{s}{p \Rightarrow s} \ast 1 \qquad\qquad \frac{s}{\text{not-}p \Rightarrow s} \ast 2$$

$$s$$

We would now like to establish some fairly sophisticated variations of the induction axiom which are often more effective than the standard inductive method.

Strong Induction

The result we establish here is a theorem that is equivalent to the induction principle. Due to the fact that it permits, in the "induction hypothesis," a stronger assumption, it is often effective in situations which do not permit proof by regular induction. For this reason it is often called "strong induction."

4.2-9 Theorem: *("Strong Induction")*

If 1) $p(1)$,   and

2) $\forall m$ $p(1)$ and $p(2)$ and . . . and $p(m) \Rightarrow p(m+1)$,

then $\forall n \in N$ $p(n)$.

Proof:

1) $p(1)$ given.

2) Let $k \in N$ and assume $p(k)$. Now $p(1) \Rightarrow p(2)$.

Therefore we have $p(1)$ and $p(2)$, but

$$p(1) \quad \text{and} \quad p(2) \Rightarrow p(3) \quad \text{(by 2) above).}$$

Hence inductively we have $p(1)$ and $p(2)$ and . . . and $p(k)$. It follows (again by 2)) that $p(k+1)$. Hence

$$\forall k \in N \quad p(k) \Rightarrow p(k+1)$$

and so by induction $\forall n \in N$ $p(n)$. □

Naturally the variations on induction described earlier also apply for strong induction.

The Well Ordering Principle

Another useful fact about natural numbers, which is logically equivalent to the induction axiom, is the "Well Ordering Principle." We shall only show here that this law holds, and leave it as an exercise for you to show that the induction axiom is implied by the Well Ordering Principle.

4.2-10 Definition: If A is an ordered set, then A is said to be *well ordered* provided any non-empty subset of A has a least element.

(That is, $(B \subset A, B \neq \varnothing) \Rightarrow (\exists x \in B \quad \forall y \in B \quad x \leq y)$.)

4.2-11 Theorem: The natural numbers N are well ordered.

Proof: Let $M = \{m \in N$: any subset of N containing m has a least element$\}$.

i) $1 \in M$ since $\forall x \in N \quad 1 \le x$.

ii) Assume $k \in M$. That is, any subset of N which contains k has a least element.

Let E be an arbitrary subset of N which contains $k + 1$. Now $S = E \cup \{k\}$ has a least element. If the least element of S is not k, then E has a least element, namely the same number which was a least element for S. If the least element of S is k, then E has $k + 1$ as a least element, since there are no natural numbers between k and $k + 1$. (See Exercise 10(f), 3.3.)

Then, by induction, $M = N$. That is, $\forall n \in N$, any subset of N which contains n as an element possesses a least element. Hence any non-empty subset of N has a least element. $\square$

We shall have occasion in the next few sections to call on these two very important forms of induction.

Exercises   4.2

1.   Show, without using induction, that if $n \ne 1$, then $1 < n$, where $n \in N$. (*Hint:* Use the uniqueness of the starting number 1. That is, 1 is the only natural number which is not a successor.)

2.   Consider an induction axiom which reads: If $H \subset N$ and

    1) $x \in H$ and $\forall n \quad \varphi(n) \ne x$,   and

    2) H is hereditary,

then $H = N$.

Show that if $\forall n \quad \varphi(n) \ne x$ and $\forall n \quad \varphi(n) \ne y$, then $x = y$. (That is, show that we need not have axiomatically assumed the uniqueness of the "first natural number.")

3.   Show that the Well Ordering Principle is sufficient to guarantee the induction principle.

4.   Define $\bigcup_{i=1}^{n} S_i$ and $\bigcap_{i=1}^{n} S_i$, where S_i is a sequence of sets,

    a) using a recursive definition;

    b) in terms of index sets.

5.   Let A_i be a sequence of sets. Define:

a) $\overset{1}{\underset{i=1}{\times}} A_i = A_1$ *b*) $\overset{k+1}{\underset{i=1}{\times}} A_i = A_{k+1} \times \left(\overset{k}{\underset{i=1}{\times}} A_i \right)$

If $A_1 = \{a, b, c\}, \quad A_2 = \{a, b, d\}, \quad A_3 = \{a, e\}$, find:

d) $\overset{3}{\underset{i=1}{\times}} A_i$ *e*) $\overset{3}{\underset{i=1}{\bigcup}} A_i$ *f*) $\overset{3}{\underset{i=1}{\bigcap}} A_i$.

6.   Prove by induction:

$$\sum_{i=1}^{n} i(i+1)^2 = \frac{n(n+1)(n+2)(3n+5)}{12}$$

7. Show that for each positive integer n, there exists a positive integer c such that $5^{2n} - 1 = 24c$. (Keep in mind that c can depend on n.)

8. Show by induction that the number of subsets of a finite set with n elements is 2^n. (That is, $\#2^A = 2^n$ if $\#A = n$.)

9. Use the Well Ordering Principle to show that $A \cup B$ is finite, provided A and B are finite.

4.3 Existence of the gcd, and The Euclidean Algorithm

Euclid's Lemma and the Fundamental Theorem of Arithmetic

In Section 3.7 we introduced and used the fact that any pair of integers has a greatest common divisor. We apologized then for not presenting its proof and promised to present it in the present chapter. The proof is interesting in that the induction principle is applied in the alternate form we discussed in the last section: the Well Ordering Principle. The proof is also interesting because we develop in it a result of importance for further number theoretic results.

4.3-1 Theorem: If $a, b \in Z$, then there exists an element $d \in Z$, $d \geq 0$ such that $(d|a$ and $d|b)$ and $(d'|a$ and $d'|b) \Rightarrow d'|d$. (That is, given $a, b \in Z$, $gcd(a, b)$ exists.)

Proof: If $a = b = 0$, then $d = 0$ satisfies the theorem. Therefore assume that $a \neq 0$ and let $S = \{p \in N: p = ax + by$ for some $x, y \in Z\}$. Now $p = aa + b0 \in N$, therefore $S \neq \emptyset$.

By the Well Ordering Principle, S has a smallest natural number d, where $d = ax + by$ for some $x, y \in Z$. We shall show that d satisfies the conditions of the theorem. Clearly $d > 0$. By the division theorem, there exists q and r such that $a = dq + r$ and $0 \leq r < d$. Thus

$$r = a - dq = a - (ax + by)q = a - axq - byq = a(1 - xq) + b(-yq).$$

If $r > 0$, then $r \in S$. But this would contradict the fact that d is the smallest element in S, since $r < d$. Hence $r = 0$, from which we get $a = dq$. Therefore $d|a$, and similarly $d|b$. Now if $d'|a$ and $d'|b$, then $d'|ax + by$ (i.e., $d'|d$). $\square$

4.3-2 Corollary: (To the proof) If d is a $gcd(a, b)$, then $d = ax + by$ for some $x, y \in Z$.

Remark: We have established now that for $a, b \in Z$ there exists a unique $gcd(a, b)$ and that $gcd(a, b) = ax + by$ for some $x, y \in Z$. (For uniqueness, see Theorem 3.7-13.) Note, however, that the x and y are not unique, since $a(x + b) + b(y - a) = ax + by$.

In Chapter 3 we discussed a method for computing greatest common divisors by using the Fundamental Theorem of Arithmetic. We would now like to establish a systematic method, known as "Euclid's Algorithm", for computing this number. In order to use this algorithm, it is sufficient to be able to find $gcd(a, b)$ for any $a, b \in N$.

4.3-3 The Euclidean Algorithm
Let $a, b \in N$ and assume $a \le b$.

Let $r_0 = a$. By the division property $b = aq_1 + r_1$ where $0 \le r_1 < a$.

Also

$$a = r_0 = r_1 q_2 + r_2 \qquad \text{where} \qquad 0 \le r_2 < r_1$$
$$r_1 = r_2 q_3 + r_3 \qquad \text{where} \qquad 0 \le r_3 < r_2$$

$$\vdots \qquad\qquad\qquad\qquad \vdots$$

$$r_{n-1} = r_n q_{n+1} + r_{n+1} \qquad \text{where} \qquad 0 \le r_{n+1} < r_n$$
$$r_n = r_{n+1} q_{n+2} + r_{n+2} \qquad \text{where} \qquad 0 \le r_{n+2} < r_{n+1}$$

By continuing this recursive process of "dividing the previous remainder by the most recent remainder", one eventually gets a remainder of 0. (Note that this is an application of the Well Ordering Principle.) The last non-zero remainder in this process is the $gcd(a, b)$ because:

i) If $r_{n+2} = 0$, then $r_{n+1}|r_n$, $r_{n+1}|r_{n-1}$, etc., until finally $r_{n+1}|r_1$ and $r_{n+1}|r_0 = a$. It then also follows that $r_{n+1}|b$.

ii) If $d|a$ and $d|b$, then $d|r_1$, from which $d|r_2$, etc., until finally $d|r_{n+1}$. □

Example: Find $gcd(483, 561)$.

$$561 = 1 \times 483 + 78$$
$$483 = 6 \times 78 + 15$$
$$78 = 5 \times 15 + 3$$
$$15 = 3 \times 5 + 0$$

Hence $gcd(483, 561) = 3$.

Example: Find $gcd(64, 82)$.

$$82 = 1 \times 64 + 18$$
$$64 = 3 \times 18 + 10$$
$$18 = 1 \times 10 + 8$$
$$10 = 1 \times 8 + 2$$
$$8 = 4 \times 2 + 0$$

Hence $gcd(64, 82) = 2$.

We now progress toward the proof of the Fundamental Theorem of Arithmetic. We must first establish a result with which you are familiar. We previously asked you to prove this result, using the Fundamental Theorem.

Of course, we could not use this result in our proof without establishing its truth by some other means.

4.3-4 Theorem: (*Euclid's lemma*) Let a, $b \in Z$ and let p be prime. If $p|ab$, then $p|a$ or $p|b$.

Proof: If $p \nmid a$, then $\gcd(p, a) = 1$ (see Exercise 6) so that by Corollary 4.3-2, $1 = px + ay$ for some $x, y \in Z$. Multiplying both sides of this equation by b, we have $b = pxb + ayb = p(xb) + (ab)y$. Since $p|ab$ and $p|p$, it follows that $p|b$. □

The Fundamental Theorem of Arithmetic

We are now prepared to establish the result we promised. In the proof of the Fundamental Theorem you should notice that we use "strong induction" rather than the standard inductive principle.

4.3-5 Theorem: (*The Unique Factorization Theorem*), (*The Fundamental Theorem of Arithmetic*)

$\forall n \in N$, there exists prime natural numbers $p_1, p_2, \ldots, p_r$ such that

$$n = p_1 \cdot p_2 \ldots p_r$$
and if
$$n = q_1 \cdot q_2 \ldots q_h$$

where $q_1, q_2, \ldots, q_h$ are prime, then there is a *1-1* correspondence

$$f: \{p_1, p_2, \ldots, p_r\} \xrightarrow[onto]{1-1} \{q_1, q_2, \ldots, q_h\}$$

such that $f(p_i) = p_i$, $i = 1, 2, \ldots, r$.

Proof: (By strong induction.)

i) If $n = 2$, then clearly the result holds since 2 is a prime. Namely, $2 = 2$ is the factorization and $f(2) = 2$ is the correspondence.

ii) If n is prime, then again the result holds. If n is not prime, then $n = sm$ where $1 < s < n$ and $1 < m < n$.

Now by the induction hypothesis (strong induction) $s = p_1 p_2 \ldots p_r$ and $m = p_1' p_2' \ldots p_b'$, both unique products of prime numbers. Hence $n = p_1 p_2 \ldots p_r p_1' \ldots p_b'$. (This proves existence.)

For uniqueness, let $n = q_1 q_2 \ldots q_h = sm$. Therefore $q_1|s$ or $q_1|m$ (by Euclid's lemma). *WLOG*, assume $q_1|s$. By hypothesis, s can be factored only one way, therefore $q_1 = p_i$ for some $i \in \{1, \ldots, r\}$. *WLOG* we may assume $p_1 = q_1$ by using the commutative law. It follows that $n = q_1 q = q_1(p_2 p_3 \ldots p_r p_1' p_2' \ldots p_b')$ where $q = p_2 p_3 \ldots p_r p_1' p_2' \ldots p_b'$ and $q < n$. By the induction hypothesis, q can be factored in only one way. Therefore $q_2 q_3, \ldots q_h = p_2 p_3 \ldots p_r p_1' p_2' \ldots p_b'$ where there is a *1-1* correspondence f.

274

$$f: \{p_2, p_3, \ldots, p_r, p'_1, p'_2, \ldots, p'_b\} \xrightarrow[onto]{1\text{-}1} \{q_2, q_3, \ldots q_h\}$$

such that $f(p_i) = p_i$, $i = 2, 3, \ldots$ (taking the p'_i's into account). f can easily be extended by defining $f(p_1) = q_1 = p_1$, so that it is the *1-1* correspondence between the two factorizations of n. □

We conclude this section with a discussion of a process for finding x and y such that $gcd(m, n) = mx + ny$ for m and n positive integers. Consider the following example.

Example: $gcd(19, 23) = 1$. By repeated use of the division theorem, we have the following:

$$23 = 1 \cdot 19 + 4$$
$$19 = 4 \cdot 4 + 3$$
$$4 = 1 \cdot 3 + 1$$

Upon "solving" these,

$$4 = 23 - 19$$
$$3 = 19 - 4 \cdot 4$$
$$1 = 4 - 3$$

Now by several substitutions,

$$1 = 4 - (19 - 4 \cdot 4) = 4 - 19 + 4 \cdot 4$$
$$= 5 \cdot 4 - 19 = 5(23 - 19) - 19$$
$$= 5 \cdot 23 - 5 \cdot 19 - 19 = 5 \cdot 23 - 6 \cdot 19$$

Notice how the first steps of this process resemble the algorithm for finding the *gcd*.

Example: $gcd(10, 64) = 2$.

$$64 = 6 \cdot 10 + 4 \Leftrightarrow 4 = 64 - 6 \cdot 10$$
$$10 = 2 \cdot 4 + 2 \Leftrightarrow 2 = 10 - 2 \cdot 4$$

Now by substitution,

$$2 = 10 - 2(64 - 6 \cdot 10) = 10 - 2 \cdot 64 + 12 \cdot 10 = 13 \cdot 10 - 2 \cdot 64$$

Note also that by the remark following Corollary 4.3-2, we have $2 = (13 + 64)10 + (64 - 10) - 2$.

Exercises 4.3

1. Use the Euclidean algorithm to find:

   a) $gcd(24, 160)$ d) $gcd(139, 463)$
   b) $gcd(602, 803)$ e) $gcd(1204, 876)$
   c) $gcd(1766, 468)$ f) $gcd(138, 768)$

2. Show that if $a|b$ where $a, b \in N$, and if $a > \sqrt{b}$, then for some $c < \sqrt{b}, ac = b$. Explain how this fact can be useful in testing a number for primeness.

3. Assume that $p > 1$ such that $p|ab \Rightarrow p|a$ or $p|b$. Show that p is prime. (*Hint:* Supply some missing quantifiers.)

4. Find $x, y \in Z$ such that:

   a) $gcd(4, 6) = 4x + 6y$ *d)* $gcd(-12, 3) = -12x + 3y$

   b) $gcd(8, 14) = 8x + 14y$ *e)* $gcd(-24, -9) = -24x - 9y$

   c) $gcd(24, 36) = 24x + 36y$

5. Prove Corollary 4.3-2.

6. Without using the Fundamental Theorem of Arithmetic, prove that if $p \nmid a$, then $gcd(a, p) = 1$.

7. Investigate (prove or disprove):

   a) For every positive integer n, $n^2 + n + 17$ is prime.

   b) For every positive integer n, $n^2 + n + 41$ is prime.

   c) Every integer can be written in the form $p + 2^n$ where either p or $-p$ is prime and $n \in N$.

   d) Every integer can be written in the form $p + 2n^2$ where p or $-p$ is prime and $n \in N$.

8. Establish (prove) that every prime greater than 3 is either 1 more or 1 less than some multiple of 6.*

4.4 Decomposition of Rational Numbers into Partial Fractions†

The material in this section is designed to serve a dual purpose. The first purpose is to gain insight into an operation through decomposing or "undoing" it. The second is to consider a process in a familiar number ring (the rational numbers), which we later shall extend to a less familiar system. The process of partial fraction decomposition is a necessary skill in the solution of many problems. Although this decomposition is ordinarily done in certain function spaces, it can also be done in the set of rational numbers.

The process we wish to consider is that of "un-adding" fractions. Recall the theorem for adding rational numbers, $p/q + m/n = np + mq/qn$. For example,

$$\frac{1}{2} + \frac{2}{3} = \frac{3+4}{2 \cdot 3} = \frac{7}{6} \quad \text{and} \quad \frac{2}{5} + \frac{1}{3} = \frac{6+5}{15} = \frac{11}{15}.$$

It seems, then, that given $11/15$, we should be able to find a method for decomposing it into $2/5 + 1/3$. Some of the questions we should ask are:

---

* For more information on the distribution of primes see the *Scientific American—Prime Number Patterns*, March 1964.

† Much of the material in this section was suggested by William A. Miller, WSU—Whitewater. See "Partial Fractions for the Junior and Senior High Mathematics Programs." *School Science and Mathematics*, January, 1968.

a) When can a fraction m/n be decomposed into the sum of certain more fundamental fractions?

b) What exactly do we mean by "decompose" and "more fundamental" in *a)*?

c) How can one determine the decomposition, if it exists?

Before we study this problem further, let us consider the following theorem.

4.4-1 Theorem: If $m \in Z$, n, $k \in N$ and $gcd(n, k) = 1$, then the fraction m/nk can be expressed as the sum of two fractions with denominators n and k. That is, there exist $a, b \in Z$ such that

$$\frac{m}{nk} = \frac{a}{n} + \frac{b}{k}.$$

Proof: By Corollary 4.3-2, there exist integers x and y such that $1 = nx + ky$. Hence

$$\frac{m}{nk} = \frac{m(nx + ky)}{nk} = \frac{mnx + mky}{nk} = \frac{mx}{k} + \frac{my}{n}. \quad \square$$

Example: Decompose $\dfrac{3}{14} = \dfrac{3}{2 \cdot 7}$ into the form $\dfrac{a}{2} + \dfrac{b}{7}$. Using the method described in the last section $1 = 7 - 3.2$. Thus $\dfrac{3}{14} = \dfrac{3(7 - 3 \cdot 2)}{2 \cdot 7} = \dfrac{3}{2} + \dfrac{-9}{7}$.

Example: Decompose $\dfrac{6}{35}$ into the form $\dfrac{a}{5} + \dfrac{b}{7}$.

Now $1 = 3 \cdot 7 - 4 \cdot 5$. Therefore $\dfrac{6}{35} = \dfrac{6(3 \cdot 7 - 4 \cdot 5)}{5 \cdot 7} = \dfrac{18}{5} - \dfrac{24}{7}$.

Notice also that $1 = 3 \cdot 5 - 2 \cdot 7$ and hence

$$\frac{6}{35} = \frac{6(3 \cdot 5 - 2 \cdot 7)}{35} = \frac{18}{7} - \frac{12}{5}.$$

Question: Is there anything significant in this example associated with the fact that $gcd(18, 24) = 6 = gcd(18, 12)$?

Let us generalize this procedure somewhat to the possibility of decomposing a fraction into the sum of two fractions whose denominators are not prime.

Example: Consider the fraction $10/24 = 10/4 \cdot 6$.

We would like to write this in the form $a/4 + b/6$ even though $gcd(4, 6) = 2$. We know that $2 = 4x + 6y$ for some $x, y \in Z$. Previously we could put our fraction into the desired form by multiplying it by 1 in a special form. In this case, however, we are working with 2. We notice something special about the numerator. Namely, it contains a factor of 2. We thus have

$$\frac{10}{4 \cdot 6} = \frac{5 \cdot 2}{4 \cdot 6} = \frac{5(4x + 6y)}{4 \cdot 6} = \frac{5x}{6} + \frac{5y}{4}.$$

277

Question: Do you think you can decompose $5/24$ into the form $a/4 + b/6$? (*Hint:* Recall Exercise 10, 3.7.)

This leads us to the following generalization of Theorem 4.4-1.

4.4-2 Theorem: If m/nk is a rational number $(m, n, k \in Z)$, and if $\gcd(n, k)$ is a factor of m, then $m/nk = a/n + b/k$ for some $a, b \in Z$.

Proof: Let $d = \gcd(n, k)$ and $m = dp$. Then $d = nx + ky$ for some x, $y \in Z$, hence

$$\frac{m}{nk} = \frac{qd}{nk} = \frac{q(nx + ky)}{nk} = \frac{qx}{k} + \frac{qy}{n}. \quad \square$$

We conclude this section with a process for decomposing a fraction m/p^n, where $m, n \in N$ and p is a prime.

Example: Consider $79/7^3$. By the division theorem,

$$79 = 11 \cdot 7 + 2$$

and

$$11 = 1 \cdot 7 + 4$$

hence

$$79 = (7 + 4)7 + 2 = 7 \cdot 7 + 4 \cdot 7 + 2$$

therefore

$$\frac{79}{7^3} = \frac{7 \cdot 7 + 4 \cdot 7 + 2}{7^3} = \frac{1}{7} + \frac{4}{7^2} + \frac{2}{7^3}.$$

Example: Consider $182/5^3$. Now

$$182 = 36 \cdot 5 + 2 \qquad 36 = 7 \cdot 5 + 1 \qquad 7 = 1 \cdot 5 + 2$$

and hence

$$182 = (7 \cdot 5 + 1)5 + 2 = 7 \cdot 5^2 + 5 + 2 = (5 + 2)5^2 + 5 + 2$$
$$= 5^3 + 2 \cdot 5^2 + 5 + 2.$$

Thus

$$\frac{182}{5^3} = \frac{5^3 + 2 \cdot 5^2 + 5 + 2}{5^3} = 1 + \frac{2}{5} + \frac{1}{5^2} + \frac{2}{5^3}.$$

We state this formally in the following theorem.

4.4-3 Theorem: If $n, m, p \in N$ where p is a prime, then there exists $a \in N_0$ and $r_i \in N_0$, $i = 1, 2, \ldots, n$ where the r_i's are less than p such that

$$\frac{m}{p^n} = a + \sum_{i=1}^{n} \frac{r_i}{p^i}.$$

The proof is left as an exercise.

Exercises 4.4

1. Decompose each fraction a/b below into the sum of two fractions whose denominators are the prime factors of the denominators b:

a) $3/14$ *c)* $9/34$ *e)* $12/51$ *g)* $4/15$

b) $7/15$ *d)* $16/77$ *f)* $1/9$ *h)* $20/21$

2. Decompose each fraction a/b below into the sum of two fractions whose denominators are indicated by the way b is factored:

a) $\dfrac{9}{6 \cdot 7}$ b) $\dfrac{9}{2 \cdot 21}$ c) $\dfrac{16}{6 \cdot 10}$ d) $\dfrac{12}{15 \cdot 21}$

3. Investigate (prove or disprove):

If $m/kn = a/k + b/n$, $gcd(k, n) = 1$, and also $m/kn = c/k + d/n$, then $gcd(a, b) = gcd(c, d) = m$.

4. Decompose each of the following into an integer plus a sum of fractions according to Theorem 4.4-3:

a) $16/3^3$ b) $241/5^4$ c) $21/2^2$ d) $380/7^5$ e) $429/11^4$

5. Prove Theorem 4.4-3.

6. Can you generalize Theorem 4.4-3 to include decompositions of m/k^n where k is not prime? Use the methods described in the examples preceding Theorem 4.4-3 to decompose the following:

a) $261/4^4$ b) $743/6^5$ c) $900/15^3$ d) $276/9^4$ e) $521/8^5$

4.5   The General Completeness Theorem, Existence of Square Roots, The Archimedean Property and Its Consequences

In Chapter 3, Sections 11, 12, and 13, we made a light study of the important extension of the rational field to the real field. In this section we will establish some of the results which we left unproved, and also establish one of the basic "heavy artillery pieces" known as "the Archimedean Property."

Recall that we observed a "topological" weakness of the rational number line; it has "holes." To eliminate this deficiency, we imbedded the ordered set Q in an ordered set R just large enough to do the job. We insisted that every non-empty set of *rational numbers* bounded above by a *rational number* have a least upper bound in R. (Possibly rational or irrational.) Since we are now dealing with the larger set, we desire to generalize this property to non-empty subsets of R. We stated this theorem earlier without proof, and wish to establish it formally now.

4.5-1 Theorem: If $H \subset R$, $H \neq \varnothing$, and H is bounded above (by any element of R), then sup H exists in R.

279

Proof: By Theorem 3.11-4, H is bounded above by a rational number. Now if $x \in H$, then $x = \sup S_x$, $S_x = \{r: r < x, r \in Q\}$. Let

$$S = \bigcup_{x \in H} S_x.$$

Clearly $S \neq \varnothing$. Further $S \subset Q$, and is bounded above by a rational number since any upper bound for H is also an upper bound for S. Therefore $\sup S$ exists. If $x \subset H$, then $x = \sup S_x$ and since $S_x \subset S$, it follows that $\sup S_x \leq \sup S$ (*i.e.*, $x \leq \sup S$ for every $x \in H$), and so H is bounded above by $\sup S$. Any upper bound for H is also an upper bound for S. Therefore if b bounds H from above, then $\sup S \leq b$. Hence we have satisfied the definition for $\sup S$ to be a least upper bound for H. That is, $\sup S = \sup H$. ▢

Having solved the problem of having holes in our number line, we found ourselves faced with a new one. We no longer had a set of numbers with a nice algebra. In the rational numbers we had a very orderly algebraic system. (Q is a field.) We wished to extend this algebra to include the newly attached irrational numbers in a way that preserved as many of the familiar rational number properties as possible. We decided then to extend our operations in a fashion which would keep two numbers "close together" after being added or multiplied by a third number provided they were "close" to begin with. That is, the stretching and shrinking of intervals under the operations would not be too severe.

Example: Consider the interval $(1/7, 4/3)$. Let $S = \{3x: x \in (1/7, 4/3)\}$. Then by using properties of rational numbers and the facts mentioned above, we deduce that $S = (3/7, 4)$.

Example: Consider the interval $(1/2, 3/4)$. Let $S = \{xy: x, y \in (1/2, 3/4)\}$. Upon examination of various possibilities (usually done by multiplying rational numbers), we find that $S = (1/4, 9/16)$. In making this deduction, we liberally use the various inequality properties of rational numbers. We deduce that the irrational combinations fall in the same interval from the fact that we arranged our extension of this operation so that no number would be moved "far" from its neighbors under multiplication and addition.

In a sense, it is rather amazing that in extending our operations "$+$" and "$\cdot$" from Q to R, we preserved *all* of the field properties. Not only that, we preserved *all* of our manipulative devices for solving equations and inequalities. What more could one ask than an extension that solved a problem and cost nothing! In making this development, we "begged off" proving that R possesses all of the field properties. We still plan to take this position, since the proofs are very tedious and contribute very little to the student's understanding at this level. We do, however, hope to capture the *spirit* of such proofs and at the same time deduce some very important facts.

Recall that we promised a result guaranteeing that irrational numbers exist, and also to show that all positive rational numbers have square roots.

We could do both of these things at once, showing that all positive rational numbers have square roots in R since certain numbers have no square root in Q. We shall show only that 2 has a square root, and leave it to the students' faith that similar proofs can be given for other numbers.

4.5-2 Lemma: If r_1, r_2 are positive rational numbers such that $r_1 < r_2$, then there exists some positive rational number q such that $r_1 < q^2 < r_2$.

Question: Need r_1 be positive in order for this result to hold? We leave the proof of this result as an exercise for the student, although it is by no means an easy problem. It is a problem which can be easily understood, and the insight a student can gain by attempting to solve this problem is immeasurable.

4.5-3 Theorem: Let $x = \sup S$ where $S = \{r: r^2 < 2\}$. By the definition of multiplication for real numbers, $x^2 = \sup T$, where $T = \{r_1 r_2: r_1 \leq x$ and $r_2 \leq x\}$. It follows that $x^2 = 2$.

Note: In this theorem, all numbers r, q, x referred to are taken to be positive.

Proof: First, we claim that if $r < x$, then $r^2 < 2$ because: $r < x \Rightarrow r < q$ for some $q \in S$ since $x = \sup S$ (for otherwise r would bound S and we would have an upper bound smaller than the smallest one), from which $r^2 < q^2$, and $q^2 < 2$, since $q \in S$. Hence $r^2 < 2$. Conversely (or nearly conversely), if $r^2 < 2$, then $r \leq x$ (why?).

We now would like to argue that $x \notin Q$. We do this using the trichotomy law in each of several cases, arriving at a contradiction under the assumption that $x \in Q$. It is immediate that $x^2 \neq 2$ since 2 has no square root in Q. If $x^2 > 2$, then $x^2 > q^2 > 2$ by the lemma. It follows that $x > q$, and from the first part of this proof, we have that $q^2 < 2$, a contradiction. The third case is $x^2 < 2$. By the lemma, $x^2 < q^2 < 2$, from which we deduce that $x < q$. But since $q^2 < 2$, we know that $q \in S$. This is a contradiction, since x is an upper bound for S from which $q \leq x$.

Now we proceed with the heart of the proof. We shall establish two facts. We will show that both $x^2 \leq 2$ and $2 \leq x^2$, from which we have $x^2 = 2$. Consider $r_1 \leq x$ and $r_2 \leq x$, so that $r_1 r_2 \in T$. Since x is not rational, we know that $r_1 < x$ and $r_2 < x$, and from the first preliminary result of this proof we know that $r_1^2 < 2$ and $r_2^2 < 2$. For some rational numbers t_1 and t_2, $r_1^2 < t_1 < 2$ and $r_2^2 < t_2 < 2$. *WLOG*, assume $t_1 \leq t_2$ and therefore $r_1^2 < t_2$. It follows that $r_1^2 r_2^2 < t_2^2$ from which $(r_1 r_2)^2 < t_2^2$. Hence $r_1 r_2 < t_2 < 2$. Therefore 2 is an upper bound for T, and since x^2 is the least upper bound we have $x^2 \leq 2$.

Now in order to show that $2 \leq x^2$, we use a similar technique and an application of the preceding lemma. Let $K = \{r: r < 2\}$, so that $2 = \sup K$. For any $r \in K$, $r < 2$ and by the lemma, there is some $q > 0$ such that $r < q^2 < 2$. It follows that $q \in S$, and therefore $q \leq x$. (Why?) Hence $q^2 \in T$ and therefore $q^2 \leq x^2$. But $r < q^2$, and it follows that x^2 is an upper bound for K. Since 2 is the least upper bound for K, we have $2 \leq x^2$. □

Question: Being satisfied that each positive rational number has a square root, does this guarantee that any positive real number has a square root? How difficult would it be to guarantee this fact?

The Archimedean Law and Its Consequences

We would now like to develop some very important properties of the real numbers. These properties are strongly related to the induction axiom for natural numbers. Recall that one of the properties of natural numbers is the fact that there is no largest one. That is, you can always "count" higher than any given number. Although the real numbers do not form a "counting" type of number system, they contain N as a subset. We might be curious, then, as to whether we can count high enough to supersede any given real number.

4.5-4 Lemma: If $x \in R$, then $\exists m \in N$ such that $m > x$.

Proof: We have already shown that there is a $q \in Q$ where $q > x$ as a result of the axioms for R. Now $q = m/n$ where $m, n \in Z$. $m/n \leq |m/n| = \frac{|m|}{|n|} \leq \frac{|m|}{|n|} |n| = |m|$. Therefore $x < m/n \leq |m|$. $\square$

4.5-5 Theorem: (*The Archimedean Property*) If $x, y \in R$, $(x > 0)$, then for some $n \in N$, $y < nx$.

Proof: $y/x \in R$ since $x \neq 0$, so by the lemma $\exists n \in Z$ such that

$$y/x < n.$$

Since $x > 0$, we know that $x(y/x) < nx$, or that $y < nx$. $\square$

Thus we know that we can not only count past any real number, but, by taking natural number multiples of some positive real number, can exceed any given number.

The following are some important and useful consequences of the Archimedean Property.

4.5-6 Theorem: If $x \in R$, then there exists a unique $n \in Z$ such that

$$n \leq x < n + 1.$$

Proof: Let $A = \{m \in Z: x < m\}$. By the Archimedean Property, there is a natural number h such that $x < h \cdot 1$, and therefore $A \neq \emptyset$. Clearly A is bounded below (by x). Hence let $n + 1 = \inf A$. We know, since A is a set of integers, that $\inf A \in A$, therefore $x < n + 1$. On the other hand, $n \leq x$; otherwise $n + 1$ would not be a lower bound for A. Thus, $n \leq x < n + 1$. To show uniqueness, let $k \leq x < k + 1$ where $k \in Z$. Then

$$k \leq x < n + 1$$

and $$n \leq x < k + 1$$

so that $\quad\quad k < n + 1 \quad$ and $\quad n < k + 1.$

Therefore $\quad\quad k \leq n \quad$ and $\quad n \leq k$

and hence $\quad\quad\quad\quad k = n.$ □

4.5-7 Theorem: (*Euclidean Property*) If $x, y \in R$ and $x > 0$, then there exists a unique $n \in Z$ and a unique $r \in R$ such that

$$y = nx + r \quad \text{where} \quad 0 \leq r < x.$$

Proof: Let $A = \{m \in Z : mx \leq y\}.$

(Existence) Let $z = \max \{y, -y\}$. By the Archimedean Property $\exists k \quad z < kx$. Therefore $(-k)x < -z \leq y$, so $A \neq \emptyset$. Obviously, A is bounded above by y/x. Hence $nx \leq y$, (n being sup A) since the least upper bound for a collection of integers is always in the set. Let $r = y - nx$, so that $nx + r = y$. Further, $0 \leq r < x$, for otherwise $n + 1 \in A$, which contradicts the fact that n is an upper bound for A.

(Uniqueness) Assume $nx + r_1 = kx + r_2$, where $0 \leq r_1 < x$ and $0 \leq r_2 < x$. If $r_1 = r_2$, then immediately $n = k$. *WLOG* assume that $r_1 < r_2$, so that $r_2 - r_1 > 0$, and therefore $nx - kx > 0$. Hence $kx < nx$ and since $x^{-1} > 0$, we have $k < n$. Therefore $n - k \geq 1$. Now $r_2 = nx - kx + r_1 = (n - k)x + r_1$, but since $r_1 \geq 0$ and $n - k \geq 1$, it follows that $r_2 \geq x$, a contradiction. □

Exercises   4.5

1. Determine $\{y : y = 6x \text{ for some } x \in S\}$, where:
    a) $S = (2, 4)$
    b) $S = (-1, 4)$
    c) $S = (-1, 0) \cup (2, 3)$
    d) $S = (-4, -3) \cup (-2, -1)$

2. In each interval T below, determine $A = \{x + y : x, y \in T\}$ and $B = \{xy : x, y \in T\}$:
    a) $T = (0, 1)$ *d)* $T = (-3, -2)$
    b) $T = (1, 3)$ *e)* $T = (-2, -1) \cup (2, 4)$
    c) $T = (-1, 2)$

3. In each interval T below, determine $S = \{x/y : x, y \in T\}$:
    a) $T = (0, 1)$ *c)* $T = (-2, -1)$
    b) $T = (1, 2)$ *d)* $T = (-1, 0) \cup (0, 2)$

4. Recall that every real number in $(0, 1)$ has a unique name in terms of an infinite decimal which does not have zeros from "some point on"! Show that $(0, 1)$ is not countable. (*Hint:* Assume $(0, 1)$ is countable and look at a countable list of decimal representations. From this list build a decimal representation which is not in the

list.) [See *Mathematics: The Man-Made Universe*, S. K. Stein (W. H. Freeman and Co., San Francisco, 1963), pp. 253–255.]

5.   Prove Lemma 4.5-2.

6.   Find $n \in Z$ such that $n \leq x < n + 1$, where:

a) $x = \dfrac{5 - 3/5}{2 - 6}$

b) $x = -6.89$

c) $x = 21.63$

7.   We know by Theorem 4.5-6 that for each $x \in R$ there exists a unique $n \in Z$ such that $n \leq x < n + 1$. For each x, denote this associated integer by $[x]$. Graph, on an x, y-coordinate system, the set $\{(x, y): y = [x]\}$. That is, graph the function f where $f(x) = [x]$.

8.   In each case below, find a left end point for the interval A so that if $x, y \in A$, then $xy \in B$. (Answers are not unique.)

a) $A = (\_\_, 2), B = (2, 5)$

d) $A = (\_\_, -4), B = (2, 21)$

b) $A = (\_\_, 3), B = (7, 9)$

e) $A = (\_\_, -3), B = (4, 10)$

c) $A = (\_\_, 2), B = (-1, 5)$

f) $A = (\_\_, 6), B = (-2, 40)$

9.   Let $f(x) = 2x \quad \forall x \in R$. Determine the "smallest" interval B such that $f[S] = \{f(x): x \in S\} \subset B$, where:

a) $S = (2, 3)$

c) $S = (-1, 1)$

e) $S = (1/4, 1/2)$

b) $S = (1, 2)$

d) $S = (1/10, 2/10)$

f) Would the "smallest" set B always necessarily be an interval?

10.   Let $f(x) = x^2 + 1$. Determine S such that $f[S] = B$, where:

a) $B = (1, 2)$

d) $B = (1/2, 3/4)$

b) $B = (1/2, 1)$

e) $B = (-a, a), a > 0$

c) $B = (-1, 2)$

f) $B = (a, -a), a < 0$

11.   How big is a point? How many points does it take to fill a line? What, if anything, do these questions mean? That is, how might one measure a point, or a set of points?

12.   Show that $\{r: r^2 < 2\}$ is non-empty and bounded above.

$$(r > 0 \text{ and } r \in Q)$$

13.   Find the supremum and infimum of each of the following sets (if they exist):

a) $A = \{x: -3 \leq x^2 < 5\}$

b) $B = \{x: x^2 < 15 \text{ and } x \in N\}$

c) $C = \{x: x = (n + 1)/n \text{ for } n \in N\}$

d) $D = \{x: x = (n^2 + 1)/n \text{ for } n \in N\}$

e) $E = \{x: x = (n^3 + n + 1)/n^3 \text{ for } n \in N\}$

f) $F = \{x: x = (n - 1)/n \text{ for } n \in N\}$

4.6   Finite Arithmetic: The Equivalence Relation $\sim_n$

In this section we shall develop a class of finite number systems known as the "modular arithmetics." The elements of a given modular arithmetic are best thought of as sets of integers. We shall define addition and multiplication operations on these sets, and examine various properties which follow from the definitions. In particular, we shall be interested in seeing whether these systems are number rings or fields.

Let us consider first a very simple modular arithmetic. Denote by $\bar{0}$ the set of all even integers,

$$\bar{0} = \{\ldots, -4, -2, 0, 2, 4, 6, \ldots\}.$$

Denote $\bar{1}$ the set of all odd integers,

$$\bar{1} = \{\ldots, -3, -1, 1, 3, 5, \ldots\}.$$

Define addition and multiplication by the following tables:

$\oplus$	$\bar{0}$	$\bar{1}$
$\bar{0}$	$\bar{0}$	$\bar{1}$
$\bar{1}$	$\bar{1}$	$\bar{0}$

$\odot$	$\bar{0}$	$\bar{1}$
$\bar{0}$	$\bar{0}$	$\bar{0}$
$\bar{1}$	$\bar{0}$	$\bar{1}$

It is easy to verify that the set $\{\bar{0}, \bar{1}\}$, along with the operations $\oplus$ and $\odot$, satisfy the definition of a number ring. (The reader is asked to do so in Exercise 2.)

Notice that $\bar{0} \cup \bar{1} = Z$ and $\bar{0} \cap \bar{1} = \varnothing$, so that $\{\bar{0}, \bar{1}\}$ forms a partition of Z. By a previous theorem, it follows that we may regard this as having partitioned the integers into two equivalence classes. Given the equivalence relation, it would therefore be possible to characterize each class simply by giving an element in the class, the elements in the class being equivalent to each other. Thus, we could give a very lengthy list of names for the set $\bar{0}$ and also for the $\bar{1}$. That is, $\bar{0} = \bar{2} = \bar{4} = \overline{-2} = \ldots$, and $\bar{1} = \bar{3} = \bar{5} = \overline{-1} \ldots$, since these expressions state simply that C_0, C_2, C_4, etc., are the same equivalence class, as are C_1, C_3, C_5, etc.

Let us examine a little more closely our definitions for multiplying and adding these objects. When two even numbers are added, we obtain an even number; and when two odd numbers are added, we again have an even number. When an even number and an odd number are multiplied, we obtain an even number. If we continue in this fashion comparing our results with our multiplication tables for $\bar{0}$ and $\bar{1}$, we will notice that the sum of two classes can be determined by looking at the class which contains the sum of any two elements in the original classes. For example, $\bar{2} \oplus \bar{3} = \overline{2+3} = \bar{5} = \bar{1}$ and $\bar{7} \oplus \bar{5} = \overline{7+5} = \overline{12} = \bar{0}$. A similar statement can be made for multiplication. Thus, $\bar{2} \odot \bar{3} = \overline{2 \cdot 3} = \bar{6} = \bar{0}$, etc. The number ring we have constructed and discussed is known as "the mod-2 arithmetic." Let us now construct a modular arithmetic for arbitrary positive integers. We begin by defining an equivalence relation in $Z \times Z$.

4.6-1 Definition: Let n be a positive integer. $\forall m, p \in Z$, $m \sim_n p$ if $m - p = kn$ for some $k \in Z$.

285

As we shall see, the above definition defines an equivalence relation "$\sim_n$" in $Z \times Z$ (*i.e.*, an equivalence relation on Z), such that two integers are in the same equivalence class if their difference is divisible by n.

Remark: Recall that in our discussion of equivalence relations, we considered an example of such a relation for $n = 3$. Recall that in this case three equivalence classes are obtained:

$$C_0 = \{\ldots, -3, 0, 3, 6, 9, \ldots\},$$
$$C_1 = \{\ldots, -2, 1, 4, 7, \ldots\},$$

and

$$C_2 = \{\ldots, -1, 2, 5, 8, \ldots\}.$$

Note that the partition $\{C_0, C_1, C_2\}$ of Z induces precisely the relation $\sim_3$.

4.6-2 Theorem: If n is a positive integer, then $\sim_n$ is an equivalence relation on Z.

Proof:

i) $\forall m \in Z$, $m - m = 0 = 0 \cdot n$, so that $m \sim_n m$.

ii) $m \sim_n p$, then $m - p = kn$ for some k. It follows that $p - m = (-k)n$. Therefore $p \sim_n m$.

iii) If $m \sim_n p$ and $p \sim_n q$, then $m - p = km$ and $p - q = hm$, so that $(m - p) + (p - q) = km + hm = (k + h)m$. Thus $m - q = (k + h)m$, and hence $m \sim_n q$.

Since $\sim_n$ is reflexive (*i*), symmetric (*ii*), and transitive (*iii*), it is an equivalence relation. □

We know, of course, that the equivalence classes induced by $\sim_n$ form a partition of Z. We shall denote the collection of equivalence classes induced by $\sim_n$ by Z_n. Since Z_n is a partition of Z, it causes no confusion to denote a given class in Z_n by indicating some member p of that class. We thus agree that each member of Z_n may have a multitude of names. If p is in some equivalence class, we shall denote that class by $\bar{p}$. It is clear that $\bar{p} = \bar{q}$ if and only if $p \sim_n q^*$. That is, $\bar{p}$ and $\bar{q}$ are each names for the same set, namely the equivalence class that contains both p and q.

Example: Consider the equivalence relation "$\sim_5$".

$5 \sim_5 10$ since $5 - 10 = -5$ is divisible by 5.
$8 \sim_5 3$ since $8 - 3 = 5$ is divisible by 5.
$5 \not\sim_5 3$ since $5 - 3 = 2$ is not a multiple of 5.

The partition induced by $\sim_5$ contains five sets. $\{\bar{0}, \bar{1}, \bar{2}, \bar{3}, \bar{4}\} = Z_5$.

$\bar{0} = \{\ldots, 5, 0, 5, 10, 15, \ldots\} = \{5n : n \in Z\}$
$\bar{1} = \{\ldots, -4, 1, 6, 11, \ldots\} = \{5n + 1 : n \in Z\}$
$\bar{2} = \{\ldots, -8, -3, 2, 7, 12, \ldots\} = \{5n + 2 : n \in Z\}$
$\bar{3} = \{\ldots, -7, -2, 3, 8, 13, \ldots\} = \{5n + 3 : n \in Z\}$
$\bar{4} = \{\ldots, -6, -1, 4, 9, 14, \ldots\} = \{5n + 4 : n \in Z\}$

* This is frequently denoted by $p \equiv q(mod\ n)$, read "p is congruent to q modulo n."

Operations on the Equivalence Classes

Let us now define a multiplication and an addition for Z_n, where as usual, n is some positive integer.

4.6-3 Definition: If $\bar{p}, \bar{q} \in Z_n$, then $\bar{p} \oplus \bar{q} = \overline{p + q}$ and $\bar{p} \odot \bar{q} = \overline{p \cdot q}$.

We must examine this definition carefully to see if we have really defined binary operations. Since each element in Z_n has a multitude of names, and since we have defined addition (multiplication) in terms of some given names for the sets, we must show that the result of addition (multiplication) is independent of the names being used.

Remark: What we are asking here is whether $\oplus$ and $\odot$ are "well defined" in the sense of being functions. We want to establish that $\oplus : Z_n \times Z_n \to Z_n$, and $\odot : Z_n \times Z_n \to Z_n$, so that equivalent pre-images are mapped to the same image under the two operations.

Example: Consider $Z_5 = \{\bar{0}, \bar{1}, \bar{2}, \bar{3}, \bar{4}\}$, where $\bar{0} = \{-10, -5, 0, 5, \ldots\}$, $\bar{2} = \{-3, 2, 7, 12, \ldots\}$, etc. Also $\bar{0} = \overline{-10} = \bar{5} = \overline{10}$, etc., and $\bar{2} = \overline{-3} = \bar{7} = \overline{12}$, etc. Now $\bar{0} \oplus \bar{2} = \overline{0 + 2}$ by the definition above. The question is whether we obtain the same result if we use a different representative for the set $\bar{0}$ or $\bar{2}$. We see that we should have $\bar{0} \oplus \bar{2} = \bar{5} \oplus \overline{12}$, since $\bar{0} = \bar{5}$ and $\bar{2} = \overline{12}$. Therefore $\overline{5 + 12}$ should be $\bar{2}$. (Why?) Is it true that $\bar{5} \oplus \overline{12} = \bar{2}$? Also $\bar{5} \odot \overline{12}$ should be $\bar{0}$, since $\bar{0} \odot \bar{2} = \bar{0}$. Is it true that $\bar{5} \odot \overline{12} = \bar{0}$?

These questions concerning addition and multiplication in Z_n are settled by the following theorem.

4.6-4 Theorem: If $\bar{p_1} = \bar{p_2} \in Z_n$ and $\bar{q_1} = \bar{q_2} \in Z_n$, then

a) $\overline{p_1 + q_1} = \overline{p_2 + q_2}$

and

b) $\overline{p_1 \cdot q_1} = \overline{p_2 \cdot q_2}$.

That is, if $p_1 \sim_n p_2$ and $q_1 \sim_n q_2$, then $p_1 + q_1 \sim_n p_2 + q_2$ and $p_1 \cdot q_1 \sim_n p_2 \cdot q_2$.

Proof: $p_1 - p_2 = k_1 n$ and $q_1 - q_2 = k_2 n$. (Why?) Thus

$$p_1 - p_2 + q_1 - q_2 = k_1 n + k_2 n$$
$$(p_1 + q_1) - (p_2 + q_2) = (k_1 + k_2)n$$

so that $p_1 + q_1 \sim_n p_2 + q_2$. The proof of the theorem for multiplication is analogous and is left as an exercise for the student. $\square$

When it is clear from the context that one is dealing with a given modular arithmetic, it is customary to delete the bar from over the integer which designates the set.

287

Example: Let $5, 7 \in Z_3$. Then $5 + 7 = 12 = 0$ and $5 \cdot 7 = 35 = 2$. What is really meant here is that if $\bar{5}, \bar{7} \in Z_3$, then

$$\bar{5} \oplus \bar{7} = \overline{12} = \bar{0} \quad \text{and} \quad \bar{5} \odot \bar{7} = \overline{35} = \bar{2}.$$

It might be pointed out here that when Glenda Gibson first encountered mod arithmetics in college, she went home and told her father that, "Nowadays $5 + 7 = 0$, and $5 \cdot 7 = 2$." The sad result was that Gurney immediately withdrew her from college. It would seem advisable then, when explaining mod arithmetics, to point out clearly that this is really a different plus and times on a different number system; everything except the names has been changed.

Exercises 4.6

1. Consider the equivalence relation "$\sim_3$" as defined.
   a) Is $3 \sim_3 0$?
   b) Is $5 \sim_3 0$?
   c) Is $9 \sim_3 0$?
   d) What integers belong to the class $\bar{0}$
   e) How many elements are in Z_3?
   f) How many elements are in $\bar{5}$?
   g) Prove that $\bar{3} \# \bar{5}$ (cardinal equivalence).

2. a) Verify that $\{\bar{0}, \bar{1}\}$ forms a number ring under the operations $\oplus$, $\odot$ defined in the "operation tables".
   b) Is this system a field?

3. a) How many elements are in Z_7?
   b) Describe the elements in Z_7 using set selectors. (Recall the division algorithm.)

4. How many elements are in Z_n?

5. Let $\bar{5}, \bar{6} \in Z_5$. Compute $\bar{5} \oplus \bar{6}$ and $\bar{5} \odot \bar{6}$.

6. Let $\bar{3}, \overline{-7} \in Z_{17}$. Compute $\bar{3} \oplus \overline{-7}$ and $\bar{3} \odot \overline{-7}$.

7. Show that Z_n forms a number ring.

8. Prove the second half of Theorem 4.6-4 concerning multiplication.

9. Show that Z_4 is not a field.
   (*Hint:* Find a non-zero number with no multiplicative inverse.)

10. Show that Z_5 is a field, and find all multiplicative inverses.

11. Under what conditions on n do you suppose Z_n is a field?
    In the remaining exercises we omit the "circles" and "bars" from the notation.

12. In Z_7 compute:

    a) $(3 + 7)6 - 4$

    b) $(12 - 4)2 + 6 \times 5$

    c) $(4 - 7) + 8(6 + 2)$

    d) $(21 + 3 \cdot 4) - (4 + 2)^2$

13. Find all numbers in Z_7 which have square roots.

14. Solve the following equations in Z_5. Keep in mind that Z_5 is a field.

    a) $7x + 3 = 1$

    b) $16x + 2 = 3x - 4$

    c) $16x + 2 = 7 - 3x$

    d) $-3x + 11 = 2x + 1$

15. In Z_4 expand the following binomials. (The exponents are not to be thought of as elements of Z_4.)

    a) $(2 + 3)^2$

    b) $(1 + 3)^3$

    c) $(3 + 7)^3$

16. Let $x, y \in Z_n$ such that $xy = 0$. Show that $(x + y)^n = x^n + y^n$.

17. Formally apply the quadratic formula to the following equations in Z_7. Test your results. (Use the results of Exercise 13 to determine whether square roots exist.)

    a) $2x^2 + 2x + 2 = 0$

    b) $3x^2 + x + 1 = 0$

    c) $x^2 - 4x + 2 = 0$

    d) $5x^2 + 2x - 1 = 0$

    e) $2x^2 + 5x + 2 = 0$

18. Consider the mod arithmetic Z_n. Can you decompose Z_n into three disjoint sets $Z_n^- \cup \{0\} \cup Z_n^+$ such that

    a) $\forall x \neq 0$ $x \in Z_n^+$ or $-x \in Z_n^+$ but not both?

    b) $\forall x, y$ if $x, y \in Z_n^+$, then $x + y \in Z_n^+$ and $xy \in Z_n^+$?

19. a) Can you state (using the language of mod arithmetic) a characterization for an integer to be divisible by 9?

    b) Recall that if $a \equiv b$ (mod m) and $c \equiv d$ (mod m), then $a + c \equiv b + d$ (mod m) and $ac \equiv bd$ (mod m). (See Theorem 4.6-4.)

    c) Now $10 \equiv 1$ (mod 9). Show therefore that $\forall n \in N$ $10^n \equiv 1$ (mod 9).

    d) Now $477 = 4 \times 10^2 + 7 \times 10^1 + 7 \times 10^0$
    $$\equiv 4 \times 1 + 7 \times 1 + 7 \times 1 \text{ (mod 9)}.$$

But $4 \times 1 + 7 \times 1 + 7 \times 1 = 18 = 10 + 8$
$$\equiv 1 + 8 \equiv 9 \equiv 0 \text{ (mod 9)}.$$

Is 477 divisible by 9?

    e) Which of the following are divisible by 9?

       i) 4,986

       ii) 13,756,824

       iii) 298,456,598,358

20. Using Exercise 19 as a model, devise a technique to determine whether a number is divisible by

    a) 3

    b) 4

    c) 6

21. Show that a modular arithmetic Z_n is an inductive system. That is, show that:

    if   i) $p(a)$ for some a in Z_n

        ii) $p(k) \Rightarrow p(k + 1)$ for each k in Z_n,

    then $\forall b \in Z_n \, p(b)$.

289

5

GRAPHING TECHNIQUES
AND SOME SPECIAL
RELATIONS AND
FUNCTIONS

In this chapter we shall investigate some special properties of functions. Some of these properties are easily interpreted graphically; in fact, some of them are *suggested* by graphical considerations. The main objective is to acquaint the student with various properties of functions that are useful in later applications. Much of our work will emphasize the ability to recognize these properties from an examination of the description of a function. Among other considerations, this will often involve sketching a graph of the function under investigation, which in turn is useful in "understanding" the function.

5.1   x and y Descriptions and Symmetries

Recall that a relation f whose domain and range contain only real numbers is a subset of $R \times R$ ($f \subset R \times R$). It is natural, then, to graph the relation by constructing a pictorial representation of the elements (ordered pairs) in the relation. A function in $R \times R$ is a subset of $R \times R$ with the "single valuedness" property. This is stated graphically by the observation that "each vertical line on the plane can intersect f at no more than one point." (See Figure 5.1.)

Many relations in R (subsets of $R \times R$) can be described in terms of a statement (involving variables x and y) which completely determines the elements in the relation. When this is possible, it is common to refer to the function (or relation) by the statement, instead of giving a complete name or description.

Example: Let $f = \{(x, y): y = x^2\}$.

It is common in this case to refer to "the function $y = x^2$", with the understanding that "the function f,

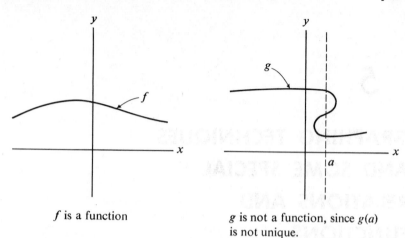

f is a function   *g* is not a function, since *g*(*a*)
                            is not unique.

FIG. 5.1

where $\forall x, y = f(x) = x^2$"
is what is really intended.

Recall our remark that in certain instances one refers to "the function $f(x)$" or "the function $y = f(x)$." Again, it is to be understood that the function f is intended, and that $f(x)$ actually means the image of the pre-image x, whereas $y = f(x)$ is the set selector which determines the ordered pairs that make up f (*i.e.*, $f = \{(x, y): y = f(x)\}$). As a notational convenience, we have agreed to write "f," "$f(x)$," or "$y = f(x)$" each as the name of the function involved. The context should make it clear, for example, whether "$f(x)$" refers to the image of x or the function f.

If f is a relation described by

$$f = \{(x, y): p(x, y) = q(x, y)\},$$

then it is often said that f is *implicitly* given by the equation

$$p(x, y) = q(x, y).$$

In this case, if one can *uniquely* solve the equation for y, then it immediately follows that f is a function.

Question: What can you say if the equation $p(x, y) = q(x, y)$ can be uniquely solved for x?

Example: Let $f = \{(x, y): 2x + 3 = 5y\}$.

The equation $2x + 3 = 5y$ has the same solution set as the equation $2x/5 + 3/5 = y$. Therefore $\forall x \quad f(x) = 2x/5 + 3/5$.

It is due to this traditional consistent use of x's and y's in describing certain functions that the collection

$$\{(x, 0): x \in R\} \qquad \text{is called the } x\text{-axis}$$

and the collection

$$\{(0, y): y \in R\} \qquad \text{is called the } y\text{-axis.}$$

We shall henceforth label these axes as "x" and "y" in our graphs.

In the work that follows, we shall almost always make use of this traditional language in discussing functions and relations. It should be clear that by eliminating a great deal of the set notation, no clarity is lost, whereas the reading and writing are greatly simplified. The *meaning* remains the same; the *notation* has been simplified after a firm understanding of this meaning has been mastered.

Symmetries

In Chapter 1, we defined a relation T in $R \times R$ to be *symmetric*, provided $T = T^{-1}$. We also noted that the graph of T^{-1} is the reflection of T across the line $x = y$. That is, replacement of (a, b) in T by (b, a) in T^{-1} results in a reflection of the point (a, b) across the line $y = x$ to the point (b, a).

Example: Let T be defined by $y^2 + 1 = x$. Then T^{-1} is defined by $x^2 + 1 = y$. (Explain!) Note that $T \neq T^{-1}$.

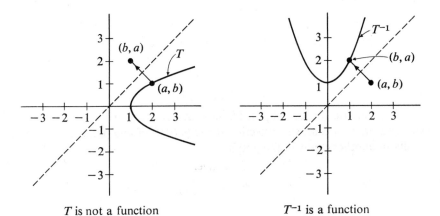

T is not a function T^{-1} is a function

FIG. 5.2

Although in general symmetric *functions* are rare, there are other kinds of "symmetry" that are possessed by certain functions, and a knowledge of these will help a great deal in graphing them.

5.1-1 Definition: A relation $f \subset R \times R$ is said to possess *symmetry through the origin*, provided that

$$(x, y) \in f \Rightarrow (-x, -y) \in f.$$

Note that this means that the graph of a function f, symmetric through the origin, has the property that any point on the graph must have a reflection through $(0, 0)$ that is also on the graph. (See Figure 5.3.)

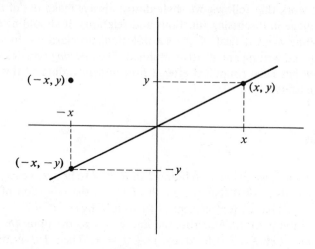

FIG. 5.3 The reflection of the point (x, y) through the origin $(0, 0)$ results in the point $(-x, -y)$.

Example: The relations in $R \times R$ described by

$$y = x^3,$$
$$\{(x, y): x^2 + y^2 \leq 4\},$$
and $\qquad\{(1, -1), (-1, 1)\}$

are all symmetric through $(0, 0)$. These relations are graphed in Figure 5.4. Note that in each case, the reflection through $(0,0)$ of *any* point in the graph results in another point in the graph.

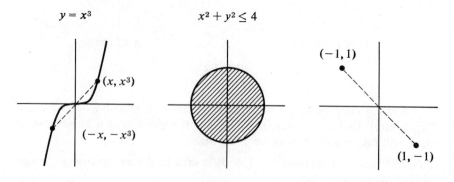

FIG. 5.4

Although the above definition concerning "symmetry through the origin" applies to all relations (including functions), there is a special term used with respect to functions.

5.1-2 Definition: Let $f: R \rightarrow R$ such that

$$\forall x \in R \quad f(-x) = -f(x).$$

Then f is called an "odd" function.

Note that an odd function is symmetric through the origin.

Example: Let $f(x) = 2x^3$. Then

$$f(-x) = 2(-x)^3 = -(2x^3) = -f(x),$$

thus $2x^3$ is an odd function.

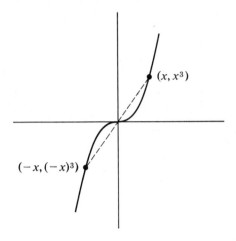

FIG. 5.5

Another type of symmetry which has special application to functions is symmetry about the ordinate, or y-axis.

5.1-3 Definition: A relation $f \subset R \times R$ is *symmetric about the ordinate* iff

$$(x, y) \in f \Rightarrow (-x, y) \in f.$$

Note that this means that the reflection of a point on the graph across the y-axis results in a point also on the graph.

The graphs of two relations with symmetry about the ordinate are shown in Figure 5.7.

5.1-4 Definition: A function $f: R \rightarrow R$ is called an "even" function iff

$$\forall x \quad f(-x) = f(x).$$

Note that an even function is symmetric across the y-axis.

295

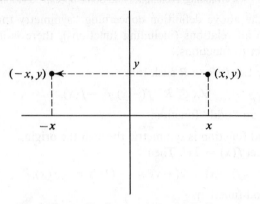

FIG. 5.6 Reflecting (x, y) across the line $x = 0$ results in the point $(-x, y)$.

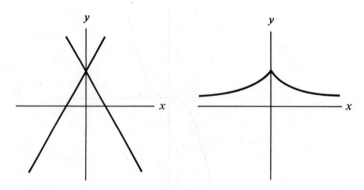

FIG. 5.7

Example: Let $f(x) = x^2$ for all x. Then

$$f(-x) = (-x)^2 = x^2 = f(x),$$

so f is even.

5.1-5 Definition: A relation $f \subset R \times R$ is *symmetric about the abscissa* provided that

$$(x, y) \in f \Rightarrow (x, -y) \in f.$$

Graphically speaking, a relation is symmetric about the abscissa provided that the reflection of any point of the graph across the x-axis results in a point on the graph.

Question: If $f: R \to R$, and f is symmetric about the abscissa, then $\forall x \quad f(x) = \underline{\quad\quad}$?

Remark: Note that saying "a relation is *symmetric*" implies only that it possesses one kind of symmetry: symmetry about the line $y = x$. In order

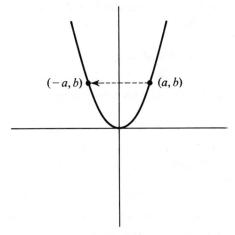

FIG. 5.7b

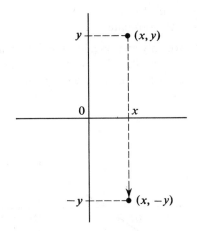

FIG. 5.8 The reflection of (x, y)
across the line $y = 0$ is the point
$(x, -y)$.

to specify other kinds of symmetry we should use the entire description, such as "symmetry through the origin," or "symmetry about the abscissa," or "symmetry about the y-axis."

We may be able to determine whether a relation possesses the various types of symmetry from its description. If we can do so, this will help greatly in graphing it, since in effect, we need only graph half of the relation in such cases; the other half being obtained by the appropriate reflection. Suppose a relation under consideration is described by an equation of the form $y = f(x)$. In order to check for symmetry through $(0, 0)$ we can see whether replacing x by $-x$ and y by $-y$ results in a description equivalent to the original one. If this does happen, we know the relation has symmetry through the origin.

Example: The relation described by

$$y^3 = 2x - 1/x$$

has symmetry through $(0, 0)$, since upon replacing y by $-y$ and x by $-x$ we obtain

$$(-y)^3 = 2(-x) - 1/(-x),$$

which is equivalent to the original equation. (Verify this.)

Example: $xy = 1$ is symmetric through $(0, 0)$ since $(-x)(-y) = xy$.

The reader is asked to develop similar methods of checking descriptions of relations to determine whether they possess the other types of symmetry.

5.1-6 Theorem: If a relation possesses any two of the following types of symmetry, then it possesses the third:

  i) symmetry through $(0, 0)$.
  ii) symmetry about the abscissa.
  iii) symmetry about the ordinate.

Proof: We shall prove only one case, leaving the other two for the reader, since the proofs are quite similar. Suppose, then, that f is a relation in $R \times R$ with *i)* and *iii)*. (See Figure 5.9.) We must show that it also has *ii)*.

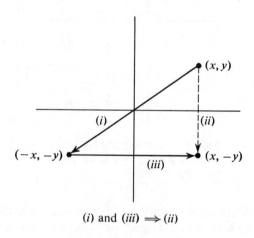

(*i*) and (*iii*) $\Rightarrow$ (*ii*)

FIG. 5.9

Now for any $(x, y) \in f$, we have $(-x, -y) \in f$ by *i)*. This implies $(-(-x), -y) \in f$ by *iii)*. That is, $(x, -y) \in f$. Thus *i)* and *iii)* yield

$$(x, y) \in f \Rightarrow (x, -y) \in f,$$

which is precisely *ii)*. ◻

Exercises 5.1

1. Graph the reflection of $y = x^2$
   a) through the origin.
   b) through the ordinate.
   c) through the abscissa.
   d) through the line $x = y$.
   e) through the line $y = -x$.

2. Test each of the following relations for symmetries:
   a) $x^2y^2 = 1$
   b) $xy = 5 - x^2y$
   c) $5 - xy = x^2$
   d) $y = 2 - 3x^2$

3. Graph, as best you can, each relation, and test it for symmetries:
   a) $xy = 5$
   b) $3xy = 1 - x^2$
   c) $y = 2x$
   d) $-xy = 1$
   e) $y = x$

4. Each of the following is a set selector for a function. Decide in each case whether it is an odd or an even function (maybe neither):
   a) $y = x^2 + 1$
   b) $y = x^4 + 2x^2 + 5$
   c) $y = x^6 + 5x^2$
   d) $y = x^8 + 2x$
   e) $y = x^3 + x$
   f) $y = x^5 + 4x$
   g) $y = 13x^7 + 3x^3 + 5x$
   h) $y = 4x^5 + 2x^2$

5. Reflect each graph below
   a) through its origin.
   b) through the ordinate.
   c) through the abscissa.
   d) through the line $y = x$.

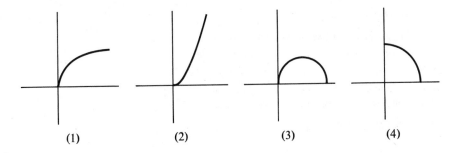

(1)   (2)   (3)   (4)

FIG. 5.9a

In each case, decide if the resulting graph and the original gives a function. If they are functions, decide whether they are odd or even functions.

6. When is the function $ax^7 + bx^6 + cx^5 + dx^4 + ex^3 + fx^2 + gx + h$ odd and when is it even? Make a guess. (*Hint:* Look at Exercise 4 above.) Try to prove your conjecture.

7. *a)* Show that an even function is symmetric about the y-axis.

b) Show that an odd function is symmetric about the origin.

8. Suppose that f and g are two functions having symmetry through the origin. What can you say about the symmetry of:

   a) $f \vee g$ *b)* $f + g$ *c)* $f \cdot g$ *d)* $f \circ g$ *e)* f^2

9. Same as Exercise 8 under the assumption that f and g have symmetry about the ordinate.

   (*Hint:* Note that f and g are assumed to be *functions*.)

10. *a)* Find a relation in $R \times R$ having all *four* types of symmetry.

   b) Is there such a *function* in $R \times R$?

11. *a)* Show that if the description of a relation T is given by $y^n = x^p$ (where n, p are in N), then T has symmetry through $(0, 0)$ if $n + p$ is even.

   b) Find conditions on n and p that will guarantee that T has symmetry.

   c) Same as *b)* except T has symmetry about $x = 0$.

   d) Same as *b)* except T has symmetry about $y = 0$.

12. Develop a method of checking descriptions of the form $y = f(x)$ to determine whether the relation described has

   a) symmetry.

   b) symmetry about the x-axis.

   c) symmetry about the y-axis.

   (*Hint:* Recall that checking for symmetry through $(0, 0)$ turned out to involve replacement of (x, y) by its reflection through $(0, 0)$.)

   d) Use the methods of a, b, and c to test the following relations for symmetry:

   1) $5xy = 1$ 4) $xy^3 + x^3y = 0$

   2) $xy^2 + x^2 = 3$ 5) $x^4 + 3y^3 = 1$

   3) $x^3y^5 + x^2y = 3$

13. Prove the other two cases of Theorem 5.1-6.

   (*Hint:* Prove   *i)* and *ii)* $\Rightarrow$ *iii)*,

and   *ii)* and *iii)* $\Rightarrow$ *i)*.)

Are you convinced that these two cases, together with the one given in the proof following the statement of the theorem, exhaust all the possibilities?

14. Classify the following functions as either even or odd (or both):

   a) $y = x$ *c)* $y = 4x^4 - 3x^2 + 2$

   b) $y = x^2$ *d)* $y = x^3 - x$

   e) can you guess how the "even" and "odd" terminology originally arose?

15. *a)* Show that the relation defined by $|x| + |y| = 1$ has all four types of symmetry.

   b) Graph the relation of part *a)* by finding its graph in quadrant I (assuming $x \geq 0$ and $y \geq 0$), then using reflections to obtain the remainder of the graph.

5.2 Restriction and Extension of Functions, Periodicity

We have already observed that it may be possible to change the domain of a function $f: A \rightarrow B$ by enlarging it to a set containing A (*extension*), or decreasing it to a subset of A (*restriction*). In this section we shall discuss some useful applications of these ideas.

Recall that a variable in a statement must always be quantified—either explicitly, or assumed from the context. In this connection, we may encounter statements that are used to describe functions for which the domain is not prescribed. Thus, for example, we make statements such as, "consider the function $f(x) = \dfrac{x^2 - 4}{x - 2}$." Now we need to know the domain D_f in order to describe f completely, but information as to what it should be is absent. In such cases we make use of the following convention.*

Convention of the Maximal Domain

A function f in $R \times R$, which is described by a statement of the form $y = f(x)$, is assumed to have as its domain

$$D_f = \{x \in R : f(x) \text{ is defined and is an element of } R\},$$

unless otherwise specified.

Thus, unless specifically defined otherwise, the domain of a function is taken as "large" as possible. For example, the function in $R \times R$ described by

$$f(x) = \frac{x^2 - 4}{x - 2}$$

is assumed to have domain

$$D_f = R - \{2\}.$$

(Why isn't $2 \in D_f$?)

Exercise: Find the domains of the following functions in $R \times R$:

a) $y = 1/x$ b) $y = \sqrt{x + 2}$

There are many instances in which we wish to extend a function to a new domain in such a way that certain properties or conditions are retained. For example, recall that we first defined the addition operation for the natural numbers, so that we could view addition as a function

$$+ : N \times N \rightarrow N.$$

* J. F. Gray, *Sets, Relations, and Functions*, Holt, Rinehart, and Winston, 1962.

Thus $+$ maps the pair $(2, 3)$ to the image 5, $+(7, 9) = 16$, etc. We established certain properties of the function "$+$" and then extended it to the set of integers

$$+ : Z \times Z \to Z,$$

in such a way that these properties were retained in the extended system. Finally, we extended the function "$+$" to Q, R, and $\mathcal{C}$. We see that in this case the extensions were made in a very special way, so that certain properties were preserved.

A principle upon which to base an extension might also be "symmetry" of some sort. For example, suppose $f(x) = x$ describes a function from $[0, \infty)$ into R. Suppose we wish to extend f to R in such a way that its graph is symmetric about the y-axis (See Figure 5.10.). (That is, so that the ex-

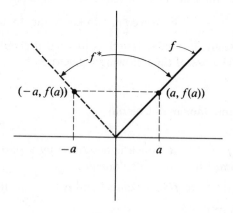

FIG. 5.10

tended function f^* is even.) This means that we must introduce ordered pairs of the form $(-a, f(a))$ into f^*. Note that the extension f^* of f to R is the function described by $y = |x|$.

We shall later encounter more important and more subtle ways in which a function can be extended to a larger domain. One of the most useful of these is the extension of a function to accommodate periodicity.

Periodic Functions

Another type of "symmetry" that a function or relation can have involves invariance under *translations* rather than reflections of some sort. We call this property "periodicity." In the present section we shall discuss some properties of periodic functions. In Chapter 7, we shall discuss some very important examples of periodic functions: the trigonometric functions.

It is very natural to find that the notion of "cycles" is considered to be important. We observe many cyclic phenomena in the real world in which we find ourselves. For example, man very early observed the stages of the moon, the day-night-day sequence, the summer-winter-summer cycle, the life cycle, and so on. He then naturally wondered whether other things occurred in some cyclic fashion. He formulated such theories as "the giant wind from the north comes every three summers," and "I flunk every other math course." In fact, efforts are made to use "cycles" in the formulation of models for diverse phenomena, such as business activity, and sunspot activity. We shall see that periodic functions exhibit this "cyclic" notion. Thus, it should not surprise the reader to learn that periodic functions are often used in the formulation of mathematical models.

We are going to define a class of functions known as "periodic functions." These are functions which "periodically" take on the same values again and again as one evaluates the function at pre-images along the real line.

5.2-1 Definition: A function $f: R \rightarrow R$ is a *periodic function* iff
$$f(x + p) = f(x) \text{ for some } p > 0.$$

Example: Consider the function f graphed in Figure 5.11.

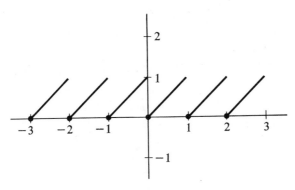

FIG. 5.11

Note also that
$$\forall x \quad f(x + 2) = f(x) \quad \text{and} \quad \forall x \quad f(x + 3) = f(x).$$

5.2-2 Definition: If f is a periodic function, the smallest $p > 0$ such that
$$\forall x \quad f(x + p) = f(x)$$
is called *the period of f.* (If there is such a p.)

303

Notice that our definitions have allowed the constant functions to be periodic, although they have no period (explain this!). This may at first seem strange, but it is a common way to state the definitions, and it proves useful.

Example: Let *f* be as graphed in Figure 5.12.

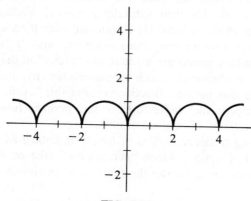

FIG. 5.12

Then *f* is periodic, with period 2.

Recall that every real number α is either an integer, or lies between two integers (*i.e.*, $n \le \alpha < n + 1$ for some unique $n \in Z$). A popular function from R to R using this fact is "the greatest integer function," denoted [ ].

5.2-3 Definition: $\forall x \in R$, $[x]$ (the "greatest integer in x") is the unique integer n such that $n \le x < n + 1$.

A sketch of the graph of the greatest integer function is given in Figure 5.13.

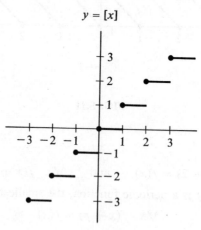

$y = [x]$

FIG. 5.13

This is not a periodic function, as is clearly seen, but the associated function f, described by

$$\forall x \quad f(x) = x - [x]$$

(called the "fractional part of x") *is* periodic.

$y = x - [x]$

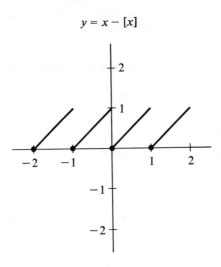

FIG. 5.14

Question: What is the period of the "fractional part" function?
Example: Suppose

$$f(x) = \begin{cases} x - 2n \text{ for } x \in [2n, 2n + 1) \\ -x + 2n \text{ for } x \in [2n - 1, 2n) \end{cases} \quad n \in Z.$$

The graph of $f: R \to R$ is shown in Figure 5.15.

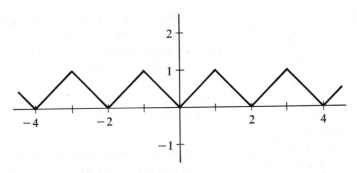

FIG. 5.15

We note that by "translating" the graph to the right or left by two units, we obtain the same graph. That is, for each x,

$$f(x - 2) = f(x + 2) = f(x).$$

(Verify this, using the definition of f.) Since 2 is the *smallest* positive real number p for which $f(x + p) = f(x)$, f is periodic with period 2.

We shall next prove a very interesting thing about the class of periodic functions in $R \times R$, namely that the class is *not* closed under function addition.

5.2-4 Theorem: Suppose f and g are periodic functions with periods p and q, respectively. Then

  i) $f + g$ is periodic iff $p/q \in Q$, and

  ii) if $p/q \in Q$ and if $f + g$ has a period T, then T is the least common multiple of p and q.

  Proof: i) We know that $f(x + p) = f(x)$ and $g(x + q) = g(x)$. By definition,

$$(f + g)(x) = f(x) + g(x)$$

so that

$$(f + g)(x + S) = f(x + S) + g(x + S) \qquad \forall S \in R.$$

We therefore want to find conditions under which there is a smallest positive S such that

$$f(x + S) + g(x + S) = f(x) + g(x). \tag{1}$$

Now if $p/q = a/b$ where $a, b \in N$, then (1) is satisfied for $S = bp$. In order to verify this, note that if $a/b = p/q$, then $bp = aq$, so that (by induction, for example)

$$f(x + S) + g(x + S) = f\left(x + \sum_{i=1}^{b} p\right) + g\left(x + \sum_{i=1}^{a} q\right) = f(x) + g(x),$$

since f and g have periods p and q, respectively. On the other hand, if p/q is irrational, then (1) is satisfied only if $f(x + S) = f(x)$ and $g(x + S) = g(x)$. But this implies that S is a common multiple of p and q (why?) which is a contradiction (why?).

  ii) By the above proof, we know that if $p/q = a/b$ ($a, b \in N$), then the definition is satisfied for $S = bq$. Now suppose the fraction a/b is expressed in lowest terms. If the period T of $f + g$ was smaller than bp, then T would be of the form $b'p$ for some $0 < b' < b$. Similarly we would have $T = a'q$ for $0 < a' < a$, thus

$$b'p = a'q$$
which implies $\qquad$ $p/q = a'/b'$,

a contradiction. (Why?) $\square$

  Remark: Note that in the above proof we have assumed that the least common multiple of p and q is the number bp obtained from the fraction expression in *lowest terms* of the rational number p/q.

Periodic Extension

5.2-5 Definition: Suppose A is some half open finite interval in R. That is, suppose A is a set of the form:

   i) $(a, b]$, or

   ii) $[a, b)$, where $a < b$.

If $f: A \to R$, then *the periodic extension of f to R* is the function f^* defined by

$$\forall x \in A \quad f^*(x) = f(x)$$

and

$$\forall x \in R \quad f^*(x + p) = f^*(x),$$

where $p = b - a$.

   Example: Suppose $A = [0, 2)$ and $\forall x \in A \quad f(x) = x$. Then f and f^* have the graphs shown in Figure 5.16.

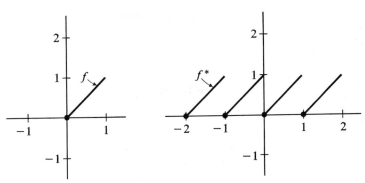

FIG. 5.16

We know that such a uniquely determined function actually exists by the following theorem.

5.2-6 Theorem: Let $a < b$, $a, b \in R$. Then $\forall x \in R$, there exists a unique $n \in Z$ such that

$$x + n(b - a) \in [a, b).$$

   Proof: By a previous result we know that there is a unique $n \in Z$ such that

$$(n - 1)(b - a) < a - x \leq n(b - a).$$

But

$$(n - 1)(b - a) = nb - b + a - na,$$

so that

$$nb - b + a - na < a - x,$$

or equivalently

$$n(b - a) + a - b < a - x.$$

That is,

$$n(b - a) < a - x + b - a = b - x.$$

Therefore

$$a - x \leq n(b - a) < b - x,$$

from which it follows that

307

$$a \leq x + n(b - a) < b,$$
(*i.e.*, $\qquad x + n(b - a) \in [a, b)).$

The proof for $(a, b]$ is similar. $\square$

Example: Let $f(x) = x^2 - 4$ $\forall x \in (2, 4]$, and let f^* be the periodic extension of f. (Note that the period will be no larger than $4 - 2 = 2$.)

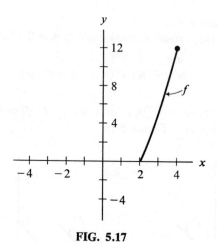

FIG. 5.17

We wish to determine $f^*(1/2)$. Since

$$f^*(1/2) = f^*(2 + 1/2)$$
and $\qquad 2 + 1/2 \in (2, 4],$
we must have $\qquad f^*(1/2) = f(2 + 1/2).$

This process is used to find $f^*(x)$ for any real pre-image x.

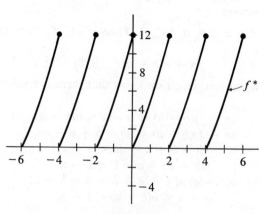

FIG. 5.18

The concept of periodicity, and periodic extensions, need not be re-stricted to functions in $R \times R$, but can easily be extended to functions in $R \times A$, where A is any non-empty set. When we develop the trigonometric functions, we shall find this concept useful.

Exercises 5.2

1. What is the maximal domain for each of the following functions?

   a) $f(x) = 2x^2/(1 - x)$

   b) $f(x) = (x^2 + 2)/(x^2 + 1)$

   c) $(x^2 + 2x)/x$

   d) $(2x^2 + x + 5)/(x^2 - 5)$

2. Extend each of the following by symmetry about the ordinate, and graph the extension: $\forall x \in [0, \infty)$

   a) $f(x) = 2x + 1$

   b) $f(x) = x^2 + 1$

   c) $f(x) = x^3$

   d) $f(x) = (x^2 + 1)/(x - 1)$

3. Extend by periodicity, and graph the extension:

   a) $f(x) = 2x^2, x \in [0, 2)$

   b) $f(x) = 2 + x, x \in (4, 7]$

   c) $f(x) = 3x + 4, x \in [-2, 1)$

4. Let f and g be periodic with periods p and q, respectively. Which of the following are periodic?

   a) $f \cdot g$

   b) f^2

   c) F where $F(x) = f(x^2)$

   d) $f \circ g$

   e) $f \lor g$

   f) $f \land g$

   If the function is periodic, find its period or show that it has none.

5. Let $f(x) = \begin{cases} 1 & \text{if } x \in [2n, 2n + 1) \text{ for some } n \in Z. \\ -1 & \text{otherwise} \end{cases}$

   a) Sketch a graph of f.

   b) Show that f is periodic, and find its period.

6. Prove that if $f(x + p) = f(x)$ for a given $p \in R$, then

   a) $f(x + np) = f(x)$ for any $n \in Z$.

   b) $(h \circ f)(x + p) = (h \circ f)(x)$ for any function $h: R \to R$.

   c) $\forall m \in R, f(x + m) = f(x) \Rightarrow m = np$ where $n \in N$.

7. Sketch a graph representing (or argue that no such function exists):

   a) a periodic odd function that is not even.

   b) a periodic 1-1 function.

   c) a periodic even function that is not odd.

   d) a periodic function which is even and odd.

8. Investigate (prove or disprove):

   a) If a function is periodic, it is not symmetric.

   b) If f and g are periodic functions with different periods and $af + bg = 0$, then $a = b = 0$.

   c) If f is periodic with period p, and S is a positive real number such that $f(x + S) = f(x)$, then $S = p^n$ for some $n \in N$.

d) The sum of two periodic functions with periods p and q, if periodic, has period bounded above by $p \cdot q$.

9. Show that Theorem 5.2-4 remains true if the symbol "$f + g$" is replaced by "$f \vee g$" throughout.

5.3 Boundedness and Monotonicity

Boundedness of a Function

We have previously defined "boundedness" for sets of real numbers. Recall that a set is bounded above by B provided that all elements of the set are not greater than B, and similarly for being bounded below. We say that a set is *bounded* provided it is bounded both above and below. We wish to state a similar definition for "boundedness of functions," where the "boundedness" refers to the range of the function.

5.3-1 Definition: Let f be a function such that $R_f \subset R$. Then f is said to be bounded (bounded above) (bounded below) if R_f is bounded (bounded above) (bounded below).†

Example: Let $f(x) = x^2$. Then $R_f = [0, \infty)$, so f is bounded below but not above.

Example: Let $f(x) = 5$ if $x \geq 0$ and $f(x) = -2$ if $x < 0$. $R_f = \{5, -2\}$ so f is bounded above and below and hence bounded.

Monotonic Functions

One interesting attribute that many functions have is that their graphs don't "weave up and down," but rather continue in one general trend (either generally "up to the right" or "down to the right"). Such functions might justly be called "monotonous." In fact, mathematicians use many terms to describe such functions, such as "increasing," "non-decreasing," and "monotonic." A function is called "monotonic" provided it is either "*non-decreasing*" or "*non-increasing*" as x is increased. This is made more definite by the following.

5.3-2 Definition: A function $f: R \to R$ is *monotonic increasing* if and only if

$$\forall x, y \in R \quad x < y \Rightarrow f(x) \leq f(y).$$

† This kind of statement is common in mathematics. You should read it as the three distinct statements:
1. f is bounded if R_f is bounded.
2. f is bounded above if R_f is bounded above.
3. f is bounded below if R_f is bounded below.

f is *strictly monotonic increasing* iff

$$\forall x, y \in R \quad x < y \Rightarrow f(x) < f(y).$$

Example: Let $f(x) = x$ for all $x \in R$. As x increases, the functional values (images) increase. *f* is strictly monotonic increasing.

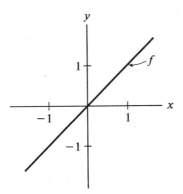

FIG. 5.19   A strictly increasing function.

Example: Let $f(x) = [x]$ (the greatest integer function).

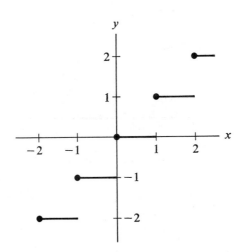

FIG. 5.20   An increasing function.

Here *f* is monotonic increasing, but not strictly increasing. (Note that we occasionally omit the word "monotonic" in our description, saying "strictly increasing" rather than "strictly monotonic increasing.")

We have an analogous definition for functions which are monotonic decreasing.

5.3-3 Definition: A function $f: R \rightarrow R$ is called *monotonic decreasing* iff

$$\forall x, y \in R \quad x < y \Rightarrow f(x) \geq f(y).$$

f is called *strictly monotonic decreasing* (or simply, *strictly decreasing*) if strict inequality holds.

Example: Let $f(x) = -x$. Then f is strictly decreasing.

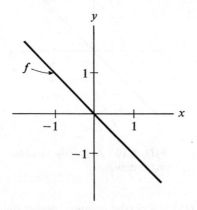

FIG. 5.21 A strictly decreasing function.

Example: Let $f(x) = 2$ for all x.

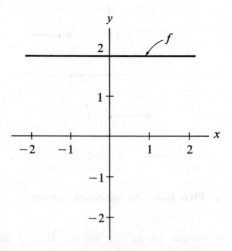

FIG. 5.22

Here f is monotonic decreasing but not strictly decreasing. f is also monotonic increasing.

We remark again that in discussions of monotonic functions, it is common practice to omit the word "monotonic." As a result, a function which is said to be "increasing" may be merely "non-decreasing." If one intends to convey the information that a function is "truly" *increasing*, then the words "strictly increasing" are used.

In the remainder of this section we shall state several properties of monotonic functions; in a later section we shall investigate a very important class of such functions: the exponential functions and their inverses. The theorems we state concerning general properties of monotonic functions could have been restricted to monotonic increasing or strictly monotonic increasing functions, since most of the statements we can make for increasing functions can be made also for monotonic decreasing or strictly monotonic decreasing functions as well. (You are urged to try to prove such statements.) Exercise 3 shows how we can routinely change a problem concerning decreasing functions into an equivalent one involving increasing functions.

One of the more important elementary results concerning monotonic functions is the following.

5.3-4 Theorem: If a function f in $R \times R$ is strictly monotonic, then f^{-1} is a function.

Proof: We shall prove only the case for a strictly increasing function and leave the decreasing case as an exercise. We do this by showing that f must be 1-1. Assume

$$\forall x, y \in R \quad x < y \Rightarrow f(x) < f(y).$$

Suppose $a, b \in R$ and $f(a) = f(b)$.

By the trichotomy law exactly one of the following holds:

   i) $a < b$
   ii) $b < a$
   iii) $a = b$.

Now $a < b \Rightarrow f(a) < f(b)$,
and $b < a \Rightarrow f(b) < f(a)$.

But $f(a) = f(b)$. Therefore we are left with only the possibility that $a = b$. Hence f is 1-1 and therefore has an inverse which is a function. □

We shall make use of this theorem later when we develop the log functions. They are defined to be the inverses of the (monotonic) exponential functions and are also functions.

Example: $f(x) = x^3$ is a strictly increasing function, and therefore has an inverse (which is a function).

313

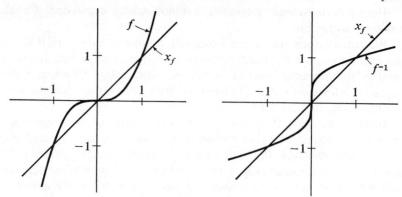

FIG. 5.23

Graphically speaking, if a function is strictly monotonic, then any *horizontal* line can intersect the function no more than once. This is sufficient to guarantee that the inverse is a function. (Recall the "vertical line test" for functions, and the fact that a horizontal line, when reflected across x_f, becomes a vertical line.)

5.3-5 Theorem: If $f: R \to R$ is strictly increasing and $g: R \to R$ is increasing, then $f + g$ is strictly increasing.

Proof: For all x and y such that $x > y$, we have $f(x) > f(y)$ and $g(x) \geq g(y)$, so that $f(x) + g(x) > f(y) + g(y)$. But this means that

$$(f + g)(x) > (f + g)(y),$$

so $f + g$ is strictly increasing. □

Using similar arguments, the reader can (and should) prove the following:

5.3-6 Theorem: If f and g are (strictly) increasing, then $f \circ g, f \vee g$ and $f \wedge g$ are (strictly) increasing.

5.3-7 Theorem: If f is (strictly) increasing, then $-f$ is (strictly) decreasing.
(Note that Theorems 5.3-6 and 5.3-7 are each "several theorems in one.")

Exercises 5.3

1. Determine whether the following functions are: monotonic, strictly monotonic, increasing, decreasing, bounded above, bounded below. (Prove your assertion.)

a) $f(x) = 2x$

b) $f(x) = -x^3$

c) $f(x) = x^2 + x + 1$

d) $f(x) = x^3 + x + 1$

e) $f(x) = 1/x$

f) $f(x) = 2^x$

2. Is it possible for a periodic function to be monotonic? (Explain!)

3. Show that Theorems 5.3-5, 5.3-6, and 5.3-7 remain valid if "increasing" is replaced by "decreasing" throughout.

4. What can you say about the pointwise product $f \cdot g$, $(f \cdot g(x) = f(x)g(x))$ with respect to monotonicity of f and g?

5. Investigate (prove or disprove):
   a) The inverse of a strictly increasing function is strictly increasing.
   b) An even function is never monotonic.
   c) A strictly monotonic function cannot be bounded.

6. Show that a function which is both monotonic increasing and monotonic decreasing is a constant function. (*Hint:* Use the trichotomy law of R.)

5.4   Sequences and Intuitive Limits

In discussing functions, and drawing their graphs, it is useful to discuss the concept of "limits." What we have in mind here is to consider what happens to functional values of a given function when the domain values are taken near some point, or are taken very large or small. Let us begin our discussion of limits with the special class of functions known as "sequences." Recall the following definition.

5.4-1 Definition: A sequence of real numbers is a function $s: N \to R$ (*i.e.*, for each natural number n, a value in R is determined). The image $s(n)$ of the natural number n is denoted by s_n, and the sequence is often listed by

$$\{s_1, s_2, s_3, \ldots\} \text{ or simply by } \{s_i\}.$$

(Beware! *Do not mistake this for a singleton set.*)

   Remark: Occasionally one encounters sequences with a domain of the form $m, m + 1, m + 2, \ldots$ for some $m \in Z$, other than $m = 1$. This simply involves relabeling the elements of the domain of a *bona fide* sequence, however, and is not a serious departure from the foregoing definition.

   Example: The sequence $\{1, 4, 7, 10, 13, \ldots\}$ (that is, the sequence $s \subset N \times N$ described by

$$\{(1, 1), (2, 4), (3, 7), (4, 10), (5, 13), \ldots\}$$

is a special case of an *arithmetic sequence*. In this sequence we note that each term differs from its predecessor by 3. Thus

$$\forall i, \quad s_{i+1} = s_i + 3.$$

This type of sequence is of interest in many applications so we give a formal definition as follows.

315

5.4-2 Definition: An *arithmetic sequence* is a sequence $\{u_n\}$ having terms such that

$$u_{n+1} - u_n = d \quad \text{for all } n \geq 1.$$

The number d is called the *common difference* of the sequence.

Example: Note that $\{n\} = N$ is an arithmetic sequence with common difference 1. We have observed previously that

$$\sum_{n=1}^{k} n = \frac{k(k+1)}{2} = \frac{k}{2}(s_1 + s_k),$$

where $s_k = k$. It is interesting that this formula for the sum of the first k terms of the arithmetic sequence $\{n\}$ is true for all arithmetic sequences.

5.4-3 Theorem: Suppose $\{a_n\}$ is an arithmetic sequence with common difference d. Then the sum of the first k terms of the sequence is given by

$$\sum_{n=1}^{k} s_n = \frac{k}{2}(s_1 + s_k).$$

Proof: We use "induction" as follows:

$$\sum_{n=1}^{k} s_n = \sum_{n=0}^{k-1} (s_1 + nd) \quad \text{(see Exercise 21)}$$

$$= \sum_{n=0}^{k-1} s_1 + \sum_{n=0}^{k-1} nd$$

$$= ks_1 + d \sum_{n=1}^{k-1} n$$

$$= ks_1 + d\left(\frac{(k-1)(k)}{2}\right)$$

$$= \frac{k}{2}[s_1 + s_1 + (k-1)d]$$

$$= \frac{k}{2}[s_1 + s_k]. \quad \square$$

Example: $1 + 4 + 7 + \ldots + 31 = 11/2[1 + 31] = (11)(16)$.
Example: Consider the sequence defined by

$$\forall n \quad s_n = 2^{-n} \quad \text{or} \quad s_n = \frac{1}{2^n}.$$

Using the slightly ambiguous but useful notation mentioned above we have

$$\{s_n\} = \{2^{-n}\} = \left\{\frac{1}{2}, \frac{1}{4}, \frac{1}{8}, \frac{1}{16}, \ldots\right\},$$

we notice several things about the sequence $\{2^{-n}\}$. First of all, it is described by a condition analogous to the "common difference" definition of the arith-
316

metic sequence of the preceding example. In this case, however, there is a common multiplicative factor involved, rather than a common additive one. Thus we see that the terms s_n of this sequence are related by

$$\forall n \in N, \quad s_{n+1} = \frac{1}{2} s_n.$$

5.4-4 Definition: A sequence $\{s_n\}$ with the property

$$\forall n \in N, \quad s_{n+1} = r s_n$$

is called a *geometric sequence* with *common ratio r*.

Note that a geometric sequence is completely determined by specification of the common ratio and some term s_j.

A theorem similar to that for sums of terms in an arithmetic sequence holds for the geometric case as well. This is given by

5.4-5 Theorem: Suppose $\{s_n\}$ is a geometric sequence with common ratio $r \neq 1$. Then the sum of the first k terms of the sequence is given by

$$\sum_{n=1}^{k} s_n = \frac{s_1(1 - r^k)}{1 - r}.$$

This is proved in a way analogous to that for the preceding theorem. (See Exercise 25.)

Another thing we notice about the sequence $\{2^{-n}\}$ is that the terms are getting smaller and smaller as n gets large. In fact, it seems that the terms are going to be very close to zero for any large n. This is expressed symbolically by writing

$$\text{``}\lim_{n \to \infty} s_n = 0.\text{''}$$

It should be emphasized that our notion that "s_n gets small as n gets large" is extremely intuitive in nature at this point. By writing "$\lim_{n \to \infty} s_n = 0$", we shall be expressing our feeling that the terms in the sequence get close to zero for all n "sufficiently" large. Actually, in order to *prove* assertions about such "limits" (such as, for example, the fact that $\lim_{n \to \infty} s_n = -\lim_{n \to \infty} -s_n$), we would have to define carefully what the symbol "$\lim_{n \to \infty} s_n$" means. This is one of the first things encountered in a calculus course. We shall content ourselves with only an intuitive discussion of "limits" in this book.

Example: Consider the sequence $\{1 + 1/n\}$. We see that the first few terms are $2, 1\,1/2, 1\,1/3, 1\,1/4, \ldots$, and that apparently the terms get close to 1 for large n. Thus we write

$$\lim_{n \to \infty} (1 + 1/n) = 1.$$

If we graph the function described by $f(n) = 1 + 1/n$, we obtain the graph in Figure 5.24

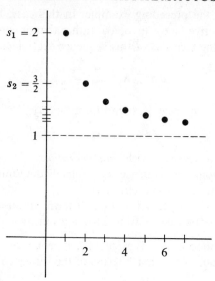

FIG. 5.24

Note that in this case, as with every sequence, the main interest is in what happens with points in its *range*. That is, since every sequence has the same domain N, the images in the range are the only interesting things about them. This is reflected in our notation for sequences; $\{s_1, s_2, s_3, \ldots\}$ being actually a list of the *range* of the function

$$\{(1, s_1), (2, s_2), (3, s_3), \ldots,\}.$$

For this reason, one often sees sequences graphed as their range only (on a real number line). Thus a graphical representation of the sequence $\{1 + 1/n\}$ might consist of only the points shown in the vertical axis in Figure 5.24.

Example: Consider the sequence $1 + \dfrac{(-1)^n}{n}$. A graph of this sequence is shown in Figure 5.25.

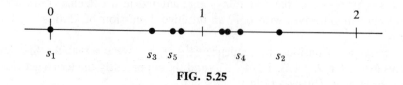

FIG. 5.25

We see that the sequence

$$\left\{0, 1\frac{1}{2}, \frac{2}{3}, 1\frac{1}{4}, \frac{4}{5}, 1\frac{1}{6}, \frac{6}{7}, \ldots\right\}$$

appears to "oscillate" around 1, and that apparently the terms *all* get close to 1 as n gets large. Thus we would state that

$$\lim_{n \to \infty} \left(1 + \frac{(-1)^n}{n} \right) = 1.$$

Very often a sequence with a limit "oscillates" about its limit point from only the right or the left side. This will occur, for example, whenever the images s_n are monotonically increasing (as n increases), so that

$$\forall n \in N, \quad s_{n+1} \geq s_n.$$

In this case we call s_n a "monotonically increasing" sequence. In general, the "increasing-decreasing" and "boundedness" terminology introduced previously for monotonic functions $f: R \to R$ is also applied to sequences $s_n: N \to R$. Note that apparently the increasing sequence "approaches its limit" (if it has one) from the left. You should think about the case for decreasing sequences. In the case of bounded monotonic sequences, it happens that the limit is directly determined by the least upper bound (*l.u.b.*, sup) or the greatest lower bound for the set of range values, depending on whether the sequence is increasing or decreasing.

Example: Consider the sequence

$$\{s_n\} = \{2 + 1/n^2\} = \left\{ 3, 2\frac{1}{4}, 2\frac{1}{9}, 2\frac{1}{16}, \ldots \right\}.$$

It appears that $\lim_{n \to \infty} s_n = 2.$

Also in this case

$$\inf \left\{ 3, 2\frac{1}{4}, 2\frac{1}{9}, 2\frac{1}{16}, \ldots \right\} = 2.$$

Recall that the *completeness axiom*, which we used in the extension to the real numbers from the rational numbers, asserted that "any non-empty set of real numbers which is bounded above has a least upper bound." A direct consequence of this real number property is the following theorem concerning limits of sequences. (Notice, in the statement of this theorem, the play of language concerning boundedness of functions, as it relates boundedness for the range set.)

5.4-6 Theorem: i) If a sequence $\{s_n\}$ is monotonically increasing and $\{s_n\}$ is bounded above, then $\lim_{n \to \infty} s_n$ exists and is given by

$$\lim_{n \to \infty} s_n = \sup \{s_n\}.$$

ii) Similarly, if $\{s_n\}$ is monotonically decreasing and is bounded below, then

$$\lim_{n \to \infty} s_n = \inf \{s_n\}.$$

The proof of this theorem is beyond the scope of this text, since it would obviously require a firm rigorous foundation for the concept of "$\lim_{n \to \infty} s_n$."

However, the theorem is interesting in that it shows a strong connection between the two different concepts ("limit" and "least upper bound") involved.

Example: Suppose $\{s_n\}$ is a geometric sequence with common ratio $0 < r < 1$. Then $\{s_n\}$ is monotonically increasing if $s_1 \leq 0$. Otherwise it is monotonically decreasing. (Verify this!) (What happens if $r \in (-1, 0)$?) If $s_1 > 0$ and $r \in [0, 1)$, then $\{s_n\}$ is decreasing and has *g.l.b.* 0 (why?). Thus in this case

$$\lim_{n \to \infty} s_n = 0.$$

If $r = 1$, note that the sequence is a constant function so that

$$\lim_{n \to \infty} s_n = s_1.$$

Thus in this case $\quad$ *g.l.b.* $\{s_n\}$ = *l.u.b.* $\{s_n\}$ = s_1.

The Number e

One of the very popular irrational real numbers (perhaps even more popular than π) which occurs in calculus is a number called "e". The number e, being an irrational number, does not have a "nice fractional name," which accounts for its special name.

Consider the sequence given by

$$s_n = (1 + 1/n)^n$$

$$\{s_n\} = \left\{2, 2\frac{1}{4}, 2\frac{10}{27}, 2\frac{113}{256}, \ldots\right\}.$$

It *appears* that the sequence is an increasing sequence, and it can indeed be shown that it is. It can also be shown that the sequence is bounded above, and so it follows that $\{s_n\}$ has a limit. The limit is the irrational number denoted by "e."

$$\lim_{n \to 8} (1 + 1/n)^n = e$$

The number e has the approximate value 2.7182818284590 . . . (see Figure 5.26).

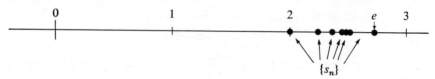

FIG. 5.26

As you may see in later work, this rather unlikely looking number is of great theoretical and practical importance.

Additional Remarks on Decimal Notation

We close this section with a few remarks similar to those made in Section 3.13 on decimal notations for real numbers. When we write a real number $r = 243.81$, we mean that r is the sum of the numbers 2, 4, 3, 8, and 1, each multiplied by an appropriate power of 10. Thus

$$r = 2 \times 10^2 + 4 \times 10^1 + 3 \times 10^0 + 8 \times 10^{-1} + 1 \times 10^{-2}.$$

We may represent real numbers as limits of certain sequences of rational numbers. Thus, the number r above is the limit of the sequence

$$\{s_n\} = \{200, 240, 243, 243.8, 243.81, 243.810, 243.8100, \ldots\}.$$

Recall that every real number is either rational or irrational. A rational number is a number expressible as the quotient of two integers. Another very useful characterization of rational numbers can be given in terms of their "decimal expansions": *A number is rational iff its infinite decimal expansion is "repeating."* By "repeating," we mean that after some point in the decimal expansion, a certain "block" of digits repeats in a cyclic fashion. This is sometimes denoted by drawing a vinculum (bar) over the repeating block. In particular, note that any *finite* decimal represents a rational number, since we may imagine the repeating block to be "$\bar{0}$" commencing at the end of the finite decimal. Thus, $243.81 = 243.81\bar{0}$ represents a rational number (namely $24381/100$).

The point of all of this is the fact that *any real number can be represented as the limit of a sequence of rational numbers.* Of course, if the real number r in question is itself rational, the sequence could be taken to be $\{s_n\}$, where the s_n's are all r (so that $\{s_n\}$ is a sequence of rational numbers). The more interesting situation is that in which r is irrational. The following example illustrates one procedure for representing an irrational number as the limit of a sequence of rational numbers.‡

Example: The irrational number

$$\pi = 3.14159265358979323846264\ldots$$

is the limit of the sequence

$$\{s_n\} = \{3, 3.14, 3.141, 3.1415, 3.14159, 3.141592, \ldots\}.$$

Since each s_n is a finite decimal, it is a rational number. Thus $\{s_n\}$ is a sequence of rationals, and we have chosen it so as to guarantee that

$$\lim_{n \to \infty} s_n = \pi.$$

Remark: Note that every number stored in a digital computer must

‡ For a very good discussion of the ideas of approximating numbers by rational numbers, see "Numbers: Rational and Irrational" by Ivan Nivan, Random House (1961).

necessarily be rational, since each digit of the number requires some memory locations, and even the largest computers have only finitely many such locations. Thus in computing, we may necessarily be faced with the idea of using rational numbers to *approximate* irrational numbers. In fact, in any numerical computation with decimals, one is necessarily forced to use only rational numbers.

Exercises 5.4

1. Why is the factor r involved in the geometric sequence called the *common ratio?*

2. Is it possible that 14, 5, and 8 are all terms of one geometric sequence? Of an arithmetic sequence?

3. The 5th term of a geometric sequence is 32 and its 10th term is 1024. Find its 16th term.

4. *a)* Show that a geometric sequence must be of the form

$$\{s_1, rs_1, r^2s_1, \ldots, r^ns_1, \ldots\}.$$

b) Find an analogous form that represents the arithmetic sequence.

5. Which of the following are geometric (arithmetic) sequences?
   a) $\{2, 6, 10, 14, 10, \ldots\}$
   b) $\{3, 1, 1/3, 1/9, 1/27, \ldots\}$
   c) $\{5, 7, 9, 12, 15, \ldots\}$

6. Suppose $s_n = c \quad \forall n \in N$. What is $\lim_{n\to\infty} s_n$?

7. Show how the number $.\overline{3}$ can be viewed as the sum of terms in a certain geometric sequence.

8. Find a "quotient" expression for the rational number

$$.317171717\ldots = .3\overline{17}.$$

9. Find $\lim_{n\to\infty} s_n$, where

a) $s_n = \dfrac{n+1}{n^2}$ *b)* $s_n = \dfrac{n}{n!}$ *c)* $s_n = \dfrac{1}{n} + 1$

10. *a)* What do you think the limit of the sequence $\{(-1)^n\}$ is?
    b) What do you think the limit of the sequence $\{2^n\}$ is?

11. *a)* Show that if the common difference k of an arithmetic sequence $\{s_n\}$ is prescribed, along with some specific term s_j, that all terms of the sequence are determined.

b) List the first seven terms of the arithmetic sequence with common difference -4 where the 20th term is 52110. (*Hint:* Do it the easy way.)

c) Find the sum of the first 31 terms of the sequence of part *b).*

12. Which of the following sequences are increasing and which are decreasing:

 a) $f_1 = 5$ *c)* $h_1 = 3$ *e)* $a_1 = 2$
   $f_n = (1/3)f_{n-1}$ $h_n = h_{n-1} - 3$

 b) $g_1 = 1$ *d)* $k_1 = 2$ $a_n = \sum_{i=1}^{n} a_1(1/3)^i$
   $g_n = 2f_{n-1}$ $k_n = k_{n-1} + 5$

13. Find the fifth term of each of the sequences in 12.

14. If $a_1 = 16$ and the common difference is 3, what are a_6 and a_{10}?

15. If $b_5 = 25$ and the common difference is -2, find b_1 and b_{15}.

16. If $y_1 = 2$ and $\forall n$ $y_n = y_{n-1} + 2$, find

 a) $y_3,\ y_4,\ y_5$ *b)* $\sum_{i=1}^{5} y_i$ *c)* $\sum_{i=1}^{125} y_i$ *d)* $\sum_{i=1}^{k} y_i$

(*i.e.*, find an *explicit* representation).

17. Consider the sequences in 12. Which were bounded above? Bounded below? Bounded?

18. If $d_5 = 3/8$ and the common ratio is $1/2$, find d_1 and d_{10}.

19. If $\{h_n\}$ is a geometric sequence and $h_5 = 20$ and $h_7 = 5/32$, find the common ratio and h_1.

20. Let $S: N \rightarrow R$ such that $S_1 = 1$. Find $\lim_{n \rightarrow \infty} S_n$ for each of the following:

 a) $S_n = \sum_{i=1}^{n} (1/2)^i$ *b)* $S_n = \sum_{i=1}^{n} (1/3)^i$ *c)* $S_n = \sum_{i=1}^{n} 5/3^i$

 (*Hint:* First find an explicit representation for S_n which does not use $\sum$.)

21. *a)* Let $\{a_n\}$ be an arithmetic sequence with common difference d. Show
$$\forall n \geq 1 \quad a_n = a_1 + d(n-1).$$

 b) Let $\{a_n\}$ be a geometric sequence with common ratio r. Show
$$\forall n \geq 1 \quad a_n = a_1 r^{n-1}.$$

22. Write each of the following in repeating decimal notation:

 a) $5/96$ *b)* $6/11$ *c)* $4/15$ *d)* $5/132$

 (*Hint:* Divide!)

23. Suppose $\{s_n\}$ is a geometric sequence with common ratio r, where $0 < r < 1$. Find:

 a) $\lim_{n \rightarrow \infty} s_n$ *b)* $\lim_{k \rightarrow \infty} \sum_{n=1}^{k} s_n$

 (*Hint:* See *hint* in Exercise 20.)

24. *a)* Find the sum of the numbers $15, 19, 23, 27, \ldots, 415$.
 b) Find the sum of the numbers $90, 30, 10, \ldots, 90/729$.

25. Prove Theorem 5.4-5.

5.5   Limits and Continuity

Limits of Other Functions

Suppose $\{f_n\}$ is a sequence such that $\lim_{n \to \infty} f_n = k$. We are interested in seeing what happens with the idea of limits when we extend the domain beyond N. If, for example, $f_n = 1 - 1/n$ describes the sequence $\{f_n\}$, we can define an extension of $\{f_n\}$ to a new function $f: (0, \infty) \to R$ by $f(x) = 1 - 1/x$. Note in particular for integer pre-images, the function f yields the same image as the sequence f_n. However, the two are not equivalent functions. (Why?) See Figure 5.27 for a comparison of the graphs of f_n and $f(x)$.

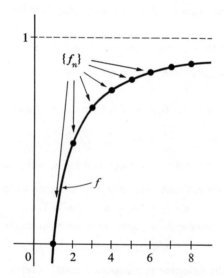

FIG. 5.27   The graphs of f_n and f coincide at the images of the integers $1, 2, 3, \ldots$, so that $f(n) = f_n$ (that is, $f|_N = \{f_n\}$).

(Note that the scales on the two axes are different to accommodate the particular problem being examined.) It seems in this case that for large n, the sequence becomes "nearly" constant—in fact, f_n monotonically increases up to $1 = \lim_{n \to \infty} f_n$. It also seems true that $f(x)$ does the same, so that we might be willing to extend our limit notation to state that

$$\lim_{x \to \infty} f(x) = 1.$$

The meaning of this statement is intuitively stated by saying that "$f(x)$ gets arbitrarily close to 1 for all x sufficiently large." The symbol is read "the limit of $f(x)$, as x gets large, is 1."

Example: Suppose $f(x) = 2/2^x$. Then as x gets large, $f(x)$ gets close to 0, so that apparently

$$\lim_{x \to \infty} f(x) = 0.$$

(See the graph of f (for positive values of x), Figure 5.28.)

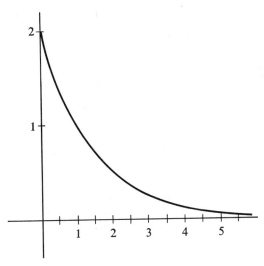

FIG. 5.28

Example: If $f(x) = x$, we see that as x gets large, $f(x)$ gets large, so that there is no number α such that

$$\lim_{x \to \infty} f(x) = \alpha$$

in this case. We shall say that "$f(x)$ converges to ∞" in this case, and write

$$\lim_{x \to \infty} f(x) = \infty.$$

It is to be emphasized that "∞" is meaningless standing alone. It may make sense only in conjunction with entire statements of the form above. (You should compare this use of the symbol "∞" with its use in interval notation of the form $(0, \infty)$.)

We next consider what happens on the graph of a function $f: R \to R$ as x gets "close" to some point a. The question is: "Does $f(x)$ *necessarily* also get 'close' to some point b?" We shall see that it may or may not, depending upon the behavior of f near a. If the answer to our question is "yes," we write

$$\lim_{x \to a} f(x) = b.$$

325

The meaning of the above symbol intuitively is this: There is a number b such that $f(x)$ is "close" to b for any x "sufficiently close" to a. For the time being, we avoid defining exactly what we mean by "close" and "sufficiently close" in the above statement. However, it must be understood that *we do not care what happens to $f(x)$ at the point $x = a$ itself!* The function may not be well behaved at a; in fact, a may not be a point in D_f. It turns out to be more convenient to have the limit be a "neighborhood" property, rather than a property involving only the point a.

Example: $\lim_{x \to 3} 4x = 12$. (Do you agree that $4x$ gets close to 12 for x close to 3?)

Example: The function in $\lim_{x \to 2} \dfrac{x^2 - 4}{x - 2}$ is not defined at $x = 2$ (why?), but the limit exists and is equal to $\lim_{x \to 2} (x + 2) = 4$. In this case it is crucial that the student understands the difference between the functions defined by

$$f_1(x) = \frac{x^2 - 4}{x - 2} = \frac{(x - 2)(x + 2)}{(x - 2)}$$

and

$$f_2(x) = x + 2.$$

The second function is an extension of the first, since $2 \notin D_{f_1}$, and

$$f_1(x) = f_2(x) \qquad \forall x \in D_{f_1}.$$

In order to find $\lim_{x \to 2} f_1(x)$, if this limit exists, it is not necessary to be able to compute $f_1(2)$ (indeed, it doesn't exist). The limit can be interpreted graphically as indicated in Figure 5.29.

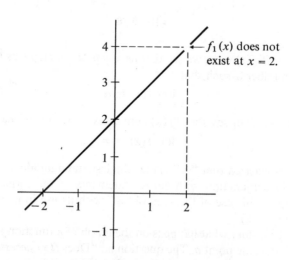

FIG. 5.29   The graph of f_1 indicates that $f_1(x)$ gets close to 4 as x gets close, but not equal, to 2. Thus we say that $\lim_{x \to 2} f_1(x) = 4$.

Example: a) $\lim_{x \to a} x = a$.

b) $\lim_{x \to a} |x| = |\lim_{x \to a} x.|$

(The student should verify these statements!)

The property exhibited by the absolute value function above is interesting. We see that apparently $|x|$ is a function in which we can interchange the order of "function" and "limit." That is, we have a function f such that (at least at the point a),

$$\lim_{x \to a} f(x) = f(\lim_{x \to a} x).$$

Such functions are of great interest, and thus this property is given a special name.

5.5-1 Definition: A function $f: A \to B$ is said to be *continuous* at the point $a \in A$ if $\lim_{x \to a} f(x) = f(a)$.

Remark: Note that the condition "$\lim_{x \to a} f(x) = f(a)$" is equivalent to the condition of "interchangeability of f and lim," inasmuch as $f(\lim_{x \to a} x) = f(a)$. Thus "continuity" is precisely the condition that allows one to interchange the process of taking the limit and evaluating the function. Note also that the condition "$\lim_{x \to a} f(x) = f(a)$" really implies three things:

1) that $\lim_{x \to a} f(x)$ exists.
2) that a is in the domain of f (so that $f(a)$ is defined).
3) that the limit is the value $f(a)$.

5.5-2 Definition: A function $f: A \to B$ is called *continuous at every point in A* (or simply *continuous*) iff

$$\forall a \in A \quad \lim_{x \to a} f(x) = f(a).$$

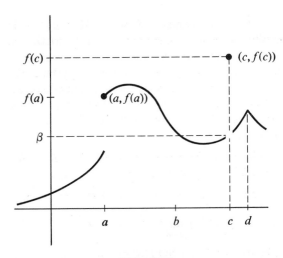

FIG. 5.30

The condition of continuity of a function is very strong. Graphically, it means roughly that the graph of the continuous function does not have "jumps" or "holes." Suppose, for example, that $f(x)$ has the graph shown in Figure 5.30. We see that f has "discontinuities" at the points a, b, and c, since in the first case, pre-images close to a are not all mapped to images near any real number (and thus certainly not all close to $f(a)$). In fact, apparently $\lim_{x \to a} f(x)$ does not exist in this case. In the second case, we have a different problem. Here $\lim_{x \to b} f(x)$ exists, but $f(b)$ does not. Finally, at c we have both $\lim_{x \to c} f(x)$ and $f(c)$ existing, but the two are not equal ($f(x) \neq \lim_{x \to c} f(x) = \beta$). Do you agree that f is continuous at d?

Early attempts to characterize continuity of a function were sometimes expressed as follows: "The function is continuous if its graph can be traced without lifting the pencil from the paper." While this expression does characterize the *spirit* of continuity, the wording is too vague to be of much use in rigorous work.

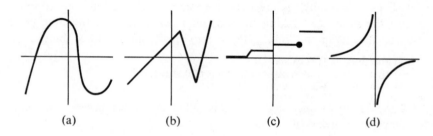

(a)   (b)   (c)   (d)

FIG. 5.31

Example: Of the four graphs in Figure 5.31, only the first two correspond with continuous functions. Note that the restriction of the function in (d) to $[1, \infty)$, for example, *is* continuous.

We conclude this section by stating a very important theorem concerning limits and its connection with extensions of functions. Since continuity is a "limit condition," this theorem can be used to prove analogous statements about continuity. A proof of the "Limit Theorem" would require a rigorous definition of limits.

5.5-3 Theorem: (*The Limit Theorem*) Suppose $f: R \to R$, $g: R \to R$, and that $\lim_{x \to a} f(x) = \alpha$ and $\lim_{x \to a} g(x) = \beta$. Then

> *i*) $\lim_{x \to a} (f + g)(x) = \lim_{x \to a} f(x) + \lim_{x \to a} g(x) = \alpha + \beta$.

> *ii*) $\lim_{x \to a} f \cdot g(x) = \lim_{x \to a} f(x) \cdot \lim_{x \to a} g(x) = \alpha \cdot \beta$.

> *iii*) $\forall c \in R, \lim_{x \to a} cf(x) = c \lim_{x \to a} f(x) = c\alpha$.

iv) if f is continuous,

$$\lim_{x \to a} f(g(x)) = f(\lim_{x \to a} g(x)) = f(\beta).$$

Remark: Note that c in *iii*) can be taken to be -1 in particular, so that *i*) can be extended to subtraction as well. Similarly one can use *ii*) to express a similar property for division (provided the denominator limit is non-zero). You might observe that *iii*) is only a special case of *ii*). (Explain!)

Extensions by Continuity

A commonly encountered criterion upon which extensions of functions are based, is continuity. In some cases, we may have a function which is not a continuous function in $R \times R$, but which can be "extended by continuity" to such a function. An example of this is the function $f(x) = (x^2 - 4)/(x - 2)$ discussed previously. Using the maximal domain convention we conclude that $D_f = \widetilde{\{2\}}$. Recall that f is continuous at each point in its domain, so in order to extend f on D_f to f^* on R by continuity, we would like to define a value for f^* at $x = 2$. In order for the function f^* to be continuous at 2, we must make a specific choice for $f^*(2)$, namely:

$$f^*(2) = \lim_{x \to 2} f(x).$$

Since
$$\lim_{x \to 2} (x^2 - 4)/(x - 2) = 4,$$

we define $f^*(2) = 4$. Thus the extended function f^*, defined by

$$f^*(x) = \begin{cases} (x^2 - 4)/(x - 2) & \text{if } x \neq 2 \\ 4 \text{ if } x = 2 \end{cases}$$

is a continuous function in $R \times R$. In fact in this case, note that

$$f^*(x) = x + 2 \qquad \forall x \in R.$$

Example: Let $f(x) = (x^2 - 1)/(x + 1)$. f is undefined at -1 but

$$\lim_{x \to -1} f(x) = -2.$$

Therefore, if we define $f(-1) = -2$, the function f is extended to include (-1) and the extension is made in a way to accommodate continuity. (Note that we are using the same symbol (f) for the original and extended versions in this case.)

It may seem that the functions we have chosen to extend by continuity up to now have been rather "rigged." This is true, but in general, the idea of extension by continuity is a very important one. Essentially, when we extended exponentiation to include arbitrary real number exponents we applied this concept.

Example: Let $f(x) = 2^x$ where $x \in Q$, so that f is defined on all rational numbers. If we extend f to the reals by continuity, then we say in effect that a real number is mapped close to the point where rational numbers near it are mapped.

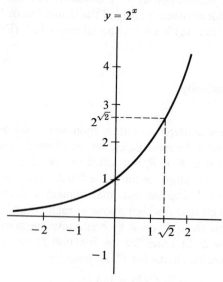

FIG. 5.32

This is the essence of our extension of exponentiation to include all real numbers by using least upper bounds. Continuity is thus very closely related to the completeness axiom for the real numbers. (You might find it interesting to review Section 3.13 with this idea in mind.)

Exercises 5.5

1. Find the following limits:

   a) $\lim_{x \to \infty} 2x$ c) $\lim_{x \to \infty} (2 + 1/x)$ e) $\lim_{x \to \infty} 1/2^x$

   b) $\lim_{x \to \infty} 2/x$ d) $\lim_{x \to \infty} 2^{-x}$

2. Let $f, g \subset R \times R$ such that $f > g$. (Recall that $f > g$ if $\forall x \ \ f(x) > g(x)$.) Argue that if $\lim_{x \to a} f(x) = b$, then $\lim_{x \to a} g(x) \leq b$ if the limit exists.

3. Suppose $f: (0, \infty) \to R$, and that the sequence $\{s_n\}$ is the restriction of f to N. (That is, $\{s_n\} = f|_N$.) Then argue for or against:

   a) $\lim_{x \to \infty} f(x) = \alpha \Rightarrow \lim_{n \to \infty} s_n = \alpha$.

   b) $\lim_{n \to \infty} s_n = \alpha \Rightarrow \lim_{x \to \infty} f(x) = \alpha$.

4. *a)* Show that the sum of continuous functions is continuous.

   b) Show that the product of continuous functions is continuous.

   c) Show that a constant times a continuous function is continuous.

   d) Show that the composition of continuous functions is continuous. (*Hint:* Use the limit theorem and the definition for continuity.)

5. *a)* Show that if c_f is continuous and x_f is continuous, then $f(x) = 5x^3 - 2x^2 + 3x - 9$ is a continuous function.

   b) Sketch a graph of $f(x)$.

6. *a)* Show that if $f: R \to R$ is a continuous function, then for any real number α, there is a sequence $\{r_n\}$ of rational numbers such that $\lim_{n\to\infty} r_n = \alpha$ and $\lim_{n\to\infty} f(r_n) = f(\alpha)$. (*Hint:* Use a remark of the preceding section.)

   b) Do you think the converse of the above statement is true?

7. Find the indicated limits, if they exist, of each of the following:

   a) $\lim\limits_{x\to 2} \dfrac{x+3}{x+4}$

   c) $\lim\limits_{b\to\infty} \dfrac{b+1}{b^2+1}$

   b) $\lim\limits_{a\to -3} \dfrac{a^2+4x+3}{x+3}$

   d) $\lim\limits_{y\to 2} \dfrac{y^2-5y+6}{y-2}$

8. Which of the following functions are continuous on the reals? Of those that are not continuous on R, at what points are they not continuous:

   a) $1/x + 1/y = 1$

   b) $y = (x^2 + 5x)^3$

   c) $y = (x-1)/(x+1)$

   d) $y = [x]$

   e) $y = x - [x]$

   f) $y = |[x]|$

   g) $y = [|x|]$

   h) $y = \begin{cases} x - 2n, & \text{if } x \in [2n, 2n+1) \\ 2n - x, & \text{if } x \in [2n-1, 2n) \end{cases}$

9. State a theorem about $\lim_{x\to a} (f \vee g)(x)$ in terms of $\lim_{x\to a} f(x)$ and $\lim_{x\to a} g(x)$.

5.6 Asymptotes, Big O and Little o

Asymptotes

It is interesting to see how certain limits can be interpreted graphically. Suppose, for example that f is a function in $R \times R$ such that $\lim_{x\to\infty} f(x) = 5$. Then we know that, for sufficiently large x, the function must behave essentially as the function 5_f. Knowing this is a great help in graphing f, since we need not worry about finding ordered pairs and "plotting" f for large x in such a case. Suppose that it is also known that $\lim_{x\to -\infty} f(x) = 0$. (That is, $f(x)$ is close to zero for sufficiently small x.) Then in order to graph f, it is only necessary to check its behavior for x values relatively close to the origin.

Example: Consider the function $f(x) = 2^x$. Note that $\lim_{x \to -\infty} 2^x = 0$, since taking 2 to very large *negative* powers results in numbers close to zero. Thus we know that the graph of f approaches the x-axis for small x (see Figure 5.33). Noting that $\lim_{x \to \infty} 2^x = \infty$ tells us that, for positive x-values, the graph trails up into the 1st quadrant. The graph is completed very easily by finding a few ordered pairs such as $(0, 1)$ and $(1, 2)$.

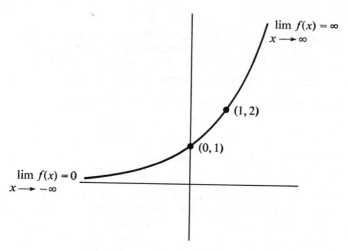

$$\lim_{x \to \infty} f(x) = \infty$$

$(1, 2)$

$(0, 1)$

$$\lim_{x \to -\infty} f(x) = 0$$

FIG. 5.33 Graph of $y = 2^x$.

When the graph of a function (or relation) approaches a horizontal line for very large positive or negative values of the variable, we call that line a *horizontal asymptote* of the function.

5.6-1 Definition: If $\lim_{x \to \infty} f(x) = a$, then the line, $y = a$, is called a *horizontal asymptote of f in the positive direction*. If $\lim_{x \to -\infty} f(x) = b$, then $y = b$ is a *horizontal asymptote of f in the negative direction*.

It is also possible that the graph of f approaches a vertical line for x values near some point a. Then we obtain vertical asymptotes if $\lim_{x \to a} f(x) = \infty$ or $\lim_{x \to a} f(x) = -\infty$.

Example: Consider the "hyperbola," $y = 1/x$. In this case we have

$$\lim_{x \to \infty} f(x) = 0, \tag{1}$$

$$\lim_{x \to -\infty} f(x) = 0, \tag{2}$$

$$\lim_{x \to 0^+} f(x) = +\infty, \tag{3}$$

$$\lim_{x \to 0^-} f(x) = -\infty, \tag{4}$$

where "$\lim_{x \to 0^+} f(x) = \infty$" denotes that $f(x)$ gets large for *positive* x values near zero. Similarly "$\lim_{x\to 0^-} f(x) = -\infty$" means that $f(x)$ gets small for *negative* x values near zero. These limits are called the "limit from the right" and "limit from the left" of f as x goes to zero, respectively. Equations (1) through (4) tell us a great deal about the graph of f (and hence a great deal about f itself). By (1) and (2), we know that the x-axis is a horizontal asymptote in both the positive and negative directions. By (3) and (4) we know that the y-axis is a vertical asymptote as x approaches zero from the right and also from the left. The graph of f (Figure 5.34) is very easily completed by checking a few ordered pairs (such as $(1, 1)$ and $(-1, -1)$) and noting the symmetries of f. (There are two kinds. What are they?)

Remark: Limit statements such as "$\lim_{x\to a} f(x) = b$" are often written in the form "$f(x) \to b$ as $x \to a$." Thus statement (4) could be written "$y \to -\infty$ as $x \to 0^-$." This notation is used in Figure 5.34.

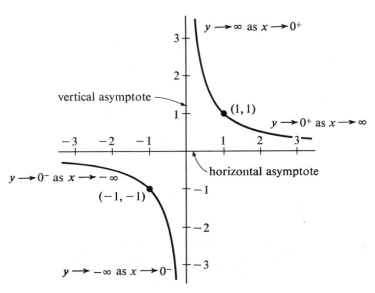

FIG. 5.34   The graph of $y = 1/x$.

The idea of vertical and horizontal asymptotes is easily generalized. First of all, we might be willing to relax the condition that an asymptote which the graph "approaches" be a vertical or horizontal line. Thus we can consider *oblique asymptotes*, as well as horizontal and vertical ones. However, it seems rather strict to insist that the graphs in question always approach *lines*. We might be willing to take "asymptotes" to be familiar curves of various kinds, in addition to straight lines.

Example: Consider the function $f(x) = x - 1/x$. Note that

$\lim_{x \to 0^+} f(x) = -\infty$, and also that $f(x) \to +\infty$ as $x \to 0^-$. (Recall that $\lim_{x \to a} (h + g)x = \lim_{x \to a} h(x) + \lim_{x \to a} g(x)$.) Thus we know the behavior of the graph of $f(x)$ near the origin. In order to determine the function's behavior "in the large" (that is, for x values far from the origin), we compute $\lim_{x \to \infty} f(x) = \infty$, $\lim_{x \to -\infty} f(x) = -\infty$. Unfortunately, this does not tell us exactly *how* f goes in quadrants I and III. A close inspection of $f(x)$ reveals the following useful information: As $x \to \infty$, $f(x)$ becomes essentially the function x_f (*i.e.*, the line $y = x$) since $1/x \to 0$. Similarly, for large negative values of x we have $f(x) \to x$. Thus it appears that the line $y = x$ is an oblique asymptote. (See Figure 5.35.)

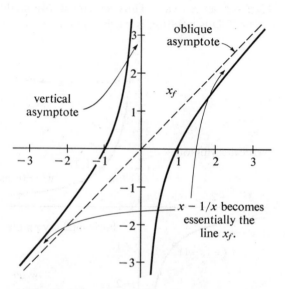

FIG. 5.35 The function $f(x) = x - 1/x$ becomes essentially the function x_f for x values far from the origin. Thus x_f is an oblique asymptote.

Example: Consider the function described by $f(x) = (x^2 + 2)/x^3$. Note that $D_f = \{\bar{0}\}$, and that $f \to +\infty$ as $x \to 0^+$, while $f \to -\infty$ as $x \to 0^-$. Thus the line $x = 0$ is a vertical asymptote. Note that $f(x)$ becomes essentially the function $1/x$ for very large values of $|x|$. This is easily seen by writing

$$f(x) = x^2/x^3 + 2/x^3 = 1/x + 2/x^3.$$

Now x^3 gets large much "faster" than x so that $2/x^3$ goes "rapidly" to zero, leaving the $1/x$ function. Recalling the behavior of the $1/x$ function, we easily complete the graph with the aid of a few ordered pairs in f, and a consideration of symmetry through $(0, 0)$. (See Figure 5.36.)

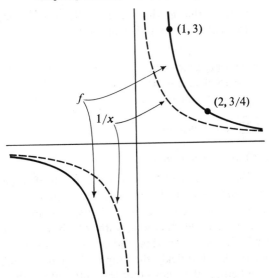

FIG. 5.36   The graph of $f(x) = (x^2 + 2)/x^3$ has a vertical asymptote at $x = 0$, and behaves "in the large" as the function $1/x$.

Big O and Little o

In the last two examples we noticed that for large x, the functions under consideration behave essentially as certain simple functions with which we are familiar, such as $y = x$ or $y = 1/x$. This idea is formalized by the following definition.

5.6-2 Definition: We write $f = O(g)$ as $x \to a$ if $\lim_{x \to a} f(x)/g(x) = 1$. ("$f$ is big O of g" or "f is the same order as g.") Similarly, we write the statement $f = o(g)$ as $x \to a$ if $\lim_{x \to a} f(x)/g(x) = 0$. ("$f$ is little o of g" or "f is small compared to g.")

Remark: We can easily extend this notation to such expressions as $f = O(g)$ as $x \to \infty$, $f = O(g)$ as $x \to -\infty$, etc. Note that if $f = O(g)$ as $x \to \infty$, then the functions f and g are essentially the same for x values sufficiently large. That is, since

$$\lim_{x \to \infty} \frac{f(x)}{g(x)} = 1$$

we apparently must have

$$\lim_{x \to \infty} f(x) = \lim_{x \to \infty} g(x)$$

if these limits are non-zero. But this means that for sufficiently large x, there is not much difference between f and g. On the other hand, to say that

335

$f = o(g)$ as $x \to \infty$ means that g "dominates" f. That is, $|g(x)|$ gets very large with respect to $|f(x)|$ for x values sufficiently large.

Example:

a) $(1 + 1/x) = O(1)$ as $x \to \infty$.

b) $(x - 1/x) = O(x)$ as $x \to \infty$.

c) $(x - 1/x) = o(x^{-2})$ as $x \to 0$.

d) $x^n = O\left(\sum_{i=1}^{n} a_i x^i\right)$ as $x \to \infty$.

e) $x^n = o(x^m)$ as $x \to \infty$ if $m > n$.

Thus we see that the task of sketching the graph of some function that is not familiar to us may be considerably eased by taking care of its "behavior in the large" in one step. The real power of this, of course, is to utilize our knowledge of certain simple functions with which we are familiar. With some practice we hope to develop this, and other notions, to a point that will enable the reader to sketch quickly the graph of *any* reasonably simple function. For the time being, let us note that the "ultimate authority" in graphing is ordered pairs. Thus, if all else fails, the student may have to prepare a list of some of the ordered pairs in the function he is trying to graph, and plot them in order to get some idea of how the graph looks. As we become more skillful in using some of the ideas such as asymptotes, we will often be able to avoid the hard labor of preparing long lists of ordered pairs. In fact, often we may not need to find any at all.

Exercises 5.6

1. Find the vertical asymptotes for each of the following functions. Graph each function.

a) $f(x) = 3/(2x - 1)$

b) $f(x) = 2/(x + 2)$

c) $f(x) = x/(2x^2 + x - 2)$

d) $f(x) = (x - 1)/(x^2 - 1)$

2. Graph each of the following functions.

a) $f(x) = 3 + 1/(x - 1)$

b) $f(x) = x(x^2 + 1)/(x^2 + x)$

c) $f(x) = x + 1/x$

d) $y = x^2 + 1/x^2$

3. a) Characterize horizontal asymptotes in terms of the big O or little o notation.

   b) Do the same as in a) for oblique and vertical asymptotes, if possible.

4. If $f = O(g)$ as $x \to \infty$, does it follow that $g = O(f)$ as $x \to \infty$?

5. If $f = o(g)$ as $x \to a$, what can you say about $\lim_{x \to a} g(x)/f(x)$?

6. Is it possible to have $f \vee g = f$ and also $f = o(g)$?

7. Suppose $f = O(x)$ as $x \to \infty$ and $g = O(x^2 + 2x + 1)$ as $x \to \infty$. What can you say about:

a) $f \wedge g$

b) $f \circ g$

c) $f + g$

d) f/g

e) $f \cdot g$

8. *a)* Suppose $\mathfrak{F}$ is the class of functions in $R \times R$ with domain R. Define $f \, O \, g$ to be the relation in $\mathfrak{F}$ described by $f \, O \, g$ iff $f = O(g)$ as $x \to \infty$. Show that "0" is an equivalence relation.

   b) What can you say about the equivalence classes induced by "0"?

5.7   Slopes and Tangent Lines

Lines and Slope

Let us discuss briefly the conditions under which the Cartesian graph of a function $f: R \to R$ is a straight line.

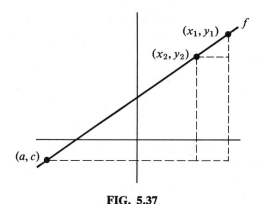

FIG. 5.37

The graph of a function f will be a line, provided that given any two points (x, y) and (a, c) in f, $(a \neq x)$, it follows that

$$\frac{y - c}{x - a} = m$$

for some fixed m. We feel this way because of certain ratios which are involved in similar triangles (see Figure 5.37). Simplifying this result slightly we see that a function $f: R \to R$ will graph as a straight line if and only if

   $f(x) = mx + b$ for some fixed $m \in R$ and some fixed $b \in R$.

Hence the following definition.

5.7-1 Definition: Let $f: R \to R$. Then f is called a *linear function* if $f(x) = mx + b$ for some m and b in R.

   Example: Let $f(x) = 2x + 1$. The graph of f is shown in Figure 5.38.

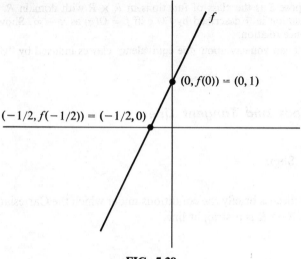

$(0, f(0)) = (0, 1)$

$(-1/2, f(-1/2)) = (-1/2, 0)$

FIG. 5.38

Notice that

$$f(3 + 1) = 2(3 + 1) + 1$$
$$= 2 \cdot 3 + 2 + 1$$
$$= 2 \cdot 3 + 1 + 2$$
$$= 7 + 2 = f(3) + 2.$$

The functional value of f increased by 2 as the domain value increased by 1. We note that this is independent of the point chosen. For example

$$f(4 + 1) = 2(4 + 1) + 1$$
$$= 8 + 1 + 2$$
$$= 9 + 2 = f(4) + 2.$$

Note that the amount which $f(x)$ increases as x increases by one unit corresponds to the m in the preceding definition (which in this particular case is 2). Let us show that this is always true.

5.7-2 Theorem: If $f: R \to R$ is linear (*i.e.*, $f(x) = mx + b$), then

$$\forall x \in R \quad f(x + 1) - f(x) = m.$$

Proof: Let $x \in R$.

$$f(x + 1) - f(x) = (m(x + 1) + b) - (mx + b)$$
$$= mx + m + b - mx - b$$
$$= m. \quad \square$$

We see then that the defining m is a measure of the increase of the functional values with respect to a unit increase of the values of the domain variable. Also notice that $(0, b) \in f$. Hence the following definition.

5.7-3 Definition: If $f: R \to R$ given by $f(x) = mx + b$, then f is said to have *slope m*. The number b is called the *y intercept*.

Example: Let $f(x) = 1/2x + 2$. f passes through the point $(0, 2)$ and $f(x)$ increases by $1/2$ as x increases by 1. The graph of f is given in Figure 5.39.

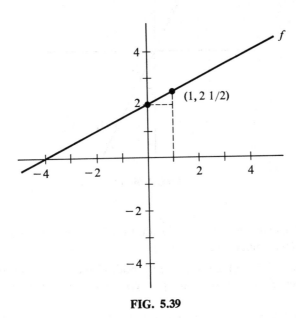

FIG. 5.39

We next show that this "measure of increase" can be used without reading changes of exactly one unit "along the *x*-axis."

5.7-4 Theorem: If $f(x) = mx + b$ and $h \in R$, then

$$\forall x \quad f(x + h) - f(x) = mh.$$

The proof is left as an exercise.

5.7-5 Corollary: $\forall h \neq 0, \forall x \quad \dfrac{f(x + h) - f(x)}{h} = m.$ ☐

The above theorem asserts that if f is a linear function with slope m, then, as x increases by an amount h, $f(x)$ increases by an amount mh. The corollary states the same fact in terms of a ratio. That is, the ratio of the increase in $f(x)$ to the increase in x is the slope m.

Example: Let $f(x) = -2x$. Clearly $(0, 0) \in f$ and if x increases an amount h, then $f(x)$ increases an amount $-2h$. Hence if h is positive (an increase to the right), then $f(x)$ decreases (an increase downward). (See Figure 5.40.)

339

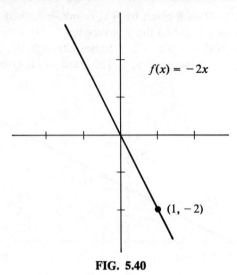

$f(x) = -2x$

$(1, -2)$

FIG. 5.40

We shall shortly make use of one additional property of linear functions, the fact that two points determine a line.

5.7-6 Theorem: If (x_1, y_1) and (x_2, y_2) are both elements of a linear function $f: R \to R$, then f has slope $m = (y_2 - y_1)/(x_2 - x_1)$ and y-intercept $b = y_1 - mx_1$.

Proof: Suppose $(x, y) \in f$, where $x \notin \{x_1, x_2\}$. (Note that necessarily $x_1 \neq x_2$ (why?).) Then

$$\frac{y - y_1}{x - x_1} = m = \frac{y_2 - y_1}{x_2 - x_1}$$

(verify this), so that $y = mx + b$, where m and b are as claimed in the theorem. ☐

Tangent Lines and Slopes of Curves

We wish to examine the possibility of extending the slope concept to functions which are not linear (*i.e.*, graphed as lines).

In geometry, a line tangent to a circle (at a point of the circle) is taken to be a line which intersects the circle at only one point. This idea does not lend itself well to curves in general. Intuitively, we want a line to be called "tangent to a curve at d" if it intersects the curve at d, and all points on the curve "close" to d "lie close to" the tangent line. In Figure 5.41, we have three examples of lines tangent to a curve f.

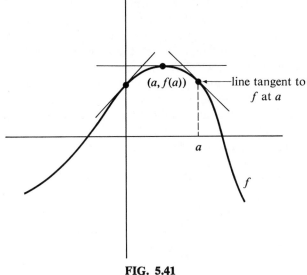

FIG. 5.41

Geometrically, we can imagine a "smooth" curve as having a tangent line at each point, and thus extend the concept of slope to functions from R to R which graph as "smooth" curves. The slope of the *tangent line* at a given point is apparently determined, hence we can define the slope of the function in terms of the slope of the tangent line.

In order to do this, we need to decide what particular characteristics of a function determine whether it graphs as a "smooth" curve. Let us examine some examples.

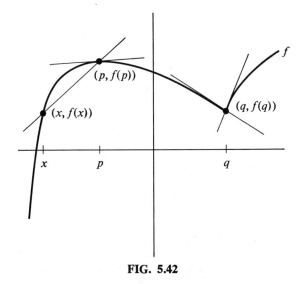

FIG. 5.42

Example: Consider a function f whose graph is given in Figure 5.42. First consider the point $(p, f(p))$. We notice that if a line intersecting $(p, f(p))$ and some arbitrary point $(x, f(x))$ on the curve is considered, then as x "approaches" p, the line "approaches" the tangent line at p. This is true, regardless of the side from which x "approaches" p. On the other hand, at the point $(q, f(q))$ there is not a unique tangent line, since one arrives at a different line depending on whether one considers $x \to q^-$ or $x \to q^+$. Apparently, then, a curve has a tangent line at a point d only if the curve is "smooth" at d (*i.e.*, has no "sharp corners" or "jumps").

As you may have guessed, this concept of slope "at a point" for certain functions is related to the notion of limit. We consider a motivating Figure 5.43 and then make a "reasonable" definition of slope at a point.

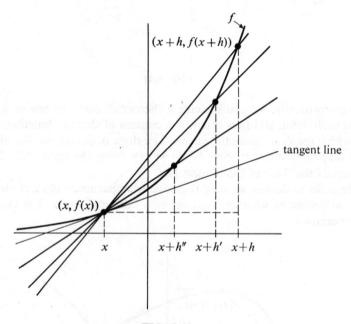

FIG. 5.43

5.7-7 Definition: If $f: R \to R$ and if $\lim_{h \to 0} \dfrac{f(a + h) - f(a)}{h}$ exists, then this limit is called the "slope of f at a."

Example: Let $f(x) = x^2$. Then

$$\frac{f(2 + h) - f(2)}{h} = \frac{(2 + h)^2 - 2^2}{h}$$

$$= \frac{2^2 + 4h + h^2 - 2^2}{h}$$

$$= 4 + h \quad (\text{provided } h \neq 0)$$

and hence $\lim_{h \to 0} \dfrac{f(2 + h) - f(2)}{h}$ exists and is equal to 4. We assert therefore that a tangent line exists at $(2, f(2))$; moreover, it has slope 4. Similarly,

$$\frac{f(0 + h) - f(0)}{h} = \frac{(0 + h)^2 - 0^2}{h} = \frac{h^2}{h} = h,$$

and therefore

$$\lim_{h \to 0} \frac{f(0 + h) - f(0)}{h} = \lim_{h \to 0} h = 0.$$

Also, $\dfrac{f(-2 + h) - f(-2)}{h} = \dfrac{(-2 + h)^2 - (-2)^2}{h}$

$$= \frac{4 - 4h + h^2 - 4}{h}$$

$$= -4 + h. \qquad \text{(Again we assume } h \neq 0.\text{)}$$

Hence $\lim_{h \to 0} \dfrac{f(-2 + h) - f(-2)}{h} = \lim_{h \to 0} (-4 + h) = -4.$

We now know that f has a tangent line at $(0, 0)$ with slope 0, one at $(2, 4)$ with slope 4, and one at $(-2, 4)$ with slope -4. This serves as an aid in graphing f as we see in Figure 5.44.

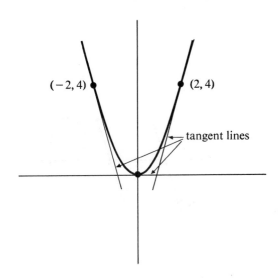

FIG. 5.44

Remark: In evaluating the limits above, you should note that we did not "evaluate" the ratio $\dfrac{f(x + h) - f(x)}{h}$ at $h = 0$. In fact, we found it necessary to insist that $h \neq 0$. Also note the limit as $h \to 0^+$ would be the same as the limit as $h \to 0^-$, which is necessary in order for the limit to exist.

Example: Let $g(x) = x^3$.

$$\lim_{h \to 0} \frac{g(0 + h) - g(0)}{h} = \lim_{h \to 0} h^2 = 0$$

$$\lim_{h \to 0} \frac{g(1 + h) - g(1)}{h} = \lim_{h \to 0} \frac{(1 + h)^3 - 1^3}{h}$$

$$= \lim_{h \to 0} \frac{1 + 3h + 3h^2 + h^3 - 1}{h}$$

$$= \lim_{h \to 0} (3 + 3h + h^2)$$

$$= 3$$

and $$\lim_{h \to 0} \frac{g(-1 + h) - g(-1)}{h} = \lim_{h \to 0} \frac{-1 + 3h - 3h^2 + h^3 - (-1)}{h}$$

$$= \lim_{h \to 0} (3 - 3h + h^2)$$

$$= 3.$$

Using this information, we graph the points $(0, 0), (1, 1), (-1, -1)$ along with the tangent lines at these points in Figure 5.45.

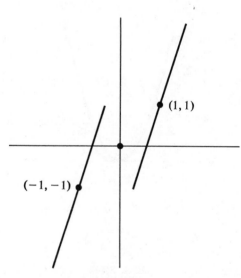

(1, 1)

(-1, -1)

FIG. 5.45

Using imagination, optimism, the fact that g is an odd function, and the knowledge

$$\lim_{x \to \infty} x^3 = \infty \quad \text{and} \quad \lim_{x \to -\infty} x^3 = -\infty,$$

one obtains a fair picture of the function (see Figure 5.46).

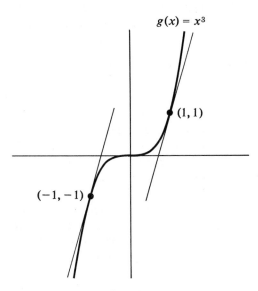

$g(x) = x^3$

$(1, 1)$

$(-1, -1)$

FIG. 5.46

Example: In the above examples, we computed the slope for a given function at several different points. In each case, we could have determined a formula which gave the slope at an arbitrary point b in the domain of the function. For example, consider the function f where

$$f(x) = 2x^2 - 1.$$

The slope at $(b, f(b))$ is given by

$$\lim_{h \to 0} \frac{f(b + h) - f(b)}{h} = \lim_{h \to 0} \frac{2(b + h)^2 - 1 - (2b^2 - 1)}{h}$$

$$= \lim_{h \to 0} \frac{2b^2 + 4bh + 2h^2 - 1 - 2b^2 + 1}{h}$$

$$= \lim_{h \to 0} \frac{4bh + 2h^2}{h}$$

$$= \lim_{h \to 0} 4b + 2h = 4b.$$

Hence, at each point b in the domain of f, the slope of f at $(b, f(b))$ is $4b$.

345

Thus,   at $(0, -1)$ f has slope 0

at $(-1, 1)$ f has slope -4

at $(1, 1)$ f has slope 4.

This information should be very helpful in drawing a graph of f.

Remark: Note that tangent lines have positive slope where the function is increasing and negative slope where the function is decreasing.

Linear Interpolation for Functional Values

In many problems of interest, one has a table of functional values for a given function $f: R \to R$ which lists $f(x_1), f(x_2), f(x_3)$, etc., where $|x_i - x_{i+1}| = k$ for some fixed positive k. (Clearly, one cannot list functional values for all real numbers.) If the function is such that values are difficult to compute, then it is useful to approximate $f(x)$ for x's not listed in the available table of values. One common method of making such approximations is that known as "linear interpolation." (This method, for example, is of interest in dealing with logarithms and circular functions, which we shall consider later.)

Consider $f: R \to R$, and a partial table of values in which $f(x_1)$, $f(x_2)$, $f(x_3)$ are listed, along with the knowledge that the function is "fairly well behaved" between the points for which values are given. Figure 5.47 is the graph of f.

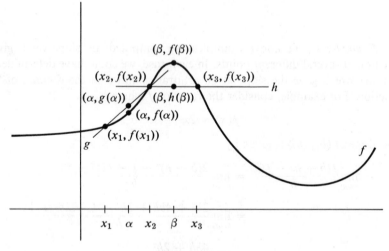

FIG. 5.47

If we wish to determine an approximate value for $f(\alpha)$, $x_1 < \alpha < x_2$ (as shown in Figure 5.47), then we determine $g(\alpha)$, where g is the linear function whose graph passes through $(x_1, f(x_1))$ and $(x_2, f(x_2))$. This is easily done, since by Theorem 4.7-6, $g(\alpha)$ is determined by solving the equation

$$\frac{f(x_2) - f(x_1)}{x_2 - x_1} = \frac{g(\alpha) - f(x_1)}{\alpha - x_1}.$$

We then feel that $f(\alpha)$ is "approximately" $g(\alpha)$, and we use $g(\alpha)$ in our computations in place of the unknown $f(\alpha)$. This process is known as *linear interpolation*, and its success depends on the fact that with certain functions (namely, those which are continuous), the functional values associated with neighboring pre-images, are near each other. Notice that linear interpolation between x_2 and x_3 (Figure 5.47) would apparently yield an approximation, $h(\beta)$, of $f(\beta)$ that is not very good. (Why?) There are other methods of approximation which may be better for some problems. (Some of these methods are well suited to use in computer applications.)

Exercises 5.7

1. Graph, and determine the slope of each function:
   a) $f(x) = 3x - 4$ c) $f(x) = (1/2)x + 1/3$
   b) $f(x) = -2x + 2$ d) $f(x) = -3x - 2/5$

2. Graph, and determine the slope of each function:
   a) $f = \{(x, y): y = 2x - 3\}$ d) $f = \{(x, y): y - x = 0\}$
   b) $f = \{(x, y): 3y = 2x - 3\}$ e) $f = \{(x, y): 2y + x - 1 = 0\}$
   c) $f = \{(x, y): 3y - 1 = 4x + 2\}$

3. What role do you suppose b plays in the graphing of a linear function $f(x) = mx + b$? (*Hint: b* is called "the *y*-intercept"!)

4. If $f(x) = 7x + 29$, then how much does $f(x)$ increase as
   a) x increases by one unit?
   b) x increases by $1/3$ of a unit?
   c) x increases by 7 units?
   d) x increases by π units?
   e) x decreases by 2 units?

5. Let $f(x) = 3x^2 + 2$. Determine the slope of f at $(0, f(0)), (1, f(1)), (-1, f(-1))$, if it exists. Then use this information and other limit concepts along with symmetry to graph f.

6. Compute the slope at select points, and use limit values in the large to graph f where:
   a) $f(x) = 2x^3 - 1$
   b) $f(x) = 2x^2 - 1/2$
   c) $f(x) = x^4$

7. If $f(5) = 9$ and $f(5.6) = 9.52$, then use linear interpolation to (hopefully) approximate:
   a) $f(5.3)$ b) $f(5.2)$ c) $f(5.11)$ d) $f(5.47)$

8. Use Definition 5.7-7 ("slope of f at a") to find the slope of $f(x) = mx + b$ at a. (Note that this coincides with the definition of the slope of a linear function given in Definition 5.7-3.)

9. Find the slope of the line which passes through the two given points, then graph the line:

a) $(2, -3)$ and $(0, 1)$ c) $(5, 0)$ and $(7, 0)$

b) $(-5, -3)$ and $(-1, -2)$ d) $(5, 0)$ and $(5, 3)$

10. Find the linear function f that passes through the given point and has slope m.

a) $(0, 1)$ and $m = -1$ c) $(-2, -1)$ and $m = 4$

b) $(2, 5)$ and $m = -3$ d) $(-3, 4)$ and $m = \pi$

11. Find the line tangent to the curve $y = 2x^2 + 4x - 3$ at $(1, 3)$.

12. Find the slope of each of the following functions at the indicated point, and then at an arbitrary point $(b, f(b))$.

a) $y = 5x^3 - 3x^5$ at $(1, 2)$

b) $y = \dfrac{x^5}{5} - \dfrac{x^3}{3} + \dfrac{x^2}{2} + x + 2$ at $\left(2, \dfrac{146}{15}\right)$

c) $y = 3 + 4x - x$ at $(-1, -2)$

13. Suppose that when an atomic particle is in a certain magnetic field, the equation of its path is $4x^2 - 8x + 1$. If the field is removed at any instant, the path of the particle will be along the tangent line to the curve at that point where the field is removed. What will be the equation of the line which the particle will follow if its field is removed when the particle is at $(5, 61)$ (neglecting direction)?

14. Prove Theorem 5.7-4.

15. Find the linear function containing the points $(1, 2)$, $(-1, 4)$.

5.8   Zeros, Slope, and Continuity, Applied to Graphing

When graphing a function $y = f(x)$, it is useful whenever possible to determine all *zeros* of the function, that is, all points x such that $f(x) = 0$. In many cases, this information along with knowledge of symmetry, asymptotes, and limits in the large, will give one a fairly clear idea of how the entire graph of the function looks. For example, suppose

$$f(x) = (x - 1)(x - 2)(x + 1).$$

Note that f has zeros at 1, -1, and 2. That is,

$$f(1) = 0 \qquad f(-1) = 0 \qquad f(2) = 0.$$

(Moreover, there are no other zeros.) On the other hand,

$$f(x) = x^3 - 2x^2 - x + 2$$

and so $\lim\limits_{x\to\infty} f(x) = \infty$ $\lim\limits_{x\to-\infty} f(x) = -\infty$.

(Also, $f = O(x^3)$.) (Why?) We have, then a rough picture of the function's graph (see Figure 5.48).

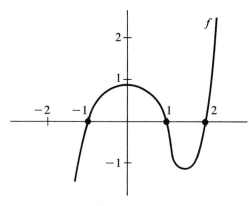

FIG. 5.48

There are several questions to be answered, however, before we should feel confident that this is a very reliable graph.

Question: What would prevent the function f from being graphed as in Figure 5.49 (*i.e.*, is Figure 5.49 consistent with the information we have established about f)?

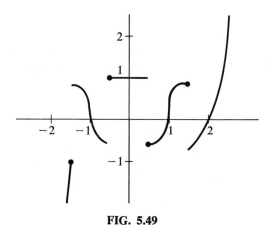

FIG. 5.49

We have drawn the graph so that f has the zeros in the proper places. We have the values growing large to the right and small to the left. What additional information does one need in order to be sure that the graph does not look as we have drawn it here? The answer, of course, is the knowledge that f *is continuous* at each point, in which case the breaks cannot occur. It can be shown that f is continuous, and therefore the "broken places" cannot occur as shown. (Once again, the proof must await a rigorous definition of limits, although you should be able to justify it using the limit theorem.)

Consider then Figure 5.50 as a possible graph of f.

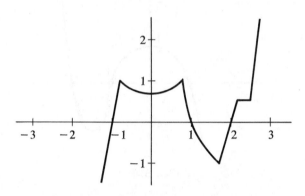

FIG. 5.50

We have now drawn the graph to accommodate "values in the large," "zeros," and "continuity," but once again the graph is considerably different from the one we first drew. We notice that the critical question involved here concerns the existence of unique tangent lines at each point on the curve. Let us then examine

$$\lim_{h \to 0} \frac{(x + h)^3 - 2(x + h)^2 - (x + h) + 2 - x^3 + 2x^2 + x - 2}{h}$$

(why?). By computing, simplifying, and applying some intuitive limit facts, one finds this limit to be

$$3x^2 - 4x - 1,$$

which is defined at each point x. It follows that a unique tangent exists at each point on the curve (why?), and hence the "kinks" we have drawn in Figure 5.50 cannot be allowed. We know therefore that the graph of f looks much as we drew it in the first place. By plotting some well chosen ordered pairs, we can get an even better picture.

$$f(-2) = (-2 - 1)(-2 + 1)(-2 - 2) = (-3)(-1)(-4) = -12$$
$$f(0) = (-1)(1)(-2) = 2$$

$$f\left(\frac{3}{2}\right) = \left(\frac{3}{2} - 1\right)\left(\frac{3}{2} + 1\right)\left(\frac{3}{2} - 2\right) = \left(\frac{1}{2}\right)\left(\frac{5}{2}\right)\left(-\frac{1}{2}\right) = -\frac{5}{8}$$

$$f(3) = (3 - 1)(3 + 1)(3 - 2) = (2)(4)(1) = 8$$

Using all the information at our disposal, we have an approximate graph of f shown in Figure 5.51.

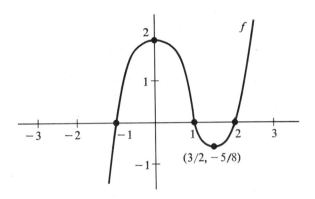

FIG. 5.51

Notice that we are only guessing here as to the point on the curve at which a "hump" reaches its highest or lowest point. How might one determine this? What is the slope of the function (slope of the tangent line) at such a point?

Zeros of Functions and Solutions of Equations

Notice the strong relationship between solving equations and finding zeros of functions.

Example: Consider the function

$$y = x^2 - x - 2 \qquad (f(x) = x^2 - x - 2).$$

Finding the zeros of f is equivalent to finding all solutions of the equation

$$x^2 - x - 2 = 0.$$

Now $\qquad\qquad x^2 - x - 2 = (x - 2)(x + 1).$

Therefore, the solutions of the equation (and hence the zeros of the function) are 2 and -1.

Due to the strong connection between solutions of equations and zeros of functions, it is often possible to obtain solutions of an equation by seeking zeros of the corresponding function. This technique is useful because of the large body of "extra information" that can be applied when looking at the function. This has the effect of allowing us to bring certain "heavy artillery" to bear upon the problem of "solving equations."

Example: What are the solutions of the equation

$$x^3 + \frac{1}{6} x^2 - \frac{85}{18} x + \frac{25}{9} = 0?$$

We do not intend to locate the solutions, but merely obtain some information as to where they must lie. Consider the function

$$f(x) = x^3 + \frac{1}{6}x^2 - \frac{85}{18}x + \frac{25}{9}.$$

Now $\quad \lim_{x \to \infty} f(x) = \infty \quad$ and $\quad \lim_{x \to -\infty} f(x) = -\infty.$

That is, in the large, the graph of f goes upward indefinitely toward the right and downward indefinitely to the left. ($f = 0(x^3)$.) Let us evaluate f at some convenient points.

$$f(0) = \frac{25}{9}$$

$$f(1) = 1 + \frac{1}{6} - \frac{85}{18} + \frac{25}{9} = -\frac{14}{18} = -\frac{7}{9}$$

$$f(-1) = -1 + \frac{1}{6} + \frac{85}{18} + \frac{25}{9} = \frac{120}{18} = \frac{20}{3}$$

It seems, then, that f might be graphed as in Figure 5.52.

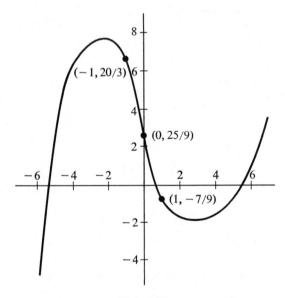

FIG. 5.52

That is, we feel that if the function is smooth and continuous, the zeros must be at least three in number, and, moreover, that there must be:

a) one zero between 0 and 1,
b) one zero to the left of -1 and,
c) one zero to the right of 1. (Why?)

How can one be sure that the curve actually crosses the x-axis and does not "skip over" it? Could we use linear interpolation to approximate the zeros of f? If so, how would you do it?

Inequalities and Continuity

Let us now use some facts about continuity and limits to help analyze inequalities.

Example: Solve and graph the solution set described by

$$\frac{(x - 2)(x + 1)}{x} \geq 0.$$

Solution: Let $f(x) = \dfrac{(x - 2)(x + 1)}{x}$ and graph f. Now f has zeros at 2 and -1. Also

$$\lim_{x \to 0^+} f(x) = -\infty \quad \text{and} \quad \lim_{x \to 0^-} f(x) = \infty. \quad \text{(Why?)}$$

If f is continuous at all points other than 0, then the graph of f should be similar to Figure 5.53.

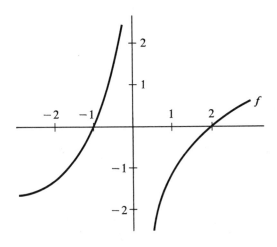

FIG. 5.53

Hence the solution set is the collection of numbers which have non-negative functional values (*i.e.*,

$$[-1, 0) \cup [2, \infty)).$$

This solution set is graphed on a real number line in Figure 5.54.

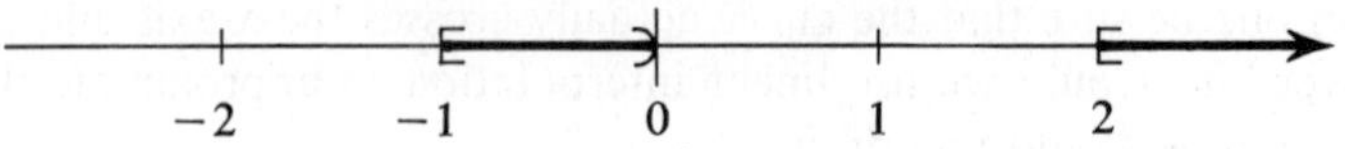

$$\begin{array}{ccccc} & & & & \\ -2 & -1 & 0 & 1 & 2 \end{array}$$

FIG. 5.54

Example: Solve $(x - 1)(x + 2)x < 0$.

Solution: Let $\qquad f(x) = (x - 1)(x + 2)x$.

f has zeros at $1, -2, 0$.

$$f(2) = (2 - 1)(2 + 2)2 = 8.$$

Also, f is continuous (and smooth), so that the graph of f is somewhat like Figure 5.55.

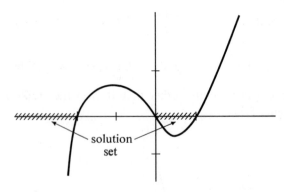

FIG. 5.55

Hence, the solution set is

$$(-\infty, -2) \cup (0, 1). \quad \text{(Explain!)}$$

We have been using the fact that in order for the values of a continuous function to shift from positive to negative, it must first pass through zero. This is a useful and important fact which we state here without proof.

5.8-1 Theorem: (The Intermediate Value Theorem)
Let $f: R \to R$ be continuous. If $u < v$ and $f(u) > 0$ and $f(v) < 0$ (or $f(u) < 0$ and $f(v) > 0$), then for some $x \in (u, v), f(x) = 0$.

Exercises 5.8

1. Graph each of the following:

   a) $y = (x + 3)(x - 4)(x - 1)$

   b) $y = (2x - 4)(3x + 1)(x + 1)$

   c) $y = \dfrac{3(x - 1)x}{(x - 2)}$

   d) $y = 2x^2 - 5x + 3$

2. Solve:

a) $\dfrac{(x - 1)(x + 2)}{x} \geq 0$

c) $\dfrac{(2x - 3)(5x - 1)(x + 2)}{(x - 2)(x - 1)} > 0$

b) $(2x - 3)(x + 2)(x - 1) < 0$

d) $\dfrac{(x - 3)(x + 2)(x - 1)x}{(x - 4)(x + 4)} \leq 0$

3. a) Is the x in Theorem 5.8-1 unique?

b) Generalize Theorem 5.8-1 by showing that

$$\text{if } \beta \in (f(v), f(u)) \qquad (f \text{ continuous}),$$

then for some $x \in (u, v), f(x) = \beta$.

(*Hint:* Consider zeros of $h(x) = f(x) - \beta$.)

4. Use the quadratic formula along with continuity facts and the intermediate value theorem to solve and graph the following inequalities.

a) $\dfrac{3x^2 + 2x - 1}{x - 1} < 0$

c) $\dfrac{7x + 2}{x^2 - 7x + 10} \leq 0$

b) $(x^2 - 3x + 2)(2x + 1) \geq 0$

d) $\dfrac{2x^2 + 4x + 3}{2x - 1} > 0$

5. Graph $f(x) = x^3 + 2x^2 + x - 3$ and use linear interpolation to find an approximate root for the equation $x^3 + 2x^2 + x - 3 = 0$.

6. Graph $f(x) = 2x^3 - x^2 - 2x + 1$ and use your graph to approximate roots for the equation $2x^3 - x^2 - 2x + 1 = 0$.

7. Give a convincing argument that a cubic equation

$$ax^3 + bx^2 + cx + d = 0$$

can have no more than three roots, based on the assumption that a quadratic equation can have no more than two roots. (*Hint:* Show that the curve $y = ax^3 + bx^2 + cx + d$ can have no more than two "peaks" or "valleys." First compute a formula for the slope of the curve and use the fact that this slope is zero at a "peak" or "valley.")

5.9   Linear Functions in R × R:

Previously we discussed several types of functions which were defined by general conditions of the behavior of the function at certain points or combinations of points. For example, recall that an *odd function* is a function f such that

$$f(-x) = -f(x) \qquad \text{for all } x$$

and that a *periodic* function is a function g such that, for some positive real number α,

$$g(x + \alpha) = g(x) \qquad \text{for all } x.$$

In the present section we shall investigate the class of continuous functions which satisfy a similar condition, namely the condition of additivity:

$$\ell(x + y) = \ell(x) + \ell(y) \qquad \forall x, y \in D_\ell \qquad (1)$$

The main aim of this section is to show that this condition is sufficient to guarantee that such a function $\ell: R \to R$ has as its graph a straight line passing through the origin. For this reason, the class of functions satisfying condition (1) is called the class of *homogeneous linear functions*. The behavior of these functions in turn leads to the abstract definition of "linearity."

5.9-1 Theorem: Suppose ℓ is a continuous function

$$\ell: R \to R$$

such that $\qquad \forall x, y \in R, \qquad \ell(x + y) = \ell(x) + \ell(y). \qquad (2)$

Then $\ell(x) = mx$, where m is the real number $\ell(1)$.

Remark: Before stating a proof of this theorem, we make some observations regarding the proof. The path we follow is roughly that discussed in Chapter 3 in the development of the real number system R. We start by restricting the domain D_ℓ of ℓ to the set Z, then extend it to the rational numbers, and finally to the set of real numbers. In the first part of the proof, where we are dealing with integers and rational numbers, the conclusion of the theorem is obtained by algebraic manipulation on the assumption expressed in equation (2). The extension of the conclusion to hold for a function ℓ with

$$D_\ell = R$$

utilizes the assumed continuity of ℓ.

This kind of argument is encountered frequently in various branches of mathematics. The general format of this type of argument is sketched in the following diagram.

	First Stage	Second Stage	Final Stage
Results	Proof of the conclusion using some small subclass of the totality of objects for which the conclusion is supposed to hold.	Proof for class of objects larger than that used in 1st stage.	Proof for the entire class of objects claimed in the statement of the theorem.
Example	Proof for $D_\ell = Z$	Proof for $D_\ell = Q$	Proof for $D_\ell = R$
Method	algebraic manipulation	algebraic manipulation and 1st stage result	previous stage and a limit concept (such as continuity)

Proof (of Theorem 5.9-1): *First Stage.* Recall that we have assumed that $\ell(x)$ is a real number for $x \in R$. The number $\ell(0)$ is determined to be zero, as follows:

$$\ell(0) = \ell(0 + 0) = \ell(0) + \ell(0) \qquad \text{(Why?)}$$
$$= 2\ell(0).$$

Therefore $\ell(0) = 0$ (why?).

We have assumed $\ell(1) = m$. $\ell(2)$ is obtained as follows:

$$\ell(2) = \ell(1 + 1) = \ell(1) + \ell(1) = 2\ell(1) = 2m.$$

In general, for any positive integer k,

$$\ell(k) = mk \Rightarrow \ell(k + 1) = \ell(k) + \ell(1) = mk + m = m(k + 1),$$

and hence by induction $\ell(n) = mn$ for all $n \in N$.

On the other hand,

$$0 = \ell(0) = \ell(k + (-k)) = \ell(k) + \ell(-k)$$

which implies that

$$\ell(-k) = -\ell(k) = -mk,$$

so

$$\ell(x) = mx \qquad \forall x \in Z.$$

Thus the conclusion holds at least for each integer.

Second stage. $\quad m = \ell(1) = \ell\left(k\left(\frac{1}{k}\right)\right) \qquad$ for any $k \in N$.

But

$$\ell\left[k\left(\frac{1}{k}\right)\right] = \ell\left(\sum_{i=1}^{k} \frac{1}{k}\right) = \sum_{i=1}^{k} \ell\left(\frac{1}{k}\right) = k \cdot \ell\left(\frac{1}{k}\right),$$

and hence we have

$$m = k \cdot \ell\left(\frac{1}{k}\right)$$

or

$$\ell\left(\frac{1}{k}\right) = m \cdot \frac{1}{k}.$$

Now for any positive rational number a/k (where $a \in N$) we have

$$\ell\left(\frac{a}{k}\right) = \ell\left(a \cdot \frac{1}{k}\right) = \ell\left(\sum_{j=1}^{a} \frac{1}{k}\right) = \sum_{j=1}^{a} \ell\left(\frac{1}{k}\right)$$
$$= \sum_{j=1}^{a} \left(m \cdot \frac{1}{k}\right)$$
$$= a\left(m \cdot \frac{1}{k}\right) = m\left(\frac{a}{k}\right).$$

Thus for any $x \in Q$,

$$\ell(x) = mx$$

since

$$\ell\left(-\frac{a}{k}\right) = -\ell\left(\frac{a}{k}\right). \qquad \text{(Why?)}$$

357

Final stage. In the previous stage, we have shown that the conclusion of the theorem holds for any *rational number x*. Now suppose α is an irrational number. Then, as discussed previously, there is a sequence $\{r_n\}$ of rational numbers such that

$$\lim_{n \to \infty} r_n = \alpha.$$

At each point r_n we have $\ell(r_n) = m \cdot r_n$, and using the assumed continuity of the function ℓ we have

$$\ell(\alpha) = \ell \left(\lim_{n \to \infty} r_n \right) = \lim_{n \to \infty} \ell(r_n) = \lim_{n \to \infty} mr_n$$

$$= m \lim_{n \to \infty} r_n = m\alpha.$$

Thus it follows that

$$\ell(x) = mx \qquad \forall x \in R. \;\square$$

We thus see that any function $f \colon R \to R$ which is continuous and additive (has the property that $f(x + y) = f(x) + f(y)$) can be described by $f(x) = mx$. It follows that f graphs as a line through $(0, 0)$.

Let us next observe an interesting property of functions of the sort we have been discussing.

5.9-2 Theorem: If ℓ is a continuous and additive function, and $a, b \in R$, then

$$\forall x \in R \qquad \ell(ax + b) = a\ell(x) + \ell(b).$$

The proof is left as an exercise.

This leads us to the following definition for linear functions in general.

5.9-3 Definition: A function $f \colon A \to B$ is *linear* if $\forall x, y \in A$ and for any real number a

$$f(ax + y) = af(x) + f(y).$$

Note that in order to apply this definition, it must be possible to "multiply" elements in A and B by real numbers a. That is, A and B must be closed under multiplication by real numbers. This is sometimes expressed by saying that "A and B are closed under *scalar* multiplication and addition." Here the term "scalar" refers to the set of real numbers. (Actually, the class of numbers containing the element a may be different from the set of real numbers. It is common, for example, to generalize the definition to include complex numbers.)

Under our definition of linear functions, it is seen that the homogeneous additive functions are indeed linear functions from R to R, but the class of all linear functions from R to R also includes functions of the more general form

$$f(x) = mx + b.$$

The graphs of linear functions $f \colon R \to R$ are thus straight lines, and m and b have the graphical interpretation discussed in Section 5.7.

The definition of linear functions does not require that the domain or range of such a function necessarily be the set of real numbers. The student will encounter "spaces" of linear functions in many contexts which do not use real number domains and ranges. (A systematic study of such spaces will be given in Chapter 8.)

Linear Equations

We saw above that a linear function from R into R is described by the equation $y = mx + b$, where m and b are real numbers. In fact, the class $\mathfrak{F}$ of *all* linear functions from R into R can be put into *1-1* correspondence with the set of all pairs (m, b) of real numbers. Formally, this fact could be stated

"a *1-1* correspondence between $\mathfrak{F}$ and $R \times R$ is established by the function $\theta(mx + b) = (m, b)$."

(Note that this immediately implies that $\mathfrak{F} \# R \times R$.)

The numbers m and b are often called *parameters* of the family of all linear functions, and $\mathfrak{F}$ is sometimes referred to as a "two-parameter" family of functions. The name "parameter" associated with the numbers m and b refers to the fact that in discussing an arbitrary member of $\mathfrak{F}$, the numbers m and b

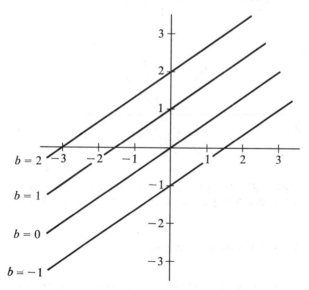

FIG. 5.56   Here are shown graphs of linear functions in the family defined by $y = (3/2)x + b$ for $b \in \{-1, 0, 1, 2\}$. The class of all such functions (*i.e.*, the class $\{f \in \mathfrak{F}: m = 3/2\}$) would be called a "one-parameter subclass of $\mathfrak{F}$."

359

may be left unspecified, although they are assumed fixed. The term "two-parameter family" here refers to the fact that ordered pairs of real numbers can be used as labels for the members of $\mathfrak{F}$, since $\mathfrak{F} \# R \times R$. That is, $\mathfrak{F}$ can be indexed by a *one-one* correspondence using $R \times R$ as the index set.

It is interesting to investigate the subclasses of $\mathfrak{F}$ which are obtained by considering one of the parameters held fixed and allowing the other parameter to vary. Suppose, for example, that m is held fixed, and b is allowed to vary over R. We thus obtain a subclass of elements in $\mathfrak{F}$. Such a subclass will consist of parallel lines.

The graphs of some members of the family of lines all having slope 3/2 but different y-intercepts are shown in Figure 5.56. The graphs of some members of the family of all linear functions having y-intercept -3, but with different slopes, are shown in Figure 5.57.

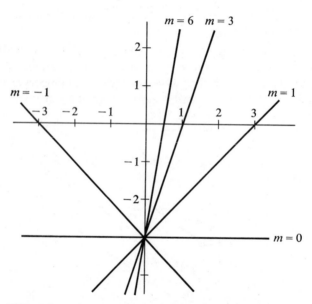

FIG. 5.57   The graphs of some members of the one-parameter family of functions with y-intercept -3.

Equation Forms for Linear Functions

We next catalogue some useful "form" descriptions of the linear functions. Certain *standard forms* for some functions and relations are useful in isolating pertinent information which will help in sketching graphs. This same information is also useful determining an analytical (equation) description when certain geometric facts are known.

5.9-4 Theorem: (General Form) An equation

$$Ax + By + C = 0 \quad \text{where} \quad A, B, C \in R$$

describes a linear function, provided that $B \neq 0$. That is, if

$$f = \{(x, y): Ax + By + C = 0\},$$

then f is a linear function.

Proof: The proof merely consists of observing that the equation can be solved for y in the form $y = mx + b$. Here we have

$$y = -\frac{A}{B}x - \frac{C}{B}. \quad \square$$

Remark: It is equally clear that any equation $y = mx + b$ can be put in the general form.

5.9-5 Theorem: A) Point slope form. A linear function with slope m which contains the pair (α, β) can be described by

$$(y - \beta) = m(x - \alpha).$$

B) Two point form. A linear function which contains the two distinct pairs (α, β) and (c, d) can be described by

$$y - \beta = \frac{d - \beta}{c - \alpha}(x - \alpha).$$

C) Intercept form. A linear function which has a graph that intersects the y-axis at $(0, b)$ and the x-axis at $(a, 0)$ can be described by

$$\frac{x}{a} + \frac{y}{b} = 1,$$

provided a and b are non-zero.

D) The form of the description we have been using ($y = mx + b$) is called the *slope-intercept form* of a linear equation.

The student should verify statements *A)* through *C)* above. This can be done by showing that each description is equivalent to the equation given in Definition 5.7-1, where m and b are numbers such that the conditions imposed in each case are satisfied. (Here we make use of the fact that a function f: $R \rightarrow R$ is linear *if* it can be described by the equation $y = mx + b$, with some choice of the numbers m and b.)

We have seen that given the slope m of a member of $\mathfrak{F}$, the member is determined to within a one-parameter subset of $\mathfrak{F}$ (whose members have graphs that are parallel lines). That is, linear functions with equal slopes have graphs that are parallel lines.

In Section 5.14 we return to analyze, in a different setting, certain geometric properties of linear equations and their related functions.

361

Exercises 5.9

1. Assume ℓ is an additive function in $R \times R$. Show that if $a_1, a_2, \ldots, a_n$ are elements in D_ℓ, then

$$\ell\left(\sum_{i=1}^{n} a_i\right) = \sum_{i=1}^{n} \ell(a_i)$$

(*i.e.*, "pairwise" additivity of ℓ implies "finite" additivity of ℓ).

2. Can you show that an additive function in $R \times R$ is monotonic?

3. Assume $f: R \to R$ is such that $\forall x, y$ $f(x + y) = f(x) + f(y)$. Prove or disprove that:

a) $\forall n \in N$ $\forall x$ $f(nx) = nf(x)$.
b) $\forall r \in Q$ $\forall x$ $f(rx) = rf(x)$.
c) If $f(y) \neq 0$, then $f(ry) \neq 0$ $\forall r \in Q$.

4. Assume $f: R \to R$ is such that $\forall x, y$ $f(x + y) = f(x) + f(y)$. Prove or disprove that:

a) $\forall x$ $\forall y$ $f(xy) = xf(y)$.
b) If $f(y) \neq 0$, then $f(xy) \neq 0$ $\forall x \in R$.

5. Assume $f: R \to R$, f is continuous and $\forall x, y$ $f(x + y) = f(x) + f(y)$. Prove or disprove that:

a) $\forall x$ $\forall y$ $f(xy) = xf(y)$
b) If $f(y) \neq 0$, then $f(xy) \neq 0$ $\forall x \in R$.

6. Let $f: \mathcal{C} \to \mathcal{C}$ be defined by $\forall z \in \mathcal{C}$ $f(z) = 2iz$. Show that f is a linear function. Keep in mind that az is defined for $a \in R$, $z \in \mathcal{C}$.

7. Which of the following functions from $\mathcal{C}$ to $\mathcal{C}$ are linear?

a) $f(z) = (2 + i)z - 1$ d) $f(z) = 1/z + i$
b) $f(z) = 3z + 2i$ e) $f(z) = (z + 1)/2z$
c) $f(z) = 2z^2 + i$

8. a) Let f, g be linear functions in $\mathcal{C} \times \mathcal{C}$. Show that the functions $f + g$ and af ($a \in \mathcal{C}$) are also linear.

b) Is the composite function $f \circ g$ linear?

9. Prove that the inverse of a linear function with non-zero slope is a linear function. (What happens if $m = 0$?)

10. Determine the equation in slope-intercept form for the linear function passing through the two points given.

a) $(0, 2), (1, 1)$ c) $(2, 3), (-2, 3)$
b) $(1, 3), (2, 4)$ d) $(-1, 4), (0, 2)$

11. Determine the equation in intercept form for the linear function passing through the points given.

a) $(1, 0), (0, 2)$ c) $(-3, 0), (0, -2)$
b) $(-2, 0), (0, 4)$ d) $(-1, -1), (-2, 3)$

5.10   Exponential Functions and Their Inverses

In Chapter 3, we developed the concept of exponents. Recall that we have defined b^x, where b is any nonnegative real number and x is any real number (with the understanding that 0^0 is undefined). Here we wish to introduce a class of associated functions, and to investigate certain of their properties.

5.10-1 Definition: Let b be a positive real number. Then define

$$\forall x \in R \qquad E_b(x) = b^x.$$

$E_b: R \to R$ is called the *exponential function with base b*. (E_b is often designated by saying "the function b^x" or "the function $y = b^x$.")

Although any nonnegative number will serve as a base for an exponential function, the most commonly used ones are 10 and e.

Recall $e = \text{lub} \left\{ \left(1 + \dfrac{1}{n} \right)^n : n \text{ is a positive integer} \right\}.$

The number e is irrational, and is nearly equal to the rational number 2.718281828. The reason that e is so very popular is made clear in calculus. We shall be concerned only with the fact that it is a positive real number and hence will serve as the base for an exponential function.

The following facts about exponential functions are useful.

5.10-2 Theorem: i) $E_b(x + y) = E_b(x)E_b(y)$
             ii) $E_{ab}(x) = E_a(x)E_b(x)$
             iii) $E_{b^x}(y) = E_b(xy)$
             iv) E_b is continuous

Proof: i) $E_b(x + y) = b^{x+y} = b^x b^y = E_b(x)E_b(y)$
      ii) $E_{ab}(x) = (ab)^x = a^x b^x = E_a(x)E_b(x)$
      iii) $E_{b^x}(y) = (b^x)^y = b^{xy} = E_b(xy)$
      iv) When we extended exponentiation to include irrational numbers, we did so in such a way that the exponential functions would be continuous. A rigorous proof is beyond the scope of this text since we have never carefully defined "limit." []

Let us graph some of the exponential functions.
Example: Consider $E_{10}(x) = 10^x$ for all $x \in R$.

$$E_{10}(-1) = \frac{1}{10}, \qquad E_{10}(0) = 1, \qquad E_{10}(1) = 10.$$

Recall that if $b > 1$ and $x < y$, then $b^x < b^y$. We see then that E_{10} is a strictly increasing function and hence should look as shown in Figure 5.58.

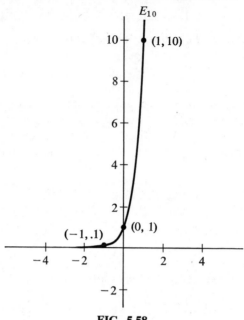

FIG. 5.58

Note that $\lim_{x \to -\infty} E_{10}(x) = 0$, and therefore the x-axis is a horizontal asymptote on the left.

Example: Consider $E_e(x) = e^x$. (E_e is often called "the" exponential function, the base e not being mentioned.) Some points on or near E_e are:

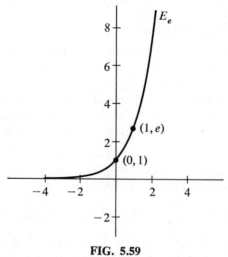

FIG. 5.59

$$E_e(1) = e \cong 2.7, \qquad E_e(-1) = \frac{1}{e} \cong .37, \qquad E_e(0) = 1.$$

Now $e > 1$, and so once again we have a strictly increasing function with horizontal asymptote on the left (see Figure 5.59).

Notice that e^x is not as "steep" as 10^x. In fact, in general as b gets larger, the graph of E_b gets steeper (has larger slope at each x). (Why?)

Let us compare this with exponential functions whose base is less than 1. For $0 < b < 1$ there is a $B > 1$ such that $b = 1/B$ (or $B = 1/b$). Now

$$b^x = (1/B)^x = (B^{-1})^x = B^{-x}.$$

That is, $\qquad\qquad\qquad E_b(x) = E_B(-x).$

Hence E_b and E_B are reflections of each other through the y-axis. (If $b > 1$, then $0 < b^{-1} < 1$ and if $0 < b < 1$, then $b^{-1} > 1$.)

Example: Consider the graphs of E_3 and $E_{1/3}$ as in Figure 5.60.

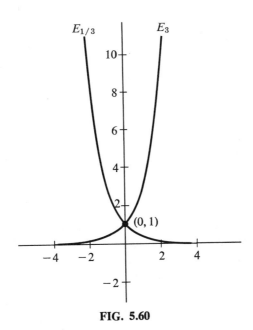

FIG. 5.60

We see that all exponential functions pass through $(0, 1)$ (prove this), and if $b < 1$, then b^x is decreasing, whereas if $b > 1$, then b^x is increasing. Further, we see that the trivial exponential function $E_1(x) = 1^x \equiv 1$ (*i.e.*, $E_1 = 1_f$) also fits into this pattern.

As b approaches 1, the graph of E_b gets more and more nearly "flat," or more like the line $y = 1$. Note, however, that no matter how near b is to 1,

$$\text{if } b > 1, \text{ then } b^x \to 0 \text{ as } x \to -\infty$$

and $\qquad\qquad\qquad$ if $b < 1$, then $b^x \to 0$ as $x \to \infty$.

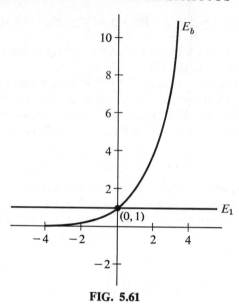

FIG. 5.61

That is, E_b^{-1} ($b > 0$) *is a function if* $b \neq 1$. This brings us to the next subject, the "logarithm functions" which are the inverses of those exponential functions having bases other than 1.

Logarithms

We have noted that if $b > 0$ and $b \neq 1$ then E_b is a strictly monotonic function whose domain is R and whose range is, as we shall shortly see, $(0, \infty)$. We have previously shown that strictly monotonic functions are *one-one*, and are therefore "invertible," in the sense that the inverse relation is a *function*.

5.10-3 Theorem: If $b > 0$ and $b \neq 1$, then

$$\forall y > 0 \qquad \exists x, \qquad E_b(x) = y.$$

Proof: We use the intermediate value theorem 5.8-1.

Since E_b is continuous, so is

$$g(x) = E_b(x) - y \qquad \text{for each fixed } y > 0.$$

WLOG we may assume that $b > 1$.

Since
$$E_b(x) \to 0 \qquad \text{as} \qquad x \to -\infty,$$
$$E_b(x) - y \to -y \qquad \text{as} \qquad x \to -\infty.$$

366

Thus for each $y > 0$, $g(x) < 0$ for some x (sufficiently small), say $x = u$. Similarly, $g(v) > 0$ for some $v > u$ since

$$\lim_{x \to \infty} E_b(x) = \infty.$$

Thus, by the intermediate value theorem, there is some $x \in (u, v)$ such that $g(x) = 0$.

But $g(x) = 0$ iff $E_b(x) = y$. □

We have now established the fact that E_b ($b > 0$, $b \neq 1$) is a *one-one* function from the reals onto the positive reals. Hence we can state the following definition.

5.10-4 Definition: If $b > 0$ and $b \neq 1$, then $\log_b = E_b^{-1}$.

(log: $(0, \infty) \xrightarrow[\text{onto}]{1\text{-}1} R$. $\log_b$ is called the *logarithm function with base b.*)

Keep in mind that in order to graph the inverse of a function, one merely reflects the graph of the function through the line $x = y$.

Question: Does the continuity of E_b imply that $\log_b$ is continuous? (*Hint:* Think about the graphical interpretations of the notions involved.)

Example: Let us graph E_e and E_e^{-1} (or $\log_e$). ($\log_e$ is called the *natural log function* and often denoted by "*ln*".) (See Figure 5.62.)

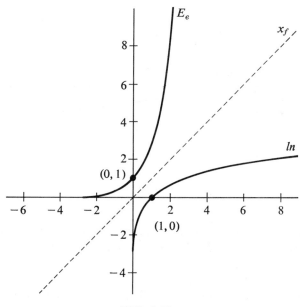

FIG. 5.62

Example: Graph $\log_{10}$ (usually denoted by "log"). (See Figure 5.63.)

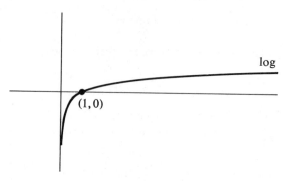

FIG. 5.63

Notice that every $\log_b$ function passes through $(1, 0)$. Several members of the (one-parameter) family of all $\log_b$ functions are shown in Figure 5.64.

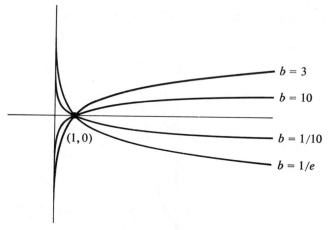

FIG. 5.64

Questions: What can you say about the slopes (at $(1, 0)$) of curves representing $\log_b$, where $b < 1$? What would be a convenient way to index the class of log functions?

The following theorem states a result which makes logarithms useful for computation. This theorem shows that it is possible to perform multiplication of positive numbers in terms of addition of the logarithms of the numbers. Similarly, exponentiation is performed by doing multiplication.

5.10-5 Theorem: i) $\log_b (xy) = \log_b (x) + \log_b (y)$

ii) $\log_b x^m = m \log_b x$.

Proof: Keep in mind that $\log_b = E_b^{-1}$, so that

$$E_b (\log_b (x)) = x \quad \text{and} \quad \log_b (E_b(x)) = x.$$

(Composition of a function with its inverse yields the identity, x_f.)

i) $\log_b (x) + \log_b (y) = \log_b E_b (\log_b (x) + \log_b (y))$

$\qquad\qquad\qquad\quad = \log_b (E_b \log_b (x) \cdot E_b \log_b (y))$

$\qquad\qquad\qquad\quad = \log_b (x \cdot y).$

ii) $m \log_b x = \log_b E_b(m \log_b x) = \log_b (b^{m \log_b x})$

$\qquad\qquad\quad = \log_b (b^{\log_b x})^m = \log_b (E_b \log_b (x))^m$

$\qquad\qquad\quad = \log_b x^m. \;\square$

Due to the fact that we use a decimal (base 10) numeration system, the most popular logarithm base for computation is base 10. In fact, one needs only a computed table of logarithms for numbers between 1 and 10. This is because $\log_{10} (x)$ for $x \not\in [1, 10)$ can easily be reduced to the sum of an integer and the $\log_{10} (y)$ where $y \in [1, 10)$.

Example: $\log_{10} (564.32) = \log_{10} (100 \times 5.6432)$.

Now applying i) of the previous theorem we have

$$\log_{10} (564.32) = \log_{10} (100) + \log_{10} (5.6432).$$

It is easy to compute

$$\log_{10} (100) = 2,$$

since $10^2 = 100$ and $\log_{10} = E_{10}^{-1}$ (*i.e.*, $\log_b x$ is the number to which b must be raised to obtain x). Thus,

$$\log_{10} (564.32) = 2 + \log_{10} (5.6432),$$

and the problem of finding $\log_{10} (564.32)$ is reduced to that of finding the logarithms of a number in $[1, 10)$.

Example: (We use the convention $\log = \log_{10}$.)

$$\log (.000132) = \log (1.32 \times 10^{-4})$$

$$= \log (1.32) + \log 10^{-4}$$

$$= \log (1.32) - 4.$$

We see, then, that for quick computational purposes, when using $\log_{10}$ it is only necessary to have on hand a table of logarithm values for pre-images between 1 and 10. Since we can't list all such pre-images, tables such as Table I are common. To approximate the image for pre-images not listed, one can use linear interpolation, as discussed previously in Section 5.7.

The properties given in the previous theorem are often useful in solving equations.

Example: Solve $2^x = 3$.

Solution: Since a $\log_{10}$ table is available, let us take the logarithms of both sides and apply ii) of the theorem. Since $2^x = 3$, it follows that

369

$$\log 2^x = \log 3 \quad \text{(why?)}.$$

Thus, $$x \log 2 = \log 3,$$

and $$x = \frac{\log 3}{\log 2} \cong \frac{.4771}{.3010}.$$

(Note that using $\log_b$ (for any base b) in the above argument would yield $x = \dfrac{\log_b 3}{\log_b 2}$. This suggests the "base changing formula" that we consider below.)

Example: Solve $12^{2x} = 19$.

$$\log 12^{2x} = \log 19$$
$$2x \log 12 = \log 19$$

$$x = \frac{\log 19}{2 \log 12} \cong \frac{1.2788}{2(1.0792)}.$$

Since tables of values (actually, only partial tables of values) for logarithm functions of base 10 and base e are available, it is useful to be able to change from one base to another for a given number.

5.10-6 Theorem: (*Base changing formula*) Let $a, b \in (0, 1) \cup (1, \infty)$, then

$$\forall x > 0 \quad (\log_b a)(\log_a x) = \log_b x$$

(*i.e.,*) $$\log_a x = \frac{\log_b x}{\log_b a}.$$

Proof: Let $x > 0$, then

$$a^{\log_a x} = b^{\log_b x}$$

(*i.e.,*) $$E_b E_b^{-1} = x_f),$$

but $$a = b^{\log_b a}$$

hence $$(b^{\log_b a})^{\log_a x} = b^{\log_b x}$$

but using a property of exponents (which one?) we have

$$b^{(\log_b a)(\log_a x)} = b^{\log_b x}$$

from which it follows that

$$(\log_b a)(\log_a x) = \log_b x. \quad \text{(Why?)} \quad \square$$

5.10-7 Corollary: $\log_a b = 1/\log_b a$.

Example: Find $\log_2 15$ using a log table (Table I).

$$\log_2 15 = \frac{\log_{10} 15}{\log_{10} 2} \cong \frac{1.1761}{.3010}$$

Example: Find $\log_{15} e$ using a $\log_{10}$ table.

$$\log_{15} e = \frac{\log_{10} e}{\log_{10} 15} \cong \frac{.4342}{1.1761}$$

(Verify these logs using Table I.)

370

Exercises 5.10

1. Sketch a graph of:
   a) E_2 b) $E_{1/2}$ c) $\log_2$ d) $\log_{1/2}$

2. i) Reduce each of the following to the sum of an integer plus the log (base 10) of a number between 1 and 10.
   a) $\log 365.41$ c) $\log .00213$ e) $\log (.0013)^3$
   b) $\log .412$ d) $\log 6.001$ f) $\log 35.61$
   ii) Calculate, using logarithms:
   a) $(365.41)(6.001)$ b) $(.412)^{1/5}$ c) $35.61/412$

3. i) Determine each of the following *in terms of* $\log_{10}$:
   a) $\log_{16} 32$ b) $\log_2 560$ c) $\log_{1/2} 5.4$
   ii) Evaluate (approximately) each of the above using linear interpolation where necessary.

4. Solve for x:
   a) $10^x = 9.51$ c) $5^x = 3.71$
   b) $10^x = 3.14$ d) $6^x = 54.1$

5. Solve for x:
   a) $\log x = 5.103$ c) $\log x = 56.102$
   b) $\log x = 2.143$ d) $\log_5 x = 11.2$

6. Solve for x:
   a) $\ln 16/5 - \ln 10/3 + \ln 5/6 = \ln x$
   b) $3^{1-2x} = 4$
   c) $\log (x^2 - 3x - 10) - \log (x - 5) = 3$
   d) $\log_4 (x + 1) - \log_4 x = 1/2$
   e) $6^{x^2-2x+8} = 7$

7. "Knowing" only that $\log_5 2 = .4306$, $\log_5 3 = .6825$, and $\log_5 7 = 1.2090$, find each of the following:
   a) $\log_5 10 =$ b) $\log_5 21/2 =$ c) $\log_5 72/35 =$

8. Using Exercise 7 above find each of the following:
   a) $\log_3 7 =$ b) $\log_2 35 =$ c) $\log_7 5 =$ d) $\log_7 28 =$

9. Suppose $g: R \xrightarrow{1\text{-}1} R^+$. Then show that
   a) g increasing $\Rightarrow g^{-1}$ strictly increasing.
   b) g decreasing $\Rightarrow g^{-1}$ strictly decreasing.
   c) $a = b \Leftrightarrow g(a) = g(b)$.
   d) Do you think that g continuous $\Rightarrow g^{-1}$ continuous?

10. a) Examine graphically the process of linear interpolation to find logarithms of numbers not listed in a table. For example, suppose you know only that log 3.120 = .4942 and log 3.130 = .4955, but we desire to find log 3.124.

371

b) Do you think linear interpolation produces a better approximation of the logarithm of a number near 1 or one near 10? (Explain!)

11. With your *eyes shut*, draw a graph of:

   a) e^x *b)* $\log_e x$ *c)* 10^x *d)* $\log_{10} x$

12. One of the important characteristics of the function e^x is that the slope at each point (x, e^x) is given by e^x (*i.e.*, the slope is equal to the functional value). Under the assumption that this is true for e^x, show that it is also true for ce^x for all c. (*Remark:* This is the only class of functions which has this property.)

5.11 Hyperbolic Functions and Their Inverses

In this section we define, and examine briefly, two very important functions which are defined in terms of the exponential functions e^x and e^{-x}. They are called the "hyperbolic sine" and the "hyperbolic cosine" (written "sinh" and "cosh").

5.11-1 Definition: $\forall x \in R$

$$\sinh x = \frac{e^x - e^{-x}}{2}$$

$$\cosh x = \frac{e^x + e^{-x}}{2}.$$

At this point, it is natural for the student to be curious about the names we have chosen for these functions. However, since certain geometric figures (hyperbolas) have a special relationship with these functions, they are called "hyperbolic." Further, since they bear a great resemblance to certain trigonometric functions (to be studied later) they also incorporate these names.

Let us now graph the functions sinh and cosh. We first observe the following useful fact.

5.11-2 Theorem: sinh is a strictly increasing function.

Proof: Suppose $x_1 < x_2$. Then

$$\sinh x_2 - \sinh x_1 = \frac{e^{x_2} - e^{-x_2}}{2} - \frac{e^{x_1} - e^{-x_1}}{2}$$

$$= \frac{e^{x_2} - e^{x_1} + e^{-x_1} - e^{-x_2}}{2} > 0$$

since $e^{x_2} > e^{x_1}$ and $e^{-x_1} > e^{-x_2}$.   (Why?)

But the above inequality implies that sinh is strictly increasing. $\square$

Remarks: It follows that $\sinh^{-1}$ is a function. (Why?) Also, note that the continuity of e^x implies the continuity of sinh and cosh. (Explain!)

Note that

$$\sinh(-x) = \frac{e^{-x} - e^{--x}}{2} = -\frac{e^x - e^{-x}}{2} = -\sinh(x).$$

Thus, sinh is odd, so we need only reflect through $(0, 0)$ to graph the left part of sinh once we have the right hand part. Two points on the function are given by

$$\sinh(0) = 0 \quad \text{and} \quad \sinh(1) = \frac{e - e^{-1}}{2} \cong 1.17.$$

Note also that

$$\sinh = 0 \left(\frac{e^x}{2} \right) \text{ as } x \to \infty \quad \text{and} \quad \sinh = 0 \left(\frac{-e^{-x}}{2} \right) \text{ as } x \to -\infty.$$

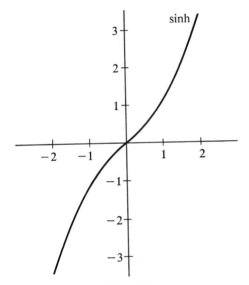

FIG. 5.65a

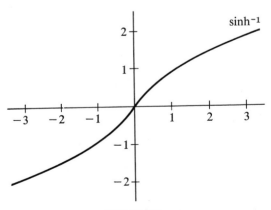

FIG. 5.65b

We next sketch a graph of cosh and cosh⁻¹.

Note that

$$\cosh(-x) = \frac{e^{-x} + e^{--x}}{2} = \frac{e^x + e^{-x}}{2} = \cosh(x).$$

Since cosh x is an even function, we need only look at the right hand side and reflect in the y-axis. Some ordered pairs in cosh are given by

$$\cosh(0) = \frac{e^0 + e^0}{2} = \frac{2}{2} = 1,$$

and

$$\cosh(1) = \frac{e + 1/e}{2} \cong 1.54.$$

Finally,

$$\cosh = 0\left(\frac{e^x}{2}\right) \text{ as } x \to \infty,$$

and

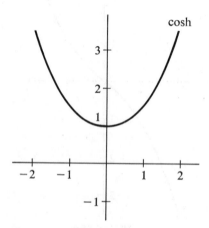

FIG. 5.66a

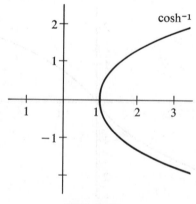

FIG. 5.66b

$$\cosh = 0 \left(\frac{e^{-x}}{2}\right) \text{ as } x \to -\infty.$$

It is obviously necessary to consider some restriction of cosh, if we want an inverse *function* "cosh⁻¹." It is common practice to speak of Cosh⁻¹ as a function to mean that portion of cosh⁻¹ which lies in the first quadrant. Thus

$$\text{Cosh}^{-1} = (\cosh|_{[0,\infty)})^{-1}.$$

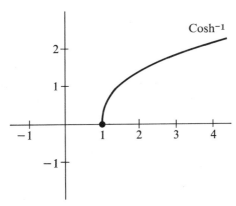

FIG. 5.67

It is interesting to superimpose the graphs of sinh and cosh.
The graph in Figure 5.68 suggests the following interesting questions.

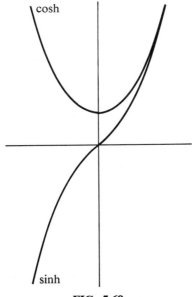

FIG. 5.68

Questions: a) Does there exist a solution for the equation $\cosh x = \sinh x$? That is, will the graphs ever intersect? If so, how often?

b) If not, how "close" do they get?

Solution: Let us seek a solution for

$$\frac{e^x + e^{-x}}{2} = \frac{e^x - e^{-x}}{2}.$$

Equivalently

$$e^{-x} = -e^{-x} \quad \text{or} \quad e^{-x} + e^{-x} = 0,$$

and the answer to *(a)* is clearly "No", since $R_{E.} \subset (0, \infty)$. We leave the remaining question *(b)* as an exercise.

There are many useful theorems (called identities) concerning these two functions. The following are the most common and most useful. They may seem familiar to students who have seen similar trigonometric identities.

5.11-3 Theorem: $\cosh^2 - \sinh^2 = 1$

(i.e., $\qquad \forall x \in R \qquad \cosh^2 x - \sinh^2 x = 1$).

Proof: $\cosh^2 x - \sinh^2 x = \dfrac{(e^x + e^{-x})^2}{4} - \dfrac{(e^x - e^{-x})^2}{4}$

$$= \frac{(e^{2x} + 2e^x e^{-x} + e^{-2x}) - (e^{2x} - 2e^x e^{-x} + e^{-2x})}{4}$$

$$= \frac{4e^x e^{-x}}{4} = 1. \ \square$$

5.11-4 Theorem: $\sinh(x + y) = \sinh x \cosh y + \cosh x \sinh y \quad \forall x, y \in R.$

Proof:

$$\sinh x \cosh y + \cosh x \sinh y = \frac{e^x - e^{-x}}{2} \cdot \frac{e^y + e^{-y}}{2} + \frac{e^x + e^{-x}}{2} \cdot \frac{e^y - e^{-y}}{2}$$

$$= \frac{e^x e^y - e^{-x} e^{-y} - e^{-x} e^y + e^x e^{-y} + e^x e^y - e^{-x} e^{-y} + e^{-x} e^y - e^x e^{-y}}{4}$$

$$= \frac{2e^x e^y - 2e^{-x} e^{-y}}{4} = \frac{e^{x+y} - e^{-(x+y)}}{2}$$

$$= \sinh(x + y). \ \square$$

5.11-5 Theorem: $\cosh(x + y) = \cosh x \cosh y + \sinh x \sinh y.$

Proof: $\cosh x \cosh y + \sinh x \sinh y$

$$= \frac{e^x + e^{-x}}{2} \cdot \frac{e^y + e^{-y}}{2} + \frac{e^x - e^{-x}}{2} \cdot \frac{e^y - e^{-y}}{2}$$

$$= \frac{e^x e^y + e^{-x} e^{-y} + e^{-x} e^y + e^x e^{-y} + e^x e^y + e^{-x} e^{-y} - e^{-x} e^y - e^x e^{-y}}{4}$$

$$= \frac{2e^x e^y + 2e^{-x} e^{-y}}{4} = \frac{e^{x+y} + e^{-(x+y)}}{2}$$

$$= \cosh(x + y). \ \square$$

Since the functions e^x and $ln\ x$ are inverses of one another, it seems reasonable that the function $\sinh^{-1}$ would in some way be related to ln, sinh being defined in terms of the exponential function. In the next theorem, we observe that such a relationship does exist.

5.11-6 Theorem: $\forall x,\quad \sinh^{-1}(x) = ln(x + \sqrt{x^2 + 1})$

Proof: Let $y = \sinh^{-1}(x)$. Therefore

$$\sinh y = \sinh(\sinh^{-1}(x)) = x,$$

so that
$$x = \frac{e^y - e^{-y}}{2} = \frac{e^{2y} - 1}{2e^y}.$$

That is,
$$2e^y x + 1 - e^{2y} = 0,$$

which can be expressed as a quadratic equation in e^y by writing

$$(e^y)^2 - 2x(e^y) - 1 = 0.$$

Hence
$$e^y = x + \sqrt{x^2 + 1}$$

or
$$e^y = x - \sqrt{x^2 + 1}.$$

But since $\sqrt{x^2 + 1} > x$ for all x (why?), making $x - \sqrt{x^2 + 1} < 0$, we must rule out the possibility that $e^y = x - \sqrt{x^2 + 1}$ (why?). We have then that

$$e^y = x + \sqrt{x^2 + 1}.$$

Solving for y we have

$$y = ln(x + \sqrt{x^2 + 1}),$$

hence
$$\forall x \in R,\quad \sinh^{-1} x = ln(x + \sqrt{x^2 + 1}).\ \square$$

Exercises 5.11

1. Determine all symmetries of cosh and sinh.

2. *a)* Show that $\cosh x = 0(\sinh x)$ as $x \to \infty$.
   b) What can you say concerning $\cosh x$ and $\sinh x$ as $x \to -\infty$?

3. Show that:
   a) $\sinh(2x) = 2 \sinh x \cosh x$
   b) $\cosh(2x) = \cosh^2 x + \sinh^2 x$

4. Show that:
   a) $\cosh 2x = 2 \cosh^2 x - 1$
   b) $\cosh 2x = 2 \sinh^2 x + 1$

5. Define tanh and sech by

$$\forall x \quad \tanh x = \frac{\sinh x}{\cosh x} \quad \text{and} \quad \text{sech } x = \frac{1}{\cosh x}.$$

Graph:

 a) tanh *b)* sech

(Use Table III if necessary for computing values.)

6. Show that:

 a) $\sinh(x - y) = \sinh x \cosh y - \cosh x \sinh y$

 b) $\cosh(x - y) = \cosh x \cosh y - \sinh x \sinh y$

7. Try to find a relation between $\cosh^{-1}$ and ln, similar to that of Theorem 5.11-6 for $\sinh^{-1}$ and ln.

8. Define $\coth x = \dfrac{\cosh x}{\sinh x}$ and $\operatorname{csch} x = \dfrac{1}{\sinh x}$. Graph:

 a) $\coth x$ *b)* $\operatorname{csch} x$

9. In each of the following the value of one of the six hyperbolic functions for a is given. Find the remaining 5:

 a) $\sinh a = -3/4$

 b) $\operatorname{sech} a = 3/5$

 c) $\operatorname{csch} a = 5/12$

10. Prove that sinh is odd and cosh is an even function. Are any of the other four hyperbolic functions odd or even?

11. Show that $(\cosh x + \sinh x)^n = \cosh nx + \sinh nx$.

12. Use Table III and linear interpolation to compute:

 a) $\sinh(1.23)$ *c)* $\tanh(3.99)$

 b) $\cosh 2.54$ *d)* $\sinh 4.02$

13. Find sinh y where:

 a) $y = 6.2$ *b)* $y = 7.1$ *c)* $y = 10$ *d)* $y = 8.9$

14. With your eyes shut, graph $\cosh x$ and $\sinh x$.

5.12 Equations and Inequations

Graphs of Inequations

We have discussed previously the connection between equations in two variables x and y and the related function f described by $y = f(x)$, provided the equation can be solved uniquely for y. We wish now to consider *inequations* in two variables x and y.

Example: Graph the set of all $(x, y) \in R \times R$ such that $y \le 2x$.

Solution: The graph of $y = 2x$ is given by a line.

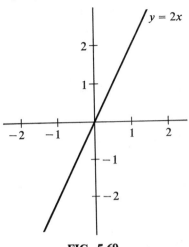

FIG. 5.69

It follows that the collection of all points (x, y) where $y \leq 2x$ would either lie *on* the line or *under* it. That is,

$$\{(x, y): y \leq 2x\} = \{(x, y): y = 2x\} \cup \{(x, y): y < 2x\}.$$

Hence the graph of the inequation § $y \leq 2x$ is given in Figure 5.70.

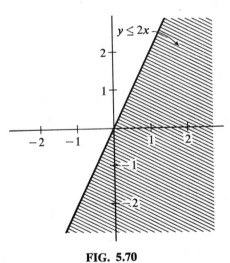

FIG. 5.70

Example: Graph the set of all $(x, y) \in R$ such that $2y - 3 > 5x$. Now this inequality is satisfied iff $2y > 5x + 3$. Hence, an equivalent inequality is

§ More precisely, "a sketch of the graph of the relation described by the inequality $y \leq 2x$." It is small wonder that we agree to certain language conventions!

379

$y > (5/2)x + 3/2$. All points (x, y) which satisfy this inequality must lie *above* the line $y = (5/2)x + 3/2$. Thus the graph of $2y - 3 > 5x$ is Figure 5.71.

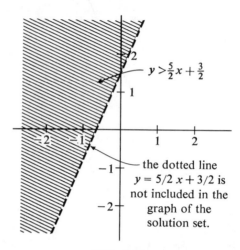

FIG. 5.71

We will have occasion to make use of relations defined as all points above (or all points below) a line. Such a set of points will be called a "half-space."

5.12-1 Definition: Suppose f is a linear function from R to R. The relations defined by

$$H = \{(x, y): y \geq f(x)\}$$

and $\qquad M = \{(x, y): y \leq f(x)\}$

are called *half-spaces* bounded by f.

Remarks: Occasionally relations of the form

$$\{(x, y): y > f(x)\} \qquad \text{or} \qquad \{(x, y): y < f(x)\}$$

are considered. Such relations (in which points in the bounding function f are not included) are called *open* half-spaces. Note that the complement of a half-space is an open half-space and vice-versa.

We will also refer to relations composed of all points on one side of a vertical line as half-spaces. Thus quadrants I and IV together with the y-axis form the graph of the half-space defined by $\{(x, y): x \geq 0\}$.

Our method of graphing half-spaces as either "everything above the line" or "everything below the line" can be interpreted in terms of unions. Note, for example, that

$$T = \{(x, y): y \geq mx + b\} = \bigcup_{x \in R} \{(x, y): y \in [mx + b, \infty)\}.$$

Thus the relation T can be viewed as a union of vertical line segments, where each line segment lies "above" the line $y = mx + b$. Similarly, T may be viewed as the union of horizontal line segments.

Let us consider a more general case. Suppose that f is given by

$$f = \{(x, y): y = f(x)\},$$

and f has the graph in Figure 5.72.

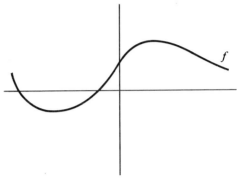

FIG. 5.72

Then the set $S = \{(x, y): y \leq f(x)\}$ is the collection of all points on or under the curve. (See Figure 5.73.)

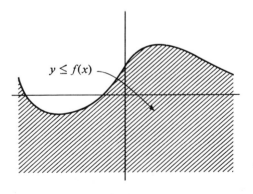

FIG. 5.73

Similarly the collection of points (x, y) such that $y \geq f(x)$ all lie on or above the curve. For strict inequalities, we "dot" the curve to indicate that its points are *not* included in the relation involved.

381

Example: A graph of the set of all (x, y) such that $y \geq 2x^2$ is given in Figure 5.74.

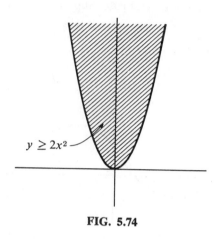

$y \geq 2x^2$

FIG. 5.74

Simultaneous Equations

Let us consider two equations $y = f(x)$ and $y = g(x)$. The points (x, y) which satisfy both equations are called *simultaneous solutions* for the two equations. More appropriately, any ordered pair (a, b) such that $b = f(a)$ and $b = g(a)$ is said to be a solution of the system of equations $y = f(x)$ and $y = f(x)$. Thus the solution set is simply the intersection of the relations involved. Graphically, any such solution must lie at a "meeting point" for the curves f and g.

In Figure 5.75 (x_1, y_1), (x_2, y_2), and (x_3, y_3) are all elements of the solution

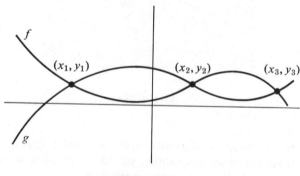

f

(x_1, y_1) (x_2, y_2) (x_3, y_3)

g

FIG. 5.75

set for the "system" of two equations. That is, they are all members of S, where

$$S = \{(x, y): y = f(x) \text{ and } y = g(x)\}$$
$$= \{(x, y): y = f(x)\} \cap \{(x, y): y = g(x)\}.$$

Many simultaneous equation problems are solvable by simple substitution and algebraic manipulation.

Example: What are the solutions of the equations $y = 2x + 1$ and $y = x - 2$?

Solution: We wish to find points (x, y) which satisfy both equations, therefore "we equate the y variable," to obtain

$$x - 2 = 2x + 1.$$

That is, if (x, y) is to satisfy both equations, then it is necessary that $x - 2 = 2x + 1$. Therefore we have $x = -3$. By returning now to either of the given equations we find then that it is necessary that $y = -5$. Hence $(-3, -5)$ is a solution. (Do you think it is the *only* solution?) Graphically, we see in Figure 5.76 that $(-3, -5)$ is the point at which the two lines determined by $y = x - 2$ and $y = 2x + 1$ intersect.

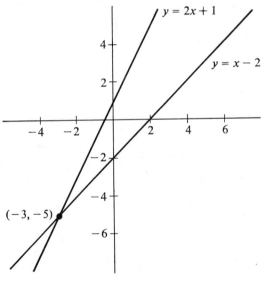

FIG. 5.76

Since linear equations in x and y graph as straight lines, it is clear that two distinct linear equations in x and y can have at most one solution.

Question: When will two linear equations have *no* solutions?

Let us consider a case in which two equations have more than one point in common.

Example: Suppose $y = 2x^2 + 1$ and $y = 3x + 2$ are the equations to be "solved simultaneously." We wish to determine all points (x, y) of intersection of their graphs.

Set $\qquad\qquad\qquad\qquad 2x^2 + 1 = 3x + 2.$

Then $\qquad\qquad\qquad\quad 2x^2 - 3x - 1 = 0,$

so that $\qquad\qquad x = \dfrac{3 + \sqrt{17}}{4} \qquad$ or $\qquad x = \dfrac{3 - \sqrt{17}}{4}.$ ‖

By substituting in the second of the two equations we have that

$$\left(\frac{3 + \sqrt{17}}{4}, \frac{17 + 3\sqrt{17}}{4}\right) \quad \text{and} \quad \left(\frac{3 - \sqrt{17}}{4}, \frac{17 - 3\sqrt{17}}{4}\right)$$

are points in the solution set. The graph in Figure 5.77 suggests that these are the *only* solutions of the system.

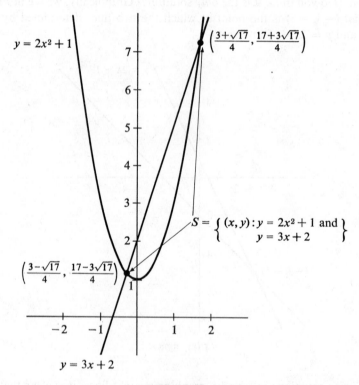

FIG. 5.77

‖ This would very often be expressed as $x = \dfrac{3 \pm \sqrt{17}}{4}.$

Example: Graph the set S of all (x, y) such that $y \leq 3x + 2$ and $y \geq 2x^2 + 1$. Note that this is the intersection of the relations

$$\{(x, y): y \leq 3x + 2\} \quad \text{and} \quad \{(x, y): y \geq 2x^2 + 1\}.$$

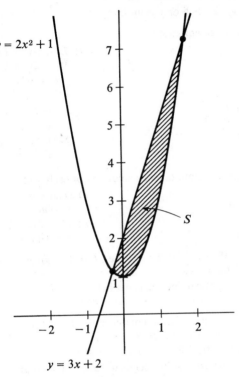

FIG. 5.78

Question: Which element $(x, y) \in S$ has the largest y component?
Solution: Clearly it is the point which appears highest in the set on the graph. That is, the point $\left(\dfrac{3 + \sqrt{17}}{4}, \dfrac{17 + 3\sqrt{17}}{4}\right)$.

Question: Would the solution above remain valid if the inequalities in the description of S had been strict?

Exercises 5.12

1. Graph the solution set of each inequality:
   a) $x + 2y > 3$
   b) $-4x + y \leq 3$
   c) $-2x - 3y < 24$
   d) $9x - 2y < 0$
   e) $9x + 2y \geq 3$
   f) $4x + 2y > 1$

2. Graph the set S where:

   a) $S = \{(x, y): 3x + 2y > 5 \text{ and } x + 4y > 2\}$

   b) $S = \{(x, y): 3x - 2y > 6 \text{ and } 2x + y/2 < 5\}$

   c) $S = \{(x, y): 3x < 10 \text{ and } -2x > 4\}$

   d) $S = \{(x, y): 2x > 6 \text{ or } y \text{ is an integer}\}$

3. Solve the system of equations:

   a) $x + 2y = 4$
      $3x - 2y = 12$

   b) $6x + 2y = 0$
      $4x + y = 1$

   c) $5x + 3y = 12$
      $-3x + 2y = 8$

   d) $7x + 5y = 13$
      $3x - 2y = 18$

   e) $x/6 - y/3 = -(1/6)$
      $x/8 - y/12 + 7/24 = 0$

   f) $\dfrac{3x + 2y}{2} - \dfrac{3x - 2y}{3} = 1$

      $\dfrac{2x + 3y}{3} + \dfrac{2x - 3y}{2} = -1$

4. Find and graph the simultaneous solutions of each system:

   a) $y^2 + x = 0$
      $3x - 1 = y$

   b) $xy = 1$
      $x + y \leq 1$

   c) $\cosh x < y$
      $x = \ln y$

   d) $x^3 + 2x + 1 = y$
      $y = \sinh x$

5. Consider the half space $y \leq 2x + 1$ (*i.e.*, $T = \{(x, y): y \leq 2x + 1\}$). Express T (using R for an index set) as

   a) the union of vertical line segments below $y = 2x + 1$.

   b) the union of horizontal line segments below $y = 2x + 1$.

6. Let T be the half space of all points in the plane above the line $y = -3x - 1$. Express T (using R for an index set) as

   a) the union of vertical line segments above $y = -3x - 1$.

   b) the union of horizontal line segments above $y = -3x - 1$.

7. Determine the highest point (largest y value) in the set $T \cap S$ where:

   a) $T = \{(x, y): y \leq 7x + 2\}$, $S = \{(x, y): y \leq -2x + 1\}$

   b) $T = \{(x, y): y \leq x - 3\}$, $S = \{(x, y): y \leq -2x + 4\}$

   c) $T = \{(x, y): y \leq \sinh x\}$, $S = \{(x, y): y \leq 2x^2 + 1\}$

5.13 Graphing Functions from C into C

In studying functions from R into R, we found it very useful to sketch models or graphs to represent them. One of the most useful graphing techniques for studying real valued functions of a real variable is to sketch a Cartesian graph. However, in studying complex valued functions of a complex variable, we cannot use a similar method since the complex numbers are represented by a plane rather than a line. (Thus, a function in $\mathcal{C} \times \mathcal{C}$ would require 4-dimensional graph paper, which is expensive and bulky to store.)

A common graphing technique in studying functions from $\mathbb{C}$ into $\mathbb{C}$ is to find what happens to some particular region of the complex plane under the mapping. That is, we consider a region or subset of the plane A and compare it with the region

$$f[A] = \{x \in \mathbb{C}: x = f(a) \text{ for some } a \in A\}.$$

Example: Let $f: \mathbb{C} \to \mathbb{C}$ be defined by $f(z) = 2z$. Consider the "unit disc" $C = \{z: |z| \leq 1\}$. (See Figure 5.79.)

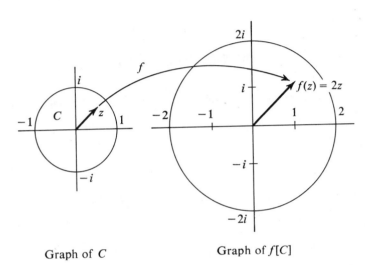

Graph of C Graph of $f[C]$

FIG. 5.79 The function f maps all the points in C to all the points in the disc shown on the right.

Now let us compare C with the set

$$f[C] = \{w: w = f(z) \text{ for some } z \in C\}.$$

We see that

$$f[C] = \{w: w = 2z \text{ and } |z| \leq 1\}.$$

Now $|z| \leq 1$ iff $|2z| \leq 2$ and hence $f[C]$ is a disc with radius 2.

Example: Let $f(z) = z^2$ and consider the unit square

$$S = \{x + iy: x, y \in [0, 1]\}   \text{(See Figure 5.80).}$$

We wish to determine what region S is mapped onto. In doing this, let us examine some particular range values. We note that

$$f(0) = 0^2 = 0 \quad f(1) = 1^2 = 1 \quad f(i) = i^2 = -1$$
$$f(1 + i) = (1 + i)^2 = 1 + 2i + i^2 = 2i.$$

387

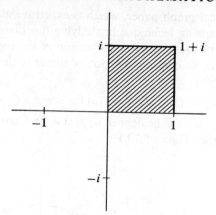

FIG. 5.80 The graph of S.

We know now where the corners of the square are mapped under the mapping f. (See Figure 5.81.)

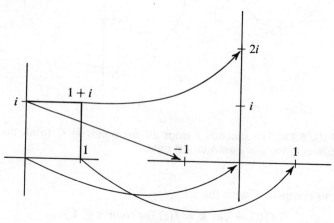

FIG. 5.81

It is reasonably clear that the line segment $[0, 1]$ maps onto itself, and that the segment from 0 to i is sent to $[-1, 0]$. If we could determine where the other two edges are mapped, we would have a fairly clear idea of what $f[S]$ looks like. Consider the points $1 + 1/4i$, $1 + 1/2i$, and $1 + (3/4)i$.

$$f\left(1 + \frac{1}{4}i\right) = \left(1 + \frac{1}{4}i\right)^2 = 1 + \frac{2}{4}i + \left(\frac{1}{4}i\right)^2$$

$$= 1 - \frac{1}{16} + \frac{1}{2}i = \frac{15}{16} + \frac{1}{2}i$$

$$f\left(1 + \frac{1}{2}i\right) = \frac{3}{4} + i \quad \text{and} \quad f\left(1 + \frac{3}{4}i\right) = \frac{7}{16} + \frac{3}{2}i$$

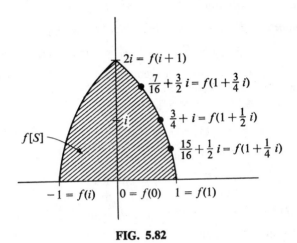

FIG. 5.82

Since $|z^2| = |z|^2$, it is clear that if B is the boundary of S, then $f[B]$ is the boundary of $f[S]$. We now know the shape of the region in $\mathcal{C}$ which is the image of S under f. This in turn gives us some idea of how f maps other regions as well.

Transformations

Let S be a subset of $\mathcal{C}$ (geometrically S is some sort of geometric figure, although in general S could be rather unusual). If $T: \mathcal{C} \to \mathcal{C}$, then $T[S]$, the trace of S under T ($T[S] = \{T(z): z \in S\}$) is also some geometric figure.

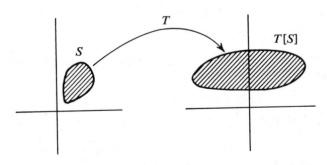

FIG. 5.83

389

We then think of T as a transformation which transforms certain figures into other figures. In this section we wish to consider only a very restricted type of transformation. For the purpose of our study, let us consider only some "rigid transformations."

5.13-1 Definition: $T: \mathbb{C} \to \mathbb{C}$ is called a *rigid transformation* iff

$$\forall u, v \in \mathbb{C} \qquad |u - v| = |T(u) - T(v)|$$

(*i.e.,* any two points in the plane remain the same distance apart after the transformation as they were before).

Example: Let $T(z) = z + 5 + i$.

$$|(2 + i) - (1 - i)| = |1 + 2i| = \sqrt{1 + 4} = \sqrt{5}$$

(*i.e.,* $2 + i$ and $1 - i$ are $\sqrt{5}$ units apart).

$$T(2 + i) = 2 + i + 5 + i = 7 + 2i$$

and $\qquad T(1 - i) = 1 - i + 5 + i = 6.$

Now $\qquad |T(2 + i) - T(1 - i)| = |7 + 2i - 6| = |1 + 2i| = \sqrt{5}.$

Similarly for arbitrary u and v.

$$|T(u) - T(v)| = |u + 5 + i - (v + 5 + 1)| = |u - v|.$$

Hence if $\qquad T(z) = z + 5 + i$ for all $z \in \mathbb{C}$,

then T is a rigid transformation.

Question: What happens to a figure S under the transformation $T(z) = z + 5 + i$?

Let us identify a large class of rigid transformations.

5.13-2 Theorem: If $\alpha, \beta \in \mathbb{C}$ and if $|\alpha| = 1$, then T is a rigid transformation where

$$T(z) = \bar{\alpha}z + \beta \qquad \forall z \in \mathbb{C}$$

Proof: Let $u, v \in \mathbb{C}$

$$\begin{aligned}|T(u) - T(v)| &= |(\alpha u + \beta) - (\alpha v + \beta)| \\ &= |\alpha u - \alpha v| = |\alpha(u - v)| = |\alpha| \, |u - v| \\ &= |u - v|\end{aligned}$$

since $|\alpha| = 1$. $\square$

Notice that if T is a rigid transformation, $T(z) = \alpha z + \beta$, then $T = T_2 \circ T_1$ (composed backwards) where

$$T_1(z) = \alpha z \qquad \text{and} \qquad T_2(z) = z + \beta$$

for if $z \in \mathbb{C}$, then

$$T_2 \circ T_1(z) = T_2(\alpha z) = \alpha z + \beta.$$

For this reason, let us separate these rigid transformations into two classes.

390

Translations

5.13-3 Definition: If $T: \mathcal{C} \to \mathcal{C}$ such that $T(z) = z + \beta$ where $\beta \in \mathcal{C}$, then T is called a *translation.* (Keep in mind here that $\beta = a + bi$ for some $a, b \in R$.)

Example: Consider the effect of T on the unit square (see Figure 5.84) $S = \{x + iy: 0 \leq x \leq 1 \text{ and } 0 \leq y \leq 1\}$ where

$$T(z) = z + (2 + 3i) \qquad \forall z \in \mathcal{C}.$$

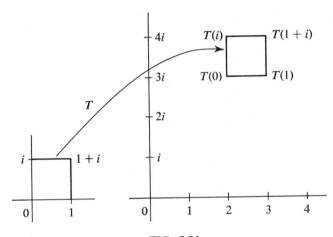

FIG. 5.84

Consider the effect of the same translation on the unit circle,

$$C = \{z: |z| = 1\}.$$
$$T(z) = z + (2 + 3i) = (a + bi) + (2 + 3i) \text{ where } z = a + bi.$$

Therefore
$$T(z) = (a + 2) + (b + 3)i$$
$$|T(z) - (2 + 3i)| = |a + 2 + bi + 3i - 2 - 3i|$$
$$= |a + bi| = |z|$$

and if $z \in C$, then $|z| = 1$. Therefore $T[C]$ is the collection of all points with distance 1 from $2 + 3i$. (See Figure 5.85.)

In general, we see that a translation $T(z) = z + (a + bi)$ merely "moves" any point $z \in \mathcal{C}$, a-units to the right and b-units up (where, of course, a negative number of units to the right is really a positive move to the left).

Example: If $T(z) = z + 3 - 2i$, then

$$T(0) = 3 - 2i, \qquad T(2) = 5 - 2i, \qquad T(1 + i) = 4 - i.$$

(See Figure 5.86.)

391

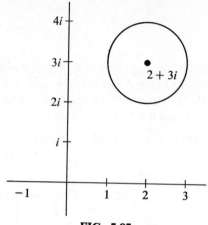

FIG. 5.85

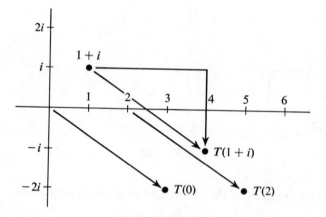

FIG. 5.86

Note also that a translation $T(z) = z + (a + bi)$ can be thought of as translating (sliding with no rotation) the whole plane $\mathcal{C}$ into a plane $\mathcal{C}'$ in such a way that the zero of $\mathcal{C}'$ is at the point $a + bi$ in $\mathcal{C}$. It is then very easy to graph $T[S]$ where $S \subset \mathcal{C}$.

Example: Let $T(z) = z + (1 + 2i)$. Let S be the darkened set (Figure 5.87).

Rotations

5.13-4 Definition: If $T: \mathcal{C} \to \mathcal{C}$ and $T(z) = \alpha z$ for all $z \in \mathcal{C}$ where $|\alpha| = 1$, then T is called a *rotation*.

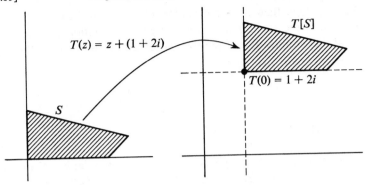

$$T(z) = z + (1 + 2i)$$

$$T(0) = 1 + 2i$$

FIG. 5.87

Example: Consider $T(z) = \left(\dfrac{1}{\sqrt{2}} + \dfrac{1}{\sqrt{2}} i\right) z$ and its effect on the unit square (see Figure 5.88).

$$T(0) = 0 \qquad\qquad T(1) = \frac{1}{\sqrt{2}} + \frac{1}{\sqrt{2}} i$$

$$T(1 + i) = \sqrt{2}\, i \qquad T(i) = -\frac{1}{\sqrt{2}} + \frac{1}{\sqrt{2}} i$$

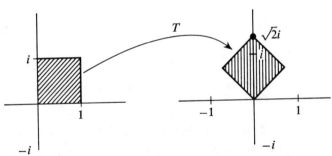

FIG. 5.88

We shall study rotations in more detail after we have developed the circular functions (trigonometric functions). Let us keep in mind now that any rigid transformation where $T(z) = \alpha z + \beta$ can be expressed as the composition of a translation and a rotation. Notice, however, that the order in which this composition is performed is important.

Example: Let $T_1(z) = \alpha z$ (a rotation)

$$T_2(z) = z + \beta \qquad \text{(a translation)}.$$

Then $\qquad\qquad T_2 \circ T_1(z) = T_2(\alpha z) = \alpha z + \beta,$

but $\qquad\qquad T_1 \circ T_2(z) = T_1(z + \beta) = \alpha(z + \beta) = \alpha z + \alpha\beta.$

We see, then, that a transformation of the form $T(z) = \alpha z + \beta$ is the composition of the rotation αz followed by the translation $z + \beta$, and is not in general the composition of the translation $z + \beta$ followed by the rotation αz.

Exercises 5.13

1. Graph $T[S]$ where S is the unit square (*i.e.*, $S = \{x + iy: x, y \in [0, 1)\}$) and:

   a) $T(z) = 2z + (1 + 3i)$

   b) $T(z) = iz$

   c) $T(z) = -iz + (1 - i)$

   d) $T(z) = (1 + i)z$

   e) $T(z) = \left(\dfrac{\sqrt{3}}{2} + \dfrac{1}{2}i\right) z$

   f) $T(z) = z - (2 - i)$

   Which of the above are "rigid transformations?"

2. Show that $T(z) = \bar{z}$ (the conjugate of z) is a rigid transformation. (This rigid transformation is called a *reflection*.)

3. Can $T(z) = \bar{z}$ be described in the form $T(z) = \alpha z + \beta$?

4. Graph $T[S]$ where S is the unit square and:

   a) $T(z) = \bar{z} + 2 + i$ b) $T(z) = \overline{z + 2 + i}$ c) $T(z) = (2 + i)\bar{z}$

5. Show that any map $T: \mathcal{C} \to \mathcal{C}$ such that $T(z) = \alpha z + \beta$, $\alpha, \beta \in \mathcal{C}$, $\alpha \neq 0$ is one-one onto. (*Hint:* $\mathcal{C}$ is a field.)

6. If C is the unit disc as in the first example and $f(z) = z^2$, what is $f[C]$?

7. Show that points on the line $z = x + xi$ are mapped into the vertical axis by the mapping $f(z) = z^2$.

8. Let $A = \{z \in \mathcal{C}: |z| > 0\}$. Find a mapping $f: A \xrightarrow[\text{onto}]{1\text{-}1} A$ such that points outside the unit circle are mapped to points inside the unit circle and vice-versa. (*Hint:* Try $f(z) = 1/z$.)

9. Graph in C the sets A and B where

   $A = \{x + iy: y = 2x - 1\}$ and $B = \{x + iy: y = -x + 1\}$.

   a) Graph $A \cup B$.

   b) Find $A \cap B$.

   If $T(z) = iz + (1 + 2i)$, then

   c) graph $T[A]$ and $T[B]$.

   d) graph $T[A \cap B]$.

10. Investigate (prove or disprove): Every rigid transformation can be expressed as the composition of a rotation, and a translation or the composition of a rotation, a translation, and a reflection. (That is, if T is a rigid transformation, then $T(z) = \alpha z + \beta$ or $T(z) = \overline{\alpha z + \beta}$ for some α, β.)

5.14   Geometric Figures and the Complex Plane

The complex number system is very useful in describing and analyzing geometric properties. We may think of the complex number system as being a plane since as a set $\mathscr{C} = R \times R$. Much of the work we do here with geometric figures could be accomplished by considering only the plane as the set $R \times R$, but since we have gone to the bother to develop an algebra on the set, we find it appropriate to consider the plane to be $\mathscr{C}$ and to apply the algebra whenever it appears useful.

In this section we shall consider circles and lines as subsets of $\mathscr{C}$ (geometric figures), and analyze some of their properties.

Circles

A circle is defined as a collection of points whose distance from some given point (called the center) is a given fixed number (called the radius). Using the fact that $|u - v|$ where $u, v \in \mathscr{C}$ is the distance between u and v, we can establish a constraining equation on the components of the numbers which make up a circle. This equation is called the equation of the circle. Let us begin by considering a circle whose center is at 0.

Example: Consider the circle K with center at 0 and with radius 2 (see Figure 5.89).

$$K = \{z: |z| = 2\},$$

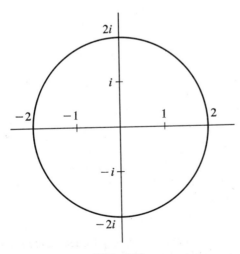

FIG. 5.89

but if we put this description in terms of the components x and y where $z = x + iy$, we have

$$K = \{x + iy: |x + iy| = 2\}$$
$$= \{x + iy: \sqrt{x^2 + y^2} = 2\}$$
$$= \{x + iy: x^2 + y^2 = 4\}.$$

Here the constraining equation $x^2 + y^2 = 4$ is called the equation for the circle K. $|z| = 2$ is also the equation of the circle K.

Example: Consider the circle with center at $2 + 3i$ and radius 3.

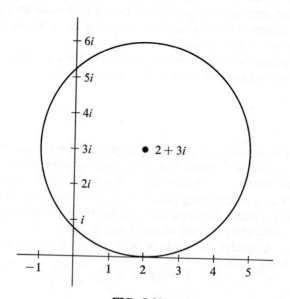

FIG. 5.90

$$H = \{z: |z - (2 + 3i)| = 3\} = \{x + iy: |x + iy - 2 - 3i| = 3\}$$
$$= \{x + iy: |(x - 2) + (y - 3)i| = 3\}$$
$$= \{x + iy: (x - 2)^2 + (y - 3)^2 = 9\}.$$

The constraining equation

$$(x - 2)^2 + (y - 3)^2 = 9$$

is called the equation of the circle with center at $2 + 3i$ and radius 3. (Note that this entire discussion could be immediately transferred to "points," ordered pairs in $R \times R$.) We could expand the equation $(x - 2)^2 + (y - 3)^2 = 9$ into the equivalent form

$$x^2 - 4x + y^2 - 6x = -4.$$

But in its present form it is extremely easy to determine the critical information (center and radius) about the circle it determines.

5.14-1 Theorem: If K is a circle with center at $a + bi$ and radius r, then the equation for K is

$$(x - a)^2 + (y - b)^2 = r^2$$

(i.e., $K = \{x + iy: (x - a)^2 + (y - b)^2 = r^2\}$.)

Proof: By definition

$$K = \{z: |z - (a + bi)| = r\}$$

but by expressing z in the real and imaginary component form $z = x + iy$, we have

$$\begin{aligned}
K &= \{x + iy: |(x + iy) - (a + bi)| = r\} \\
&= \{x + iy: |(x - a) + (y - b)i| = r\} \\
&= \{x + iy: \sqrt{(x - a)^2 + (y - b)^2} = r\} \\
&= \{x + iy: (x - a)^2 + (y - b)^2 = r^2\}. \;\square
\end{aligned}$$

By reading the steps of the proof in reverse, one immediately arrives at the converse as well. That is, if

$$K = \{x + iy: (x - a)^2 + (y - b)^2 = r^2\},$$

then K is the circle with center at $a + bi$ and radius r. Hence, an equation in x and y is the constraining equation for a circle if and only if it can be put in the form

$$(x - a)^2 + (y - b)^2 = r^2.$$

Example: Graph the equation

$$x^2 + y^2 - 4x + 4y = 1$$

(i.e., graph the set of points

$$\{x + iy: x^2 + y^2 - 4x + 4y = 1\}).$$

Let us complete the square in x and y.

$$x^2 - 4x + y^2 + 4y = 1$$
$$(x - 2)^2 + (y + 2)^2 = 1 + 4 + 4 = 9$$
$$(x - 2)^2 + (y + 2)^2 = 3^2$$

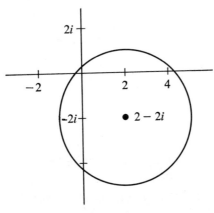

FIG. 5.91

Hence the equations represent the circle with center at $2 - 2i$ and radius 3.

Example: Graph the equation

$$x^2 + y^2 - x + 6y + \frac{17}{4} = 0.$$

We put the equation in the "standard form" for a circle by the following steps:

$$x^2 - x + y^2 + 6y = -\frac{17}{4}$$

$$\left(x - \frac{1}{2}\right)^2 + (y + 3)^2 = -\frac{17}{4} + \frac{1}{4} + 9 = 5$$

$$\left(x - \frac{1}{2}\right)^2 + (y + 3)^2 = (\sqrt{5})^2$$

which is the equation for a circle with radius $\sqrt{5}$ and center at $1/2 - 3i$.

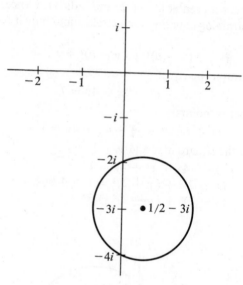

FIG. 5.92

Lines

Using the information in Section 5.9 on linear functions as a guide, we make the following definition for a line in $\mathbb{C}$.

5.14-2 Definition: Let $L \subset \mathbb{C}$. L is a line if

$$L = \{x + iy: y = mx + b\} \text{ for some } m, b \in R.$$

(m is called the slope of L and b is called the y-intercept) or

$$L = \{x + iy: x = a\} \text{ for some } a \in R.$$

(Here L is said to have "no slope.")

Question: What is the distinction between saying

$$"L = \{x + iy: y = mx + b\} \text{ for some } m, b \in R"$$

and saying

$$"L = \{x + iy: y = mx + b \text{ for some } m, b \in R\}"?$$

If L is of the form

$$L = \{x + iy: x = a\}$$

we say that L is a *vertical line.* If L has slope m where $m = 0$ we say that L is a *horizontal line.*

Example: Consider the set

$$L = \{x + iy: y = 2x + 3\}.$$

By setting $x = 0$ in the equation $y = 2x + 3$, we see that $y = 3$ (*i.e.*, $0 + 3i \in L$). By selecting various values for x and solving for y we see that the following points are also in L:

$$1 + 5i, \quad -1 + i, \quad -2 - i.$$

Note that the line passes through the imaginary axis at $3i$ and hence the name y-intercept.

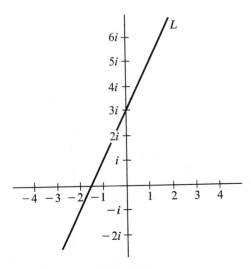

FIG. 5.93

When the equation for a line is given in the form $y = mx + b$, it is said to be in the *slope-intercept form.* In this form one can easily graph the line by looking only at m and b.

Example: Graph the line $y = -3x + 1$

(*i.e.*, $L = \{x + iy: y = -3x + 1\}$).

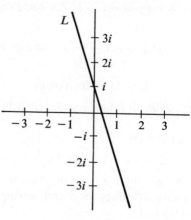

FIG. 5.94

If a line is determined by the equation $x = a$, then it is a vertical line whose points all have real component a.

Example: Graph $\{x + iy: x = 2\}$.

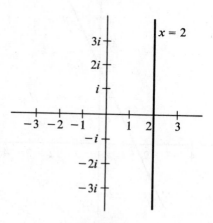

FIG. 5.95

There are several convenient forms for the equation of a non-vertical line.

Two Point Form

Any line can be determined by knowing two distinct points on the line. Consider a line passing through $a + bi$ and $c + di$ where $a \neq c$. (If $a = c$ and $b \neq d$, then the line is the vertical line whose equation is $x = a$.)

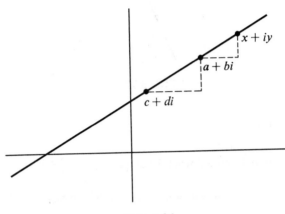

FIG. 5.96

Allow $x + iy$ to be an arbitrary point on the line. Since the slope is some fixed number for every point on the line, we can equate the ratios $(y - b)/(x - a)$ and $(b - d)/(a - c)$. That is, the equation for a line passing through $a + bi$ and $c + di$ is given by

$$\frac{y - b}{x - a} = \frac{b - d}{a - c}$$

or by

$$y - b = \frac{b - d}{a - c}(x - a)$$

(two point form).

Example: Graph the line passing through $2 + i$ and $1 - i$. Find the equation for the line and change it to slope intercept form.

Solution: The equation is

$$\frac{y - 1}{x - 2} = \frac{1 - (-1)}{2 - 1}$$

(i.e.,

$$y - 1 = 2(x - 2) = 2x - 4$$
$$y = 2x - 3).$$

401

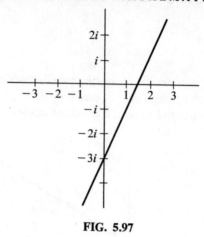

FIG. 5.97

Point Slope Form

A line is fully determined when its slope and one point through which it passes is given.

Consider then a line whose slope is m and which passes through $a + bi$.

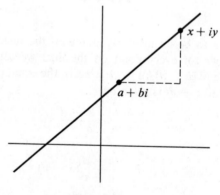

FIG. 5.98

Let $x + iy$ be an arbitrary point on the line. We then have

$$\frac{y - b}{x - a} = m$$

or $(y - b) = m(x - a)$ (*point slope form*).

Example: Graph the line with slope -2 which passes through $1 + i$. Find the equation for the line and change it to slope-intercept form.

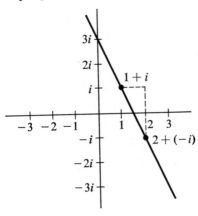

FIG. 5.99

Solution:

$$\frac{y-1}{x-1} = -2$$

$$y - 1 = -2(x - 1) = -2x + 2$$
$$y = -2x + 3$$

Parallel and Perpendicular Lines

At this point in our geometry of the complex plane, we have not given a definition for lines being either parallel or perpendicular. It is clear that such definitions should be given in terms of slope. We are prepared to give a definition for parallel lines, but the definition for perpendicularity must await some geometrical analysis.

5.14-3 Definition: Lines L_1 and L_2 are said to be parallel if
  a) neither L_1 nor L_2 has a slope or
  b) L_1 and L_2 have equal slope.
  Example: Let $L_1 = \{x + iy: y = 2x + 1\}, L_2 = \{x + iy: y = 2x + 2\}$.
L_1 is parallel to L_2.
  Although we do not have a definition for two lines being perpendicular we do know what we have in mind. With this in mind along with some applications of simple Euclidean geometry let us derive a relationship between the slopes of two lines which we wish to be perpendicular.
  We can make this derivation with lines passing through 0 since lines intersecting at an arbitrary point p can be translated by $T(z) = z - p$ into lines intersecting at 0.

403

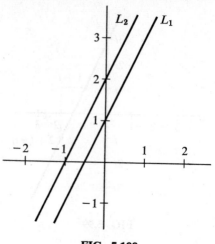

FIG. 5.100

Derivation

Consider lines

$$L_1 = \{x + iy: y = mx\} \quad \text{and} \quad L_2 = \{x + iy: y = kx\}$$

as shown in Figure 5.101 (neither line horizontal).

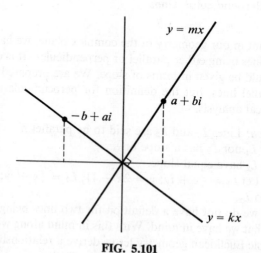

FIG. 5.101

Select $a + bi \neq 0$ on L_1. Then from our intuitive feeling about perpendicularity we know that $-b + ai$ must lie on L_2 if L_2 and L_1 are to be perpendicular (why?). Since $a + bi \in L_1$ we have $b = ma$ and since $-b + ai \in L_2$ we have $a = k(-b)$ from which we have $k = -(1/m)$. Hence we make the following definition.

5.14-4 Definition: If L_1 has slope $m \neq 0$, then L_2 is *perpendicular* to L_1 iff the slope of L_2 is $-(1/m)$. Otherwise, horizontal lines are perpendicular to vertical lines and vice-versa.

Example: Find the equation of a line L_2 perpendicular to

$$L_1 = \{x + iy: y = 3x + 2\}$$

which passes through $1 + i$. Now the slope of L_2 must be $-(1/3)$. By using the point slope form we have

$$y - 1 = (x - 1)\left(-\frac{1}{3}\right)$$

(*i.e.* $$y = -\frac{1}{3}x + \frac{4}{3}.$$ (see Figure 5.102))

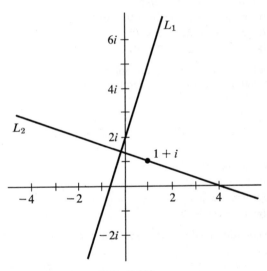

FIG. 5.102

Question: At what point do L_1 and L_2 intersect? Solving simultaneously we have:

$$3x + 2 = -\frac{1}{3}x + \frac{4}{3}$$

$$x = -\frac{1}{5} \quad \text{and} \quad y = 3\left(-\frac{1}{5}\right) + 2 = \frac{7}{5}$$

(*i.e.*, $$L_1 \cap L_2 = \left\{-\frac{1}{5} + \frac{7}{5}i\right\}.$$

405

Exercises 5.14

1. Write the equations for circles with
   a) center at $1 + i$ and radius 3.
   b) center at $2 + 3i$ and radius 7.
   c) center at 1 and radius 2.
   d) center at 0 and radius $\sqrt{3}$.
   e) center at $-1 + 2i$ and radius $\sqrt{7}$.
   f) center at $-2 - 3i$ and radius 10.

2. Graph each of the following sets:
   a) $\{x + iy: x^2 + y^2 < 25\}$
   b) $\{x + iy: (x - 1)^2 + (y + 2)^2 < 7\}$
   c) $\{z: |z + 1 + i| < 4\}$

3. Graph each of the following sets:
   a) $\{x + iy: x^2 + y^2 - 6x + 2y - 9 = 0\}$
   b) $\{x + iy: x^2 + y^2 + 2x - 1 = 0\}$
   c) $\{x + iy: x^2 + y^2 + 2x + 2 = 0\}$

4. Let L be a line passing through the points a and bi ($a \neq 0$ and $b \neq 0$) (i.e., a, $bi \in L$). Show that the equation of L can be put in the form $x/a + y/b = 1$ (i.e., $L = \{x + iy: x/a + y/b = 1\}$).

5. Let $L = \{x + iy: y = mx\}$, $L' = \{x + iy: y = -(1/m)x\}$, and $L'' = \{iz: z \in L\}$. Show that $L' = L''$. (What does this say in general about the function $f(z) = iz$?)

6. Graph each of the following sets:
   a) $\{x + iy: y = 3x - 4\}$
   b) $\{x + iy: y < 4x + 1\}$
   c) $\{x + iy: y \geq x/3 - 2\}$

7. Write the equation in slope intercept form for a line L such that:
   a) $2 + 3i \in L$ and $1 - i \in L$ d) $-3 + i \in L$ and slope $L = -1$
   b) $0 \in L$ and $4 + i \in L$ e) $-2 - 2i \in L$ and slope $L = 3$
   c) $3 + i \in L$ and slope $L = 2$

   Graph each line.

8. Write the equation of a line parallel to $L = \{x + iy: y = 3x + 2\}$ which
   a) passes through $1 + i$.
   b) passes through $2 - 3i$.
   c) passes through $4 + 2i$.

   Graph L and the lines called for in a), b), c).

9. Write the equation of a line perpendicular to $L = \{x + iy: y = 2x - 3\}$ which
   a) passes through $2 - i$.
   b) passes through $2 + i$.
   c) passes through $1 - 3i$.

   Graph L and the lines called for in a), b), c).

10. If T is a rigid transformation, and L is a line, then show that $T[L]$ is a line. (*Hint:* Show that ratio of the change in y to the change in x is constant.)

5.15 Parametric Equations for Figures in C

It is often convenient to describe a figure in $\mathbb{C}$ by allowing two real valued functions on R to determine the x and y components of the numbers making up the figure. For example, if we define x and y as follows:

$$x = 2t \qquad \forall t \in R$$
$$y = t^2 \qquad \forall t \in R$$

For each $t \in R$ a real number $x = 2t$ is determined and a real number $y = t^2$ is determined. Thus for each real number t, a complex number

$$x + iy = 2t + it^2$$

is determined. If we allow t to vary over all real numbers, then some sort of figure is traced out in $\mathbb{C}$. Let us consider this example further by first defining $f: R \to \mathbb{C}$ by

$$f(t) = 2t + it^2.$$

Let us first list a few critical functional values.

$$f(0) = 0 \qquad\qquad f(1) = 2 + i \qquad\qquad f(2) = 4 + 4i$$
$$f(3) = 6 + 9i \qquad\qquad f(4) = 8 + 16i$$
and $f(-1) = -2 + i \qquad f(-2) = -4 + 4i \qquad f(-3) = -6 + 9i$
$$f(-4) = -8 + 16i.$$

We see then as t increases, both the x and y values of $f(t)$ increase, but the y value tends to increase much faster. As t takes on negative values to the left of zero, the y values of $f(t)$ are the same as for $f(-t)$, but the x values are the negatives of those for $f(-t)$. The set

$$f[R] = \{2t + it^2 : t \in R\}$$

is shown in Figure 5.103.

15-1 Definition: Let X and Y denote functions from R into $\mathbb{C}$. The equations

$$x = X(t)$$
and $\qquad\qquad y = Y(t)$

are called the *parametric equations* of the curve K where

$$K = \{x + iy : x = X(t) \text{ and } y = Y(t), t \in R\}.$$

The variable "t" is called the *parameter*.

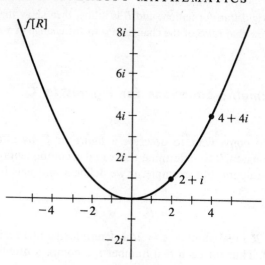

FIG. 5.103

Example: Graph the curve

$$K = \{x + iy: x = t^2 \text{ and } y = t^2\}.$$

(This same problem might be worded "graph the curve $x + iy$ with parametric equations $x = t^2$ and $y = t^2$.")

Again we can consider this as determining the trace of R under the function $f: R \to \mathbb{C}$ given by

$$f(t) = t^2 + it^2.$$

That is,
$$f[R] = \{t^2 + it^2: t \in R\}.$$

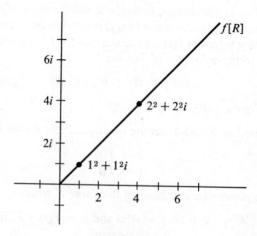

FIG. 5.104

By listing a few critical functional values and then applying our knowledge of real numbers, we arrive at the graph given in Figure 5.104. (Note that the entire curve is given in the first quadrant. Why?)

As a final example of curves determined parametrically, we would like to look at the trace of $h: R \to \mathbb{C}$ where

$$h(t) = \cosh t + i \sinh t, \qquad \forall t \in R.$$

Recall that $\cosh t \to \infty$ both as $t \to \infty$ and as $t \to -\infty$. Also recall that $\sinh t \to \infty$ as $t \to \infty$ but that $\sinh t \to -\infty$ as $t \to -\infty$. With this information and a few well chosen functional values we graph $h[R]$.

$$h(0) = 1$$

$$h(1) = \frac{e + 1/e}{2} + i \frac{e - 1/e}{2}$$

$$h(-1) = \frac{1/e + e}{2} + i \frac{1/e - e}{2}$$

$$= \frac{e + 1/e}{2} - i \frac{e - 1/e}{2} = \overline{h(1)}$$

In fact for each $t \in R$ $h(-t) = \overline{h(t)}$ (*the complex conjugate*). The graph then is as in Figure 5.105.

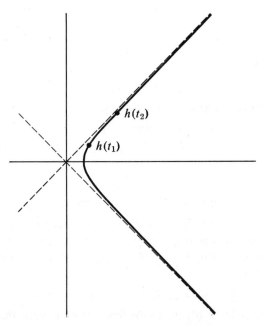

FIG. 5.105   The partial hyperbola $\{\cosh t + i \sinh t : t \in R\}$.

This curve along with its reflection in the y-axis is a special case of a particular type of figure known as a *hyperbola*. Hence the name "hyperbolic" is given to these functions.

One of the very interesting features of this particular hyperbola is the fact that the length along the curve between two points $h(t_1)$ and $h(t_2)$ is given by $|t_1 - t_2|$. That is, the curve is as if the real line were "picked up" and lain along the curve with "no stretching." We cannot of course prove this since we have given no workable definition for length along a curve. (How do you suppose one might define length along a curve?)

Eliminating the Parameter

It is often convenient, when a curve is defined parametrically, to eliminate the parameter and describe the curve in terms of a constraining equation in the variables x and y.

Example: Let $K = \{t^2 + it: t \in R\}$. We have

$$K = \{x + iy: x = t^2, y = t, t \in R\}.$$

If we substitute for t in the equations

$$x = t^2 \quad \text{and} \quad y = t$$

we arrive at a constraining equation

$$x = y^2.$$

Hence $\qquad\qquad K = \{x + iy: x = y^2\}.$

Example: Describe the set

$$\{3t - it^2: t \in R\}$$

by a constraining equation on two variables.

Let $\qquad\qquad x = 3t \quad \text{and} \quad y = -t^2$

hence $\qquad\qquad\qquad y = -\dfrac{x^2}{9}.$

That is, in this case

$$\{3t - it^2: t \in R\} = \{x + iy: 9y = -x^2\}.$$

One should be careful in eliminating the parameter to be sure that no constraining information is lost, thus allowing more points. For example, the set described parametrically by $x = t^2$ and $y = t^2$ is not the same as the set described by $x = y$

(*i.e.,* $\qquad\qquad \{t^2 + it^2: t \in R\} \neq \{x + iy: y = x\}$).

All points in the set $\{t^2 + it^2\}$ are in the first quadrant while the set $\{x + iy: y = x\}$ allows points also in the third quadrant. In order to describe this set using constraints on x and y, one would need an extra condition. For example,

$$\{t^2 + it^2 : t \in R\} = \{x + iy : y = x \text{ and } x \geq 0\}.$$

Comparison of Subsets of C With Subsets of R × R

We conclude this section with some remarks concerning $R \times R$ as compared with $\mathcal{C}$. As a set $R \times R = \mathcal{C}$, hence many of the analytic facts about sets in $\mathcal{C}$ discussed in Sections 5.14 and 5.15 can be interpreted as regarding sets in $R \times R$, and hence can be used in graphing functions and relations in $R \times R$.

Example: Graph the function

$$f(x) = 3x^2 - 6x + 5.$$

This is equivalent with graphing the set

$$\{(x, y): y = 3x^2 - 6x + 5\} = \{x + iy : y = 3x^2 - 6x + 5\}.$$

By examining the constraining equation

$$y = 3x^2 - 6x + 5 = 3(x^2 - 2x) + 5$$

and completing the square in x we have

$$y = 3(x - 1)^2 - 3 + 5$$

or equivalently

$$(y - 2) = 3(x - 1)^2.$$

As discussed earlier, one can make a transformation, perhaps by allowing the substitution

$$y' = y - 2$$

and

$$x' = x - 1$$

and graphing the equation

$$y' = 3x'^2$$

superimposed on the x, y coordinate system. (See Figure 5.106.)

Similar work can be done with rotations, but in general it entails details which we shall not consider in this text.

Exercises 5.15

1. Let $f(t) = (2 + t) + it^2$. Compute and graph each of the following points in $\mathcal{C}$.

   a) $f(0)$ c) $f(-1)$ e) $f(-2)$ g) $f(-3)$
   b) $f(1)$ d) $f(2)$ f) $f(3)$

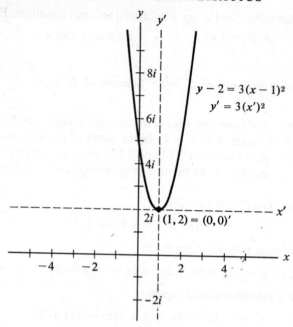

$$y - 2 = 3(x - 1)^2$$
$$y' = 3(x')^2$$

$(1, 2) = (0, 0)'$

FIG. 5.106

2. Graph the trace of R under each of the following functions from R into $\mathbb{C}$.

a) $f(t) = 2t + it^2$

b) $f(t) = 3 + it$

c) $f(t) = t^2 + 2i$

d) $f(t) = t^3 + 2t^2 i$

e) $f(t) = \cosh t + it$

f) $f(t) = it + i \sinh t$

g) $f(t) = \sinh t + i \cosh t$

h) $f(t) = -\sinh t + i \cosh t$

3. Interpret graphically the condition that $f(-t) = f(t)$ for all $t \in R$ where $f: R \to \mathbb{C}$.

4. If $h(t) = \cosh t + i \sinh t$, then show that $\forall t \in R \quad h(-t) = \overline{h(t)}$.

5. If $f(t) = X(t) + iY(t)$ and if $\lim_{t \to \infty} \dfrac{Y(t)}{X(t)} = 1$ (i.e., $Y = 0X$), then what can you say about the points $f(t)$ as $t \to \infty$?

6. Graph the trace of R under each of the following functions from R into $\mathbb{C}$.

a) $f(t) = \dfrac{1}{t} + it^2$

b) $f(t) = t - \dfrac{1}{t} i$

c) $f(t) = -\dfrac{1}{t^2} - \dfrac{i}{t}$

d) $f(t) = t - \dfrac{i}{t^2}$

7. Graph $f_0(t) = t^2 + it$ and then graph:

a) $f_1(t) = if_0(t)$

b) $f_2(t) = if_1(t)$

c) $f_3(t) = if_2(t)$

d) $f_4(t) = if_3(t)$

8. Describe each of the following sets by giving constraints on $y = Y(t)$ and $x = X(t)$ rather than in parametric form as given. Graph each set.

  a) $\{x + iy : x = 2t \text{ and } y = t^2\}$
  b) $\{x + iy : 2x = t^2 \text{ and } y = 1 - t\}$
  c) $\{x + iy : x = t^2 - 2 \text{ and } y + 1 = 2t^2\}$
  d) $\{x + iy : t = x^2 \text{ and } y = 2t\}$

9. Use "completing the square" and translation techniques to graph the following equations:

  a) $y = x^2 + 4x + 5$
  b) $2y = 3x^2 - 6x + 1$
  c) $y = 4x^2 + 8x + 7$

  d) $y = 4x^2 + 24x + 31$
  e) $3y = 5x^2 + 10x + 14$

5.16 Summary of Graphing Techniques

In this section we shall review several general principles that should be kept in mind when faced with the task of graphing a function from R into R. In fact, it is very often desirable to make such observations even when the function does not have to be formally sketched. This should enable the student to "get the feel" of the function involved, possibly a very important step in the solution of the problem in which it arises. We shall review various principles and make short comments on them.

Domain and Range

It is often useful at the outset to ascertain what the domain is, using, if necessary, the principle of the maximal domain. A knowledge of the domain and range will at least lead to a very rough idea of what kind of ordered pairs are in f, and, perhaps even more significantly, some that are *not* in f.

Symmetry

As we have seen, it is often possible to quickly recognize certain types of symmetry that a function possesses from a consideration of the description of the function. Thus, for example, the function $|x^3|$ is symmetric about the y-axis, as is x^4. Knowing this, we need (in effect) only to sketch "half" of the function's graph, the other half being obtained by reflection.

Zeros and y-intercepts

Experience tends to verify that these special ordered pairs in the function are especially "informative," provided that they are relatively easy to find. When making the final sketch, the graph should be drawn through these plotted points.

Continuity

Remember that continuous functions have graphs without "jumps" or "holes," but may have "sharp corners."

Tangent Lines

If a curve has a tangent line at a point, the curve must be "smooth" *and continuous* in a neighborhood of the point. If the tangent line at a point has positive slope, the function is increasing in the "neighborhood" of the point; similarly zero or negative slope means local "level" or decreasing behavior. Thus slopes of tangent lines can be used to gain information about monotonicity, at least near a point. Note that points at which the tangent line has zero slope *might* coincide with the "top of a hump" or "bottom of a dip" in the function's graph. This information is considerably more useful after a study of calculus in which more sophisticated techniques are developed for finding slopes.

Asymptotes and Properties in the Large

Obtaining information about the behavior of a function for $|x|$ large is often easily accomplished. This enables one to concentrate on finding the behavior of the function for pre-images "close" to the origin.

Translation and Rotation

Often one can perform such transformations in such a way that the resulting description is easily graphed. Remember to transform such a graph back to the original system!

414

Standard Forms

This very important principle of graphing depends upon your memory and experience. You will find that certain functions are used often enough so that you will remember their graphs, thus short-cutting the usual procedure of graphing. By the time you have worked through this book, you should be able to recognize immediately such functions as the polynomials, trigonometric functions, exponential functions, absolute value function, and their inverses in most cases.

Composition

It is often possible to use the idea of composition of functions to great advantage in graphing. For example, suppose you are asked to graph $f(1/x)$ where f is the "fraction part of x" function (see Section 5.2). If you use the fact that this is a composition $f \circ g(x)$, where $f = $ "fraction part" and $g(x) = 1/x$, you can use your knowledge of the two familiar functions f and g to advantage. Thus since g maps pre-images far from zero to images near zero, we see that in the composition $f \circ g$, all the periods of f outside $(-1, 1)$ will wind up inside $(-1, 1)$. (In fact, g maps points outside the interval $(-1, 1)$ to points inside, and vice-versa.) Noting moreover that $D_g = \overline{\{0\}}$ and $R_f = [0, 1)$, you should be able to "guess" that $f \circ g$ has the graph sketched in Figure 5.107 (plotting some points in addition, if necessary).

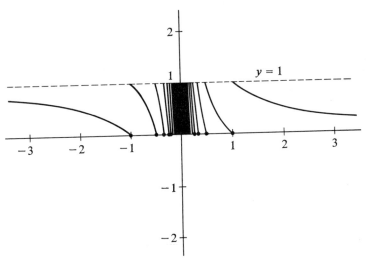

FIG. 5.107   The graph of $f \circ g(x) = \dfrac{1}{x} - \left[\dfrac{1}{x}\right]$.

Geometric Addition

This is a particular kind of composition of functions which can be constructed on the graph by the familiar process of adding ordinates at each point in the domain.

Ordered Pairs

Remember that the "final authority" on graphing is the plotting of ordered pairs in the functions. If all else fails, we must rely upon plotting sufficiently many ordered pairs so that we can guess the graph by "connecting the dots." It is usually a good idea to plot a few ordered pairs when graphing any function. These particular points should be chosen in such a way that they are either easy to find, or especially informative about the graph involved.

In the problems that follow, you are asked to apply as many of the foregoing principles as is necessary to enable you to sketch the required graphs.

Exercises 5.16

Graph each of the following:

1. $y^2 = x^2 - 5$
2. $y = (x + 1)/(x - 1)$
3. $y = 4^x$
4. $y = x + [x]$
5. $|y| = x^2$
6. $|x| + |y| = 5$
7. $xy = 4$
8. $y = |\cosh x|^2$
9. $y^5 x^3 = 1$
10. $y = x^{1/4}$
11. $yx^{1/2} = 1$
12. $y = \dfrac{1}{x^{3/5}}$
13. $y = \ln |x|$

14. $y = e^{x^2}$

15. $y = e^{-1/2x^2}$

16. $y = \cosh(\sinh(x))$

17. $y = \cosh(\cosh^{-1}(x))$

18. $y = x^x$

19. $y = \dfrac{1}{1 + \dfrac{1}{1 + 1/x}}$

20. $y = e^x$

21. $y = 1 + x + x^2/2 + x^3/3$

6

COUNTING METHODS
AND PROBABILITY
MODELS

Introduction

In this chapter we shall see how useful some of the notions we have developed thus far can be. We start with a consideration of "counting problems." The answer to the question "In how many ways . . .?" is, as we shall see, useful in connection with the assignment of probabilities to events. Thus after we have sufficiently developed an ability to enumerate, we shall branch into an area of great mathematical interest; that of Probability Theory. The body of mathematics described as "probability theory" is very broad, and we will not be able to consider a complete development of the theory. It is hoped, however, that the reader will be able to gain an understanding of the most fundamental concepts involved.

Our work in this chapter, then, should serve a dual purpose; to introduce the fundamental notions of probability upon which you can later build, and to provide an important example showing how the concepts of functions, sets, classes of sets closed under set operations, and enumeration of sets all tie together in a useful mathematical model.

6.1 Permutations

We begin our approach to counting methods with a consideration of a particularly simple and elegant type of function, the *permutation*.

6.1-1 Definition: A permutation on some finite set A is a function $v\colon A \xrightarrow[\text{onto}]{1-1} A$.

Remark: Note that ν^{-1} is a permutation on A and also that the identity mapping is a permutation on A.

WLOG we may take $A = \{1, \ldots, n\}$ for some $n \in N$, since otherwise it would at most involve relabeling the original elements.

Example: Let $A = \{a, b, c\}$. If we let $x_1 = a$, $x_2 = b$, and $x_3 = c$, then $A = \{x_1, x_2, x_3\}$. Thus, any study of the permutations on A (*one-one* correspondences between A and A) can be essentially accomplished by studying the permutations on $\{1, 2, 3\}$.

The reason we wish to examine this particular type of function is due to the interpretation it gives with respect to solving certain physical problems involving arrangements. For example, consider the problem of determining the number of ways in which one can "arrange" the members of A where $A = \{1, 2, 3, 4\}$. (More precisely, how many strict linear orderings exist on A?) This problem can be solved by allowing four slots, 1.____ , 2.____ , 3.____ , 4.____ , and then determining all possible ways to fill the slots with the elements of A, using each element exactly once. Clearly, any such arrangement of the elements of A determines a *one-one* correspondence from A to A. That is, any "arrangement" (strict linear ordering) of the elements of A determines a permutation on A and vice-versa. Hence, in order to study the number of ways one can arrange the elements of finite sets, we need only undertake a study of permutations on the sets $\{1, \ldots, n\}$, $n \in N$.

Let us then consider the problem of counting the permutations on the set $A = \{1, \ldots, 4\}$. Denote for example, the permutation ν, where $\nu(1) = 2$, $\nu(2) = 1$, $\nu(3) = 4$, $\nu(4) = 3$, by

$$\nu = \begin{pmatrix} 1 & 2 & 3 & 4 \\ 2 & 1 & 4 & 3 \end{pmatrix}.$$

We see that any given permutation is decided when we have filled each of the "slots" below the numbers, 1, 2, 3, 4, with an element of A in such a way that each member is used exactly once. In counting these permutations then we notice that in selecting a number for the "first" position we have four choices. In selecting a number for the second position, however, we have only three choices since we cannot re-use the element which appears in the first position. (A *one-one* function must send distinct pre-images to distinct images.) Similarly, we have two ways in which to choose the element in the third position and only one way to choose the last number. We deduce then that the number of permutations on $A = \{1, 2, 3, 4\}$ is given by

$$4 \cdot 3 \cdot 2 \cdot 1 = 4!$$

We generalize this result in the following lemma.

6.1-2 Lemma: The number of permutations on $A_n = \{1, \ldots, n\}$ is $n!$.

Proof: By induction on n.

  i) Clearly the number on $A_1 = \{1\}$ is $1 = 1!$.

  ii) Assume that the number of permutations on $A_k = \{1, \ldots, k\}$ is $k!$.

Consider an arbitrary permutation v on A_k,

$$v = \begin{pmatrix} 1, & 2, & \ldots, & k \\ a_1, & a_2, & \ldots, & a_k \end{pmatrix}$$

then $\mu = \begin{pmatrix} 1, & 2, & \ldots, & k, & k+1 \\ a_1, & a_2, & \ldots, & a_{k_0} & k+1 \end{pmatrix}$

is a permutation on $A_{k+1} = \{1, \ldots, k+1\}$. Further, by interchanging $k+1$ with any one of the first k, a_i's we have a different permutation on A_{k+1}. For example,

$$\mu' = \begin{pmatrix} 1, & 2, & \ldots, & k, & k+1 \\ k+1, & a_2, & \ldots, & a_k, & a_1 \end{pmatrix}$$

is a permutation on A_{k+1}. Hence given v, a permutation on A_k, we have determined $k+1$ permutations on A_{k+1}. Clearly any permutation on A_{k+1} can be gotten from such an interchange from some permutation on A_k.

  Since any two different permutations on A_k must differ in at least two places (see Exercise 5), it follows that no duplication occurs when one uses this method to construct permutations on A_{k+1} by beginning with distinct permutations on A_k. We have argued that

  a) for each permutation on A_k there are $k+1$ distinct permutations on A_{k+1}.

  b) no duplications occur when different permutations on A_k are considered.

  c) no permutation on A_{k+1} has been left uncounted.

We conclude that there are $k+1$ times as many permutations on A_{k+1} as on A_k. That is, there are

$$k! \cdot (k+1) = (k+1)!$$

permutations on A_{k+1}. (Are *a)*, *b)*, and *c)* all necessary to make this claim? Are they sufficient?) □

  Remark: The above proof is often given in a somewhat "looser" form as follows: Each permutation v can be determined by choosing the image of 1, then the image of 2, next the image of 3, and so on. $v(1)$ can be chosen in n ways, since any of the elements in $\{1, \ldots, n\}$ could be the image of 1 under v. Having chosen $v(1)$, $v(2)$ can be chosen in $n-1$ ways, since there are $n-1$ elements other than $v(1)$ that could serve as $v(2)$. Similarly, given the choices for $v(1)$ and $v(2)$, $v(3)$ could be chosen in $(n-2)$ ways. This process is continued down to the stage at which we are choosing $v(n)$. Given that the images $v(1), v(2), \ldots, v(n-1)$ have been chosen, there is only one way

421

to choose $\nu(n)$. (Keep in mind that we are "building" functions that are *one-one*.) Thus the total number of ways of choosing the images $\nu(1)$, $\nu(2)$, $\ldots$, $\nu(n)$ is $n(n-1)\ldots(1) = n!$.

Example: How many possible ways can 10 people be seated in a room containing 10 chairs? The answer is deduced to be 10! by observing that this is equivalent with asking how many permutations on $\{1, \ldots, 10\}$ there are. (That is, by labeling first the chairs and then the people with distinct numbers in $\{1, \ldots, 10\}$.)

We have considered so far, the very simple problem of counting the number of permutations on a set with n elements. In determining this number, we applied a special case of a slightly more general counting principle which we shall discuss shortly. First, however, we wish to establish two familiar counting principles and examine some examples and applications.

6.1-3 Theorem: (First basic counting principle)

If A and B are finite sets, then

$$\#(A \cup B) = \#A + \#B - \#(A \cap B).$$

Proof left for the reader.

Example: Gurney allows 20 animals in the cow barn C, where he allows only cows and pigs. He allows 17 animals in the horse barn H where he allows only horses and pigs. He has 30 animals allowed in both barns total. How many horses, cows, and pigs does he have?

Solution: $\#(H \cup C) = \#H + \#C - \#(H \cap C)$

(i.e., $\qquad 30 = 17 + 20 - $ (number of pigs)).

Hence, Gurney has 7 pigs, 13 cows, and 10 horses.

6.1-4 Theorem: (Second basic counting principle)

Let $A_1, \ldots, A_n$ be non-empty finite sets. The number of functions from $\{1, \ldots, n\}$ into $A_1 \cup \ldots \cup A_n$ such that $f(i) \in A_i$ is

$$\#A_1 \cdot \#A_2 \cdot \ldots \cdot \#A_n.$$

Equivalently, the number of n-tuples whose ith component is a member of A_i is

$$\prod_{i=1}^{n} (\#A_i). \qquad (i.e., \#\underset{i=1}{\overset{n}{\text{X}}} A_i = \prod_{i=1}^{n} (\#A_i)).$$

Proof: By induction on n.

i) Clearly the number of functions from $\{1\}$ into A_1 is $\#A_1$.

ii) Assume the result holds for k. That is, the number of functions from $\{1, \ldots, k\}$ into $\cup_{i=1}^{k} A_i$ such that $f(i) \in A_i$ is given by $\prod_{i=1}^{k} (\#A_i)$. To each such function and each element in A_{k+1} there corresponds a function from $\{1, \ldots, k+1\}$ which takes its $(k+1)^{th}$ value in A_{k+1}. Hence, if we have not omitted any possibilities, there will be $\#A_{k+1}$ times as many functions as before. That is, we will have

$$\#A_{k+1} \cdot \prod_{i=1}^{k} (\#A_i) = \prod_{i=1}^{k+1} (\#A_i)$$

n-tuples whose ith component is in A_i. ☐

Exercise: Rewrite the proof of the above theorem using the idea of extension and restriction of functions.

This result can be applied to the problem of determining the number of different ways certain finite sequences of events can be accomplished.

Example: The state in which Gurney Gibson resides designates automobile license plates using three letters and three digits. Thus Gurney's license number is TIP 424. How many distinct such license plates are possible using this scheme?

Solution: The first letter can be chosen in 26 ways; the second and third similarly. The digits can each be chosen in 10 ways. Thus the total number of such plates is

$$\#(A \times A \times A \times T \times T \times T) \quad \text{where } A = \{a, b, c, \ldots, x, y, z\}$$
$$\text{and } T = \{0, \ldots, 9\}.$$

We compute 26 times 26 times 26 times 10 times 10 times 10 = 17,576,000

= (# of ways of choosing 1st letter) × (# of ways of choosing 2nd letter)
× (# of ways of choosing 3rd letter) × (# of ways of choosing 1st digit)
× (# of ways of choosing 2nd digit) × (# of ways of choosing 3rd digit).

On the other hand, if the plates are to be designated in such a way that no symbol is used more than once, the number of license plates is

$$26 \times 25 \times 24 \times 10 \times 9 \times 8 = 11,232,000.$$

Remark: The *process* of counting the elements in $A \times A$ with distinct components is not the same as counting the elements in $A \times (A - \{a\})$. (Although the answer is the same.) Why?

Example: How many ways can one seat 4 people at a bridge table from a group of 12?

(The order in which they are seated is important.) The first place can be filled in 12 different ways while the second can be filled 11 ways, the third 10, and the fourth 9. Hence, the number of possibilities is $12 \cdot 11 \cdot 10 \cdot 9$. This problem is essentially a permutation type of problem where only part of the permutations on $\{1, \ldots, 12\}$ are considered. Note that

$$12 \cdot 11 \cdot 10 \cdot 9 = \frac{12!}{8!} = \frac{12!}{(12 - 4)!}.$$

This brings us to the next theorem.

6.1-5 Theorem: (Third basic counting principle)

Suppose $B \subset \{1, \ldots, n\}$ and that $\#B = r$. The number of distinct restrictions to B of permutations on $\{1, \ldots, n\}$ is $\dfrac{n!}{(n - r)!}$. Equivalently, given a universal set with n elements, the number of ordered r-tuples $(r \leq n)$ with distinct components that can be formed is

$$n(n - 1) \ldots (n - r + 1) = \frac{n!}{(n - r)!}.$$

Proof left as an exercise.

It is common to rephrase this description simply as *"the number of permutations of n things taken r at a time,"* and to denote this number by P_r^n.

6.1-6 Definition: $P_r^n = \dfrac{n!}{(n - r)!} = (n - 1) \ldots (n - r + 1)$.

Remark: Observe the missing quantifiers in the preceding definition. In fact, note that P_r^n is a function. Its domain is the set $\{(n, r): n \in N, r \in \{0, \ldots, n\}\}$, and its range is in N. Instead of writing the image of the pair (n, r) as $P(n, r)$ we have adopted the commonly used notation P_r^n.

Example: How many ways can 12 of 20 cars be parked? The answer is determined to be $P_{12}^{20} = \dfrac{20!}{8!}$ since the first space can be filled 20 ways, the second 19 ways, until the last space, which can be filled 9 ways, is filled. That is,

$$P_{12}^{20} = 20 \cdot 19 \cdot \ldots \cdot 9.$$

In this example, it could be argued that there are really not that many ways to park the cars since the important thing is not the order but whether or not a given car is parked. In the next section we will examine the case in which the absence of order is taken into account. However, there are many counting problems which can be solved with the machinery at hand, and you should work some exercises before we move on.

Exercises 6.1

1. At Eagle Beak High where every student must take math or English, there are 85 students taking math and 106 students taking English. There are 20 students taking both math and English. How many students are there at E.B.H.?

2. Each of 5 schools needs a teacher. There are 9 applicants for the positions. How many ways can the position be filled?

3. In how many ways can a dime, a quarter, and a nickel be distributed among 5 boys?

4. Show that the composition of two permutations on a finite set A is again a permutation.

5. Show that if ν and ν' are permutations on a finite set and $\nu \neq \nu'$, then ν and ν' differ in at least two places. (That is, $\exists x, y \quad x \neq y, \nu(x) \neq \nu'(y)$.)

6. In how many distinct ways can five distinct objects be distributed among three distinct containers?

7. *a)* How many numbers with three digits can be formed using the digits 1, 4, 5, or 7?

b) How many numbers with three distinct digits can be formed using 1, 4, 5, or 7?

8. How many possible ways can a dime, a quarter, and a nickel land (with respect to heads and tails)?

9. Compute:

a) P_3^5 *b)* P_2^7 *c)* $P_4^7 \cdot P_2^4$

10. Compute $\prod_{i=1}^{n} P_1^i$.

11. *a)* A telephone dial has holes numbered 0 to 9 inclusive. How many different seven-digit telephone numbers are possible where the first digit cannot be 0 or 1?

b) If the telephone dial had holes numbered 0 to 5 inclusive, how many digits long would each telephone number need to be in order to have at least as many possible numbers as in *a)*? (The same rule holding on the first digit.)

12. A man tries to choose the winner of each of 16 basketball games. Assuming no ties, how many different predictions are possible?

13. How many possible ways to select a "daily double" ticket if there are ten horses in the first race and 9 in the second? (The desire is to select the winner in both races.)

14. A photographer has at hand eleven photographic negatives. He wishes to select 5 and make in succession one print from each. In how many ways can this task be accomplished?

15. *a)* Evaluate $P_5^5 + P_3^5 + P_1^5$.

b) Solve for *x* if $P_6^x = 7P_2^x$.

c) Show that $P_r^n = nP_{r-1}^{n-1}$.

6.2 Combinations

The four Gibsons want a family portrait. They realize that one of them must man the simple box camera with which the picture is to be taken. Glenda (being a college girl) explains that there are many arrangements of the order in which the "chosen ones" can stand in front of the camera (from left to right, say). In fact she claims that the total number of possible arrangements is $P_3^4 = 24$. Gurney, being more experienced than Glenda, claims that the *order* in which the people are standing in the portrait is not of importance. The only thing of importance, he claims, is the people to be included. Glenda then applies her knowledge of set theory. She explains that Gurney is talking about the number of three element subsets of $\{1, \ldots, 4\}$, and that there are four such subsets. (Sometimes Gurney wonders why he sends Glenda to college, but at times like these, he realizes the value of an education.)

The importance of this example is that it points out the necessity of deciding whether one is trying to count the number of ordered *k*-tuples with

425

distinct components, or only the number of k-element subsets (in which the concept of order is absent). We know that P_r^n is the number of ordered arrangements of r things chosen from a universe of n elements. It is common to call the number of arrangements *not* taking order into account "the number of *combinations* of n things taken r at a time," and to denote this number by $\binom{n}{r}$ (or sometimes by C_r^n).

6.2-1 Definition: If A is a finite set with cardinality n and if $r \leq n$, then we denote by "$\binom{n}{r}$" the number of distinct subsets of A with r-elements.

6.2-2 Theorem: $\binom{n}{r} = \dfrac{P_r^n}{r!} = \dfrac{n!}{r!(n-r)!}$

Proof: We argue somewhat informally as follows: The formation of an ordered r-tuple with distinct components can be accomplished by first choosing the r elements to be included, then choosing the particular order of these r elements. Thus the total number of such ordered r-tuples (P_r^n) is the product of the number of ways of selecting the r elements, $\binom{n}{r}$, and the number of arrangements of these elements (P_r^r). That is,

$$P_r^n = \binom{n}{r} P_r^r.$$

Hence $\quad\quad \binom{n}{r} = P_r^n / P_r^r = \dfrac{n!}{(n-r)!} \cdot \dfrac{1}{r!}. \quad \square$

Example: A committee consisting of 3 people is to be formed in a club with a membership of 14 couples (a total membership of 28 people). How many committees are there?

$$\left(Answer: \binom{28}{3} = \frac{28!}{25!\,3!} = \frac{28 \cdot 27 \cdot 26}{6} \right)$$

How many committees are there with 2 men and 1 woman?

(Answer: The number of ways of selecting the men is $\binom{14}{2}$, and the number of ways of selecting the women is $\binom{14}{1}$, therefore the total number of ways of selecting the committee is $\binom{14}{2}\binom{14}{1} = \dfrac{14 \cdot 14 \cdot 13}{2}$.)

Remark: It is interesting to note that when one selects r objects from a universe of n elements, he leaves $n - r$ elements. It should then be true that the number of ways of "selecting" r elements is the same as the number of ways of "leaving" $n - r$ elements. That is,

$$\binom{n}{r} = \binom{n}{n-r}.$$

This is easily verified and is left as an exercise.

426

In determining the number of combinations of r things (unordered) taken from a set of n elements, we first determine the number of permutations (ordered) and then divide by the number of ways to order the objects which we desire to leave unordered. This idea can be extended and used to solve other problems as well.

Example: How many different ways can three men be dealt 5 card poker hands from a 52 card deck? We might analyze this in the following two ways.

1) The first man can get 5 from 52 cards, the second 5 from 47 and the third 5 from 42. Thus the total number of possible hands is $\binom{52}{5}\binom{47}{5}\binom{42}{5}$.

2) We now view the process as dealing 15 cards around and see that there are P_{15}^{52} ways to distribute the cards in this fashion provided each position is distinct. However, only some of the positions are considered to be distinct. If we divide by the number of ways a given man's hand can be arranged, we then have the number of unarranged possibilities. By doing this for each person we have

$$\frac{P_{15}^{52}}{5!\ 5!\ 5!}$$

which reduces to the expression derived in the first analysis. (Verify this.)

Question: In this example, have we taken into account the order in which the men are seated?

Total Number of Subsets Using Combinations

In view of the fact that $\binom{n}{r} = \dfrac{n!}{r!(n-r)!}$ is the number of subsets with r elements (from a set with n elements), we should be able to determine the total number of subsets by adding the numbers for all possible cases.

Example: Let $\#S = 4$.

The number of 4 element subsets of S is $\binom{4}{4}$, the number of 3 element subsets of S is $\binom{4}{3}$, etc. The total number of subsets of S should be

$$\binom{4}{4} + \binom{4}{3} + \binom{4}{2} + \binom{4}{1} + \binom{4}{0} = 1 + 4 + 6 + 4 + 1 = 16.$$

This corresponds with the previous information in that we expected to get $2^4 = 16$. The generalization of this fact is a special case of the *Binomial Theorem* which we look at in the next section.

6.2-3 Theorem: $\displaystyle\sum_{j=0}^{n} \binom{n}{j} = 2^n.$

Proof left as an exercise.

Perhaps it is worth mentioning again that $0! = 1$, from which $\binom{n}{0} = 1$ and $P_0^n = 1$.

Exercises 6.2

1. Show that $\binom{n}{r} = \binom{n}{n-r}$ as remarked earlier.

2. Show that $\binom{n+1}{r} = \binom{n}{r-1} + \binom{n}{r}$ for $1 \le r \le n$.

   (*Hint:* Expand both sides into quotients of factorials.)

3. *a*) In how many ways can two dice (one red, the other green) be tossed to give a total of 3? A total of 7? A total of 9?

   b) Which of the above totals is most likely to be thrown on a given toss of the dice?

4. *a*) With an ordinary deck of 52 cards, in how many ways can a 5 card hand be drawn? (*Hint:* A "hand" depends only upon the cards present, not upon the order in which they were dealt.)

   b) In how many ways can a hand be drawn which contains 4 aces?

   c) In how many ways can a hand be drawn which contains two aces?

   d) In how many ways can a "full house, queens over tens" be drawn (*i.e.*, the hand must contain three queens and two tens)?

5. Gurney Gibson has five shirts (two of which are indistinguishable), and two pairs of pants. In how many distinguishable ways can he dress?

6. *a*) Using the 26-letter alphabet, how many three letter "words" can be formed? (We are very liberal here, any three letters in a row form a word.)

   b) How many of the "words" in part *a*) have a letter used more than once? (*Hint:* Find the number without a repeated letter and subtract.)

7. *a*) The Eagle Beak baseball team is composed of ten men, most of whom are specialists (*i.e.*, can play only one position). However, the three men who play 1st, 2nd, and 3rd bases are quite versatile. One of them can play at 1st or at 3rd. Another can play at 1st or at 2nd. The third man can play any of the three positions. In how many ways can the team be assigned?

   b) Answer the above if every man on the team can play every position.

8. *a*) Suppose that in a collection of n objects, n_1 are of the same type, n_2 are of a second type, n_3 of a third type, etc., up to n_r objects of type r, where $\sum_{i=1}^{n} n_i = n$. Assuming that arrangements of objects in the collection are distinguishable only up

to the types of items, show that the total number of distinguishable arrangements
is $\dfrac{n!}{n_1!n_2!\ldots n_r!}$.

b) Explain why this reduces to $\dbinom{n}{n_1}$ if $r = 2$.

9. Prove Theorem 6.2-3.

10. *a)* Prove that $\forall n \in N, r \in \{0, \ldots, n\}, \dbinom{n}{r} \leq P_r^n$.

b) Under what conditions will the equality be assumed?

11. Consider the expression

$$(x + y)^6 = (x + y)(x + y)(x + y)(x + y)(x + y)(x + y).$$

In this product, one obtains 2^6 terms by selecting either the x or the y from each factor.

a) How many different ways can one select four x's and two y's?

b) What will the coefficient be on the x^4y^2 term after simplifying?

c) Why will this be the same as the coefficient on the x^2y^4 term?

12. Given a bowl with three white beads and two black beads. How many combinations of three beads are there of which one is black and two are white?

13. A student has three large books, six medium-sized books, and four small books.

a) In how many ways can they be arranged on a shelf so that all books of the same size are together?

b) In how many ways can they be arranged as in *a)* so the medium-sized group is between the large group and small group?

c) In how many ways can they be arranged if one insists also that the large books be on the left?

6.3   The Binomial Theorem

The functions $\dbinom{n}{r}$ are of great interest. An amazing number of identities and theorems have been (and are being) published in the mathematics journals concerning them. We shall limit ourselves here to a consideration of only a few such properties. The major aim of this section is the development of an important theorem concerning multiplication, the so-called "Binomial Theorem."

Consider what happens when we take the binomial expression $(a + b)$ to integral powers, 0, 1, 2, $\ldots$, etc. The first few expressions are:

$$(a + b)^0 = 1$$
$$(a + b)^1 = a + b$$
$$(a + b)^2 = a^2 + 2ab + b^2$$
$$(a + b)^3 = a^3 + 3a^2b + 3ab^2 + b$$
$$(a + b)^4 = a^4 + 4a^3b + 6a^2b^2 + 4ab^3 + b^4$$

By examining these expressions carefully, we make the following observations: For $n \in \{0, 1, 2, 3, 4\}$,

a) $(a + b)^n$ is the sum of $n + 1$ terms.

b) each term in this sum is of the form $k \cdot a^r b^{n-r}$, where $k \in N$, and $r \in \{0, \ldots, n\}$.

We wonder if this "pattern" remains as we take n larger and larger. Moreover, we wonder whether it is possible to give an explicit expression for the coefficient k involved. The affirmative answer to these questions is furnished by the Binomial Theorem.

6.3-1 Theorem: (Binomial Theorem) $\forall a, b \in \mathcal{C}$, $\forall n \in N_0$,

$$(a + b)^n = \sum_{j=0}^{n} \binom{n}{j} a^j b^{n-j}.$$

Example: If $n = 5$, $\sum_{j=0}^{5} \binom{5}{j} a^j b^{5-j}$

$$= \binom{5}{0} a^0 b^5 + \binom{5}{1} a^1 b^4 + \binom{5}{2} a^2 b^3 + \binom{5}{3} a^3 b^2 + \binom{5}{4} a^4 b^1 + \binom{5}{5} a^5 b^0$$

$$= b^5 + 5ab^4 + 10a^2b^3 + 10a^3b^2 + 5a^4b^1 + a^5 \text{ (verify this!).}$$

Of course, this is the same expression as that obtained by taking the product

$$(a + b)^4(a + b) = (a^4 + 4a^3b + 6a^2b^2 + 4ab^3 + b^4)(a + b)$$

in the usual "longhand multiplication" manner.

Proof (of Theorem *6.3-1*): We use mathematical induction on n.

i) If $n = 0$, then $\sum_{j=0}^{0} \binom{0}{j} a^j b^{0-j}$ consists of the single term $\binom{0}{0} a^0 b^0 = 1$. Hence

$$(a + b)^0 = \sum_{j=0}^{0} \binom{0}{j} a^j b^{0-j}.$$

(To avoid the assumption that $a + b \neq 0$, one should begin this induction at 1.)

ii) Suppose now that $(a + b)^k = \sum_{j=0}^{k} \binom{k}{j} a^j b^{k-j}$.

Now $(a + b)^{k+1} = (a + b)(a + b)^k = a(a + b)^k + b(a + b)^k$

$$= a\left(\sum_{j=0}^{k}\binom{k}{j} a^j b^{k-j}\right) + b\left(\sum_{j=0}^{k}\binom{k}{j} a^j b^{k-j}\right)$$

$$= \sum_{j=0}^{k}\binom{k}{j} a^{j+1} b^{k-j} + \sum_{j=0}^{k}\binom{k}{j} a^j b^{k-j+1}$$

$$= a^{k+1} + \sum_{j=0}^{k-1}\binom{k}{j} a^{j+1} b^{k-j} + \sum_{j=1}^{k}\binom{k}{j} a^j b^{k-j+1} + b^{k+1}.$$

(1)

The first summation in the expression can be written

$$\sum_{j=0}^{k-1}\binom{k}{j} a^{j+1} b^{k-j} = \sum_{j=1}^{k}\binom{k}{j-1} a^j b^{k-j+1} \tag{2}$$

since this involves only "relabeling" the index of summation, and leads to the addition of precisely the same terms. Thus expression (2) can be substituted into (1), which leaves us with

$$a^{k+1} + \sum_{j=1}^{k}\binom{k}{j-1} a^j b^{k-j+1} + \sum_{j=1}^{k}\binom{k}{j} a^j b^{k-j+1} + b^{k+1}$$

$$= a^{k+1} + \sum_{j=1}^{k}\left(\binom{k}{j-1} + \binom{k}{j}\right) a^j b^{k-j+1} + b^{k+1}$$

$$= a^{k+1} + \sum_{j=1}^{k}\binom{k+1}{j} a^j b^{k+1-j} + b^{k+1} \quad \text{(by Exercise 2, 6.2).}$$

But since $\binom{k+1}{0} = 1$ and $\binom{k+1}{k+1} = 1$, this expression reduces to

$$\sum_{j=0}^{k+1}\binom{k+1}{j} a^j b^{k+1-j}. \quad \square$$

Example: Show that

$$\sum_{j=0}^{n}(-1)^j\binom{n}{j} = \binom{n}{0} - \binom{n}{1} + \binom{n}{2} - \binom{n}{3} + \ldots = 0 \quad (n \neq 0).$$

Solution: $0 = (-1 + 1)^n = \sum_{j=0}^{n}\binom{n}{j}(-1)^j(1)^{n-j} = \sum_{j=0}^{n}(-1)^j\binom{n}{j}.$

Example: Find the term in $(4x^2 - 2y)^{12}$ which involves x^{14}.

Solution: Since $(4x^2 - 2y)^{12} = \sum_{j=0}^{12}\binom{12}{j}(4x^2)^j(-2y)^{12-j}$, we need only

find the value of j at which $x^{14} = (x^2)^7$ appears. Clearly this value is $j = 7$, so that the entire term involving x^{14} is

$$\binom{12}{7}(4x^2)^7(-2y)^5 = -\binom{12}{7}2^{19}y^5x^{14}.$$

It is interesting to compare the coefficients of the terms in $(a + b)^n$ for various n. This is conveniently done by construction of "Pascal's Triangle" as follows:

Expansion   *Coefficients of terms in expansion*

Expansion									
$(a + b)^0$					1				
$(a + b)^1$				1		1			
$(a + b)^2$			1		2		1		
$(a + b)^3$		1		3		3		1	
$(a + b)^4$	1		4		6		4		1

$(a + b)^5$ 1   5   10   10   5   1

$(a + b)^6$ 1   6   15   20   15   6   1

$(a + b)^7$ 1   7   21   35   35   21   7   1

$(a + b)^n$ $\binom{n}{0}$ $\binom{n}{1}$ $\binom{n}{2}$ - - - - - - - - - - - - - - - - - - $\binom{n}{n-1}$ $\binom{n}{n}$

Note that each row of coefficients is obtained from the one directly above it by adding the adjoining numbers in the top row, and placing one's on both ends. Thus, for example, the row of coefficients in $(a + b)^4$ is found from the row above it (the row of coefficients for $(a + b)^3$ as follows:

$(a + b)^3$ 1   3   3   1
                 add   add   add

$(a + b)^4$ 1   4   6   4   1

Of course, this involves the fact that

$$\binom{n-1}{j-1} \quad + \quad \binom{n-1}{j}$$
$$\text{add}$$

$$\binom{n}{j}$$

as you showed earlier in Exercise 2, 6.2.

From Pascal's triangle we can obtain some interesting relationships among the numbers $\binom{n}{r}$. Suppose, for example, that we add the numbers lying along the diagonals of Pascal's triangle.*

* See "A Generalization of the Connection Between the Fibonacci Sequence and Pascal's Triangle," Joseph A. Raab, Wisconsin State College, The Fibonacci Quarterly, volume 1, number 3, October 1963.

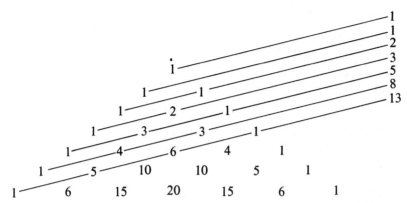

The resultant sequence $\{u_n\} = \{1, 1, 2, 3, 5, 8, 13, 21, 34, 55, \ldots\}$ is called the "Fibonacci sequence." Note that, for $n > 2$,

$$u_n = u_{n-1} + u_{n-2},$$

so that each term (after the first two) is obtained by adding the two preceding terms. The Fibonacci numbers are of great interest in mathematics. In fact, there is a mathematical journal, "The Fibonacci Quarterly," which is primarily devoted to the publication of number theoretic results related to these amazing numbers.

Exercises 6.3

1. Show that $\sum_{j=0}^{n} \binom{n}{j} = 2^n$. (*Hint:* $1 + 1 = 2$.)

2. Find the terms in $(x + 5)^{10}$ involving:
    a) x^{10} b) x^5 c) x^0

3. How many terms are in the expansion of $(9a - 5/7b)^{23}$?

4. Find $\left(\sum_{j=0}^{9} \binom{9}{j} x^j 2^{9-j} \right) \left(\sum_{k=0}^{12} \binom{12}{k} 2^k x^{12-k} \right)$. (*Hint:* Do it the "short" way!)

5. a) Suppose A is the set of the first 15 Fibonacci numbers, and P is the set of prime integers. Find $\#(A \cap P)$.
    b) Do you think there are infinitely many prime Fibonacci numbers?

6. Note that the Pascal triangle is symmetric about a vertical line passing down its "center." Explain why this is true, using the definition for the combination symbol $\binom{n}{r}$ and $\binom{n}{n-r}$.

7. Prove that $\sum_{j=0}^{n} \binom{n}{j} a^i b^{n-i} = \sum_{j=0}^{n} \binom{n}{j} b^j a^{n-i}$,

a) using only the Binomial Theorem.

b) using only Exercise 6 above.

8. Expand and simplify:

a) $(2x + 3y)^5$

b) $(x - y^2)^6$

c) $(-x^2 - 2y)^7$

d) $(3x + 4y^3)^5$

9. a) Determine the 15th line in Pascal's triangle.

b) Write a formula for a sequence which would give the 200th line in Pascal's triangle.

10. a) How many ways can one select a subset from $\{1, \ldots, 10\}$ which has either 4 members or 5 members?

b) How many ways can one select a subset of $\{1, \ldots, 20\}$ which has 6, 9, or 18 members?

c) How many ways can one select a subset from a set S whose cardinality is n, which has either p members or k members ($p \neq k$ and $p, k \in \{1, \ldots, n\}$)?

11. Given an urn with 10 black balls and an urn with 12 white balls, how many ways can one place either 4 black balls or 2 black balls in a first basket and 5 white balls or 3 white balls in a second basket?

12. Given seven coins, how many ways can they be arranged with either 4 heads or 2 heads showing?

6.4 Elementary Probability Notions

Mathematical Models

The basic idea of probability theory is to formulate mathematical models of phenomena which are observed to occur in the physical universe. That is, we wish to use a mathematical system (which in some sense is analogous to the particular physical process under consideration) to gain information about the process under investigation. The usefulness of formulating such a "mathematical model" depends upon many factors. However, if the model reflects "faithfully" in mathematical terms the attributes of the physical process involved, then we may be able to use mathematical methods in our model to arrive at conclusions about the model which also may be interpreted as conclusions about the physical process. The procedure of using a mathematical model can be schematically diagrammed as follows:

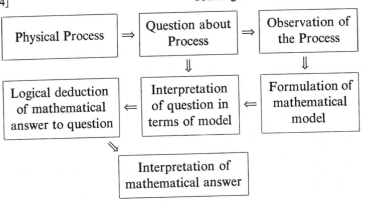

A good example of the use of models to "explain" observed phenomena is associated with the problem of accounting for observed planetary motion. An early model of our solar system, the Ptolemaic model, used the assumption that the earth was the center of the system. Planetary motion (and the motion of the sun) was interpreted by the use of circles, and circles within circles, etc. (Such orbits were called "epi-cycles.") This view was held by educated men for several centuries, until it was superseded by the familiar model of Copernicus, in which the sun is assumed to be the center of the solar system. The point of all this is that each model could be used to explain the observed motions of the planets, but in order to do so, the Ptolemaic system became very complicated, whereas the Copernican system remains relatively simple. Thus in adopting the Copernican system, we rule in favor of the simpler and more workable of these two alternate explanations of the observed "motion."

There are many cases in which several alternative models each have merits and drawbacks. Consider the case of explaining the observed phenomena associated with light. Two main models are called the "wave theory" and the "corpuscular theory" of light. Each model can be used to explain certain phenomena that the other cannot; hence no clear choice between the two can be made. Since each of the models is useful, each is used. To use one of the models is *not* to claim that light *is* actually of the particular form involved. Thus there is a very important distinction between a useful *model* of light and a claim as to what light actually *is*.

Probability and Sample Spaces

In probability theory we begin with a universal set called the *Sample Space*. We shall restrict our study to the case of finite sample spaces, although the theory can be extended to the infinite case. (It should be recalled that the

435

word "space" can be interpreted as meaning a set whose members satisfy certain conditions.) The physical phenomenon that we are attempting to model in probability is often called the "experiment." We may think of the following experiment as an example. The experiment consists of the toss of a certain coin. The outcome of a performance of this experiment is the side of the coin that shows "up"—that is, either "heads," "tails," or "edgies." (From a rigorous point of view, we shall adopt the word "experiment" as an undefined term.)

6.4-1 Definition: A *Sample Space S* for an experiment is a set with an element representing every possible outcome of the experiment.

For example, in the coin tossing example our sample space might be described by

$$S = \{H, T, E\}$$

where

H represents the outcome "heads"
T represents the outcome "tails"
E represents the outcome "edgies."

The sample space for an experiment is by no means unique. We usually try to choose one which will be simple, yet sufficiently sophisticated to yield a useful model. For example, we might be willing to take the sample space for the coin-tossing experiment to be $S = \{H, T\}$. In this case, we argue that deletion of the outcome "edgies" will not seriously affect the usefulness of our model. In fact (unless the coin is unusually thick), the deletion or inclusion of the outcome E will "not make much difference" one way or the other. The precise sense in which the deletion of E doesn't affect the model is that the probability results we would get would be nearly the same using either sample space. Thus, we feel that for an ordinary coin, we "probably" won't observe "edgies" anyway.

This brings us to another object in our model: the *probability function.* One of the first things we must emphasize is that the domain of a probability function is *not* the sample space, but rather a set of subsets of the sample space. Before we undertake a rigorous definition of the probability function and its domain, we make some observations concerning how most people intuitively expect probabilities to behave. In the first place, we usually talk about the "probability" that something will occur when the future performance of the experiment is observed. For example, we hear such phrases as "it will probably rain tomorrow" and "the probability that I will pass this course is almost zero." If we examine these statements closely, it appears that a numerical "index" is being assigned to something that may or may not happen in the future. Moreover, these numbers reflect the "likelihood" (in some sense) that the thing described will actually occur; numbers near 1 being used to indicate that it very likely will occur, while numbers near zero reflect a feeling that it most likely will not occur. In our probability model we shall see that the "things" whose likelihood of occurrence or non-occurrence is being indexed by the probabilities assigned are subsets of the sample space. Thus our model will involve the assignment of numerical images ("probabilities") to pre-images in a certain domain called the "event space."

In the coin tossing example, we may feel that a future performance of the experiment (a future toss of the coin) is equally likely to result in the outcome "H" as it is the outcome "T." Thus in the probability model used to describe this experiment, we may feel that the number 1/2 should be assigned to the event $\{H\}$ and also the event $\{T\}$. (Note that the events we speak of here are subsets of the sample space.)

Let us consider another simple example. Suppose the experiment consists of the toss of a single die, the outcome being considered to be the number of spots showing "up." In this case, an acceptable (but by no means the only) sample space would be

$$S = \{1, 2, 3, 4, 5, 6\}.$$

Suppose, moreover, that the die is "fair," so that we are equally likely to observe any of the six points in S upon a particular toss of the die. Then we assign probabilities 1/6 to the six elementary events $\{1\}, \{2\}, \ldots, \{6\}$. Note that inclusion of the ordered pair $(\{1\}, 1/6)$ in a probability function P would reflect ("model") our notion that the "chances of throwing a 1" on a toss of the die are "one in six." Suppose however, that we are not particularly interested in finding the probability of the six elementary events $\{1\}, \{2\}, \ldots, \{6\}$, but rather want to find the probabilities that

a) "an even number is tossed,"

and that

b) "the number thrown is greater than 3."

We see that in such cases we are describing pre-images made up of various subsets of S, subsets other than the simple singleton events $\{1\}, \{2\}, \ldots, \{6\}$. Thus the description in a) above defines the set

$$\{2, 4, 6\},$$

while that in b) describes

$$\{4, 5, 6\}.$$

It thus becomes apparent that assigning probabilities only to the singleton subsets of S will not suffice for the more interesting probability questions that we wish to answer. For this reason we insist on a more complete domain for our probability function.

6.4-2 Definition: An *event space* $\mathcal{E}$ for an experiment having finite sample space S is a set of subsets of S such that:

437

1) $S \in \mathcal{E}$

2) $A, B \in \mathcal{E} \Rightarrow A \cap B \in \mathcal{E}$

3) $A \in \mathcal{E} \Rightarrow \overline{A} = S - A \in \mathcal{E}$

The elements of $\mathcal{E}$ are called *events*.

Remark: Note that the three conditions in this definition can be stated alternately as

1) S is an event.

2) $\mathcal{E}$ is closed under intersections.

3) $\mathcal{E}$ is closed under complementation (with respect to S) (*i.e.*, the complement of an event is an event).

Example: For any experiment having a finite sample space S, it follows that

$$\{\phi, S\} \quad \text{and} \quad 2^S \text{ (the collection of all subsets of } S)$$

may be event spaces. (There are, in general, many possible choices of an event space.)

Example: For the die tossing example, an acceptable event space, from the point of view of the questions a) and b) that we want answered, would be the minimal extension of $\{\{2, 4, 6\}, \{4, 5, 6\}\}$ to an event space. You should verify in this case that the smallest event space containing $\{2, 4, 6\}$ and $\{4, 5, 6\}$ is

$$\begin{aligned}
\mathcal{E} = \{&\{2, 4, 6\}, \{4, 5, 6\}, \{2, 4, 5, 6\}, \{1, 3, 5\}, \\
&\{1, 3, 4, 5, 6\}, \{1, 2, 3, 4, 5, 6\}, \phi, \{1, 2, 3\}, \\
&\{1, 3\}, \{1, 2, 3, 4, 6\}, \{2\}, \{4, 6\}, \{5\}, \\
&\{2, 5\}, \{1, 3, 4, 6\}, \{1, 2, 3, 5\}\}.
\end{aligned}$$

For example, $\{4, 6\} \in \mathcal{E}$ since

$$\{2, 4, 6\} \quad \text{and} \quad \{4, 5, 6\} \Rightarrow \{2, 4, 6\} \cap \{4, 5, 6\} = \{4, 6\} \in \mathcal{E}.$$

But then $\overline{\{4, 6\}} = \{1, 2, 3, 5\} \in \mathcal{E}$. Also $\{1, 2, 3, 5\} \cap \{4, 5, 6\} = \{5\} \in \mathcal{E}$. Of course, the larger set 2^S would also serve as an event space for this experiment.

Example: Consider the experiment of letting two distinct coins fall. One might let the sample space be the following collection of ordered pairs.

$$S = \{(H, H), (H, T), (T, H), (T, T)\}.$$

The minimal event space containing the events $\{(H, H), (T, T)\}$ (the event that both coins fall heads or both fall tails) and $\{(H, T), (T, H)\}$ (the event that the coins fall differently) is

$$\mathcal{E} = \{\phi, S, \{(H, H), (T, T)\}, \{(H, T), (T, H)\}\}.$$

Question: What do you think should be the probability assigned to the event $\{(H, H), (T, T)\}$?

438

Now that we have established that the objects having probabilities are events, we can proceed with our investigation of the probability function itself. Note that in the die tossing example (with event space 2^S, say) we would assert that the probability of the event described in *a*) is $1/2$ since we feel that the chances are "50-50" that an even number is tossed. Thus we feel that $P(\{2, 4, 6\}) = 1/2$. Note that this ties in with our idea of assigning probability $1/6$ to each of the singleton events $\{2\}$, $\{4\}$, and $\{6\}$, since

$$P(\{2\}) + P(\{4\}) + P(\{6\}) = \frac{1}{6} + \frac{1}{6} + \frac{1}{6} = \frac{1}{2} = P(\{2, 4, 6\}). \qquad (1)$$

Also note that

$$P(\{2, 4, 6\}) = \frac{\#\{2, 4, 6\}}{\#S} = \frac{3}{6} = \frac{1}{2}$$

in this particular case. The reason that the probability of an even number being tossed is expressible as the ratio above is that each of the singleton events $\{1\}$, $\{2\}$, ..., $\{6\}$ in $\mathcal{E}$ is "equally probable," or "equally likely." We shall return to this idea shortly, but first let us see how the idea expressed in equation (1) can be represented in a general form. Note that (1) can be stated in the form

$$P(\{2, 4, 6\}) = P(\{2\} \cup \{4\} \cup \{6\}) = P(\{2\}) + P(\{4\}) + P(\{6\}).$$

This fact, together with the fact that the event S is the set of all possible outcomes, motivates the following definition.

6.4-3 Definition: A *probability function* for an experiment having finite sample space S and an event space $\mathcal{E}$ is a mapping $P: \mathcal{E} \to [0, 1]$ such that

    1) $P(S) = 1$,

and

    2) if $A_1, A_2, \ldots, A_k$ are disjoint events (*i.e.*, $A_i \cap A_j = \phi$ if $i \neq j$), then

$$P\left(\bigcup_{i=1}^{k} A_i \right) = \sum_{i=1}^{k} P(A_i) \qquad (additivity\ property).$$

Example: For the coin tossing experiment with a sample space $S = \{H, T\}$ and event space $2^S = \{\{H\}, \{T\}, \{H, T\}, \phi\}$, the probability function which reflects our notion that the coin is "fair" is the set

$$P = \left\{ \left(\{H\}, \frac{1}{2} \right), \left(\{T\}, \frac{1}{2} \right), (\{H, T\}, 1), (\phi, 0) \right\}.$$

If the coin is biased in some way, for example, if it is bent in such a way that the side having "H" is rounded, we might find that a more useful model would involve the probability function $P': \mathcal{E} \to [0, 1]$ such that $p'(\{H\}) = 1/3$ and $P'(\{T\}) = 2/3$.

In many elementary experiments we assume, as part of our model, that the singleton events are "equally likely." Of course, in order that

439

$\{a\} \in \mathcal{E}$ for each $a \in S$, it is necessary to have the event space $\mathcal{E} = 2^S$ (verify this!). In the remainder of this section, let us assume that the event space selected is 2^S. It follows that the probability of any event (any subset of S) can be found once the probabilities have been assigned to the singleton events. This is done using the "additivity property" of the probability function. Thus, if a, b, c are points of S, then the image of the event $\{a, b, c\}$ under P is expressed as

$$P(\{a\}) + P(\{b\}) + P(\{c\})$$

since $\{a\}$, $\{b\}$, and $\{c\}$ are pairwise disjoint, and

$$\{a\} \cup \{b\} \cup \{c\} = \{a, b, c\}.$$

Now if, in addition, we are willing to assume that the experiment is conducted in such a way that each of the singleton events is equally likely, then we must assign each the probability

$$P(\{a\}) = \frac{1}{\#S}.$$

That this is true is seen as follows: Suppose the elements are relabeled, for convenience, as $a_1, a_2, \ldots, a_n$, where $\#S = n$. Now each of the singleton events $\{a_i\}$ is supposed to have the same probability, say p. Thus

$$\forall i, \qquad P(\{a_i\}) = p.$$

Thus $\qquad 1 = P(S) = P\left(\bigcup_{i=1}^{n} \{a_i\}\right) = \sum_{i=1}^{n} P(\{a_i\}) = \sum_{i=1}^{n} p = np.$

Therefore $\qquad p = \dfrac{1}{n} = \dfrac{1}{\#S}$

as claimed.

Using a similar argument, we easily establish the following important and useful theorem.

6.4-4 Theorem: Suppose an experiment has a finite sample space S and the event space 2^S. Suppose moreover that each singleton event is equally likely. Then for any event $B \subset S$,

$$P(B) = \frac{\#B}{\#S}.$$

The proof is left as an exercise.

Example: Suppose the experiment consists of choosing at random a single card from a well shuffled deck of 52 cards. Find the probability that
a) the card is a 7.
b) the card is red.
c) the card is a red 7.

Solution: We feel that since the deck is "well shuffled," and the card is chosen "at random," the chosen card is equally likely to be any card in the deck. Thus each particular card has probability 1/52 of being chosen. Now

440

a) P (card is a 7) $= \dfrac{\text{\# ways of obtaining a 7}}{\text{\# ways of drawing a card}} = \dfrac{4}{52} = \dfrac{1}{13}.$

b) P (card is red) $= \dfrac{\text{\# red cards}}{\text{\# cards}} = \dfrac{26}{52} = \dfrac{1}{2}.$

c) P (card is a red 7) $= \dfrac{\text{\# red 7's}}{52} = \dfrac{2}{52} = \dfrac{1}{26}.$

We should note that the sample space for this experiment consists of 52 points of the type A-H, 2-S, Q-D, etc., where H means hearts, S spades, etc. Thus, for example, the event described by "the card is a red 7" is the *set*

$$\{7\text{-}H, 7\text{-}D\}$$

so that in part c) above we actually calculate

$$P(\{7\text{-}H, 7\text{-}D\}) = \frac{\#\{7\text{-}H, 7\text{-}D\}}{\#S} = \frac{2}{52}.$$

Example: Suppose a poker hand (5 cards) is drawn from a well shuffled deck. What is the probability of getting 3 aces and 2 queens?

Solution: Note that the sample spaces consist of all "possible hands." More precisely, S contains points of the form

$$\{A\text{-}D, 2\text{-}H, 3\text{-}H, Q\text{-}S, Q\text{-}C\}.$$

(Note that *order* within a hand is not considered. Why?) The event E described as "3 aces and 2 queens" contains several points. For example,

$$\{A\text{-}D, A\text{-}C, A\text{-}H, Q\text{-}S, Q\text{-}H\} \in E.$$

How many "hands" are there in E? We use the counting principles developed earlier to conclude that

$$E = (\text{ways of drawing 3 aces})(\text{\# ways of drawing 2 queens})$$

$$= \binom{4}{3} \cdot \binom{4}{2}.$$

Note that $$\#S = \binom{52}{5}.$$

Thus $$P(E) = \frac{\#E}{\#S} = \frac{\binom{4}{3}\binom{4}{2}}{\binom{52}{5}}.$$

Some initial confusion can occur in the example if one is not clear on the following two points.

  i) the elements (points) of S are sets (5 card hands).
  ii) the elements of $\mathcal{E}$ are families of sets (collections of 5 card hands).

  Let us conclude this section with a theorem concerning probability functions.

6.4-5 *Theorem:* If P is a probability function and A and B are elements (sets) in the event space, then

$$P(A \cup B) = P(A) + P(B - A).$$

(B-A is an event. See Problem 3.)

Proof: $P(A \cup B) = P(A \cup (B - A))$ (since $A \cup B = A \cup (B - A)$)

$\qquad\qquad\quad = P(A) + P(B - A)$ (since $A \cap (B - A) = \phi$). □

Corollary: $P(A \cup B) = P(A) + P(B) - P(A \cap B).$

Proof: $P(A \cup B) = P((A - B) \cup (B - A) \cup (A \cap B))$ (Why?)

$\qquad\qquad\quad = P(A - B) + P(B - A) + P(A \cap B)$ (Why?)

$\qquad\qquad\quad = P(A \cup B) - P(B) + P(A \cup B) - P(A) + P(A \cap B)$

$\qquad\qquad\qquad\qquad\qquad\qquad\qquad\qquad\qquad\qquad$ (by the theorem).

Upon solving for $P(A \cup B)$ we have the desired result. □

Exercises 6.4

1. Describe a suitable sample space for the experiment of "tossing" four coins: a penny, a nickle, a dime, and a half dollar.

2. Let $S = \{1, 2, 3, 4, 5\}$. Determine the minimal event space which includes the events:

   a) $\{1, 2\}$ and $\{2, 4\}$

   b) ϕ, $\{3, 4\}$, and $\{3, 4, 1\}$

   c) $\{1, 2, 3\}$ and $\{4\}$

3. Show that if $\mathcal{E}$ is an event space then

   a) $\phi \in \mathcal{E}$.

   b) $A, B \in \mathcal{E} \Rightarrow A - B \in \mathcal{E}$.

   c) $A, B \in \mathcal{E} \Rightarrow A \cup B \in \mathcal{E}$. (*Hint:* Use De Morgan's Laws.)

4. In the "poker hand" example, what is the probability of drawing a hand with

   a) no aces?

   b) exactly one ace?

   c) exactly two aces?

   d) exactly three aces?

   e) four aces?

   f) more than two aces?

Why should the probabilities found in *a)–e)* add to 1?

5. An urn contains 4 white balls, 2 red balls, 5 green balls. Two balls are drawn at random from the urn. What is the probability that the balls

   a) are both red?

   b) are of different colors?

    c) are both of the same color?

    d) have at least one white?

    e) have exactly one white?

Describe the event space $\mathcal{E}$ for the experiment.

6. Prove Theorem 6.4-4.

7. A shipment consists of ten good articles, four articles with minor defects, and two with major defects. One is drawn at random. Find the probability that it

    a) has no defect.

    b) has no major defect.

    c) is either good or has a major defect.

8. Let the sample space S for an experiment of tossing three distinct coins be the set $S = \{H, T\} \times \{H, T\} \times \{H, T\}$. Describe the subset of 2^S (event) which represents the event described by

    a) all three coins heads.

    b) the first coin heads and the other two tails.

    c) the first coin heads or the other two tails.

    d) at least one head.

Determine the probability of each event (under the assumption that singleton events are equally likely).

9. Consider the experiment consisting of tossing three indistinguishable coins.

    a) Would it be possible to use the following sample space:

$$S = \{(H, H, H), (T, T, T), (H, T, T), (T, H, H)\}\,?$$

    b) What, if any, would be the disadvantages of using this sample space?

10. Let P be a probability function. Show that:

    a) $P(\phi) = 0$

    b) $P(\overline{A}) = 1 - P(A)$

    c) $A \subset B \Rightarrow P(B - A) = P(B) - P(A)$

    d) $A \subset B \Rightarrow P(A) \leq P(B)$

11. Let $\{A_i : i \in \{1, \ldots, n\}\}$ be a partition of S, and assume

$$\forall i \in \{1, \ldots, n\}, \qquad A_i \in \mathcal{E}.$$

    a) Show that $P(A_1) + P(A_2) + \ldots + P(A_n) = 1$.

    b) Show that $\forall B \in \mathcal{E}, P(B) = \sum_{i=1}^{n} P(B \cap A_i)$.

12. Consider the experiment of throwing a regular die. Take $\mathcal{E}$ to be the minimal extension of $\{\{1, 2\}, \{3, 4\}, \{5, 6\}\}$ to an event space.

    a) Describe S by a list.

    b) Describe $\mathcal{E}$ by a list.

    c) Make a satisfactory probability assignment.

13. How many distinct ways are there to form an event space in the die example?

14. a) Prove that if $\#(S) = k$, where $k \in N$, then 2^S satisfies the conditions for an event space.

b) Prove that the "smallest" class satisfying the conditions for an event space is $\{\phi, S\}$.

Note: Show two things: $\{\phi, S\}$ does satisfy the conditions, and the $\{\phi, S\} \subset \mathcal{E}$ for any event space $\mathcal{E}$.

15. Investigate (prove or disprove): If $\mathcal{E}$ is an event space and A and B are events and P a probability function, then

a) $A \triangle B \in \mathcal{E}$ $(A \triangle B = (A - B) \cup (B - A))$.

b) $P(A \triangle B) = P(A) + P(B)$.

c) $P(A \triangle B) = P(A) - P(B)$.

16. Investigate (prove or disprove):

a) $P(A) = 0 \Rightarrow A = \phi$

b) $P(A) = 1 \Rightarrow A = S$

17. Six fair coins are tossed. Suppose that the outcome of the experiment is considered to be the number of heads thrown.

a) List an acceptable sample space S for this experiment.

b) Suppose the event space is 2^S. How many singleton events are there?

c) Are the singleton events in $\mathcal{E}$ equally likely? If not, find their individual probabilities.

d) Find the probability that a prime number is observed.

e) Compare the probabilities of the singleton events with the terms in the binomial expansion of $(1/2 + 1/2)^6$.

6.5 Probability Applications

Much of the early work in probability theory grew out of questions about gambling devices and games. Although the theory has more widespread uses today, it is helpful at the elementary level to consider various questions which involve at least the spirit of gambling.

Example: Grant Gibson and his father Gurney have developed the following game that they play. Each night just before supper, Gurney carelessly tosses three one-cent coins onto the table while Grant is in the washroom. If there are at least two heads showing, he places a cup over one coin leaving two heads showing. If there are not at least two heads showing, he tosses them again, etc., until at least two heads show. When Grant comes in, he guesses whether the coin under the cup shows heads or tails. If he guesses correctly, he keeps the three cents, otherwise he pays his father a nickel. Grant is very superstitious and always calls tails. Who do you suppose is winning at this game?

Grant plays a similar game with his sister Glenda. Each night after supper he takes three one-cent coins and tosses first one, then another, until two heads have shown. Glenda then guesses the outcome of the third coin while it is in the air. If she is correct, she keeps the three cents, otherwise she pays Grant a nickel. Glenda has the same superstitions as her brother and always calls tails. Who is winning this game?

We shall not answer these questions directly, since to do so would be stealing some of your fun. Instead, let us explore some more elementary probability theory with the hope that you soon will be able to decide the probable answer.

Assigning a Sample Space

One of the first things one must do in assaulting a probability problem is to determine the sample space he is using. In general there are several sample spaces one can use for any given problem; however, it is often most convenient to choose a sample space for which the singleton events in the event space are assigned equal probabilities (*i.e.*, $P(\{a\}) = \dfrac{1}{\#S}$ for all $a \in S$).

Recall, that in such cases one can apply Theorem 6.4-4.

Example: In the experiment of tossing two indistinguishable coins, it would be possible to use the sample space $S = \{H, T, D\}$ where we use H to denote the outcome in which both coins fall heads, T for both tails, and D for the coins being different. We would not, however, wish to assign the probability $1/3$ to each of these outcomes. (Why?) Perhaps the space

$$S' = \{(H, H), (T, T), (H, T), (T, H)\}$$

would be more useful, in that we feel that singleton events

$$\{(H, H)\}, \qquad \{(T, T)\}, \qquad \{(H, T)\}, \qquad \text{and} \qquad \{(T, H)\}$$

should be assigned the same probability measure.

Question: In this example, what probabilities should be assigned to the singleton events if one were to use the same space S?

Compounding Experiments

Many experiments can be considered to be a sequence of simpler experiments. For example, consider an experiment in which one tosses a coin and a regular die. One can view this as first tossing the coin and then tossing the die, or vice-versa. An acceptable sample space for the coin tossing experiment along is $S_1 = \{H, T\}$ and one for the die experiment is $S_2 = \{1, 2, 3, 4, 5, 6\}$. In both cases, the singleton events in the event space 2^{S_i} will have equal probabilities. That is,

$$P_1(\{H\}) = P_1(\{T\}) = \frac{1}{2}$$

445

and

$$P_2(\{1\}) = P_2(\{2\}) = \ldots = P_2(\{6\}) = \frac{1}{6}.$$

An acceptable sample space for the combined experiment is $S = S_1 \times S_2$ and each singleton event can be viewed as equally probable with probability $1/12 = 1/2 \cdot 1/6$.

Example: In the coin, die experiment discussed above, what is the probability that a head will show along with a 1 or a 6? The event which we have described is

$$E = \{(H, 1), (H, 6)\}$$

hence $\qquad\qquad P(E) = \frac{\#E}{\#S} = \frac{2}{12} = \frac{1}{6}.$

Notice that this can be answered in terms of probabilities in the two elementary probability functions P_1 and P_2. That is,

$$P_1(\{H\}) = \frac{1}{2} \qquad P_2(\{1, 6\}) = \frac{2}{6} = \frac{1}{3}$$

$$P(E) = P_1(\{H\}) \cdot P_2(\{1, 6\}) = \frac{1}{2} \cdot \frac{1}{3} = \frac{1}{6}.$$

One could also express this as

$$P(\{H\} \times \{1, 6\}) = P_1(\{H\}) \cdot P_2(\{1, 6\}).$$

Example: Consider the experiment of drawing two cards from a regular deck and rolling a regular die. What is the probability of ending with at least one queen and a 2 or a 3?

Solution: Let the sample space S_1 for the card drawing experiment be the set of all two card hands. $\left(\#S_1 = \binom{52}{2}. \right)$ Let the sample space for the die tossing experiment be $S_2 = \{1, 2, 3, 4, 5, 6\}$. The event of drawing at least one queen is the set of two card hands E_1 with at least one queen: ($\#E_1 = 6 + 4 \cdot 48$). The event of ending with a 2 or 3 on the die is the set $E_2 = \{2, 3\}$. The event we are interested in is the set

$$E_1 \times E_2 \subset S_1 \times S_2.$$

Let us first compute the probability, using Theorem 6.4-4, on the sample space $S_1 \times S_2$.

$$P(E_1 \times E_2) = \frac{\#(E_1 \times E_2)}{\#(S_1 \times S_2)} = \frac{198 \cdot 2}{\binom{52}{2} \cdot 6}$$

446

If we use this theorem on the two spaces S_1 and S_2, we notice that

$$P(E_1 \times E_2) = P_1(E_1) \cdot P_2(E_2)$$

$$= \frac{198}{\binom{52}{2}} \cdot \frac{2}{6}.$$

Expectation

In viewing a probability problem from a gambler's point of view, we might pose the following question: If a particular outcome of a game pays two dollars and has probability p, how much can one wager and break even with the house? We realize, of course, that we cannot necessarily expect to win, lose, or break even on any given try, but if viewed over a long period of time, we wish to break even. If $p = 1/6$, then one would expect to win (on the average) every 6th try. Hence, one should be willing to risk $1/6 \cdot 2 = 1/3$ dollar on each play.

6.5-1 Definition: If the probability of an event is p and if the value M is assigned to the event, then the amount pM is called the mathematical expectation of the event.

The mathematical expectation of an event is the amount one should be able to risk and not lose or win (in the long run).

Example: An event has probability $p = 1/3$ and pays a winner \$5. It costs \$1.75 to play the game. How will a player fare at this game? The expected value is $(1/3)$ \$5 $\cong$ \$1.67. Hence, a player loses, on the average, 8¢ a play.

Example: How much should one be willing to pay to play the following game? Three coins and two dice are tossed. The event in which exactly two coins are the same and the dice total 7 pays \$10. We need to compute the probability of this event. The probability that two coins are the same is $1 - 1/4$ (since the probability that all three are the same is $1/8 + 1/8$). The probability that the dice total 7 is $1/6$, hence the probability of the event is $3/4 \times 1/6 = 1/8$. The expectation is $1/8 \times$ \$10 $=$ \$1.25.

Exercises 6.5

1. What is the probability that not all coins show alike when four coins fall at random? (*Hint:* Compute the probability of the complementary event and use the fact that $P(A) = 1 - P(\overline{A})$.)

447

2. What is the probability that the toss of two coins and a die will yield
   a) two heads and a 6?
   b) at least one head and a 6?
   c) exactly one head and a number less than 5?
   d) both coins the same and a number over 2?

3. What would be a fair bet against $10 that two persons picked at random will not have birthdays in the same month, assuming that all months are equally likely?

4. Describe the outcome of Grant Gibson's betting with his father and his sister.

5. Five coins and two dice are tossed. What is the probability that the result is
   a) exactly three heads and a total of 8?
   b) exactly two heads and a total of 6?
   c) less than three heads and a total under 7?
   d) five heads and a total of 12?
   e) all coins alike and a total of 2 or 12?
   f) some coins alike and a total of 1?

6. a) How much should you pay to play a game in which four coins are tossed and you receive $1 for each head showing?
   b) Same as a) with five coins?

7. a) A given family has three children, two of whom are girls. What is the probability that the other child is a boy?
   b) A given family has three children and the youngest two are girls. What is the probability that the third child is a boy?

8. We have observed that a probability model is composed of three objects: two sets and an assignment of numbers (a probability function). It is convenient to describe a particular model quickly by writing these objects $(S, \mathcal{E}, P)$. When this is done, the ordered triple is usually called the "*probability space* for the experiment under consideration. Recall that the components of $(S, \mathcal{E}, P)$ must satisfy certain conditions, and by calling the triple a probability space we imply that the various conditions imposed on each component are satisfied.

Investigate (prove or disprove):
Let $(S_1, \mathcal{E}_1, P_1)$ and $(S_2, \mathcal{E}_2, P_2)$ be probability spaces.
Let $S = S_1 \times S_2$, $\mathcal{E} = \{A \times B : A \in \mathcal{E}_1, B \in \mathcal{E}_2\}$ and let P be defined on $\mathcal{E}$ by

$$P(A \times B) = P_1(A)P_2(B).$$

Then $(S, \mathcal{E}, P)$ is a probability space.

9. What is the expectation of an event that pays M and has probability p where
   a) $M = \$20$ and $p = 1/7$.
   b) $M = \$19$ and $p = 5/8$.
   c) $M = \$30$ and $p = 1$.

10. a) A lamp has three independent sockets. Of 11 bulbs, four are no good. If three bulbs are selected at random, what is the probability that there will be some light?
    b) What is the expectation if the reward for bringing light is $20?

    c) What is the expectation if the reward for having two or more lights on is $50 (with nothing for only one)?

    d) Same as *c*) but with a $10 reward for only one light.

11. Four cards are drawn from a regular deck.

    a) What is the probability that there will be at least three hearts?

    b) Exactly three hearts?

7

THE CIRCULAR
FUNCTIONS

7.1 The Sine and Cosine

In this section we shall introduce the circular trigonometric functions and some of their properties. It is difficult to give a completely rigorous and logically sound definition of the trigonometric functions; moreover, this would completely eclipse any reason for calling them circular functions. Therefore we begin with intuitive geometrical definitions, concentrating first on the cosine and sine functions.

Consider the unit circle C in $\mathcal{C}$ defined by

$$C = \{x + iy : x^2 + y^2 = 1\}.$$

It is well known that the circumference (the distance measured along the outside of C) is 2π. Now let us define a function

$$T: [0, 2\pi) \to C$$

by assigning to each number $r \in [0, 2\pi)$ the point $x + iy$ which lies on the unit circle the distance r from $1 + 0i$ measured counterclockwise along the unit circle. (See Figure 7.1.) Since the circumference of this circle is 2π, it is clear that T is a *one-one* function from $[0, 2\pi)$ *onto* C.

Now let us extend the domain of T to include all real numbers by use of the Euclidean property. Recall that, given t, there is a unique integer n and a unique real number $r \in [0, 2\pi)$ such that $t = n \cdot 2\pi + r$.

7.7-1 Definition: $\forall t \in R \quad T(t) = T(r)$, where $t = n \cdot 2\pi + r$ for $r \in [0, 2\pi)$ and $n \in Z$.

Remark: $T(t + 2\pi) = T(t) \quad \forall t \in R$, which immediately extends to

$$T(t + n \cdot 2\pi) = T(t)$$

by induction. Note then that T is periodic. Does T have a period?

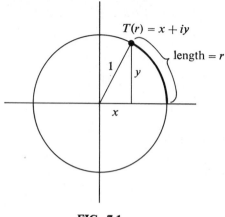

FIG. 7.1

What we have done is to extend T to include, in its domain, all reals by an "extension by periodicity."

Roughly speaking, one can view this T (trig) function as "wrapping" the real line around the unit circle somewhat like thread on a spool. The 0 on the line is placed at the point $1 + 0i = 1$ on the unit circle and then the positive part of the line wrapped counterclockwise about C and the negative part wrapped clockwise about C. (See Figure 7.2.)

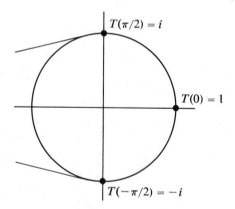

FIG. 7.2

Let us now use some simple symmetry to arrive at some useful facts concerning the trig function (or wrapping function) T. First, let us list a few obvious values for T.

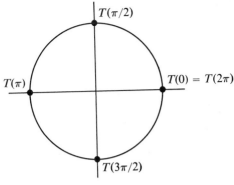

FIG. 7.3

We see in Figure 7.3 that

$$T(0) = 1 \quad T(\pi/2) = i \quad T(\pi) = -1 \quad T(3\pi/2) = -i$$

and $\qquad T(-\pi/2) = T(2\pi - \pi/2) = T(3\pi/2) = -i.$

Similarly

$$T(-\pi) = -1, \quad T(-3\pi/2) = i, \quad T(2\pi) = T(-2\pi) = T(0) = 1.$$

Now let $T(t) = a + bi$ and observe the effect on the values of T if we shift by an amount π.

For example, consider the diagram in Figure 7.4.

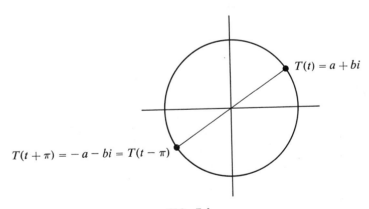

FIG. 7.4

The distance π measured on C is exactly half way around. This analysis is independent of the particular position on the circle chosen. We see in general then that

$$\forall t \in R \quad T(t + \pi) = -T(t) = T(t - \pi).$$

453

Let us consider also what happens if we shift by an amount $\pi/2$. Figure 7.5 represents two special cases from which we can easily see the general relationship.

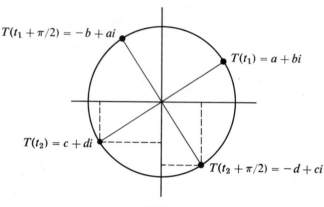

FIG. 7.5

We observe that $\forall t$ if $T(t) = a + bi$, then $T(t + \pi/2) = -b + ai$, or equivalently

$$\forall t \qquad T(t + \pi/2) = iT(t).$$

Remark: We can derive the previous identity from this one as follows

$$T(t + \pi) = T(t + \pi/2 + \pi/2) = iT(t + \pi/2)$$
$$= i(iT(t)) = -T(t).$$

We can now easily determine an identity for $T(t - \pi/2)$.

$$T(t - \pi/2) = -T(t - \pi/2 + \pi) = -T(t + \pi/2)$$
$$= -iT(t)$$

That is, if $\qquad\qquad T(t) = a + bi,$

then $\qquad\qquad T(t - \pi/2) = b - ai.$

Let us now determine some trig values for some other numbers. For example, $T(\pi/4)$ lies along the circle half way between $T(0)$ and $T(\pi/2)$. (See Figure 7.6.)

We have, then, that

$$T(\pi/4) = a + bi \qquad \text{where} \qquad a = b \qquad \text{and} \qquad a^2 + b^2 = 1.$$

(Why?) It follows that

$$a = b = \frac{1}{\sqrt{2}} = \frac{\sqrt{2}}{2}.$$

Hence we have

$$T(\pi/4) = \frac{\sqrt{2}}{2} + \frac{\sqrt{2}}{2}i.$$

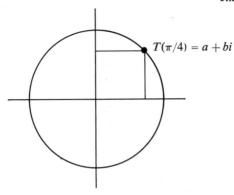

FIG. 7.6

Let us note here that if we knew all values of T for numbers between 0 and $\pi/2$, then we would essentially have a complete list of values since

$$T(t + \pi/2) = iT(t)$$

from which it follows that

$$T(t + \pi) = -T(t).$$

Thus $\quad T(t + 3\pi/2) = -iT(t) \quad$ and $\quad T(t + 2\pi) = T(t)$, etc.

Let us determine geometrically some values of T for other real numbers in $[0, \pi/2)$. For example, let us determine $T(\pi/3) = T\left(\dfrac{2}{3}\dfrac{\pi}{2}\right)$. (See Figure 7.7.)

Cutting the "first quarter of C" into three equal pieces we see that

$$T(\pi/3) = a + bi \quad \text{where} \quad a^2 + b^2 = 1 \quad \text{and} \quad a = \frac{1}{2}.$$

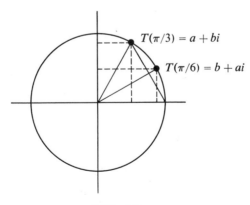

FIG. 7.7

(Why? *Hint:* Examine the equilateral triangle formed by the points 0, 1 and $T(\pi/3)$.) Hence

$$T(\pi/3) = \frac{1}{2} + \sqrt{\frac{3}{4}}\, i = \frac{1}{2} + \frac{\sqrt{3}}{2}\, i.$$

It is then immediate that

$$T(\pi/6) = \frac{\sqrt{3}}{2} + \frac{1}{2}\, i.$$

Example: Locate (approximately) on the unit circle:

 a) $T(4)$ *b)* $T(5.2)$ *c)* $T(-3)$

a) $4 = 3.14 + .86$ and hence $T(4)$ is in the third quadrant slightly more than half way toward the 4th quadrant.

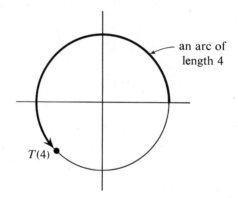

FIG. 7.8

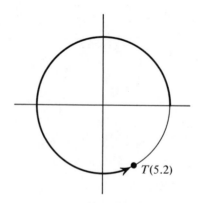

FIG. 7.9

b) Upon solving $5.2 = 2\pi x$ we have

$$x = \frac{5.2}{2\pi} \cong \frac{5.2}{6.28} \cong .83.$$

That is, $T(5.2)$ is located at $83/100$ of a complete revolution around the circle (counterclockwise). (See Figure 7.9.)

c) $3 = 3.14 - .14$ and hence $T(-3)$ is located slightly less than a half revolution (in the clockwise direction) about the unit circle. (See Figure 7.10.)

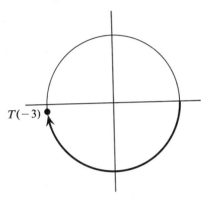

FIG. 7.10

Sine* and Cosine

We are now ready to define the two basic trigonometric functions sine and cosine whose values are determined by the real and imaginary components of the trig functions.

Remark: Throughout this text we shall use the notation "sine" to indicate the name of the function and "sin *x*" to indicate the value of the function at *x*, and similarly for "cosine" and "cos *x*." Although this is unnecessary, it may clarify (in certain instances) whether we are equating (or adding) *functions*, or *numbers*.

7.1-2 Definition: $\forall t \in R \cos t = x$ and $\sin t = y$ where $T(t) = x + iy$. That is,

$$T(t) = \cos t + i \sin t.$$

The first obvious identity we observe is that

$$\text{sine}^2 + \text{cosine}^2 = 1_f.$$

* For a historical account of the word "sine" and a historical discussion of trigonometry see "Episodes from the Early History of Mathematics" by Asger Aaboe; Random House.

That is,

$$\forall t, \quad \sin^2 t + \cos^2 t = 1. \quad \text{(Explain!)}$$

Let us now examine some values for these two functions from R to R, and sketch their graphs. Note in particular that sine and cosine are periodic functions whose periods are no greater than 2π. (Why?) Keeping in mind that $T(t) = \cos t + i \sin t$, we have the following values:

$$T(0) = 1 + 0i = \cos 0 + i \sin 0.$$

Therefore $\cos 0 = 1$ and $\sin 0 = 0$.

$$T(\pi/6) = \frac{\sqrt{3}}{2} + \frac{1}{2} i = \cos \frac{\pi}{6} + i \sin \frac{\pi}{6}.$$

Therefore $\cos \dfrac{\pi}{6} = \dfrac{\sqrt{3}}{2}$ and $\sin \dfrac{\pi}{6} = \dfrac{1}{2}$.

Similarly, we have

$$\cos \frac{\pi}{4} = \frac{\sqrt{2}}{2} \quad \text{and} \quad \sin \frac{\pi}{4} = \frac{\sqrt{2}}{2}$$

$$\cos \frac{\pi}{3} = \frac{1}{2} \quad \text{and} \quad \sin \frac{\pi}{3} = \frac{\sqrt{3}}{2}.$$

Question: What is the largest value that $\sin t$ can assume for any $t \in R$? By following the sine and cosine values as we trace $T(t)$ around the unit circle, we arrive at the following graphs for sine and cosine over $[0, 2\pi)$. (See Figure 7.11.)

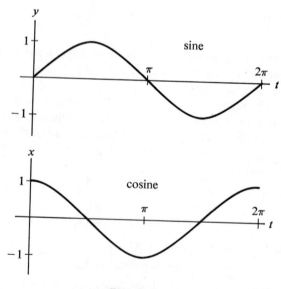

FIG. 7.11

Since we know that sine and cosine are periodic by making appropriate extensions of the functions graphed above, we immediately have the whole picture. (See Figures 7.12 and 7.13.)

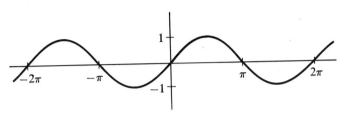

FIG. 7.12

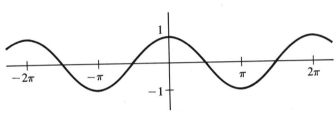

FIG. 7.13

Sine and Cosine Shifts (Translation Formulas)

Since sine and cosine are defined directly in terms of the trig function T, it follows that all values of $\sin t$ and $\cos t$ can be determined by knowing only the values for $t \in [0, \pi/2)$. Let us then derive some useful identities which are a direct result of the fact that $T(t + \pi/2) = iT(t)$.

7.1-3 Theorem: $\cos(t + \pi/2) = -\sin t$ and $\sin(t + \pi/2) = \cos t$.

Proof: $T(t + \pi/2) = iT(t)$. Therefore

$$\cos(t + \pi/2) + i \sin(t + \pi/2) = i(\cos t + i \sin t)$$
$$= -\sin t + i \cos t.$$

Therefore $\cos(t + \pi/2) = -\sin t$

and $\sin(t + \pi/2) = \cos t$

since two complex numbers $a + bi$ and $c + di$ are equal only if their respective components are equal. □

We include in the appendix a partial table of values for sine and cosine

459

in the interval $[0, \pi/2)$ (Table IV). To find values for numbers in $[\pi/4, \pi/2)$ one must read the table from the bottom upwards. We later show why it is possible to construct the table in this fashion.

Exercises 7.1

1. Using Table IV and the translation formulas find (approximate π by 3.14):
   a) sin .35
   b) cos 1.15
   c) sin $(\pi + .25)$
   d) cos $(\pi - 3.5)$
   e) sin 3.29
   f) cos 10.59
   g) sin -14.78
   h) cos -16.85

2. Use Table IV and the translation formulas to approximate the following:
   a) sin (1000)
   b) cos (2001)
   c) sin (160.3)
   d) cos (-236)
   e) sin (-27)
   f) cos (64.3)

3. Locate on the unit circle (approximately) the points:
   a) $T(648)$
   b) $T(27\pi)$
   c) $T(27\pi - 4)$
   d) $T(-64)$
   e) $T(-14.1)$
   f) $T(261)$

4. Show that if $T(t) = a + bi$, then $T(-t) = a - bi$.

5. From the definition of sine and cosine, using symmetry on the unit circle, argue that
   a) cos $(-t) = $ cos t for all $t \in R$.
   b) sin $(-t) = -$sin t for all $t \in R$.
(*I.e.*, cosine is an even function and sine is an odd function.)

6. Solve the following equations:
   a) cos $t = 1/2$
   b) cos $t = 0$
   c) sin $x = 3$
   d) .2 sin $x - 1 = 0$
   e) 2 cos $x + 1 = 0$
   f) 2 sin $x + 3 = 0$
   g) sin² $x = 1$
   h) cos $x = -2$
   i) 2 cos² $x = 1$
   j) cos $x = -.8255$
   k) sin $x = .4823$
   l) sin $x = -.8526$
   m) cos $x = .9224$
   n) sin $x = .4318$

7. Complete the following table.

t	0	$\dfrac{\pi}{6}$	$\dfrac{\pi}{4}$	$\dfrac{\pi}{3}$	$\dfrac{\pi}{2}$	$\dfrac{2\pi}{3}$	$\dfrac{3\pi}{4}$	$\dfrac{5\pi}{6}$	π	$\dfrac{7\pi}{6}$	$\dfrac{5\pi}{4}$	$\dfrac{3\pi}{2}$	$\dfrac{5\pi}{3}$	$\dfrac{7\pi}{4}$	$\dfrac{11\pi}{6}$	2π
$T(t)$																
cos t																
sin t																

8. Determine the following:

a) $T\left(\dfrac{9\pi}{4}\right)$ d) $T\left(\dfrac{28\pi}{3}\right)$ g) $T\left(\dfrac{15\pi}{2}\right)$

b) $T\left(-\dfrac{13\pi}{6}\right)$ e) $T\left(-\dfrac{7\pi}{6}\right)$ h) $T(-19\pi)$

c) $T\left(-\dfrac{3\pi}{4}\right)$ f) $T(85\pi)$

9. Knowing that π is approximately 3.14, determine which quadrant each of the following points is in.

a) $T(1)$ e) $T(3)$ i) $\cos 9 + i \sin 9$

b) $T(3.6)$ f) $T(-3.7)$ j) $\cos 4 + i \sin 4$

c) $T\left(-\dfrac{31}{3}\right)$ g) $T(7)$ k) $\cos(-14) + i \sin(-14)$

d) $T(5)$ h) $\cos 2 + i \sin 2$

10. With your eyes shut, graph cosine and sine.

7.2 The Addition Formulas and Values of Sine and Cosine for Multiples and Fractions of t

Using the fact that sine is an odd function and cosine is an even function (see Exercise 5 in previous section) along with the following basic theorem, we can establish many useful identities concerning sine and cosine.

7.2-1 Theorem: For every $u, v \in R$

$$\cos(u - v) = \cos u \cos v + \sin u \sin v.$$

Proof: Let $u = 2n\pi + y$, $v = 2m\pi + w$, where $y, w \in [0, 2\pi)$. Then

$$T(u - v) = T(2(n - m)\pi + y - w)$$
$$= T(y - w) \quad \text{(Why?)}$$

from which it follows that

$$\cos(u - v) = \cos(y - w).$$

Now either $y - w \in [0, 2\pi)$ or $w - y \in [0, 2\pi)$. (Verify this!) Further, $\cos(-t) = \cos t$ from which

$$\cos(y - w) = \cos(w - y).$$

Therefore, we may assume without loss of generality that $y > w$. Let us consider a typical situation where $y - w \in [0, 2\pi)$ (see Figure 7.14).

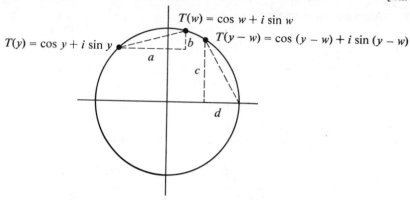

FIG. 7.14

Using the Pythagorean theorem and the geometric fact that chords across arcs of equal length have equal length, we deduce the equation

$$b^2 + a^2 = c^2 + d^2$$

as shown in the diagram. But

$$a = \cos w - \cos y \qquad b = \sin w - \sin y$$
$$c = \sin (y - w) \qquad d = 1 - \cos (y - w).$$

Hence we have

$$(\sin w - \sin y)^2 + (\cos w - \cos y)^2 = \sin^2 (y - w) + (1 - \cos (y - w))^2.$$

Expanding, we then have

$$\sin^2 w - 2 \sin w \sin y + \sin^2 y + \cos^2 w - 2 \cos w \cos y + \cos^2 y$$
$$= \sin^2 (y - w) + 1 - 2 \cos (y - w) + \cos^2 (y - w)$$

which simplifies (using the fact that $\text{sine}^2 + \text{cosine}^2 = 1_f$) to

$$\cos (y - w) = \cos y \cos w + \sin y \sin w. \qquad \text{(Verify this!)}.$$

With some thought as to other typical situations where $y - w \in [0, 2\pi)$, the student can verify that this argument is quite general. Since

$$T(2n\pi + t) = T(t) \qquad \text{for all } t,$$

we can state this in terms of the arbitrary u and v rather than the restricted y and w.

Let us use this theorem and other facts at hand to verify the following theorem.

7.2-2 Theorem: (the addition formulas) $\qquad \forall u, v \in R,$

a) $\cos (u + v) = \cos u \cos v - \sin u \sin v$

and b) $\sin (u + v) = \sin u \cos v + \cos u \sin v.$

Proof: a) $\cos(u + v) = \cos(u - (-v))$
$$= \cos u \cos(-v) + \sin u \sin(-v)$$
$$= \cos u \cos v - \sin u \sin v. \qquad \text{(Why?)}$$

We will use this fact in deducing b).

b) $\sin(u + v) = -\cos((u + v) + \pi/2) = -\cos(u + (v + \pi/2))$
$$= -(\cos u \cos(v + \pi/2) - \sin u \sin(v + \pi/2))$$
$$= -((\cos u)(-\sin v) - \sin u \cos v)$$
$$= \cos u \sin v + \sin u \cos v. \quad \square$$

From this theorem one easily deduces the following.

7.2-3 Theorem: $\forall t \in R$,

a) $\sin 2t = 2 \sin t \cos t$

and   b) $\cos 2t = \cos^2 t - \sin^2 t$.

Proof: a) $\sin(2t) = \sin(t + t) = \sin t \cos t + \cos t \sin t$
$$= 2 \sin t \cos t.$$

b) $\cos(2t) = \cos t \cos t - \sin t \sin t = \cos^2 t - \sin^2 t. \quad \square$

Among the most useful trigonometric identities in the application of calculus are the following.

7.2-4 Theorem: a) $\cos^2 t = \dfrac{1 + \cos 2t}{2}$

b) $\sin^2 t = \dfrac{1 - \cos 2t}{2}$

Proof: a) We know that
$$\cos 2t = \cos^2 t - \sin^2 t$$
$$= \cos^2 t - (1 - \cos^2 t) \qquad \text{(Why?)}$$
$$= 2 \cos^2 t - 1$$

from which $\cos^2 t = \dfrac{1 + \cos 2t}{2}$.

b) $\cos 2t = \cos^2 t - \sin^2 t$
$$= 1 - 2 \sin^2 t \qquad \text{(Why?)}$$

from which $\sin^2 t = \dfrac{1 - \cos 2t}{2}. \quad \square$

Although there are numerous identities which can be derived for these functions, the student armed with the following (along with the $\pi/2$ translation formulas) (committed to memory!) is in good shape to quickly derive almost any desired identity.

1) $\sin^2 x + \cos^2 x = 1$
2) $\cos(-x) = \cos x$
3) $\sin(-x) = -\sin x$

4) $\cos (x + y) = \cos x \cos y - \sin x \sin y$

5) $\sin (x + y) = \sin x \cos y + \cos x \sin y$

6) $\sin^2 x = \dfrac{1 - \cos 2x}{2}$

7) $\cos^2 x = \dfrac{1 + \cos 2x}{2}$

For example, consider the following.

7.2-5 Theorem: a) Suppose $1/2\, t \in [2n\pi, (2n + 1)\pi]$ for some $n \in Z$.

Then $\qquad \sin \left(\dfrac{1}{2} t\right) = \sqrt{\dfrac{1 - \cos \left(2 \left(\frac{1}{2} t\right)\right)}{2}} = \sqrt{\dfrac{1 - \cos t}{2}}$

and $\qquad \sin \left(\dfrac{1}{2} t\right) = -\sqrt{\dfrac{1 - \cos t}{2}} \qquad$ otherwise.

b) $\quad \cos \left(\dfrac{1}{2} t\right) = \sqrt{\dfrac{1 + \cos t}{2}} \qquad$ for $\qquad \dfrac{1}{2} t \in \left[\dfrac{(4n - 1)\pi}{2}, \dfrac{(4n + 1)\pi}{2}\right]$

and $\qquad \cos \left(\dfrac{1}{2} t\right) = -\sqrt{\dfrac{1 + \cos t}{2}}$

for $\dfrac{1}{2} t \in \left[\dfrac{(4n + 1)\pi}{2}, \dfrac{(4n + 3)\pi}{2}\right]$.

Proof: These come directly from 6 and 7 above where $x = \dfrac{1}{2} t$. $\quad\square$

7.2-6 Theorem: (The product formulas)

  a) $2 \sin u \cos v = \sin (u + v) + \sin (u - v)$

  b) $2 \cos u \cos v = \cos (u + v) + \cos (u - v)$

  c) $2 \sin u \sin v = \cos (u - v) - \cos (u + v)$

Proof: We merely apply the addition formulas and observe the result.

a) $\sin (u + v) + \sin (u - v)$

$\qquad = \sin u \cos v + \cos u \sin v + \sin u \cos (-v) + \cos u \sin (-v)$

$\qquad = \sin u \cos v + \cos u \sin v + \sin u \cos v - \cos u \sin v$

$\qquad = 2 \sin u \cos v$

b) $\cos (u + v) + \cos (u - v)$

$\qquad = \cos u \cos v - \sin u \sin v + \cos u \cos (-v) - \sin u \sin (-v)$

$\qquad = \cos u \cos v - \sin u \sin v + \cos u \cos v + \sin u \sin v$

$\qquad = 2 \cos u \cos v$

c) Left as an exercise. $\quad\square$

It is common practice to use the letters x and y in connection with complex numbers $x + iy$, and for this reason we *introduced* the real valued functions cosine and sine using the letter t. That is, we have defined cosine and

464

sine to be the real valued functions $X(t) = x$ and $Y(t) = y$ which paramet-rically describe the unit circle. However, this particular use of the letters x, y, and t in no way prevent us from using x and y in the ordinary fashion when dealing with them separately as real valued functions.

Exercises 7.2

1. If $\sin u = 3/5$ and $\cos v = 12/13$, determine:
   a) $\sin (u + v)$ c) $\sin (u - v)$
   b) $\cos (u - v)$ d) $\cos (u + v)$

2. If $\sin u = 5/13$ and $\cos v = 24/25$, determine:
   a) $\sin (u + v)$ c) $\sin (v - u)$
   b) $\cos (v - u)$ d) $\cos (v + u)$

3. Simplify:
   a) $\sin (\pi/4 + x) - \sin (\pi/4 - x)$
   b) $\cos (\pi/6 + t) \cos (\pi/6 - t) - \sin (\pi/6 + t) \sin (\pi/6 - t)$
   c) $\cos (\pi + t) \cos (\pi - t) + \sin (\pi + t) \sin (\pi - t)$

4. a) Express $\sin 3x$ in terms of $\sin x$.
   b) Express $\cos 3x$ in terms of $\cos x$.
   c) Express $\sin 3x$ in terms of $\cos x$.
   d) Express $\cos 3x$ in terms of $\sin x$.

5. Express each product of functional values as a sum or difference of functional values:
   a) $2 \sin 3t \cos 5t$ c) $2 \sin 3t \cos t$
   b) $2 \sin 2t + \cos 5t$ d) $2 \sin 2t \sin 9t$

6. Solve the following equations.
   a) $\sin 2x = 0$ l) $\cos 2x = \cos^2 x$
   b) $2 \sin 2t = \cos 5t$ m) $\cos 2x = -\sin^2 x$
   c) $\cos 2x = -1$ n) $\sin 2x = 2 \cos^2 x$
   d) $\cos 2x = \sqrt{3}/2$ o) $\sin x + \cos 2x = 1$
   e) $\sin 3x = -1$ p) $\cos 2x - \cos x + 1 = 0$
   f) $\sin 3x = \sqrt{3}/2$ q) $\cos 2x - (3 \cos x + 2) = 0$
   g) $\sin (1/3)x = \sqrt{2}/2$ r) $\sin 2x + \sin 4x = \sin 3x$
   h) $\sin 2x = \cos x$ s) $\sin x + \sin 5x = \sin 3x$
   i) $\cos 2x = \sin x$ t) $\sin 3x = \sin 5x$
   j) $\cos 2x = -\cos x$ u) $\sin 2x - \sin 6x = 0$
   k) $\sin 2x = \sin x$

7. Show that for all $x \in R$:
   a) $\cos^4 2x - \sin^4 2x = \cos 4x$
   b) $\sin x - \cos 2x = (2 \sin x - 1)(\sin x + 1)$

465

8. Show that

a) $\cos^6 t + \sin^6 t = 1 - 3 \sin^2 t \cos^2 t$.

b) $\dfrac{\sin^2 t}{(1 - \cos t)^2} = \dfrac{(1 + \cos t)^2}{\sin^2 t}$.

(Provide information which indicates where the ratios involved are undefined.)

c) $\dfrac{\sin^3 t + \cos^3 t}{1 - \sin t \cos t} = \sin t + \cos t$.

7.3 More Trig Functions and Their Graphs

It is useful to define other functions in terms of sine and cosine as follows.

7.3-1 Definition:

a) tangent $= \dfrac{\text{sine}}{\text{cosine}}$ $\left(i.e.,\ \forall t \in R \quad \tan t = \dfrac{\sin t}{\cos t} \right)$.

b) cotangent $= \dfrac{\text{cosine}}{\text{sine}}$ $\left(i.e.,\ \forall t \in R \quad \cot t = \dfrac{\cos t}{\sin t} \right)$.

c) secant $= \dfrac{1}{\text{cosine}}$ $\left(i.e.,\ \forall t \in R \quad \sec t = \dfrac{1}{\cos t}^\dagger \right)$.

d) cosecant $= \dfrac{1}{\text{sine}}$ $\left(i.e.,\ \forall t \in R \quad \csc t = \dfrac{1}{\sin t} \right)$.

(Here by $\forall t \in R$ we mean only those real numbers for which the ratio is defined. Recall the convention of maximal domain.)

Let us now graph these new functions starting with tangent. Let us observe some immediate facts which result from the definition

$$\tan t = \frac{\sin t}{\cos t}.$$

a) $\tan t$ is undefined where $\cos t = 0$ (*i.e.*, at $(2n + 1)\pi/2$ for $n \in Z$).

b) $\lim_{t \to a^-} \tan t = \infty$ and $\lim_{t \to a^+} \tan t = -\infty$ if $a = \dfrac{(2n + 1)\pi}{2}$.

(*Note:* Only the "one sided" limits exist.)

c) $\tan t = 0$ where $\sin t = 0$ (*i.e.*, at $n\pi$ for $n \in Z$).

Now, considering the ratio of y/x as t wraps around the unit circle (See Figure 7.15).

$\dagger$ It is important to distinguish here the difference between $1/\text{cosine}$ and cosine^{-1}. That is, $(\cos x)^{-1}$ does not mean the same as $\cos^{-1} x$.

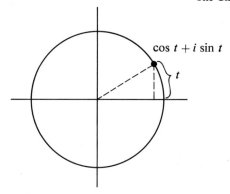

FIG. 7.15

we arrive at the following graph for tan t. (See Figure 7.16.)

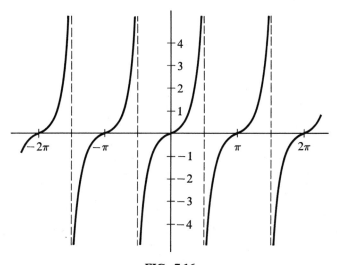

FIG. 7.16

Note that the tangent is periodic but with period π. (The known maximum would be 2π. Why?)

Let us now graph the cosecant function using a technique which we shall apply to the secant and the cotangent. By definition, $\csc t = 1/\sin t$. That is, the cosecant takes on values which are the reciprocals of the values that the sine takes. Keeping in mind that $1/1 = 1$ and $1/-1 = -1$ and that if t is small, then $1/t$ is large, and if t is large, then $1/t$ is small, then we can

467

immediately superimpose the graph of cosecant on the graph of sine. (See Figure 7.17.)

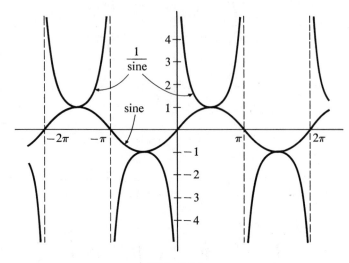

FIG. 7.17

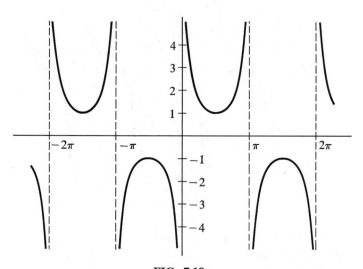

FIG. 7.18

Hence the graph of *cosecant* is shown in Figure 7.18.

Question: *a*) What is the period of cosecant? *b*) What are the asymptotes of cosecant?

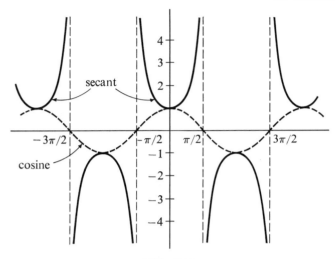

FIG. 7.19

Using a similar technique we have *secant*.

Question: a) What is the period of secant? *b)* What are the asymptotes of secant?

Similarly, the cotangent is compared to the tangent. (See Figure 7.20.)

Question: a) What is the period of cotangent? *b)* What are the asymptotes of cotangent?

Remark: Tangent and cotangent are both odd functions.

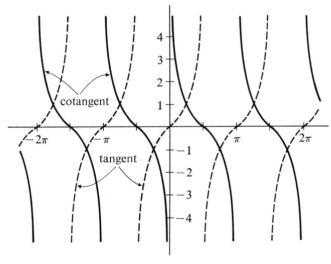

FIG. 7.20

The Co-functions

One might be curious about the names we have assigned to these various functions, especially concerning the prefix "co" on three of them. Recall that earlier we remarked that all values of sine and cosine could be computed by knowing only the values in $[0, \pi/2)$. This is true because one can evaluate $\sin t$ in terms of $\sin r$ or $\cos r$ where $r \in [0, \pi/2)$. That is

$$\sin (t + \pi/2) = \cos t$$
and
$$\cos (t + \pi/2) = -\sin t.$$

A similar thing happens with respect to the other co-functions.

7.3-2 Theorem: a) $\tan (t + \pi/2) = -\cot t.$

   b) $\sec (t + \pi/2) = -\csc t.$

Proof: a) $\tan (t + \pi/2) = \dfrac{\sin (t + \pi2/)}{\cos (t + \pi/2)} = \dfrac{\cos t}{-\sin t} = -\cot t.$

   b) $\sec (t + \pi/2) = \dfrac{1}{\cos (t + \pi/2)} = \dfrac{1}{-\sin t} = -\csc t.$ □

Similarly, $\csc (t + \pi/2) = \sec t$ and $\cot (t + \pi/2) = -\tan t$. Hence we see that in computing tables of values for the six trig functions we have a choice. We can either compute all values for sin, tan, sec in $[0, \pi)$ or we can compute values for all six functions in $[0, \pi/2)$. However, we can do even better. We can reduce the need for tabulated values for the six functions to a table of values for only the numbers in $[0, \pi/4]$. The following theorem, as you will see, makes this reduction possible.

7.3-3 Theorem: a) $\sin t = \cos (\pi/2 - t)$
and $\quad\quad\quad\quad\quad \cos t = \sin (\pi/2 - t).$
   b) $\tan t = \cot (\pi/2 - t)$
and $\quad\quad\quad\quad\quad \cot t = \tan (\pi/2 - t).$
   c) $\sec t = \csc (\pi/2 - t)$
and $\quad\quad\quad\quad\quad \csc t = \sec (\pi/2 - t).$

Proof: a) $\cos (\pi/2 - t) = \cos (t - \pi/2) = \sin t$

and $\quad \sin (\pi/2 - t) = -\sin (t - \pi/2) = --\cos t = \cos t.$

   b) $\cot (\pi/2 - t) = \dfrac{\cos (\pi/2 - t)}{\sin (\pi/2 - t)} = \dfrac{\sin t}{\cos t} = \tan t$

and $\quad \tan (\pi/2 - t) = \dfrac{\sin (\pi/2 - t)}{\cos (\pi/2 - t)} = \dfrac{\cos t}{\sin t} = \cot t.$

$c)$ $\csc (\pi/2 - t) = \dfrac{1}{\sin (\pi/2 - t)} = \dfrac{1}{\cos t} = \sec t$

and $\sec (\pi/2 - t) = \dfrac{1}{\cos (\pi/2 - t)} = \dfrac{1}{\sin t} = \csc t.$ □

Remark: If $t \in (\pi/4, \pi/2)$, then $\pi/2 - t \in [0, \pi/4]$ and hence the value of a function at a point t in $(\pi/4, \pi/2)$ can be determined by finding the value of the co-function at $\pi/2 - t$ which is in $[0, \pi/4]$. It follows then that values of the six trig functions can be determined by having only a table of values for pre-images in $[0, \pi/4]$.

Exercise: Explain how this theorem is used with respect to Table IV by reading some values from bottom to top.

Identities

Many useful identities among the six trig functions can be easily derived by application of the definitions and simple identities between sine and cosine.

Example: $\tan (u + v) = \dfrac{\tan u + \tan v}{1 - \tan u \tan v}$ (provided all values are defined).

Proof: $\tan (u + v) = \dfrac{\sin (u + v)}{\cos (u + v)}$

$\qquad = \dfrac{\sin u \cos v + \cos u \sin v}{\cos u \cos v - \sin u \sin v}$

$\qquad = \dfrac{\dfrac{\sin u}{\cos u} + \dfrac{\sin v}{\cos v}}{1 - \dfrac{\sin u \sin v}{\cos u \cos v}}$ (divide numerator and denominator by $\cos u \cos v$)

$\qquad = \dfrac{\tan u + \tan v}{1 - \tan u \tan v}.$ □

Example: $\cot (u + v) = \dfrac{\cot u - \tan v}{1 + \cot u \tan v}.$

Proof: $\cot (u + v) = \dfrac{\cos (u + v)}{\sin (u + v)}$

$\qquad = \dfrac{\cos u \cos v - \sin u \sin v}{\sin u \cos v + \cos u \sin v}$

$\qquad = \dfrac{\dfrac{\cos u}{\sin u} - \dfrac{\sin v}{\cos v}}{1 + \dfrac{\cos u \sin v}{\sin u \cos v}}$

$\qquad = \dfrac{\cot u - \tan v}{1 + \cot u \tan v}.$ □

471

Example: $\csc^2 t - \cot^2 t = 1$.

Proof: $\qquad\qquad\qquad\qquad \sin^2 t + \cos^2 t = 1$.

Therefore $\qquad\qquad\qquad 1 + \dfrac{\cos^2 t}{\sin^2 t} = \dfrac{1}{\sin^2 t}$

$$1 + \cot^2 t = \csc^2 t$$
$$\csc^2 t - \cot^2 t = 1. \;\square$$

Example: $\tan t \csc t = \sec t$.

Proof: $\qquad \tan t \csc t = \dfrac{\sin t}{\cos t} \cdot \dfrac{1}{\sin t}$

$$= \dfrac{1}{\cos t} = \sec t. \;\square$$

Question: For which values of t do the above identities fail?

In general, the best method for proving identities is to first reduce everything to sine and cosine values and proceed from there. It is a rare student who can develop facility for working with trig functions without giving it a great deal of practice. For this reason we list many identities to prove as exercises. Remember, as we mentioned earlier, "Mathematics is not a spectator sport." In order to appreciate the game, one must play.

Exercises 7.3

1. *a)* Show that tangent and cotangent are odd functions.

   b) What is the smallest interval for which one can graph the function and then extend by symmetries and periodicity to obtain the entire graph?

2. Show that

   a) $\tan (u - v) = \dfrac{\tan u - \tan v}{1 + \tan u \tan v}$.

   b) $\cot (u + v) = \dfrac{\cot u \cot v - 1}{\cot u + \cot v}$.

3. Derive an identity for:

   a) $\tan 2t$ *c)* $\cot (u - v)$ *e)* $\csc 2t$

   b) $\cot 2t$ *d)* $\sec 2t$ *f)* $\sec (u + v)$

4. Verify each of the following:

   a) $\tan (\pi/2 + t) = -\cot t$ *d)* $\csc (\pi - t) = \csc t$

   b) $\cot (\pi + t) = \cot t$ *e)* $\sec (t + 3\pi/2) = \csc t$

   c) $\tan (\pi - t) = -\tan t$ *f)* $\cot (3\pi/2 - t) = \tan t$

5. Reduce each expression to $\sin t$ and $\cos t$ and simplify.

a) $\dfrac{\tan t + \cot t}{\csc t}$

d) $\sec^4 t - \tan^4 t$

b) $\dfrac{\tan t + 1}{\cot t + 1}$

e) $\dfrac{\sin t - \csc t - \cot t}{\csc t + \cot t}$

c) $\dfrac{\sec t}{\tan t + \cot t}$

f) $\dfrac{\sec^2 t + \cot^2 t - 1}{\sec t \cot^2 t \cos t}$

6. Prove each of the following identities:
  a) $\sin t - \cos t \tan t = 0$

  b) $\dfrac{\sin t}{\csc t} + \dfrac{\cos t}{\sec t} = 1$

  c) $\dfrac{\sin t}{\cos t} - \dfrac{\sec t}{\csc t} = 0$

  d) $\tan t \csc t = \sec t$
  e) $\sin t(\cot t + \csc t) = 1 + \cos t$
  f) $(\sin t - \cos t)^2 = 1 - 2 \sin t \cos t$
  g) $\cos^2 t + \cos^2 t \tan^2 t = 1$
  h) $(1 - \sin t)(1 + \sin t) = \cos^2 t$

  i) $\dfrac{\sec^2 t - \tan^2 t + \tan t}{\sec t} = \sin t + \cos t$

  j) $\sec^2 t = \csc^2 t(\sec^2 t - 1)$

7. Evaluate (exactly, do not approximate):
  a) $\cos 7\pi/4$ d) $\cos \pi/12$ g) $\sin 13\pi/12$
  b) $\tan 5\pi/3$ e) $\cos -\pi/12$ h) $\tan 7\pi/12$
  c) $\sin 11\pi/6$ f) $\sin 5\pi/12$ i) $\tan -25\pi/6$

8. Graph f on $[0, 2\pi]$ where
  a) $f(t) = 2 \sin t.$ c) $f(t) = \cot t - \csc t.$
  b) $f(t) = \sin t + \sec t.$ d) $f(t) = \sin t + \tan t.$

9. Graph f on $[0, 2\pi]$ where

  a) $f(t) = \dfrac{\cos t}{\sec 4t} + \dfrac{\sin t}{\csc 4t}.$

  b) $f(t) = \dfrac{\sin t}{\sec 3t} + \dfrac{\cos t}{\csc 3t}.$

  c) $f(t) = \dfrac{\sin 2t}{\cos 2t} + \dfrac{\sin 4t}{\cos 4t}.$

(*Hint:* Use identities to reduce to a simpler form.)

473

10. *a)* Show that tangent restricted to $\left(-\dfrac{\pi}{2}, \dfrac{\pi}{2}\right)$ is strictly monotonic increasing.

b) Show that cotangent restricted to $(0, \pi)$ is strictly monotonic decreasing.

11. With your eyes shut, graph the tangent, cotangent, secant, and cosecant.

7.4 Angular Measure and Applications

Radian Measure

Let us now define a measure for angles, or more generally a measure for rotation. The concept of rotating something about a point is a fairly simple notion with many physical applications. When rotating an object about a point one can rotate it in either of two "directions" commonly known as "clockwise" and "counterclockwise." A common and simple measure for measuring rotation is to simply count revolutions, the number of times one makes a complete turn about the pivot point. When using this method it is often necessary to indicate fractional parts of a revolution. You are probably familiar with the rotational measure (called degree measure) in which a revolution is broken down into 360 equal parts called degrees. Here 1/2 revolution = 180°, 1/4 revolution = 90°, etc.

We wish to develop here a rotational measure (called radian measure) which is based on the fact that the circumference of a circle is 2π times its radius and in particular the circumference of the unit circle is 2π. We will find that radian measure is extremely useful due to its close connection to the circular functions and the values they take. Roughly, the definition of radian measure is: "one rotation in the counterclockwise direction is 2π radians"; however, let us describe this in a little more detail with respect to measuring angles.

Description: (*radian measure*) Consider the angle θ as shown in Figure 7.21.

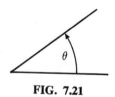

FIG. 7.21

We orient it in the complex plane with vertex at 0 and with one side along the positive real axis. (See Figure 7.22.)‡

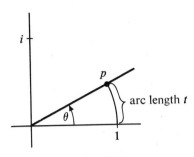

FIG. 7.22

The unit circle intersects the angle θ at 1 and at p. The arc from 1 to p has length t. The length of this arc is called the "radian measure of θ."

Example: The measure of a right angle is $\pi/2$.

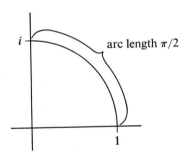

FIG. 7.23

The length of the arc on the unit circle from 1 to i is $\pi/2$. (In degree measure this is a 90° angle.)

Example: The measure of an angle given by rotating 1/8 of a revolution is $(1/8)2\pi = \pi/4$, since the length of the arc along the unit circle from 1 to p is $\pi/4$. (An angle whose radian measure is $\pi/4$ has degree measure 45°.)

‡ Note that we have not attempted to rigorously define "an angle." This can be done by letting an angle be a set of points (in our case in $\mathcal{C}$) with certain properties.

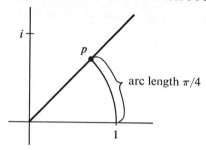

arc length $\pi/4$

FIG. 7.24

Let us now consider the size of angle whose radian measure is 1. If we measure a unit length along the arc of the unit circle from 1 to p and construct the angle which passes through 0 and p, then we have an angle with measure 1.

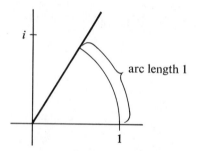

arc length 1

FIG. 7.25   One radian is approximately 57.295789°.

To measure rotations in general, we consider counterclockwise motion as positive and clockwise motion as negative. One full rotation is 2π radians and fractional parts of a rotation are measured in radians as fractional parts of 2π.

Example: Consider a wheel that has rotated 27.7 times (counterclockwise). Then the wheel has rotated through $27.7 \times 2\pi$ radians. .

Example: A wheel that has rotated 68.74 times clockwise has rotated through $-68.74 \times 2\pi$ radians.

One of the advantages of measuring a rotation by radian measure is due to the fact that if one knows the rotational measure of a wheel with radius 1, then he immediately knows the linear distance traveled by a point on the edge of the wheel.

Example: A wheel of radius 1 ft. travels west as shown in Figure 7.26.

476

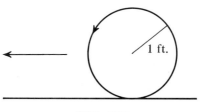

FIG. 7.26

If the wheel rotates 256 and 1/3 times, how far along the road has it traveled?
Answer: $(256 + 1/3) \times 2\pi$ ft.

Example: A belt is on a pulley whose radius is 1 ft. When the pulley spins through an angle of 2.3 radians, how far has the belt traveled?
Answer: 2.3 ft.

This useful device can be extended to wheels whose radius is not 1. The circumference of a circle K whose radius is r is given by $2\pi r$. Hence the length of the arc along K from r to p is given by rt where t is the radian measure of θ as shown in Figure 7.27.

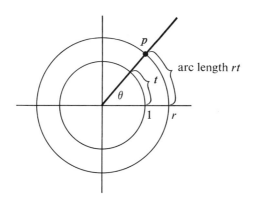

FIG. 7.27

Exercise: Use similar figures to argue that the arc length of a segment of a circle with radius r intercepted by an angle of radian measure t is given by rt.

Example: If an automobile wheel is 15 inches in radius and rotates 2500 times, then how far has the automobile traveled? (The wheel has rotated through $2500 \times 2\pi$ radians.)
Answer: $2500 \times 2\pi \times 15$ inches.

Example: A pulley with radius 2 ft. rotates through an angle whose radian measure is 2.6. How far did a belt on the pulley travel?
Answer: 2.6×2 ft.

477

By applying this principle in reverse one can determine the rotational measure (in radians) by knowing the linear distance a point on the wheel has traveled.

Example: Through how many radians has a wheel rotated if it has rolled 2000 ft. and if the wheel has radius 2 ft.?

Answer: (2000/2) radians.

In general then we have the following formula which can be solved for *d, r,* or *t.*

Formula: If a wheel with radius *r* has rotated through *t* radians and a point on the circumference has traveled a distance *d,* then

$$d = rt.$$

Example: A motor which turns a pulley *a* of radius 3″ is connected by a belt to a pulley *b* of radius 9″ which moves a conveyor belt. (See diagram in Figure 7.28.)

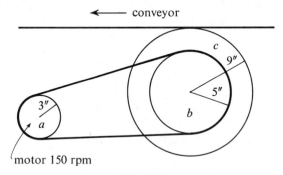

FIG. 7.28

If the motor turns 150 revolutions per minute, then how far does the conveyor belt travel in one minute?

Answer: In one minute the pulley *a* rotates through $150 \times 2\pi$ radians. Therefore the belt from *a* to *b* (and consequently the outside of *b*) travels $150 \times 2\pi \times 3$ inches. Now pulley *b* and consequently pulley *c* rotates through $(150 \times 2\pi \times 3)/5$ radians. Hence, the outside of *c* and consequently the conveyor belt travels $((150 \times 2\pi \times 3)/5) \times 9$ inches.

Example: A wheel of radius 20 inches rotates 7½ times while rolling down an inclined plane. How far did it roll?

Answer: The outside of the wheel traveled $7\frac{1}{2} \times 2\pi \times 20$ inches.

Example: A wheel of radius 7 inches rolls 5 ft. How many revolutions did the wheel turn?

Answer: The outside of the wheel rolled 60 inches. Therefore the wheel revolved 60/7 radians and hence it revolved $60/7 \times 2\pi$ revolutions.

Functions of Angles

If we have an angle θ whose radian measure is t, then we can immediately define $\sin \theta$ and $\cos \theta$ where t is the radian measure of θ.

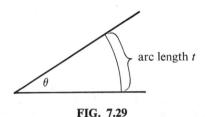

arc length t

FIG. 7.29

It is common practice, however, to make no distinction between the angle and its radian measure. That is, we use the convention of naming an angle by its measure in radians, or for that matter by its measure in degrees.

Example: $\sin 30°$ means $\sin \theta$ where the degree measure of θ is $30°$. This is determined by $\sin t$ where $t \in R$ is the radian measure of θ.

Since many available tables for the values of the circular functions over $[0, \pi/4]$ are tabulated in terms of angular measure in degrees over $[0°, 45°]$, it is useful to be adept at making the conversion. We have the simple, but useful, formula

$$2\pi \text{ radians} = 360°$$
$$\pi \text{ radians} = 180°.$$

More generally, $t \text{ radians} = \dfrac{180°}{\pi} t \text{ degrees} = S°.$

(That is, one revolution is one revolution in either measure.) Hence if $t \in [0, \pi/4]$ and one has a table which lists functional values in terms of degree measure, then

$$\sin t = \sin \left(\frac{180}{\pi} t° \right)$$

and similarly for $\cos t$, $\tan t$, etc.
Similarly,

$$S \text{ degrees} = \frac{\pi}{180} S \text{ radians} = t \text{ radians}.$$

Example: If the degree measure of θ is $60°$, then what is the radian measure of θ?

Answer: $t = \dfrac{\pi}{180} \times 60 = \dfrac{\pi}{3}.$

479

Example: If the radian measure of θ is 1.5, then what is the degree measure of θ?

Answer: $S = \dfrac{180}{\pi} \times 1.5$ degrees.

Remark: You will also find that degree measure has been broken down into smaller units, minutes and seconds, where 1 degree = 60 minutes (written 60′) and 1′ = 60 seconds (written 60″).

Exercises 7.4

1. In a circle 16 inches in diameter, how long an arc is "subtended" on the circumference by an angle of 2.4 radians? (That is, if an angle of radian measure 2.4 has its vertex at the center of the circle, then how long is the arc which is cut off by the two "rays" of the angle?)

2. How far does a 17-inch wheel roll if it turns through
   a) 27 radians?
   b) 30 revolutions?
   c) 720 degrees?

3. On a circle, if an arc 30 feet long subtends an angle of 2 radians, find the radius of the circle.

4. A runner on a circular track runs 140 yards. The diameter of the track is 200 yards.
   a) Through what angle in radians has the runner rotated?
   b) Through what angle in radians must he turn in order to run 220 yards?

5. If a flywheel is 6 ft. in diameter and if a belt over the wheel is traveling at the rate of 6000 ft. per minute, find the number of revolutions of the wheel per minute.

6. How fast in revolutions per minute must a motor turn in order to turn a ferris wheel 3 revolutions per minute where
   a) the ferris wheel has diameter 30 ft.
   b) the motor is connected to a pulley with radius 5 inches which turns a belt which turns a 20-inch (radius) pulley welded to the ferris wheel?

7. A railroad curve, in the form of an arc of a circle, is 850 yards long. If the radius of the circle is 950 yards, find the angle in degrees through which a train turns in going around the curve.

8. A packaging firm desires to have a conveyor move at a rate of 20 ft. per minute. They have a motor which runs at 200 r.p.m. (revolutions per minute) attached to a pulley 5 inches in diameter. They plan to run a belt from the motor to a pulley (which they have not yet purchased) firmly attached to a cogwheel 16 inches in diameter that turns the conveyor.
   a) What should be the radius of their new pulley?
   b) Can you determine the length of the belt they need if the motor is set 3 ft.

from the conveyor? That is, the center of the motor pulley is 3 ft. from the center of the conveyor pulley.

9. Find the degree measure of θ if the radian measure is:
   a) 1.23   c) 1   e) .321
   b) 1.1   d) 2   f) .994

10. Find the radian measure of θ if the degree measure is:
    a) 40°   c) 10°   e) 100°
    b) 60°   d) 21°   f) 124°

11. In going around a circular curve which is 645 yards long, a railroad train turns through an angle of 57°. Find the radius of the curve.

12. At the intersection of two streets, a streetcar track accomplishes a change of direction of 36° by following the arc of a circle for 185 feet. Find the radius of this circle.

13. How fast (in ft./second) is a chain driven motorcycle traveling when the engine is turning 7 revolutions per second? The driving sprocket is 3 inches in diameter; the chain is 5 ft. long; the rear wheel sprocket is 10 inches in diameter; and the rear wheel is 19 inches in diameter.

14. One day while Grant Gibson was riding on his father's hay wagon he noticed that the wheel turned 37 times between the barn and the granary. The wagon wheel is 23 inches in radius. How many feet did he travel from the barn to the granary?

7.5 The Right Triangle Theorem and Applications. Introduction to Polar Coordinates

The circular functions, sine, cosine, tangent, cotangent, secant, and cosecant, are also commonly known as trigonometric functions (*triangular functions*) as a result of some simple relationships they bear to triangles. In fact, the circular functions originated from these simple applications although today their applications are considerably more varied.

7.5-1 Theorem: (The Right Triangle Theorem) Given a right triangle with vertex angle θ (*i.e.*, whose radian measure is θ) as shown in Figure 7.30, then

1) $\cos \theta = \dfrac{a}{c} = \dfrac{\text{length of side adjacent } \theta}{\text{length of hypotenuse}}$.

2) $\sin \theta = \dfrac{b}{c} = \dfrac{\text{side opposite } \theta}{\text{hypotenuse}}$.

3) $\tan \theta = \dfrac{b}{a} = \dfrac{\text{side opposite } \theta}{\text{side adjacent } \theta}$.

4) $\cot \theta = \dfrac{a}{b} = \dfrac{\text{side adjacent } \theta}{\text{side opposite } \theta}.$

5) $\sec \theta = \dfrac{c}{a} = \dfrac{\text{hypotenuse}}{\text{side adjacent } \theta}.$

6) $\csc \theta = \dfrac{c}{b} = \dfrac{\text{hypotenuse}}{\text{side opposite } \theta}.$

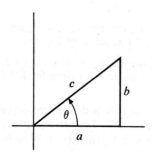

FIG. 7.30

Proof: Orient the complex plane with the vertex of θ at 0 and the side a along the real axis. Strike an arc of unit length which crosses the hypotenuse c at the point $p = x + iy$. (See Figure 7.31.) Observe that the right triangle whose hypotenuse has length 1 and whose legs have length x and y is similar to the original triangle.

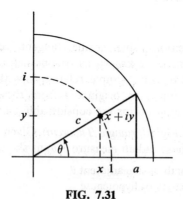

FIG. 7.31

Now $x = \cos \theta$ and $y = \sin \theta$ by definition, and by considering ratios of sides for similar triangles we see that

$$\frac{b}{c} = \frac{y}{1} = \sin \theta$$

and

$$\frac{a}{c} = \frac{x}{1} = \cos \theta.$$

The ratios for tan θ, cot θ, sec θ, and csc θ follow immediately from their definitions in terms of sine and cosine. ☐

This theorem is very useful in surveying applications because it makes it possible to measure certain lengths on a right triangle by measuring only some of the lengths and some of the angles.

Example: How tall is a building which casts a shadow 200 ft. long when the angle of elevation of the sun is 1.4 radians?

$$\frac{h}{200} = \tan 1.4$$

Therefore $h = 200 \tan 1.4 = 200 \times 5.798 = 1159.6.$

Hence the building is 1159.6 feet high.

Example: How long must a ladder be in order to reach a window 12 feet high if the angle of elevation is 60°?

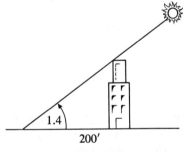

FIG. 7.32a

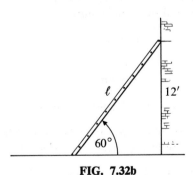

FIG. 7.32b

Proof: $\dfrac{l}{12} = \csc 60°$

Therefore $\qquad l = 12 \csc 60° = 12 \sec 30°$
$$= 12 \times 1.15 \quad \text{(approximately)}$$
$$= 13.8.$$

The ladder must be 13.8 feet long. □

Remark: Notice that a line with equation $y = mx + b$ intersects the x-axis at an angle θ where $\tan \theta = m$. (See Figure 7.33.)

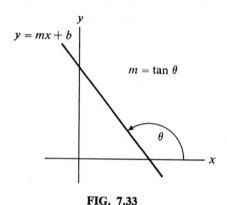

$y = mx + b$

$m = \tan \theta$

θ

FIG. 7.33

Location of a Complex Number in Polar Form

We wish now to show that the location of any non-zero complex number $a + bi$ can be determined uniquely by an ordered pair (r, θ), where $r \in (0, \infty)$ and $\theta \in [0, 2\pi)$. Conversely, given any pair (r, θ) where $r \in (0, \infty)$ and $\theta \in [0, 2\pi)$, a unique number $a + bi$ is determined. Further, the two representations will be connected by the formulas

$$a = r \cos \theta$$

and

$$b = r \sin \theta.$$

That is, $\qquad a + bi = r \cos \theta + ir \sin \theta.$

We wish, then, to establish a *one-one* correspondence between $\mathcal{C} - \{0 + 0i\}$ and the collection of ordered pairs P where

$$P = \{(r, \theta): r \in (0, \infty) \quad \text{and} \quad \theta \in [0, 2\pi)\}$$

by the mapping

$$(r, \theta) \text{ maps to } r \cos \theta + ir \sin \theta.$$

Remark: This entire process could be viewed as mapping the ordered pairs in P to the collection of all ordered pairs except $(0, 0)$ by mapping (r, θ) to $(r \cos \theta, r \sin \theta)$.

The ordered pair (r, θ) in P which determines the complex number

$$z = a + bi = r \cos \theta + ir \sin \theta$$

we shall call the *polar coordinate* of z.§

Consider now a complex number $a + bi \neq 0$.

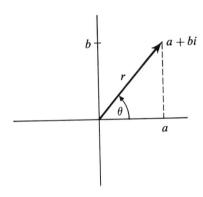

FIG. 7.34

Recall that the length (modulus) of this number is given by $\sqrt{a^2 + b^2}$. The vector which represents this number is gotten by rotating the vector $r + 0i$ through some angle θ for exactly one $\theta \in [0, 2\pi)$. By the right triangle theorem $b/r = \sin \theta$ and $a/r = \cos \theta$,

(*i.e.*, $\qquad\qquad a + bi = r \cos \theta + ir \sin \theta$).

On the other hand, if $r \in (0, \infty)$ and $\theta \in [0, 2\pi)$ are given, then a unique point $a + bi$ in the plane is determined by

$$a + bi = r \cos \theta + ir \sin \theta,$$

which is the point at the end of an arrow of length r which has been rotated by θ from the real axis.

Example: Locate the complex number whose polar coordinate is $(2, \pi/4)$. We select a vector along R^+ whose length is 2 and rotate through an angle whose measure is $\pi/4$ radians.

---

§ The polar coordinate (r, θ) of z is often called "the polar coordinates of z." This is because the idea of viewing a pair of numbers (r, θ) as a "single" object is fairly modern. Earlier usage viewed r and θ as members of a collection, and hence the plural.

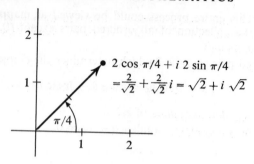

FIG. 7.35

The standard (Cartesian) coordinate for this number is $(2 \cos \pi/4, 2 \sin \pi/4)$, or when simplified, $(\sqrt{2}, \sqrt{2})$.

Example: Locate the complex number whose polar coordinates are $(3, 3\pi/4)$.

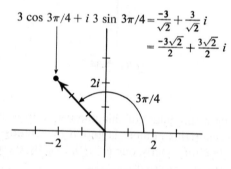

FIG. 7.36

The Cartesian coordinate for this number is $(-3/\sqrt{2}, 3/\sqrt{2})$.

If we define the ordered pair $(0, 0)$ to be the polar coordinate for the complex number 0, then we have established a *one-one* correspondence between $\mathcal{C}$ and $P' = P \cup \{(0, 0)\}$ where

$$P = \{(r, \theta): r \in (0, \infty) \quad \text{and} \quad \theta \in [0, 2\pi)\}$$

such that (r, θ) maps to $r(\cos \theta + i \sin \theta)$.

Remark: The zero point of the real number line is called the *pole*, and the half-line $[0, \infty)$ of non-negative numbers on the real number line is called the *polar axis*.

7.5-2 Definition: P' is called the collection of polar coordinates for $\mathcal{C}$, and if $(r, \theta) \in P'$ and (r, θ) maps to z, then r is called the *modulus* of z (recall that

$mod\ z = |z| = \sqrt{a^2 + b^2} = r$). θ is called the principle *argument of* z, denoted by *Arg z*.

We have established a *one-one* correspondence between $((0, \infty) \times [0, 2\pi)) \cup \{(0, 0)\}$ and $\mathcal{C}$ by the mapping f where $f(r, \theta) = r \cos \theta + ir \sin \theta$. It follows that f^{-1} exists. Let us establish a formula for finding the polar coordinate of a point in $\mathcal{C}$ when the Cartesian coordinate is known. The polar coordinate $(0, 0)$ is matched with itself, so we will examine only Cartesian coordinates (x, y) where x and y are not both 0.

We have the two defining equations

$$x = r \cos \theta \qquad y = r \sin \theta$$

from which

$$x^2 + y^2 = r^2(\cos^2 \theta + \sin^2 \theta).$$

(Square both sides of the equations and add.) It follows that

$$r = \sqrt{x^2 + y^2}.$$

Upon dividing the second equation by the first we have

$$\frac{\sin \theta}{\cos \theta} = \frac{y}{x}.$$

That is,
$$\tan \theta = \frac{y}{x}$$

from which

$$\theta = \mathrm{Tan}^{-1} \frac{y}{x}.$$

Hence, $$f^{-1}(x + iy) = \left(\sqrt{x^2 + y^2},\ \mathrm{Tan}^{-1} \frac{y}{x}\right).$$

Question: What if $x = 0$?

Exercise: Read this entire discussion again and eliminate all reference to complex numbers. Consider this as a discussion about coordinatizing $R \times R$ as a set of ordered pairs using two different systems.

Exercises 7.5

1. Find the length of the horizontal shadow of a man 6 ft. tall when the angle of elevation of the sun is 75°.

2. How tall is a chimney whose horizontal shadow is 90 ft. long when the angle of elevation of the sun is 67°?

3. A guy wire 35 ft. long is stretched from level ground to the top of a pole 25 ft. high. Find the angle between the pole and the wire.

4. How high has an airplane risen that has flown 4000 ft. upward along a straight path inclined 28° from the horizontal?

5. A painter desires to reach a window 40 ft. above the ground. Find the length of the shortest ladder he can use if it must not incline more than 78° from the horizontal.

6. Graph the complex number z whose polar coordinate (r, θ) is:

a) (2, 1.5)   c) (3, 3)   e) (0, 0)

b) (16, 2.4)   d) (5, 3.14)   f) $(3, \pi)$

7. Which complex numbers $a + bi$ have polar coordinates (r, θ) equal to their Cartesian coordinates (a, b)?

8. Determine the polar coordinates for the given complex numbers and graph the number.

a) i c) $3i$ e) $-4 - 4i$

b) $-i$ d) $4 + 4i$ f) $2 - 2i$

9. Determine the polar coordinates for:

a) $1/2 + \sqrt{2}/3\, i$ c) $2\sqrt{2} + 3i$

b) $\sqrt{2}/3 + 1/2\, i$ d) $-2 - 3/\frac{1}{2}i$

10. Show that if the polar coordinate of z is (r, θ) where $\theta \in [0, \pi)$, then the co-ordinate of z^2 is $(r^2, 2\theta)$.

11. Write a set description for all points on the unit circle using polar coordinates.

12. Graph in $\mathcal{C}$ each of the following sets:

a) $\{r(\cos\theta + i\sin\theta): r = 2\cos\theta\}$

b) $\{r(\cos\theta + i\sin\theta): \theta = 1\}$

c) $\{x + iy: x = r\cos\theta, y = r\sin\theta, r = 2, \theta \in R\}$

d) $\{r(\cos\theta + i\sin\theta): r\sin\theta = 2\}$

13. Determine the Cartesian coordinate for a number whose polar coordinate is given. Graph the number.

a) $(2, \pi)$ c) (5, 6)   e) $(2, 5\pi/12)$

b) $(3, \pi/4)$ d) (1/2, 4)

14. Let us relax the *one-one* property in mapping pairs (r, θ) to pairs (x, y) and define a mapping $f: R \times R \to \mathcal{C}$ by

$$f(r, \theta) = r\cos\theta + ir\sin\theta.$$

We can view a point in $\mathcal{C}$ as having a unique Cartesian coordinate, but many polar coordinates. Using this extension, determine the complex number $x + iy$ which has a polar coordinate as given. Graph the number.

a) $(-2, \pi)$ d) $(-3, -3\pi/4)$ g) $(6, 2000\pi)$

b) $(-7, \pi/4)$ e) (2, 20)   h) $(-20, 1000\pi)$

c) $(3, -\pi/6)$ f) $(-6, -21)$

15. Express each of the following constraining equations on the Cartesian coordi-nates of a point set as an equivalent constraining equation on the polar coordinates.

That is, determine an equation in r and θ which determines the same set of points. Graph each equation in $\mathcal{C}$.

a) $x^2 + y^2 = 25$ c) $y = -6$

b) $x = 4$ d) $x^2 - 4y^2 = 4$

16.   Express each of the following polar equations as an equivalent Cartesian equation. Graph the set described in each case.

a) $r = 7$ c) $r = 4 \cos \theta$

b) $r = 9 \sin \theta$ d) $r(1 - \cos \theta) = 2$

17.   a) Interpret symmetry (of various kinds) in polar coordinates in terms of polar descriptions of the form $r = g(\theta)$.

b) What kind of "reflection" results if the pairs (r, θ) in g are replaced by (θ, r) (interchanging r and θ)?

18.   Under what graphical circumstances will $r = g(\theta)$ describe a function g: $R \to R$?

7.6   The Law of Sines and the Law of Cosines

We now establish two useful results concerning the trig functions and triangles in general.

7.6-1 Theorem: (The Law of Sines) Let α, β, and γ be the angles of a triangle where the lengths of the sides opposite the respective angles are given by a, b, and c. (See Figure 7.37.) Then

$$\frac{\sin \alpha}{a} = \frac{\sin \beta}{b}.$$

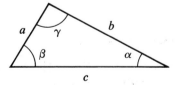

FIG. 7.37

Proof: Orient the triangle with the vertex of β at 0 and the side c along the real axis.

489

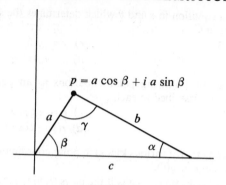

FIG. 7.38

Note that the vertex of γ is at the point $p = a(\cos \beta + i \sin \beta)$. Now translate the triangle by the translation $T(z) = z - c$. Thus,

$$T(p) = p - c = b \cos (\pi - \alpha) + ib \sin (\pi - \alpha).$$

(See Figure 7.39.)

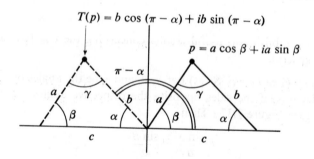

FIG. 7.39

We have then that

$$a \cos \beta + ia \sin \beta - c = b \cos (\pi - \alpha) + ib \sin (\pi - \alpha).$$

Noting that $\qquad \cos (\pi - \alpha) = -\cos \alpha$

and $\qquad \sin (\pi - \alpha) = \sin \alpha$

we have $\qquad a \cos \beta - c + ia \sin \beta = -b \cos \alpha + ib \sin \alpha.$

Setting the real and imaginary components equal, we have two equations. From the real components we have

1) $\qquad a \cos \beta - c = -b \cos \alpha$

or $\qquad\qquad c = a \cos \beta + b \cos \alpha \qquad$ *(third side formula)* which can be very useful if two sides and the two angles opposite them are known. However, from the imaginary components we have

2) $a \sin \beta = b \sin \alpha$

or $\dfrac{\sin \alpha}{a} = \dfrac{\sin \beta}{b}$ (*law of sines*). ▯

Corollary: $\dfrac{\sin \alpha}{a} = \dfrac{\sin \beta}{b} = \dfrac{\sin \gamma}{c}.$

Proof: Orient the triangle with a different vertex at 0. ▯
Example: Find the remaining parts of a triangle if $\gamma = 75°$, $\beta = 30°$, and $a = 15$.

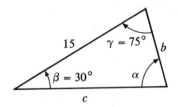

FIG. 7.40

First observe that
$$\alpha = 180° - 75° - 30° = 75°.$$

Recall, $\sin 30° = \sin \dfrac{\pi}{6} = \dfrac{1}{2}$

and $\sin 75° = \sin \dfrac{5\pi}{12} = \sin \left(\dfrac{\pi}{2} - \dfrac{\pi}{12} \right)$

$$= \cos \dfrac{\pi}{12} = \sqrt{\dfrac{1 + \cos \pi/6}{2}}$$

$$= \sqrt{\dfrac{1 + \sqrt{3}/2}{2}} = \sqrt{\dfrac{2 + \sqrt{3}}{4}}$$

$$= \dfrac{1}{2} \sqrt{2 + \sqrt{3}}.$$

Thus we have
$$\sin \alpha = \dfrac{1}{2} \sqrt{2 + \sqrt{3}}, \ \sin \beta = \dfrac{1}{2}, \quad \text{and} \quad a = 15.$$

Using the law of sines $\dfrac{\sin \beta}{b} = \dfrac{\sin \alpha}{a}$ and substitution, we obtain

$$\dfrac{1}{2b} = \dfrac{\sqrt{2 + \sqrt{3}}}{2 \cdot 15}$$

491

from which
$$b = \frac{15}{\sqrt{2 + \sqrt{3}}}.$$

Since the triangle is isosceles (has two equal angles and thus two equal sides) then

$$c = 15.$$

7.6-2 Theorem: (*The Law of Cosines*) Let α, β, and γ be the angles of a triangle where the lengths of the sides opposite the respective angles are a, b, and c. Then

$$a^2 = b^2 + c^2 - 2bc \cos \alpha.$$

Proof: Orient the triangle with the vertex of α at 0 and side c lying along the positive real axis. (See Figure 7.41.)

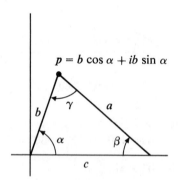

FIG. 7.41

Notice that the vertex of γ is at the point $p = b \cos \alpha + ib \sin \alpha$. The distance a is given by $|p - c|$ (the absolute value of the difference of the two complex numbers p and c). Computing this we have

$$
\begin{aligned}
a = |p - c| &= |b \cos \alpha + ib \sin \alpha - c| \\
&= |(b \cos \alpha - c) + i(b \sin \alpha)| \\
&= \sqrt{(b \cos \alpha - c)^2 + (b \sin \alpha)^2} \\
&= \sqrt{b^2 \cos^2 \alpha - 2bc \cos \alpha + c^2 + b^2 \sin^2 \alpha} \\
&= \sqrt{b^2(\cos^2 \alpha + \sin^2 \alpha) + c^2 - 2bc \cos \alpha} \\
&= \sqrt{b^2 + c^2 - 2bc \cos \alpha} \quad \text{(since } \cos^2 \alpha + \sin^2 \alpha = 1\text{).}
\end{aligned}
$$

It follows immediately that

$$a^2 = b^2 + c^2 - 2bc \cos \alpha \quad \text{(law of cosines)}. \;\square$$

Question: What do we have if α is a right angle?
Example: If $\alpha = 60°$, $b = 12$, and $c = 7$, find a.

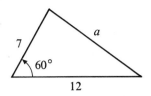

FIG. 7.42

$$a^2 = 7^2 + 12^2 - 2 \cdot 7 \cdot 12 \cos \frac{\pi}{3}$$

$$= 49 + 144 - 84 = 109.$$

Therefore $a = \sqrt{109}.$

Exercises 7.6 .

1. Interpret the law of sines if β is a right angle.

2. Interpret the law of cosines if α is a right angle.

3. Find the remaining parts of a triangle or show that no such triangle exists.

   a) $a = 3, b = 2, \gamma = 60°$ *d)* $b = 6, c = 9, \alpha = 53°$

   b) $b = 4, c = 3, \alpha = 30°$ *e)* $a = 9, b = 4, \gamma = 93°$

   c) $b = 7, c = 2, \alpha = 135°$ *f)* $a = 2, b = 2, \gamma = 45°$

4. Determine the angles of a triangle if the lengths of the sides are:

   a) 5, 7, 8   *c)* 28, 45, 53

   b) 15, 25, 30   *d)* 4, 5, 10

5. Use the law of cosines to show that the length of a given side never exceeds the sum of the lengths of the other two.

6. Given any three positive real numbers a, b, and c, does there exist a unique triangle whose sides measure a, b, and c?

7. The longer diagonal of a given parallelogram measures 20 inches. This diagonal makes angles of 37° and 26° with the sides of the parallelogram.

   a) Find the lengths of the sides of the figure.

   b) Find the length of the shorter diagonal.

8. (*Heron's formula*) Consider a triangle with sides a, b, and c, and angles opposite a with measure α.

   a) Show that the area A of the triangle is given by

   $$A = 1/2 \, bc \sin \alpha.$$

   b) Use a familiar trig identity to show that

   $$A = bc \sin (1/2 \, \alpha) \cos (1/2 \, \alpha).$$

493

c) Let $S = 1/2\,(a + b + c)$. Show that

$$\sin\frac{\alpha}{2} = \sqrt{\frac{(S - b)(S - c)}{bc}} \quad \text{and} \quad \cos\frac{\alpha}{2} = \sqrt{\frac{S(S - a)}{bc}}.$$

$\left(\textit{Hint: } \cos\dfrac{\alpha}{2} = 1/2\,(1 + \cos\alpha), \text{ and this problem appears in this section.} \right)$

d) Show that $A = \sqrt{S(S - a)(S - b)(S - c)}$. This result is called *Heron's formula*, named after the Greek geometer Heron of Alexandria who lived in the third century B.C.

9. Use Heron's formula to find the area of a triangle with legs as given.

a) 5, 7, 9   c) 5, 7, 2   e) 16, 16, 16
b) 2, 4, 1   d) 20, 14, 7   f) 3, 4, 5

10. A triangular lot at an intersection has frontage of 267 ft. on one side and 135 ft. on the other. If the third side of the lot is 356 ft. long, find the acute angle between the streets.

11. From the top of an inclined road 256 ft. long, a vertical tower at the bottom subtends an angle of 26°. If the road is inclined 40° from the horizontal, then how high is the tower?

12. The radius of the inscribed circle in a triangle is 7 ft. The area of the triangle is 450 sq. ft. Find the lengths of the sides if one angle measures 56°.

13. Gurney Gibson wishes to determine the height of an inclined ramp with angle of inclination $\pi/6$. It is constructed in such a way that it is impossible to measure this height directly. His son Grant solves this problem as follows. He rolls a tire 20 inches in diameter down the ramp and notices that the tire makes 4 1/2 revolutions as it rolls from top to bottom. How high is the ramp?

14. a) Prove that the area of any parallelogram equals the product of the lengths of a pair of adjacent sides times the sine of their included angle.

   b) Prove that the area of any convex quadrilateral is equal to one half of the product of the lengths of its diagonals times the sine of either angle formed by the diagonals.

7.7   Inverse Trigonometric Functions

Since the trigonometric functions are not *1-1*, their inverses are not functions in $R \times R$. It is possible, however, to *restrict* these functions in various ways so that the restricted versions *are 1-1* and hence the inverses of the restricted functions are functions.

For example, if we restrict the cosine function to the interval $[0, \pi]$ we will have a *1-1* function.

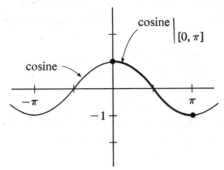

FIG. 7.43 The cosine function is not *1-1*, but its restriction cosine$|_{[0,\pi]}$ is *1-1*.

Since cosine$|_{[0,\pi]}$ is a *1-1* function, it follows that (cosine$|_{[0,\pi]})^{-1}$ is also a *1-1* function.

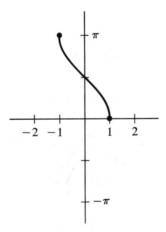

FIG. 7.44 (cosine$|_{[0,\pi]})^{-1}$ is a *1-1* function whose domain is $[-1, 1]$ and whose range is $[0, \pi]$.

There are many intervals of length π over which we could restrict the cosine and have an *invertible* function (*i.e.*, a function whose inverse is a function). Let us then define a collection of invertible functions by restricting *cosine* to various intervals of length π.

495

7.7-1 Definition: $\forall n \in Z$ cosine$_n$ is the cosine function restricted to the interval $[n\pi, (n+1)\pi]$. That is,

$$\text{cosine}_n = \text{cosine}|_{[n\pi, (n+1)\pi]}.$$

We have now a collection of invertible functions and can therefore talk about their inverses.

Example: Graph cosine$_2$ and cosine$_2^{-1}$.

Solution: cosine$_2$ = $\{(x, y): x \in [2\pi, 3\pi]$ and $y = \cos x\}$.

cosine$_2^{-1}$ = $\{(x, y): (y, x) \in \text{cosine}_2\}$.

(See Figure 7.45.)

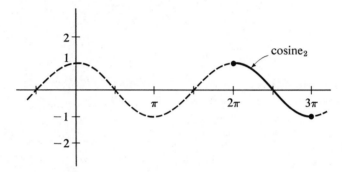

FIG. 7.45a

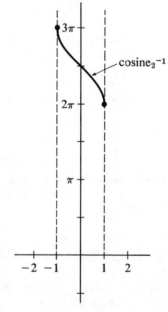

FIG. 7.45b

It should be noted that we need not necessarily restrict our domain to an interval in order to obtain a *1-1* function. Indeed, there are many ways in which one could restrict cosine to obtain an invertible function. It is most useful, however, to consider restrictions to intervals of maximum length. For example, the restriction $cosine|_{[n\pi,(n+1)\pi]}$ of the cosine function to the domain $[n\pi, (n + 1)\pi]$ is *1-1* for any n, but it is not possible to lengthen this interval and still retain the *1-1* property.

One particular member of this family of invertible functions is used more frequently than the others and as a result has a special name.

7.7-2 Definition: $cosine_0^{-1}$ is called the *Principal Inverse* of the cosine and is denoted by $Cosine^{-1}$

(i.e., $Cosine^{-1} = (cosine|_{[0,\pi]})^{-1}$

$= \{(x, y): x = cosine\ y \quad and \quad y \in [0, \pi]\}).$

In a similar fashion, let us disect the sine function into many parts by restricting it to intervals of maximum length over which no values are taken on more than once. We again have a family of functions, each of which is invertible.

7.7-3 Definition: $sine_n = sine|_{[(2n-1)\pi/2,(2n+1)\pi/2]}.$
    Example: Graph $sine_2$ and $sine_2^{-1}$.

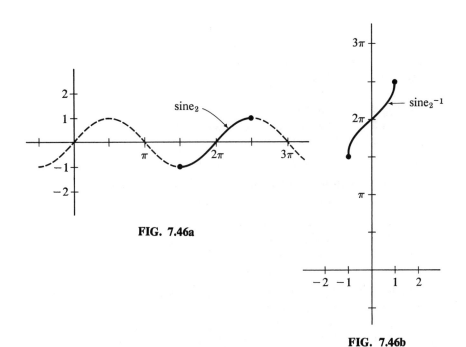

FIG. 7.46a

FIG. 7.46b

Again it is common to select a certain member of this family and call it the principal function.

7.7-4 Definition: sine_0^{-1} is called the *Principal Inverse* of the *sine* function and is denoted by Sine^{-1}

(*i.e.,* $\text{Sine}^{-1} = \text{sine}_0^{-1} = (\text{sine}|_{[-\pi/2,\pi/2]})^{-1})$.

In Figure 7.47 we have a graph of sine_0 and $\text{Sine}^{-1} = \text{sine}_0^{-1}$.

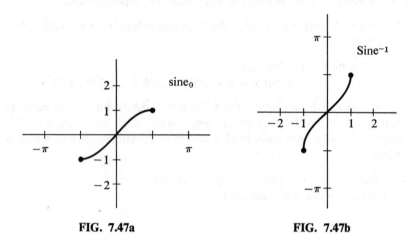

FIG. 7.47a   FIG. 7.47b

Question: What is the domain of Sine^{-1} and what is the range?

We have now that $\text{Sine}^{-1}(-1) = -\pi/2$, $\text{Sine}^{-1}(1) = \pi/2$, and for any $x \in [-1, 1]$ $\text{Sine}^{-1}(x) \in [-\pi/2, \pi/2]$.

Example: $\text{Sine}^{-1}(.3429) = .35$ since $\sin(.35) = .3429$.

Example: Solve for x where $\text{Cos}^{-1}(x) = 1$.

Solution: $\cos(\text{Cos}^{-1}x) = \cos 1$.

Therefore $x = \cos 1 = .5403$.

Let us now consider a similar process with respect to the remaining four circular functions, tangent, cotangent, secant, and cosecant.

7.7-5 Definition: $\text{tangent}_n = \text{tangent}|_{[(2n-1)\pi/2,(2n+1)\pi/2]}$.

$\text{cotangent}_n = \text{cotangent}|_{[n\pi,(n+1)\pi]}$.

$\text{secant}_n = \text{secant}|_{[n\pi,(n+1)\pi]}$.

$\text{cosecant}_n = \text{cosecant}|_{[(2n-1)\pi/2,(2n+1)\pi/2]}$.

We have made the above definition in such a way that by taking $n = 0$ one has the restricted function whose inverse is commonly called the principal inverse for the function. Graphs of these functions are shown in Figures 7.48 through 7.51.

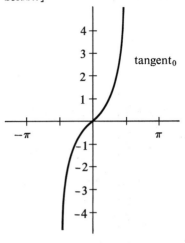

FIG. 7.48a

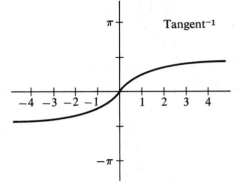

FIG. 7.48b

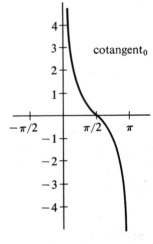

FIG. 7.49a

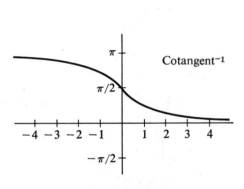

FIG. 7.49b

The principal inverses of the six trigonometric functions are often called arc-functions. That is,

$$\text{Arcsin} = \text{Sine}^{-1} \qquad \text{Arccos} = \text{Cosine}^{-1}$$
$$\text{Arctan} = \text{Tangent}^{-1} \qquad \text{Arccot} = \text{Cotangent}^{-1}$$
$$\text{Arcsec} = \text{Secant}^{-1} \qquad \text{Arccsc} = \text{Cosecant}^{-1}$$

Example: Evaluate $\text{Arctan} \sqrt{3}$.

Let $x = \text{Arctan} \sqrt{3}$ (note that $x \in [-\pi/2 - \pi/2]$).

$$\tan x = \tan (\text{Arctan} \sqrt{3}) = \tan(\text{Tan}^{-1}{}_k \sqrt{3}) = \sqrt{3}.$$

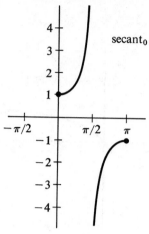

FIG. 7.50a

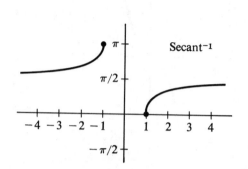

FIG. 7.50b

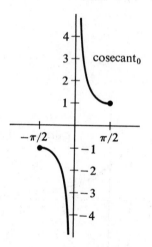

FIG. 7.51a

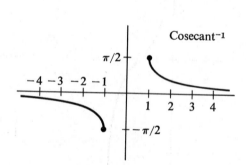

FIG. 7.51b

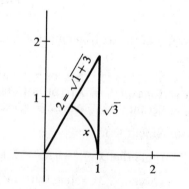

FIG. 7.52

We see that if $\tan x = \sqrt{3}$, then $\sin x = \dfrac{\sqrt{3}}{2}$. We recall then that $x = \dfrac{\pi}{3}$. We could have made an approximation of x by reading the tangent table in reverse.

Since tables of values for the six trigonometric functions are computed only for values in $[0, \pi/2)$, it follows that no negative values are listed. The following theorem is useful in extending the tables to list values for negative pre-images of the arc functions.

7.7-6 Theorem:
a) $\text{Sin}^{-1}(-t) = -\text{Sin}^{-1} t, t \in [-1, 1]$.
b) $\text{Cos}^{-1}(-t) = \pi - \text{Cos}^{-1} t, t \in [-1, 1]$.
c) $\text{Tan}^{-1}(-t) = -\text{Tan}^{-1} t$, for all t.
d) $\text{Cot}^{-1}(-t) = \pi - \text{Cot}^{-1} t$, for all t.
e) $\text{Sec}^{-1}(-t) = \pi - \text{Sec}^{-1} t$ for all $t \notin (0, 1)$.
f) $\text{Csc}^{-1}(-t) = -\text{Csc}^{-1} t$ for all $t \notin (0, 1)$.

Proof: We shall prove only the first two formulas leaving the remaining cases as exercises.

a) First, we remark that $t \in [-1, 1]$ iff $-t \in [-1, 1]$.
Let $y = \text{Sin}^{-1}(-t)$ where $t \in [-1, 1]$. Therefore

$$\sin_0 y = \sin_0 \text{Sin}^{-1}(-t) = -t$$

from which $\sin_0(-y) = t$ since $\sin e_0$ is an odd function (see Exercise 7). Hence

$$\text{Sin}^{-1} \sin_0(-y) = \text{Sin}^{-1} t$$

from which $\qquad\qquad -y = \text{Sin}^{-1} t.$
Since we let $y = \text{Sin}^{-1}(-t)$ then

$$\text{Sin}^{-1}(-t) = -\text{Sin}^{-1} t.$$

b) $\text{Cos}^{-1}(-t) = \pi/2 - \text{Sin}^{-1}(-t)$. (See Exercise 8.) Using a) above, we have

$$\text{Cos}^{-1}(-t) = \pi/2 + \text{Sin}^{-1} t.$$

Again applying Exercise 8 we have

$$\text{Cos}^{-1}(-t) = \pi/2 + \pi/2 - \text{Cos}^{-1} t = \pi - \text{Cos}^{-1} t. \;\square$$

Exercise: Interpret this theorem graphically.
Example: Find $\text{Cos}^{-1}(-.755)$. By Table IV we see that $\cos(.716) = .755$. Equivalently $\text{Cos}^{-1}(.755) = .716$. We use Theorem 7.7-6 and compute

$$\text{Cos}^{-1}(-.755) = \pi - \text{Cos}^{-1}(.755) = \pi - .716 = 2.434.$$

Example: What is $\text{Tan}^{-1}(-9.5)$? We find in Table IV that $\tan(.105) \cong 9.5$. Equivalently $\text{Tan}^{-1}(9.5) \cong .105$. Hence we have

$$\text{Tan}^{-1}(-9.5) = -\text{Tan}^{-1}(9.5) = -.105.$$

Example: What is $\text{Sec}^{-1}(-\alpha)$ if $\sec \beta = \alpha$, $\beta \in [0, \pi]$?

$$\text{Sec}^{-1}(-\alpha) = \pi - \text{Sec}^{-1} \alpha = \pi - \beta.$$

Exercises 7.7

1. What are the domain and range of:
   a) Sin^{-1}
   b) Cos^{-1}
   c) Sec^{-1}
   d) Csc^{-1}
   e) Tan^{-1}
   f) Cot^{-1}

2. What are the domain and range of:
   a) $\tan_5$
   b) $\sec_4$
   c) $\tan_{-5}^{-1}$
   d) $\sec_{-4}^{-1}$

3. Graph $\tan_2$ and $\tan_{-2}^{-1}$ and compare $\tan_{-2}^{-1}$ with Tan^{-1}.

4. Evaluate:
   a) $\text{Arctan}(-1)$
   b) $\text{Cot}^{-1}(-1)$
   c) $\text{Tan}^{-1}(.2027)$
   d) $\text{Arccot}(.0709)$

5. True-False:
   a) $\text{Sin}^{-1}(\sin(t)) = t \quad \forall t \in R$
   b) $\text{Sin}^{-1}(\sin(14)) = 14$
   c) $\text{Sin}^{-1}(\sin(1/2)) = 1/2$
   d) $\sin(\text{Sin}^{-1}(1/2)) = 1/2$
   e) $\text{Sin}^{-1}(\sin(\pi/2)) = \pi/2$
   f) $\sin(\text{Sin}^{-1}(\pi/2)) = \pi/2$

6. Show that $\forall n \in Z \quad \forall t \in R$ if t is in the domain of $\sin_n$ then $t - \pi$ is in the domain of $\sin_{n-1}$ and $\sin_n(t) = -\sin_{n-1}(t - \pi)$.

7. a) Show that sine_0 is an odd function.
   b) Why isn't cosine_0 an even function?

8. Prove that the following relationship holds between the Arcsine and Arccosine.

$$\forall t \in [-1, 1] \quad \text{Cos}^{-1} t = \pi/2 - \text{Sin}^{-1} t$$

9. Under the assumption that $a)$ and $b)$ are in the proper interval in each case, show that the identity holds. Indicate any places where it fails.

   a) $\tan(1/2 \, \text{Cos}^{-1} a) = \sqrt{\dfrac{1 - a}{1 + a}}$

   b) $\tan(\text{Tan}^{-1} a + \text{Tan}^{-1} b) = \dfrac{b + a}{1 - ab}$

   c) $\tan(\text{Tan}^{-1} a - \text{Tan}^{-1} b) = \dfrac{a - b}{1 + ab}$

10. Solve for x.
    a) Arctan $(1/3)$ + Arctan $(1/2)$ = Arcsin x
    b) Arccot $(1/3)$ + Arccot $(1/2)$ = Arccos x

11. a) Show that Csc^{-1} is an odd function.
    b) Show that Tan^{-1} is an odd function.

12. a) Given that tan $\alpha = \theta$, $\alpha \in (-\pi/2, \pi/2)$. What is $\mathrm{Tan}^{-1}(-\theta)$?
    b) Given that cot $\alpha = \theta$, $\alpha \in (0, \pi)$. What is $\mathrm{Cot}^{-1}(-\theta)$?

13. Given sin $\alpha = \theta$, cos $\alpha = \varphi$, $0 < \alpha < \pi/2$. Find:

    a) $\mathrm{Tan}^{-1}\left(-\dfrac{\theta}{\varphi}\right)$ b) $\mathrm{Cot}^{-1}\left(-\dfrac{\varphi}{\theta}\right)$

14. Without using a table, evaluate (if such a value exists):
    a) $\mathrm{Cos}^{-1} 1$ h) Arcsin $(-\sqrt{2}/2)$
    b) $\mathrm{Tan}^{-1} 1$ i) Arccos $(\sqrt{3}/2)$
    c) $\mathrm{Cos}^{-1} 0$ j) $\mathrm{Sin}^{-1}(-\sqrt{3}/2)$
    d) $\mathrm{Sec}^{-1} 2$ k) $\mathrm{Tan}^{-1} \sqrt{3}$
    e) $\mathrm{Cos}^{-1}(-1)$ l) $\mathrm{Arccot}^{-1}(-\sqrt{3})$
    f) $\mathrm{Sec}^{-1}(-2)$ m) $\mathrm{Sec}^{-1} 2/3\sqrt{3}$
    g) Arcsec $\sqrt{2}$ n) $\mathrm{Csc}^{-1}(-\sqrt{2})$

15. Without using a table, evaluate (if such a value exists):
    a) sin $\mathrm{Sin}^{-1} 3/4$ h) cos $\mathrm{Sin}^{-1} 3/5$
    b) cos $\mathrm{Cos}^{-1} 1/3$ i) sin $\mathrm{Cos}^{-1} 12/13$
    c) tan Arctan $1/2$ j) sin $\mathrm{Tan}^{-1} 3/4$
    d) sec Arccos $(-1/4)$ k) cos Arccot $8/15$
    e) cot $\mathrm{Tan}^{-1}(-4)$ l) sec $\mathrm{Tan}^{-1}(-5/12)$
    f) cos $\mathrm{Sec}^{-1} 5/2$ m) tan $\mathrm{Cos}^{-1}(-4/5)$
    g) sin Arccos $4/3$ n) sin $\mathrm{Cot}^{-1}(-24/7)$

16. Solve each of the following equations.
    a) $3 \sin x = 2$ e) $6 \sin x - \csc x + 1 = 0$
    b) $4 \cot x = 5$ f) $10 - 12 \sin^2 x + 5 \cos x = 0$
    c) $5 \cos x + 3 = 0$ g) $4 \cot x + 15 \tan x - 23 = 0$
    d) $6 \sin^2 x - 7 \sin x - 3 = 0$

17. Investigate (prove or disprove):
    a) $\forall x \in [-1, 1]$ Arccos x + Arcsin $x = \pi/2$
    b) $\forall x \notin (0, 1)$ Arcsec x + Arccsc $x = \pi/2$

    c) For all x $\mathrm{Tan}^{-1} x = \mathrm{Sin}^{-1} \dfrac{x}{\sqrt{1 + x^2}}$

    d) $\forall x \in (-1, 1)$ $\mathrm{Sin}^{-1} x = \mathrm{Tan}^{-1} \dfrac{x}{\sqrt{1 - x^2}}$

18. Graph each of the six principal inverse trig functions.

7.8   Wave Functions Derived from Sine by Composition, Simple Harmonic Motion Described by Functions A sin(mx + b)

We wish now to examine a large family of real valued functions on R which can be described by $f(x) = A \sin (mx + b)$, where A, m, and b are real numbers. In order to do this, we shall investigate independently the effect of each of the parameters A, m, and b.

Amplitude

Let us first consider the effect of the parameter A.

Example: Graph f where $f(x) = 5 \sin (x)$ for all x in R. We see that $f(x) = 0$ has the same solutions as $\sin x = 0$ and also that $f(x) < 0$ and $f(x) > 0$ have the same solutions as $\sin x < 0$ and $\sin x > 0$, respectively. Further, $f(x)$ increases or decreases accordingly as $\sin x$ increase or decreases and since $|\sin (x)|$ never exceeds 1, it follows that $|f(x)| = 5|\sin (x)|$ never exceeds 5. With these facts in mind, then, one can easily graph $y = f(x)$ by comparing it with $\sin x$. (See Figure 7.53.)

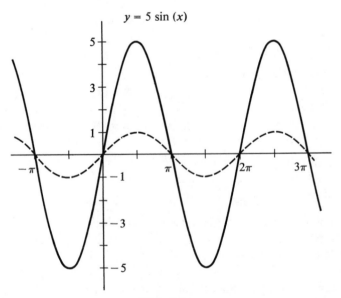

FIG. 7.53

Example: Graph $y = -1/2 \sin (x)$.

Here, if we first graph $1/2 \sin (x)$, then reflect over the x-axis, we arrive at the graph in Figure 7.54.

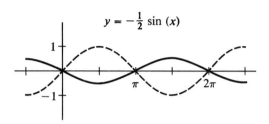

FIG. 7.54

We see that the parameter A merely has the effect of reflecting, stretching, or shrinking on the graph the image values of $\sin x$. For this reason $|A|$ is called the *amplitude*.

Frequency

We wish to study the effect of the parameter m. This parameter is closely connected to the concept of periodicity. In fact you should recall, if $g(x)$ is a periodic function with period p and m is a positive number, then $g(mx)$ is periodic with period p/m.

If f is a periodic function, then f is said to pass through one *cycle* per period. That is, if a periodic function is given by the equation $y = f(x)$, then the y values are cyclic and go through one cycle as the x values go through one period.

We consider some functions $\sin (mx)$, where $m > 0$.

Example: Let $f(x) = \sin (2x)$.

Now $\sin (t)$ goes through a complete cycle as t goes through a complete period. Notice, however, that as x passes through $[0, \pi)$ (*i.e.*, takes on all the values in $[0, \pi)$), $2x$ takes on all the values in $[0, 2\pi)$ and hence the function $\sin (2x)$ makes a complete cycle as x goes through $[0, \pi)$. Further, if x passes through $[0, 2\pi)$, then $2x$ passes through $[0, 4\pi)$ and hence $\sin (2x)$ goes through two cycles. We see then that $\sin (2x)$ will graph as a "modified" sine wave which oscillates through the real axis twice as frequently as does $\sin (x)$.

505

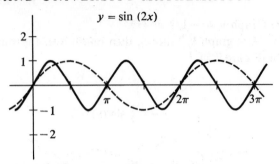

$y = \sin (2x)$

FIG. 7.55

Example: Graph sin (1/2 x).

Here the frequency with which the function passes through a complete cycle is slowed down. As x passes through $[0, 2\pi)$, $1/2\ x$ only passes through $[0, \pi)$.

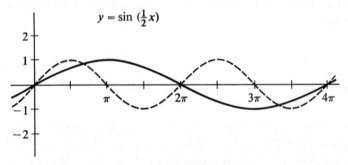

$y = \sin (\tfrac{1}{2}x)$

FIG. 7.56

In order for sin (1/2 x) to make a complete cycle x must pass from 0 to 4π.

It is clear that m is a *frequency factor.* The parameter itself is not called the frequency since it only reflects changes with respect to the natural period which is 2π. The frequency should determine the number of cycles through which the function passes as the domain variable (independent variable) passes through one unit. That is, the frequency should be the reciprocal of the period.

7.8-1 Definition: If f is a periodic function with period p, then we call $1/p$ the *frequency of f.*

Example: Let $f(x) = \sin (4x)$.

The period of f is $(2\pi)/4 = \pi/2$ and hence the frequency is $2/\pi$. That is, as x passes from 0 to 1, $f(x)$ goes through $2/\pi$ parts of a cycle.

506

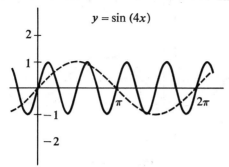

FIG. 7.57

Phase Shift

We now come to the parameter b in the function $A \sin (mx + b)$. Let us first consider the simple case $f(x) = \sin (x + b)$.

Example: Graph $\sin (x + 2)$.

If we consider the graph of $\sin u$ where $u = x + 2$, we know that as x starts at -2 and proceeds to increase, then $x + 2$ also increases. Further, as x increases by one unit then $x + 2$ increases by one unit. It follows that $\sin u$ would be a standard sine wave, but when graphed in an $(x, f(x))$ coordinate system it would begin at -2 instead of zero. That is, the "2" translates the standard sine wave two units to the left.

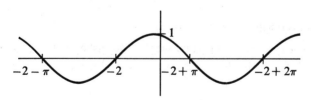

FIG. 7.58

Example: Graph $y = \sin (x - 1)$.

Now when $x = 1$, $x - 1 = 0$ and therefore we have a standard sine wave translated one unit to the right. Hence we see that $\sin (x + b)$ is a sine wave translated b units to the left using the interpretation that a negative number of units to the left is a positive number to the right.

Let us now examine $\sin (mx + b)$.

Example: Graph $y = \sin (2x + 4)$.

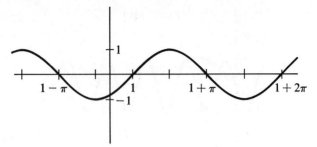

FIG. 7.59

If we write $\sin(2x + 4)$ as $\sin 2(x + 2)$ we see that we have $\sin 2u$ where $u = x + 2$. At $x = -2$, then $u = 0$ and again $x + 2$ increases at the same rate as does x. Hence we wish to graph $\sin 2u$ as being like $\sin 2x$, but translated 2 units to the left.

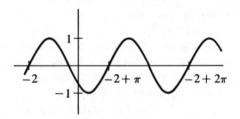

FIG. 7.60

Example: Graph $\sin(1/2\, x - 1/5)$.

We write $y = \sin 1/2\,(x - 2/5)$ and see that we wish to graph $y = \sin(1/2\, x)$ but translated 2/5 to the right (*i.e.*, $x - 2/5 = 0$ when $x = 2/5$).

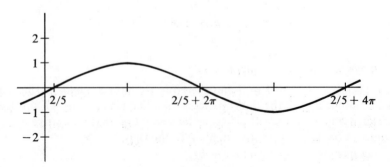

FIG. 7.61

In general, to graph $y = A \sin (mx + b)$ where A and m are positive,

we have $y = A \sin m \left(x + \dfrac{b}{m} \right)$, which graphs as a modified sine wave which

begins at $-\dfrac{b}{m}$ instead of zero. The standard sine wave is modified by changing

the amplitude to $|A|$ and multiplying the number of cycles per period by m.
If $A < 0$, then we merely reflect $|A| \sin (mx + b)$ over the x-axis.

Example: Graph $y = 2 \sin (3x - 5)$.

On solving $3x - 5 = 0$, we know to take as a starting point $x = 5/3$ and
graph a sine wave whose amplitude is 2 and which oscillates through a complete cycle three times as often as a regular sine wave (*i.e.*, the period is $2\pi/3$).

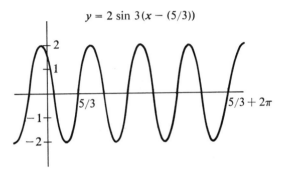

$$y = 2 \sin 3(x - (5/3))$$

FIG. 7.62

Simple Harmonic Motion

It can be shown both experimentally and theoretically that certain physical problems concerning moving bodies can be modeled by the wave functions we have described. For example, consider the problem in which a body
of mass is attached to a spring and lying on an essentially frictionless surface.

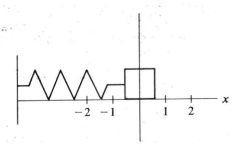

FIG. 7.63

If the spring has Hooke's constant k (*i.e.*, when the spring is stretched (compressed) x units, then the spring pulls (pushes) with a force of kx) and mass m, then the body will oscillate back and forth according to the equation

$$x = A \sin\left(\sqrt{\frac{k}{m}}\, t + \frac{\pi}{2}\right)$$

where $x = 0$ when the system is at equilibrium (in this case when the spring is unstretched), and where A is the amount the spring is initially stretched at time $t = 0$.

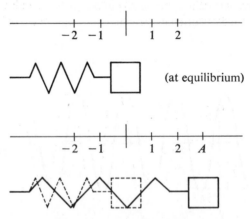

FIG. 7.64 At time $t = 0$, the body is released from a rest position with the spring stretched A units.

The position x of the body at time t after being released can be determined by $x = A \sin\left(\sqrt{\frac{k}{m}}\, t + \frac{\pi}{2}\right)$. If we make a time-position graph of this motion, we have the graph in Figure 7.65.

Note that this is also the graph of $x = A \cos\left(\sqrt{\frac{k}{m}}\, t\right)$.

Many oscillatory physical phenomena in mechanics and electronics can be modeled by functions of the form $A \sin(mx + b)$. In such cases it is said that the system vibrates with *Simple Harmonic Motion*.

More Functions by Composition

Let us conclude this section with some more elaborate variations of the sine function composed with other functions.

510

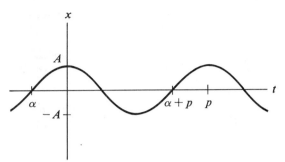

FIG. 7.65 $x = A \sin \left(\sqrt{\dfrac{k}{m}}\, t + \dfrac{\pi}{2} \right)$ has period $p = 2\pi\sqrt{m}/\sqrt{k}$. The "starting point" is $\alpha = -\pi\sqrt{m}/2\sqrt{k}$.

Example: Graph $f(x) = \sin(1/x)$.

Note that

$$f(-x) = \sin(-1/x) = -\sin(1/x) = -f(x)$$

and hence we can use symmetry through the origin to obtain the graph for $x < 0$. Now if $x \in (0, 1]$, then $1/x \in [1, \infty)$. Hence all the oscillations made by sine in $[1, \infty)$ are made by $\sin(1/x)$ in $(0, 1]$. If $x \in [1, \infty)$, then $1/x \in (0, 1]$, and since sine makes only a partial wave in $(0, 1]$, then $\sin(1/x)$ makes only a partial wave in $[1, \infty)$. It is reasonably clear after some very deep thought that $y = \sin(1/x)$ has the graph shown in Figure 7.66.

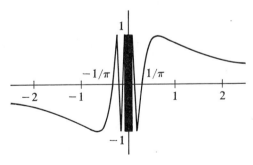

FIG. 7.66

Example: Graph $f(x) = x \sin(x)$.

First observe that

$$f(-x) = (-x)\sin(-x) = -(-x)\sin(x) = x\sin(x) = f(x).$$

511

That is, f is an even function and hence will graph symmetric about the y-axis. We compare this to $A \sin(x)$ and note here that the only variation is the fact that the function $x \sin(x)$ has an increasing amplitude as x increases. Hence we have a modified sine function whose waves are bounded by the lines $y = x$ and $y = -x$. (See Figure 7.67.)

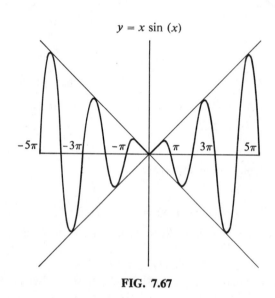

$y = x \sin(x)$

FIG. 7.67

Example: Graph $y = x + \sin(x)$.

Here we graph by adding the values of the two functions x and $\sin(x)$.

Exercises 7.8

1. Graph each of the following and determine amplitude and period.

   a) $2 \sin(x)$ f) $3 \cos(3x)$ j) $1/2 \sin(2x - 1)$

   b) $-3 \sin(x)$ g) $\sin(x + 1)$ k) $1/3 \cos(1/2\,x + 3)$

   c) $1/2 \cos(x)$ h) $\sin(x + 2)$ l) $\dfrac{1}{x} \sin x$

   d) $\sin(3x)$ i) $2 \sin(2x + 2)$ m) $x \sin\left(\dfrac{1}{x}\right)$

   e) $\cos(1/2\,x)$

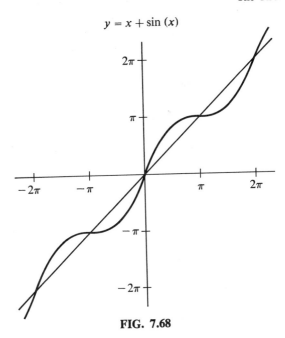

$y = x + \sin(x)$

FIG. 7.68

2. Graph each of the following.

  a) $y = 2x + \sin(x)$

  b) $y = 1/2 \, x \sin(x)$

  c) $y = e^x \sin(x)$

  d) $y = e^x + \sin(x)$

  e) $y = e^x - \sin(x)$

  f) $y = -e^x \sin(x)$

  g) $y = \sin(x^2)$

3. Graph:

  a) $\sin(e^x)$

  b) $2 \sin(e^x)$

  c) $e^{\sin(x)}$

  d) $\sin(x - e^x)$

  e) $\sin(e^{-x})$

  f) $\sin(\sin x)$

4. a) Explain why it is no restriction to assume $m > 0$ in a discussion of the family of functions $A \sin(mx + b)$ (i.e., show that if $m < 0$, then there exist numbers B, k, and c such that

$$A \sin(mx + b) = B \sin(kx + c) \quad \text{where } k > 0).$$

  b) Explain why a complete discussion of the functions $A \sin(mx + b)$ automatically includes a discussion of the function $A \cos(mx + b)$.

5. Determine the position after 23 seconds of a 1-gram block of mass which is oscillating on a spring with Hooke's constant 4 (in the proper units) which was stretched 7 cm. and released from rest at time 0. (The system is lying on a frictionless table.)

6. Graph:

  a) $y = \cos(2x - 1)$

  b) $y = -3 \cos(x + 1)$

  c) $y = 2 \tan(x + 2)$

  d) $y = \sec(2x)$

513

7. Extend as many of the techniques of this section as possible to the remaining trigonometric functions.

7.9 De Moivre's Theorem and Complex Exponents

Recall that the complex number set can be matched one to one with the set of ordered pairs

$$\{(r, \theta): r \in (0, \infty) \text{ and } \theta \in [0, 2\pi)\} \cup \{(0, 0)\}$$

where the correspondence is given by

$$(r, \theta) \text{ maps to } r \cos \theta + i r \sin \theta = r(\cos \theta + i \sin \theta).$$

That is, each non-zero complex number has a unique representation in the form

$$r(\cos \theta + i \sin \theta) \quad \text{where} \quad 0 < r \quad \text{and} \quad 0 \leq \theta < 2\pi$$

and of course many duplicate representations by changing θ by multiples of 2π or by changing θ by odd multiples of π and negating r. When a non-zero complex number is in the form $z = r(\cos \theta + i \sin \theta)$, then $|r|$ is the modulus of z and θ differs from arg (z) by some even multiple of π if $r > 0$, and by some odd multiple of π if $r < 0$. In any case, we call θ *an argument* of z since it is possible to express $z = r(\cos \theta + i \sin \theta)$.

The next theorem is one of the most interesting and useful elementary results concerning circular functions and complex numbers. Recall that $|z_1 z_2| = |z_1| |z_2|$, which tells us that when we multiply two complex numbers, the length (modulus) of the product is the product of the lengths of the two numbers which were multiplied. The following result establishes this fact and also tells us that the argument of the product is the sum of the arguments of the two numbers which were multiplied.

7.9-1 Theorem: Let $z_1 = r(\cos \theta + i \sin \theta)$ and $z_2 = s(\cos \alpha + i \sin \alpha)$. Then

$$z_1 z_2 = (rs)(\cos (\theta + \alpha) + i \sin (\theta + \alpha)).$$

Proof: $(r(\cos \theta + i \sin \theta))(s(\cos \alpha + i \sin \alpha))$

$= (rs)(\cos \theta + i \sin \theta)(\cos \alpha + i \sin \alpha)$ (by field properties)

$= (rs)((\cos \theta \cos \alpha - \sin \theta \sin \alpha) + i(\cos \theta \sin \alpha + \sin \theta \cos \alpha))$

                                             (field properties)

$= (rs)(\cos (\theta + \alpha) + i \sin (\theta + \alpha))$ (identities for sine and cosine). $\square$

7.9-2 Corollary: De Moivre's Theorem

$$\forall n \in Z \quad (r(\cos \theta + i \sin \theta))^n = r^n(\cos (n\theta) + i \sin (n\theta)).$$

Proof: Case 1. $n > 0$ (by induction on n).

1) Clearly true if $n = 1$.

2) Assume $(r(\cos \theta + i \sin \theta))^k = r^k(\cos (k\theta) + i \sin (k\theta))$.

Now $(r(\cos \theta + i \sin \theta))^{k+1} = (r(\cos \theta + i \sin \theta))^k(r(\cos \theta + i \sin \theta))$
$= r^k(\cos (k\theta) + i \sin (k\theta))(r(\cos \theta + i \sin \theta))$ (by induction hypothesis)
$= (r^k r)(\cos (k\theta + \theta) + i \sin (k\theta + \theta))$ (by the above theorem)
$= r^{k+1}(\cos (k + 1)\theta + i \sin (k + 1)\theta)$.

Hence by induction it follows that
$$\forall n \geq 1 \quad (r(\cos \theta + i \sin \theta))^n = r^n(\cos (n\theta) + i \sin (n\theta)).$$

Case 2. $n = 0$ $(r(\cos \theta + i \sin \theta))^0 = 1$

and $\qquad\qquad r^0(\cos (0) + i \sin (0)) = 1(1 + i0) = 1$.

Case 3. $n < 0$ $(i.e., -n > 0)$.

Let $m = -n$. Now
$$(r(\cos \theta + i \sin \theta)^n = \frac{1}{(r(\cos \theta + i \sin \theta))^m}$$

$$= \frac{1}{r^m(\cos (m\theta) + i \sin (m\theta))} = \frac{r^{-m}}{\cos (-m\theta) - i \sin (-m\theta)}$$
$$\text{(even and odd functions)}$$

$$= \frac{r^n}{\cos (n\theta) - i \sin (n\theta)} = \frac{r^n(\cos (n\theta) + i \sin (n\theta))}{(\cos (n\theta) - i \sin (n\theta))(\cos (n\theta) + i \sin (n\theta))}$$

$$= \frac{r^n(\cos (n\theta) + i \sin (n\theta))}{(\cos^2 (n\theta) + \sin^2 (n\theta))} = r^n(\cos (n\theta) + i \sin (n\theta)). \quad \text{(Why?)} \; \square$$

Example: Let
$$z_1 = 2(\cos (\pi/3) + i \sin (\pi/3)) \quad \text{and} \quad z_2 = 3(\cos (\pi/3) + i \sin (\pi/3)).$$
Locate $z_1 z_2$ in the complex plane. Now
$$z_1 z_2 = 6(\cos (2\pi/3) + i \sin (2\pi/3)).$$

nth Roots

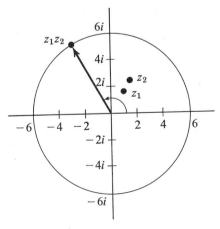

FIG. 7.69

Using De Moivre's Theorem we notice that every complex number has a square root. That is, if $z = r(\cos \theta + i \sin \theta)$, then a square root for z is

$$\sqrt{r} \, (\cos (\theta/2) + i \sin (\theta/2)).$$

Similarly, every complex number $r(\cos \theta + i \sin \theta)$ has a cube root $\sqrt[3]{r}(\cos (\theta/3) + i \sin (\theta/3))$. We shall, in fact, prove a much more general result.

7.9-3 Theorem: Let $z \in \mathcal{C}$, $z \neq 0$, and let n be a natural number. Then z has exactly n, nth roots. (That is, for exactly n distinct complex numbers u, $u^n = z$.)

Proof: Let $z = r(\cos \theta + i \sin \theta)$ where $r > 0$ and $0 \leq \theta < 2\pi$. Let

$$z_k = r^{(1/n)}\left(\cos \left(\frac{\theta + 2\pi k}{n}\right) + i \sin \left(\frac{\theta + 2\pi k}{n}\right)\right), \qquad k \in \{0, 1, 2, \ldots, n - 1\}.$$

Now by De Moivre's Theorem

$$(z_k)^n = r(\cos (\theta + 2\pi k) + i \sin (\theta + 2\pi k)) = r(\cos \theta + i \sin \theta) = z.$$

Since $\qquad 0 \leq \dfrac{\theta + 2\pi k}{n} < 2\pi \qquad$ whenever $\qquad 0 \leq k < n,$

it is immediate that we have found n distinct nth roots of z. In order to guarantee that there are no other roots, we merely notice that if

$$(s(\cos \alpha + i \sin \alpha))^n = z.,$$

then $\qquad s^n(\cos (n\alpha) + i \sin (n\alpha)) = r(\cos \theta + i \sin \theta)$

from which $\qquad n\alpha = \theta + 2\pi k \qquad$ for some $\qquad 0 \leq k < n,$

or that $\qquad \alpha = \dfrac{\theta + 2\pi k}{n}.$ ☐

Example: Locate the three cube roots of 1.

Now $1 = \cos (0) + i \sin (0)$ and hence the cube roots of 1 are:

$$1, \quad \cos (2\pi/3) + i \sin (2\pi/3), \quad \cos (4\pi/3) + i \sin (4\pi/3).$$

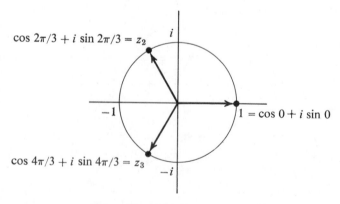

FIG. 7.70 The cube roots of 1.

That is, they lie on the unit circle distributed evenly starting with the cube root 1 itself.

Example: Find the 4th roots of $2(\cos (\pi/4) + i \sin (\pi/4))$. The roots are:

$$z_1 = \sqrt[4]{2}(\cos (\pi/16) + i \sin (\pi/16))$$
$$z_2 = \sqrt[4]{2}(\cos (\pi/16 + \pi/2) + i \sin (\pi/16 + \pi/2))$$
$$z_3 = \sqrt[4]{2}(\cos (\pi/16 + \pi) + i \sin (\pi/16 + \pi))$$
$$z_4 = \sqrt[4]{2}(\cos (\pi/16 + 3\pi/2) + i \sin (\pi/16 + 3\pi/2))$$

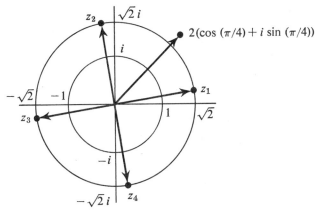

FIG. 7.71   The 4th roots of
$2(\cos (\pi/4) + i \sin (\pi/4))$.

The four roots are distributed evenly on the circle with radius $\sqrt[4]{2}$ beginning with $\sqrt[4]{2}(\cos (\pi/16) + i \sin (\pi/16))$.

Complex Exponents

In our development of the number systems from the natural numbers to the complex numbers, we managed in each case to use successfully each new collection of numbers for exponents. Exponentiation in the case of the natural numbers was a very simple idea, namely multiple addition. For the negative integers it was related to the existence of reciprocals for multiplication, while for rational numbers we needed the existence of roots along with the restriction that the base of the power be positive. We used arbitrary real numbers for exponents by making the definition in terms of supremum and infimum. In all cases we observed that certain fundamental properties of exponents are preserved, namely the facts that:

   a) $x^{a+b} = x^a x^b$

and *b*) $(x^a)^b = x^{ab}$,

along with the fact that in each case exponentiation extended to a larger number system is truly an extension and not an entirely new process. In view of this development, one might naturally explore the possibility of extending the use of exponents to include arbitrary complex numbers. Surprisingly enough, this can be done by merely denoting our trigonometric function with exponential notation.

7.9-4 Definition: $\forall \theta \in R$ $\quad e^{i\theta} = \cos \theta + i \sin \theta$ (*i.e.*, $e^{i\theta} = T(\theta)$). (This is the same irrational number e discussed earlier,

$$e = \sup \{(1 + (1/n))^n : n \in N\}. \qquad e \cong 2.71 \qquad \text{but} \qquad e > 2.71.)$$

We cannot at this time fully justify the use of the number e for this purpose. The reason for using e is made clear in a study of calculus. It is possible, however, to justify writing this in exponential form. First, let us define e^z for an arbitrary complex number z.

7.9-5 Definition: $\forall z \in \mathcal{C}$ if $z = x + iy$, then $e^z = e^{x+iy} = e^x e^{iy}$.

7.9-6 Theorem: Let $w, z \in \mathcal{C}$. Then $e^{w+z} = e^w e^z$.

Proof: Let $w = a + bi$ and $z = x + iy$.

Now $\quad e^w e^z = e^{a+bi} e^{x+iy} = e^a e^{bi} e^x e^{iy}$

$\qquad = e^a e^x (\cos b + i \sin b)(\cos y + i \sin y)$

$\qquad = e^a e^x ((\cos b \cos y - \sin b \sin y) + i(\cos b \sin y + \sin b \cos y))$

$\qquad = e^a e^x (\cos (b + y) + i \sin(b + y))$

$\qquad = e^{a+x} e^{i(b+y)} = e^{(a+x)+i(b+y)}$

$\qquad = e^{(a+ib)+(x+iy)} = e^{w+z}$. $\square$

7.9-7 Theorem: If $z \in \mathcal{C}$ and $n \in Z$, then $(e^z)^n = e^{nz}$.

Proof: This is merely a restatement of De Moivre's Theorem. Let $z = x + iy$. Now

$$(e^{x+iy})^n = (e^x(\cos y + i \sin y))^n$$
$$= (e^x)^n(\cos (ny) + i \sin (ny)) = e^{nx} e^{iny}$$
$$= e^{nx+iny} = e^{n(x+iy)} = e^{nz}. \square$$

We now have the fact that every complex number z can be expressed in the form $z = re^{i\theta}$ and that $z^n = r^n e^{in\theta}$. Not only that, but z has an nth root given by $r^{(1/n)} e^{i\theta/n}$. We do not wish to extend exponentiation using complex numbers any further at this point, but merely point out that it is possible to consistently and usefully define a^z for arbitrary $z \in \mathcal{C}$ and $a \in R^+$.

The Triangle Inequality

Let us apply some of the information now at our disposal to prove a long overdue result. Notice how closely this theorem is related to the *law of cosines.*

7.9-8 Theorem: (*The Triangle Inequality*)

If $z_1, z_2 \in C$, then $|z_1 + z_2| \leq |z_1| + |z_2|$.

Proof: Let $z_1 = re^{i\theta}$ and $z_2 = \rho e^{i\varphi}$.

Now

$$|re^{i\theta} + \rho e^{i\varphi}| = |e^{i\theta}|\,|r + \rho e^{i(\varphi-\theta)}| \quad \text{(Explain!)}$$
$$= |r + \rho\cos(\varphi - \theta) + i\rho\sin(\varphi - \theta)|$$
$$= \sqrt{(r + \rho\cos(\varphi - \theta))^2 + (\rho\sin(\varphi - \theta))^2}$$
$$= \sqrt{r^2 + 2r\rho\cos(\varphi - \theta) + \rho^2\cos^2(\varphi - \theta) + \rho^2\sin^2(\varphi - \theta)}$$
$$= \sqrt{r^2 + \rho^2 + 2r\rho\cos(\varphi - \theta)}.$$

However,

$$(|r| + |\rho|)^2 = r^2 + \rho^2 + 2|r\rho| \geq r^2 + \rho^2 + 2r\rho\cos(\varphi - \theta). \quad \text{(Why?)}$$

Therefore $\qquad \sqrt{r^2 + \rho^2 + 2r\rho\cos(\varphi - \theta)} \leq |r| + |\rho|$

and hence we have established the result. □

Exercises 7.9

1. In each case express the number in the form $r(\cos\theta + i\sin\theta)$ where $0 \leq r$ and $0 \leq \theta < 2\pi$.

   a) $-2(\cos(\pi/4) + i\sin(\pi/4))$ *c)* $-7(\cos 2 + i\sin 2)$

   b) $3(\cos(11\pi/4) + i\sin(11\pi/4))$ *d)* $4(\cos 7 + i\sin 7)$

2. Use De Moivre's Theorem, the Binomial Theorem, and the fact that $a + ib = x + iy \Rightarrow a = x$ and $b = y$ to establish the following trigonometric identities.

   a) $\cos(3\theta) = \cos^3(\theta) - 3\cos(\theta)\sin^2(\theta)$

   b) $\sin(3\theta) = 3\cos^2(\theta)\sin(\theta) - \sin^3(\theta)$

   c) $\cos(5\theta) = \cos^5(\theta) - 10\cos^3(\theta)\sin^2(\theta) + 5\cos(\theta)\sin^4(\theta)$

   d) $\sin(5\theta) = 5\cos^4(\theta)\sin(\theta) - 10\cos^2(\theta)\sin^3(\theta) + \sin^5(\theta)$

3. *a)* Determine the six 6th roots of 1.

   b) Determine the eight 8th roots of 1.

   c) When is a root of 1 real?

4. Determine and graph the three cube roots of $2e^{i(\pi/6)}$.

5. Locate each of the following numbers in the complex plane.

   a) $3e^i$ *b)* $-2e^{i7}$ *c)* $-1/2\,e^{3i}$ *d)* $2e^{3i}$

6. Determine the polar form $re^{i\theta}$ for each of the following numbers.

   a) $2 + i2$ *c)* $2 + 3i$ *e)* $-2 - 3i$

   b) $\sqrt{2}/2 + (\sqrt{3}/2)i$ *d)* $4 - 2i$ *f)* $4 - 1/2\,i$

7. Solve:

   a) $z^2 + 2i = 0$ *c)* $2z^2 + 2iz + 1 = 0$

   b) $2z^4 + 1 = 0$ *d)* $iz^2 + 3z + 2i = 0$

8. Under what conditions will the nth roots of a complex number z include a real root

   a) at $|z|^{1/n}$?

b) at $-|z|^{1/n}$?

c) at both $|z|^{1/n}$ and $-|z|^{1/n}$?

9. Locate and graph each point in $\mathcal{C}$.

a) $2/3\, e^{\,7i}$ *c)* $3/2\, e^{i}$ *e)* $-5/2\, e^{(\pi/4)i}$

b) $-5/3\, e^{2i}$ *d)* $5/2\, e^{-4i}$

10. Is De Moivre's Theorem true if $a = 0$? How many nth roots of zero are there?

11. Simplify:

a) $\dfrac{ie^{3i}e^{i}}{e^{2i}}$ *d)* $\dfrac{e^{4}e^{2-3i}}{7ie^{4+6i}}$

b) $\dfrac{ie^{2i}e^{-i}}{\sin 3 - i\cos 3}$ *e)* $(\cos 6 + i\sin 6)e^{-6i}$

c) $\dfrac{e^{-3i}e^{5i}}{ie^{5+7i}}$ *f)* $\dfrac{\cos 2 - i\sin 2}{\sin 3 - i\cos 3}e^{3i}$

12. Prove that the n numbers $|a|^{(1/n)}e^{i\frac{2k\pi}{n}}$, $k = 0, 1, 2, \ldots, n-1$ are *evenly* spaced on a circle of radius $|a|^{1/n}$ when graphed.

13. Recall the quadratic equation which was developed for fields in which certain numbers had square roots. Every non-zero complex number has two square roots; hence, the quadratic formula works in general with no restrictions in $\mathcal{C}$. Solve the following equations.

a) $2x^2 + 3ix + i = 0$ *d)* $e^{2i}x^2 + 2ix - 2e^{3i} = 0$

b) $(2 + i)x^2 - ix + 2 = 0$ *e)* $(5i + 1)x^2 - (2 + i)x - 3i = 0$

c) $x^2 + 2x - 7i = 0$

14. Let T denote the set of distinct nth roots of 5.

a) Show that $\#(T) = n$.

b) Show that T contains a real number.

c) Show that T is closed under multiplication.

d) Show that there is a number $\omega \in T$ such that each element of T can be written in the form ω^k for some $k \in N$. (Such a number ω is called a *generator* of the set T.)

e) $z \in T \Rightarrow z^n = 5$. (Hence $\omega^n = 5$.)

15. *a)* Find the 7th roots of -2.

b) Graph the 7 numbers found in *a)*.

16. *a)* Interpret graphically the effect of squaring, cubing, etc., a complex number.

b) Show that $e^{i\pi} + 1 = 0$. (This is a very interesting identity, in that it relates *five* basic constants of mathematics! This is a very pleasing (and surprising?) state of affairs.)

17. *a)* Find the set T of 4th roots of 1.

b) Show that there are two generators of T. (*Hint:* See Problem 14.)

c) Show that (-1) generates a subset of T, the set of real numbers in T.

d) Interpret the generator and its powers graphically.

18. *a)* How many roots are there to the equation $z^{m/n} = a, \dfrac{m}{n} \in Q$.

   b) Extend De Moivre's Theorem so as to give the roots of part *a)*.

7.10   Hyperbolic and Circular Functions Extended to the Complex Numbers, Parametric Equations Using $re^{i\theta}$

Often we have extended various functions to include a larger domain. In fact, in the last section we extended the exponential function E_e to include complex numbers ($E_e(z) = e^z$). It is immediate then that the two hyperbolic functions sinh and cosh have also been extended to the complex numbers. There are some very interesting relationships between the hyperbolic and circular functions and their extensions to $\mathcal{C}$.

7.10-1 Theorem: $\cosh i\theta = \cos \theta$ and $\sinh i\theta = i \sin \theta$.

   Proof:

$$\cosh i\theta = \frac{e^{i\theta} + e^{-i\theta}}{2} \quad \text{(Why?)}$$

$$= \frac{\cos \theta + i \sin \theta + \cos (-\theta) + i \sin (-\theta)}{2}$$

$$= \frac{2 \cos \theta}{2} = \cos \theta. \quad \text{(Why?)}$$

$$\sinh i\theta = \frac{e^{i\theta} - e^{-i\theta}}{2}$$

$$= \frac{(\cos \theta + i \sin \theta) - (\cos (-\theta) + i \sin (-\theta))}{2}$$

$$= \frac{2i \sin \theta}{2} = i \sin \theta. \quad \square$$

This relationship is reminiscent of the fact that $\cos (-\theta) = \cos \theta$ and $\sin (-\theta) = -\sin \theta$. Keeping in mind that $-1 = i^2$ one might be hopeful of finding a natural extension of the sine and cosine functions to $\mathcal{C}$, which ties these facts together.

7.10-2 Definition: $\forall \theta \in R, \quad \forall x \in R, \quad \forall y \in R.$

$$\sin i\theta = i \sinh \theta \quad \text{and} \quad \cos i\theta = \cosh \theta$$

and $\sin (x + iy) = \sin x \cos (iy) + \cos x \sin (iy)$

and $\cos (x + iy) = \cos x \cos (iy) - \sin x \sin (iy).$

521

Once again, there are other very strong reasons, which we are not prepared to investigate, for extending these functions in this manner. We shall, however, show that some very interesting relationships occur among the hyperbolic and circular functions with respect to the number i.

7.10-3 Theorem: $\forall z \in \mathbb{C}$

    a) $\sin iz = i \sinh z$.
    b) $\sinh iz = i \sin z$.
    c) $\cos iz = \cosh z$.
    d) $\cosh iz = \cos z$.

    Proof: Let $z = x + iy$.

    a)
$$\begin{aligned}
\sin iz = \sin i(x + iy) &= \sin(-y + ix) \\
&= \sin(-y)\cos(ix) + \cos(-y)\sin(ix) \\
&= -\sin y \cosh x + i \cos y \sinh x \\
&= -\sin y \frac{e^x + e^{-x}}{2} + i \cos y \frac{e^x - e^{-x}}{2} \\
&= \frac{e^x(-\sin y + i \cos y) - e^{-x}(\sin y + i \cos y)}{2}
\end{aligned}$$

but
$$\begin{aligned}
i \sinh z &= i \frac{e^z - e^{-z}}{2} \\
&= i \frac{e^{x+iy} - e^{-x-iy}}{2} = i \frac{e^x e^{iy} - e^{-x} e^{-iy}}{2} \\
&= i \frac{e^x(\cos y + i \sin y) - e^{-x}(\cos(-y) + i \sin(-y))}{2} \\
&= i \frac{e^x(\cos y + i \sin y) - e^{-x}(\cos y - i \sin y)}{2} \\
&= \frac{e^x(-\sin y + i \cos y) - e^{-x}(\sin y + i \cos y)}{2}.
\end{aligned}$$

    b)
$$\begin{aligned}
\sinh iz &= \sinh(-y + ix) \\
&= \frac{e^{-y+ix} - e^{y-ix}}{2} \\
&= \frac{e^{-y}(\cos x + i \sin x) - e^{y}(\cos(-x) + i \sin(-x))}{2} \\
&= \frac{e^{-y}(\cos x + i \sin x) - e^{y}(\cos x - i \sin x)}{2}
\end{aligned}$$

but
$$\begin{aligned}
i \sin z &= i \sin(x + iy) \\
&= i(\sin x \cos(iy) + \cos x \sin(iy)) \\
&= i(\sin x \cosh y + i \cos x \sinh y) \\
&= -\cos x \sinh y + i \sin x \cosh y
\end{aligned}$$

$$= -\cos x \, \frac{e^y - e^{-y}}{2} + i \sin x \, \frac{e^y + e^{-y}}{2}$$

$$= \frac{e^{-y}(\cos x + i \sin x) - e^y(\cos x - i \sin x)}{2}.$$

c) and d) are left as exercises. $\square$

7.10-4 Corollary: $\sin(-\theta) = \sin(ii\theta) = i \sinh i\theta = ii \sin \theta = -\sin \theta.$

$$\cos(-\theta) = \cos(ii\theta) = \cosh i\theta = \cos \theta.$$

Although we cannot fully justify our motives for extending sinh, cosh, sine, cosine in the particular manner we have chosen, it is nevertheless intriguing to find that there are extensions which seem to connect them all so closely. Many other functions can be extended to the complex plane in a fashion which contributes to the solutions of many physical problems. In particular, the natural logarithm function can be extended by taking restricted inverses of the exponential function e^z. (Note that e^z as extended to $\mathcal{C}$ is not a *one-one* function.) The study of complex functions is a large and fascinating field. Unfortunately, we have time in this course to do no more than scratch the surface.

Parametric Equations

Let us now use some of the information and notation involving complex exponentiation to discuss some curves in $\mathcal{C}$. If we consider the set of all Ae^{it} as t varies over R, we simply have the circle with radius $|A|$. That is, the point Ae^{it} simply revolves about 0 as t moves along the real line. Let us then examine some slight variations of this simple situation.

Example: Graph the set $\{te^{it} : t \in R\}$.

If we first graph the trace of $f(t) = te^{it}$ as t varies over $[0, \infty)$, we have a spiral. The point te^{it} is t units from 0 and t radians of rotation from the positive x-axis. (See Figure 7.72.)

If t decreases, then e^{it} spins clockwise and te^{it} again lies further and further from 0. By solving the equation $f(-t) = f(t)$ we find that these two spirals intersect at the points

$$(-1)^n(2n + 1)\frac{\pi}{2} i.$$

That is, if

$$-te^{i(-t)} = te^{it},$$

then

$$-1 = e^{i2t}.$$

Now $e^{i\theta} = -1$ whenever θ is an odd multiple of π, hence the spirals intersect when $2t = (2n + 1)\pi$ for some $n \in Z$. Thus we have the curve

$$\{te^{it} : t \in R\}$$

as shown in Figure 7.73. This curve is called the *spiral of Archimedes*.

523

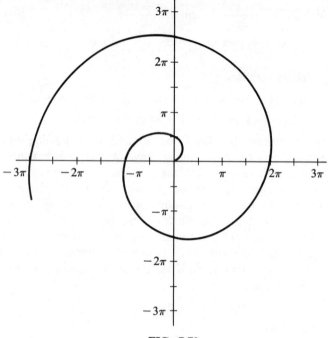

FIG. 7.72

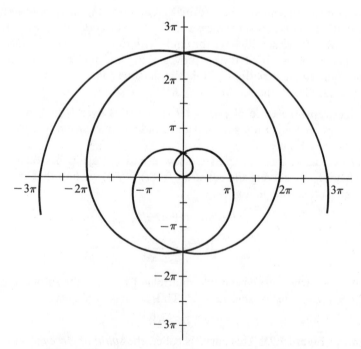

FIG. 7.73 The curve te^{it} (the spiral of Archimedes).

Example: Graph the curve given parametrically by $(\sin 2t)e^{it}$.

Let us examine the behavior of this curve as t passes through

$$[0, \pi/2], \qquad [\pi/2, \pi], \qquad [\pi, 3\pi/2], \qquad \text{and} \qquad [3\pi/2, 2\pi].$$

That is, as e^{it} rotates through each of the four quadrants. As t goes from 0 to $\pi/2$, $\sin 2t$ goes from 0 to 1 and back to 0. As t goes from $\pi/2$ to π, $\sin 2t$ goes from 0 to -1 and back to 0. Hence, the portion of the curve

$$\{(\sin 2t)e^{it}: t \in [0, \pi]\} \text{ is given in Figure 7.74.}$$

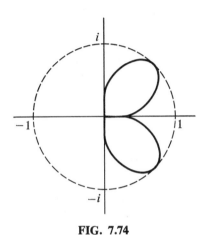

FIG. 7.74

Similarly, by following the curve through the next two quadrants and noting that

$$(\sin 2(t + 2\pi))e^{i(t+2\pi)} = (\sin 2t)e^{it}$$

we have the entire curve in Figure 7.75.

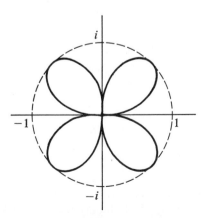

FIG. 7.75 The curve $\sin (2t)e^{it}$.

Exercises 7.10

1. Show that:
    a) $\cos iz = \cosh z$ b) $\cosh iz = \cos z$

2. Find a maximal region in the plane for which e^z could be restricted to yield an invertible (*one-one*) function.

3. Evaluate:

a) $\sin i$	c) $\cos i$	e) $\sin \pi i$	g) $\cos \pi i$
b) $\sinh i$	d) $\cosh i$	f) $\sinh \pi i$	h) $\cosh \pi i$

4. Show that $\forall z \in \mathbb{C}$:
    a) $\sinh (z + 2\pi i) = \sinh z$ c) $\sin (z + 2\pi) = \sin z$
    b) $\cosh (z + 2\pi i) = \cosh z$ d) $\cos (z + 2\pi) = \cos z$

5. Show that $\cos \theta = \dfrac{e^{i\theta} + e^{-i\theta}}{2}$ and that $\sin \theta = \dfrac{e^{i\theta} - e^{-i\theta}}{2}$. Notice how this agrees with

    $$r(\cos \theta + i \sin \theta) = re^{i\theta}.$$

6. Graph the curve in $\mathbb{C}$ given parametrically by
    a) $(\sin t)e^{it}$.   e) $(3/t)e^{it}$.
    b) $(\cos t)e^{it}$.   f) $(5 \cos 4t)e^{it}$.
    c) $(\cos 2t)e^{it}$.   g) $(1 - 2 \sin t)e^{it}$.
    d) $(\sinh t)e^{it}$.   h) $(1 - \cos t)e^{it}$.

7. a) Find a such that $(\sin at)e^{it}$ makes three loops and then repeats.
    b) Find a such that $(\sin at)e^{it}$ makes 5 loops and then repeats.

8. Locate in $\mathbb{C}$, the point
    a) $(5 + 3i)e^{i(\pi/2)}$.   c) $(2 - i)e^{i(\pi/6)}$.
    b) $(4 - 2i)e^{i(\pi/4)}$.   d) $(-2 - 4i)e^{i(-\pi/3)}$.

9. Describe in general the location of the point $(x + iy)e^{i\theta}$ in terms of x, y, and θ.

10. a) Graph the line $L = \{x + iy : y = 2x\}$. Let

    $$L_{\pi/4} = \{e^{i(\pi/4)}z : z \in L\}.$$

    Show that $L_{\pi/4}$ is a line. Graph the line.
    b) Let $L = \{x + iy : y = mx\}$ and $L_\theta = \{ze^{i\theta} : z \in L\}$. Show that $L_\theta = \{x + iy : y = kx\}$ where $k = \tan (\theta + \operatorname{Tan}^{-1} m)$.

7.11   Transformation of Coordinates, Rotation of Axes

One day Grant Gibson was lying on his stomach on the river bridge watching the water flow by. After he lay there for some time, he suddenly had the feeling that he was moving and the water was standing still. He then noticed that he could either think of the water as standing still with him moving, or as the water moving while he was still.

Changing Coordinates

We have seen that we can coordinatize the complex plane in several ways. For example, the familiar matching of each complex number $x + iy$ with its Cartesian coordinate (x, y) is a coordinatization of $\mathcal{C}$. Also, the matching of each complex number $x + iy$ with its polar coordinate $(\sqrt{x^2 + y^2}, \text{Tan}^{-1} y/x)$ is a coordinatization of $\mathcal{C}$. We wish now to investigate some very simple ways to assign new coordinates to each point of $\mathcal{C}$ and to use these new coordinates to help graph certain geometric figures. Recall, for example, that we performed certain simplification procedures (completing the square) on the constraining equation for a circle with center not at zero, and from the form of the equation, we selected a simple change of coordinates which allowed us to think of the center of the circle as being at zero. Before we proceed further, let us formalize our discussion with the following definition.

7.11-1 Definition: Let g, h be functions from $R \times R \to R$ such that

$$f(x, y) = (g(x, y), h(x, y))$$

is *one-one*. Then the complex number $x + iy$ is said to have f-coordinates (x', y') where $x' = g(x, y)$ and $y' = h(x, y)$.

Example: If $P(x, y) = (\sqrt{x^2 + y^2}, \text{Tan}^{-1} y/x)$, then the P-coordinates are the familiar polar coordinates.

Example: Let $f(x, y) = (x - 2, y - 3) = (x', y')$.

Here the f-coordinates are called translated coordinates. In this case, we could view the change of coordinates as a translation

$$T(x + iy) = x + iy - 2 - 3i = (x - 2) + (y - 3)i = x' + iy'.$$

(See Figure 7.76.)
The new coordinates are determined by the formulas

$$x' = x - 2 \qquad \text{and} \qquad y' = y - 3.$$

Hence the point $2 + 3i$ with Cartesian coordinate $(2, 3)$ has translated coordinate $(0, 0)$, the point $5 + 4i$ has translated coordinate $(3, 1)$, etc. This transformation of coordinates can be roughly viewed as either moving all points in the plane down 3 units and to the left 2 units, or as moving the reference frame up 3 units and to the right 2 units.

We find this type of transformation very useful in graphing an equation

$$(x - a)^2 + (y - b)^2 = r^2.$$

527

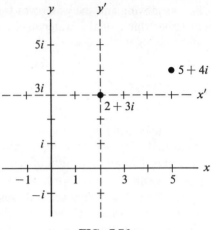

FIG. 7.76

With respect to the new coordinates, this becomes

$$x'^2 + y'^2 = r^2,$$

an equation whose graph we recognize immediately, provided we can geo-metrically connect two frames of reference for graphing in x, y and x', y'. In doing this, we are applying a procedure which is very general.

Consider for example a constraining equation (for the points in some set)

$$F(x, y) = 0$$

(constraints on the Cartesian coordinates). Assume we have f-coordinates defined by

$$f(x, y) = (g(x, y), h(x, y)) = (x', y'),$$

or equivalently by

$$x' = g(x, y) \qquad y' = h(x, y).$$

Since f is *one-one*, we should be able to solve these two equations (at least theoretically) for x and y. If we consider that we have done this where

$$x = g'(x', y') \qquad y = h'(x', y'),$$

then it follows that

$$F(g'(x', y'), h'(x', y')) = 0$$

is a constraining equation in the new coordinates. Thus, it might be the case that we can immediately determine the graph of the set of points.

Rotation of Axes

In this section we are particularly interested in transformations of coordi-nates involved when one wishes his new system to represent a geometric rotation of the standard Cartesian frame of reference.

Let us assume that we want all points $x + iy$ to have new coordinates (x', y') so that we could view the axes as having been rotated by θ as shown in Figure 7.77.

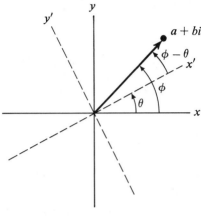

FIG. 7.77

We see that a point $a + bi$ viewed from the rotated frame would have the same modulus as viewed from the Cartesian frame. However, in viewing $a + bi$ from the rotated frame, one would see a number whose argument has been decreased by θ as compared to viewing it from the standard frame. Using this and the fact that multiplying a complex number by $e^{i\varphi}$ spins it around by an angle φ, we can determine the transformation we desire. Notice that the multiplication

$$(x + iy)e^{-i\theta}$$

has the effect of leaving a number with the same modulus and an argument that has been decreased by θ.

Now
$$\begin{aligned}
(x + iy)e^{-i\theta} &= (x + iy)(\cos(-\theta) + i\sin(-\theta)) \\
&= (x + iy)(\cos\theta - i\sin\theta) \\
&= (x\cos\theta + y\sin\theta) + i(y\cos\theta - x\sin\theta)
\end{aligned}$$

and hence we wish to change coordinates by the mapping Θ as follows.

7.11-2 Definition: The rotation of axes mapping Θ is given by

$$\Theta(x, y) = (x\cos\theta + y\sin\theta, \, y\cos\theta - x\sin\theta).$$

Equivalently
$$x' = x\cos\theta + y\sin\theta$$
$$y' = y\cos\theta - x\sin\theta.$$

These two equations can easily be solved for x and y, and you should do so now. Observe, however, that we should be able to reverse our operation of rotating points as follows.

529

$$(x' + iy')e^{i\theta} = (x' + iy')(\cos \theta + i \sin \theta)$$
$$= (x' \cos \theta - y' \sin \theta) + i(y' \cos \theta + x' \sin \theta)$$

from which

$$x = x' \cos \theta - y' \sin \theta$$
$$y = y' \cos \theta + x' \sin \theta.$$

That is, we have

7.11-3 Theorem:

$$\theta^{-1}(x', y') = (x' \cos \theta - y' \sin \theta, y' \cos \theta + x' \sin \theta)$$

(*i.e.,*)
$$x = x' \cos \theta - y' \sin \theta$$
$$y = y' \cos \theta + x' \sin \theta).$$

The General Quadratic in x and y

We would now like to consider the graphing of sets described by equations of the form,

$$Ax^2 + Bxy + Cy^2 + Dx + Ey + F = 0$$

(called the general quadratic equation in x and y). If $B = 0$, we can transform the equation into the form

$$A(x - a)^2 + C(y - b)^2 + F' = 0$$

by completing squares. It can then be reduced by a translation of axes to the simple form

$$Ax'^2 + Cy'^2 + F' = 0.$$

We shall now prove that by some appropriate rotation of axes, the general quadratic equation can be transformed into an equation with no xy term.

7.11-4 Theorem: If $B \neq 0$ and

$$Ax^2 + Bxy + Cy^2 + Dx + Ey + F = 0 \qquad (1)$$

is the constraining equation for a set then by some rotation of axes

$$x = x' \cos \theta - y' \sin \theta$$
$$y = y' \cos \theta + x' \sin \theta$$

a new constraining equation will result which is of the form

$$A'x'^2 + C'y'^2 + D'x' + E'y' + F' = 0.$$

Proof: By substituting the transformation equations into (1) we have

$$A(x' \cos \theta - y' \sin \theta)^2 + B(x' \cos \theta - y' \sin \theta)(y' \cos \theta + x' \sin \theta)$$
$$+ C(y' \cos \theta + x' \sin \theta)^2 + D(x' \cos \theta - y' \sin \theta)$$
$$+ E(y' \cos \theta + x' \sin \theta) + F = 0.$$

Thus $A(x'^2 \cos^2 \theta - 2x'y' \sin \theta \cos \theta + y'^2 \sin^2 \theta)$
$$+ B(x'y' \cos^2 \theta - x'y' \sin^2 \theta + x'^2 \sin \theta \cos \theta - y'^2 \sin \theta \cos \theta)$$
$$+ C(y'^2 \cos^2 \theta + 2x'y' \sin \theta \cos \theta + x'^2 \sin^2 \theta)$$
$$+ D(x' \cos \theta - y' \sin \theta) + E(y' \cos \theta + x' \sin \theta) + F = 0.$$

We then have

$$A'x'^2 + C'y'^2 + D'x' + E'y' + F'$$
$$+ (-2A \sin \theta \cos \theta + B(\cos^2 \theta - \sin^2 \theta) + 2C \sin \theta \cos \theta)x'y' = 0.$$

Using the identities

$$2 \sin \theta \cos \theta = \sin 2\theta \qquad \cos^2 \theta - \sin^2 \theta = \cos 2\theta$$

and setting the coefficient on $x'y'$ to zero we have

$$B \cos 2\theta = (A - C) \sin 2\theta$$

or equivalently

$$\cot 2\theta = \frac{A - C}{B}. \quad \square$$

Example: Graph the equation

$$4x^2 - 24xy + 11y^2 + 72x - 116y + 204 = 0.$$

Using the result of Theorem 7.11-4 we know that we should rotate the axes by θ where

$$\cot 2\theta = \frac{4 - 11}{-24} = \frac{7}{24}.$$

Using the identity $\tan^2 + 1_f = \sec^2$, we deduce that $\cos 2\theta = 7/25$ from which

$$\cos \theta = \sqrt{\frac{1 + 7/25}{2}} = \frac{4}{5}$$

$$\sin \theta = \sqrt{\frac{1 - 7/25}{2}} = \frac{3}{5}.$$

Let us then rotate axes by the formulas

$$x = \frac{4}{5}x' - \frac{3}{5}y'$$

$$y = \frac{4}{5}y' + \frac{3}{5}x'.$$

$$4\left(\frac{4}{5}x' - \frac{3}{5}y'\right)^2 - 24\left(\frac{4}{5}x' - \frac{3}{5}y'\right)\left(\frac{4}{5}y' + \frac{3}{5}x'\right) + 11\left(\frac{4}{5}y' + \frac{3}{5}x'\right)^2$$

$$+ 72\left(\frac{4}{5}x' - \frac{3}{5}y'\right) - 116\left(\frac{4}{5}y' + \frac{3}{5}x'\right) + 204 = 0.$$

Thus

$$4\left(\frac{16}{25}x'^2 - \frac{24}{25}x'y' + \frac{9}{25}y'^2\right) - 24\left(\frac{16}{25}x'y' - \frac{9}{25}x'y' + \frac{12}{25}x'^2 - \frac{12}{25}y'^2\right)$$

$$+ 11\left(\frac{16}{25}y'^2 + \frac{24}{25}x'y' + \frac{9}{25}x'^2\right) + \frac{288}{5}x' - \frac{216}{5}y' - \frac{464}{5}y'$$

$$- \frac{348}{5}x' + 204 = 0.$$

Collecting like terms we have

$$-5x'^2 + 20y'^2 - 12x' - 136y' + 204 = 0.$$

Now by completing the squares we have

$$-5\left(x' + \frac{6}{5}\right)^2 + 20\left(y' - \frac{17}{5}\right)^2 = -204 - \frac{36}{5} + \frac{1156}{5} = \frac{100}{5} = 20$$

which can be written

$$\left(y' - \frac{17}{5}\right)^2 - \frac{(x' + 6/5)^2}{4} = 1.$$

We now recognize that the translation

$$x'' = x' + \frac{6}{5}$$

$$y'' = y' - \frac{17}{5}$$

will simplify the equation to

$$y''^2 - \frac{x''^2}{4} = 1$$

which graphs as in Figure 7.78.

This can be determined by graphing

$$y'' = \sqrt{1 + \frac{x''^2}{4}} \quad \text{and} \quad y'' = -\sqrt{1 + \frac{x''^2}{4}}$$

separately. (Note that $y'' = 0$ $x''/2$ as $x'' \to \infty$.)

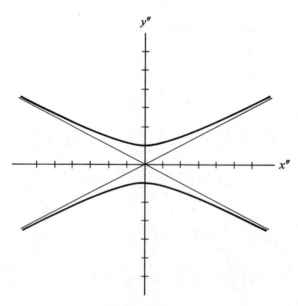

FIG. 7.78

Let us now graph this in the x, y plane (the plane $\mathcal{C}$) in view of the transformations we used. (See Figure 7.79.)

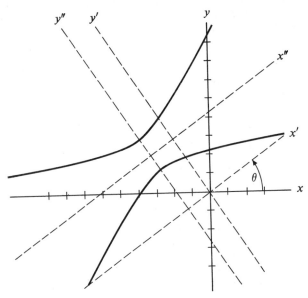

FIG. 7.79

Exercises 7.11

1. Graph each of the following curves by using symmetry, asymptotes, and by other techniques you know.

a) $9x^2 - 16y^2 = 225$

b) $9y^2 + 4x^2 = 144$

c) $3x^2 + 7y^2 = 84$

d) $11x^2 - 5y^2 + 220 = 0$

e) $x^2 + 3y^2 = 108$

f) $y^2 = 12x$

g) $x^2 + 10y = 0$

h) $2x^2 = 15y$

2. In each case, determine an angle of rotation which will give coordinates for which the constraining equation has no xy term. Change coordinates and graph the curve showing both sets of axes.

a) $x^2 + 2xy + y^2 = 2$

b) $x^2 - 3xy + y^2 = 1$

c) $8x^2 - 3\sqrt{3}\, xy + 5y^2 = 133$

d) $13x^2 + 4\sqrt{3}\, xy + 9y^2 = 105$

e) $x^2 - 4xy - 2y^2 = 1$

3. By completing the square, determine a translation which will simplify the equation to the form $Ax^2 + By^2 = F$. Make the translation and graph the curve showing both sets of axes.

a) $9x^2 - 36x + 4y^2 + 16y + 16 = 0$

b) $4x^2 - y^2 + 32x + 4y + 60 = 0$

c) $x^2 + y^2 - 10x - 24y = 0$

d) $6x^2 - 4y^2 - 12x + 16y + 34 = 0$

4. Complete the square for the variable in which a square appears, and graph the equation by making an appropriate translation.

a) $y^2 + 6y - 3x + 6 = 0$

b) $4x^2 - 4x - 32y = 15$

c) $2x^2 - 6x + 5y + 17 = 0$

d) $x^2 + 4y^2 - 12x + 16y + 16 = 0$

5. Make the appropriate transformations and graph each equation.

a) $x^2 + 24xy - 6y^2 + 4x + 48y + 34 = 0$

b) $73x^2 + 72xy + 52y^2 - 218x - 176y + 97 = 0$

c) $6x^2 + 13xy + 6y^2 - 7x - 8y + 2 = 0$

d) $9x^2 - 24xy + 16y^2 - 3x + 4y - 6 = 0$

e) $2x^2 + 4xy + 4y^2 + 2x + 3 = 0$

6. *a*) Try to simplify the equation

$$Ax^2 + Bxy + Cy^2 + Dx + Ey + F = 0$$

by first completing squares (a translation) and then by a rotation.

b) Explain this result in view of the fact that $(\alpha z) + \beta \neq \alpha(z + \beta)$. Recall that αz defines a rotation and $z + \beta$ a translation.

8

LINEARITY

In this chapter we shall investigate several interesting mathematical topics, all of which depend upon the notion of linearity which has already been introduced. Not a small part of our work will be aimed at familiarizing the reader with notation which is considered to be standard, and which will be encountered frequently in his later work. Of the concepts which are to be discussed here, possibly the two most important are:

a) The concept of linearity and associated notions, such as solutions of systems of linear equations and inequalities; and

b) The notion of maximization of functions, with an elementary treatment of linear programming as an example.

We wish to introduce the notion of a linear (vector) space and relate the notion to equation solving. We shall see that some equations have, as their solutions, points in a linear space. We shall use the concept of the linear space to develop equation solving machinery. We have time here only to introduce a few of the more elementary ideas and problems in the very large field of mathematics known as linear algebra. We will state a few abstract definitions and illustrate them with some familiar systems and problems.

Techniques are developed in this chapter which will enable the reader to solve rather interesting problems of a certain type concerning "optimal strategies." For example, consider the following problem confronting Gilbert Gibson (Gurney's father).

Gilbert runs the Gibson Grain Elevator Company. He has storage space for 100,000 bushels of wheat, of which there are three grades available: plump kernel, medium kernel, and scrawny kernel. Due to federal regulations, Gilbert must buy at least as much scrawny as plump kernel wheat. Unfortunately, there are only 50,000 bu. of medium grade available for him to purchase (although he may buy any part of this 50,000 bu. lot). Experience in the past has led Mr. Gibson to estimate that he will make a profit of 7¢/bu. on the plump wheat, 5¢/bu. on the medium wheat, and 4¢/bu. on the scrawny wheat, if only small amounts are sold. However, when large lots are sold, the profit per bushel decreases. In fact, Mr. Gibson estimates that the profit per bushel decreases to the following rates for entire lots of any of the three grades of grain in excess of 50,000 bu.:

> plump: 5¢/bu.
> medium: 4¢/bu.
> scrawny: 2¢/bu.

Mr. Gibson wants to determine the amounts of the three grades of wheat which should be purchased in order to maximize his estimated profit on selling the entire lot of wheat. What amounts of each should he purchase?

You should now attempt this problem. We later return to furnish a solution.

8.1 Linear Functions

Recall that in Chapter 5 we investigated the class of continuous functions in $R \times R$ with the property that $\ell(x + y) = \ell(x) + \ell(y)$. (We called this the "additivity property.") It was noted that $\ell(ax) = a \cdot \ell(x)$. (This is called the "homogeneity property.") Finally, a homogeneous, additive function in $R \times R$ was called a "linear function." Formally,

8.1-1 *Definition:* A function $f: A \to B$ is *linear* if $\forall x, y \in A$ and $\forall a \in R$,

$$f(ax + y) = af(x) + f(y).$$

Recall that in order to apply this definition, it must be possible to "multiply" elements in A and B by real numbers a, and to "add" elements in A and elements in B. That is, A and B must be closed under addition and under multiplication by real numbers. The class of numbers containing the elements a may be different from the set of real numbers. It is common, for example, to generalize our definition to include multiplication by complex numbers.

Linear Functions as Lines in $R \times R$

Recall that the class of all linear functions from R to R is composed of functions of the form

$$f(x) = mx + b$$

and that the graphs of linear functions $f: R \to R$ are straight lines where parameters m and b have the following graphical interpretation (see Figure 8.1).

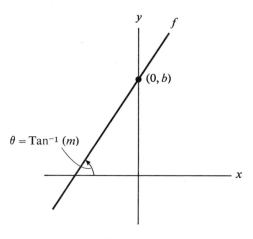

FIG. 8.1

The number m is the tangent of the angle θ from the abscissa axis to the given line (m is zero if the line is parallel to the axis of the abscissa, or, equivalently, if the function is a constant function). The number b is the y-intercept of the line (that is, the ordinate of the point of intersection of the line with the ordinate axis).

An abstract definition of linear functions does not require that the domain or range necessarily be a set of real numbers. In fact, you will soon encounter linear functions in contexts which do not use real number domains and ranges.

Linear Functions

We have discussed several alternate "forms" of the linear function in $R \times R$. The "general form"

$$Ax + By + C = 0$$

of the linear equation is very easily generalized to universes of higher dimension. For example, in "three space" (that is, in the universal set $R \times R \times R$), the linear function is described by

$$Ax + By + Cz + D = 0. \tag{1}$$

This equation describes a function

$$f \colon R \times R \to R$$

of the form $z = f(x, y)$ provided $C \neq 0$. The function can be viewed as the set of ordered pairs

$$\left\{ ((x, y), z) \colon z = \frac{-Ax - By - D}{C} \right\},$$

537

and the notation

$$f(x, y) = z = \frac{-Ax - By - D}{C}$$

indicates that the image of the point $(x, y) \in R \times R$ is the point $(-Ax - By - D)/C \in R$. The graph of f in this case is a plane (see Figure 8.2).

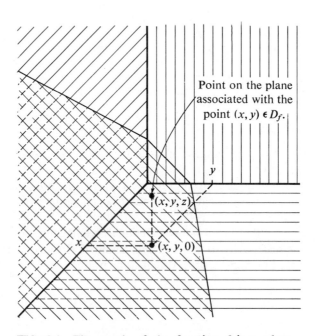

FIG. 8.2 The graph of the function f is a plane. Above we have the portion of f in the first octant. The graph consists of the ordered triples of the form $(x, y, (-Ax - 3y - D)/C)$. The set $D_f \times \{0\}$ is the "horizontal" plane containing the x and y axes. This plane is often called the "x, y" plane.

It is convenient to relabel the constants and variables of equation (1) as follows:

$$A = a_1 \qquad x = x_1$$
$$B = a_2 \qquad y = x_2$$
$$C = a_3 \qquad z = x_3$$
$$D = -a_0$$

Using the new notation, the form of equation (1) is

$$a_1x_1 + a_2x_2 + a_3x_3 = a_0,$$

or, using summation notation,

$$\sum_{i=1}^{3} a_i x_i = a_0.$$

This "general form" of the linear function in $R \times R \times R$ is easily generalized to universal sets of the form $X_{i=1}^{n} R$. Thus we say that the equation

$$\sum_{i=1}^{n} a_i x_i = a_0 \tag{2}$$

defines a linear function

$$f: \underset{i=1}{\overset{n-1}{\times}} R \to R$$

(provided $a_n \neq 0$). In this case we associate the $(n-1)$-tuples $(x_1, x_2, \ldots, x_{n-1})$ with points in the domain of f, and x_n as the image of this $(n-1)$-tuple under f. The graph of the linear function described by (2) is called a *hyperplane*. Note that it is not possible to give a graphical sketch of a hyperplane if $n > 3$. If $n = 3$, the hyperplane is an ordinary plane in $R \times R \times R$. If $n = 2$, the hyperplane is a line in $R \times R$.

You will have occasion later to deal with expressions such as that appearing in the left hand side of equation (2). The term "linear combination" is used to describe such an expression.

8.1-2 Definition: Suppose V is a universal class of objects closed under addition and scalar multiplication for some set of scalars S. An element

$$\sum_{i=1}^{n} a_i x_i$$

of V is called a *linear combination* of the x_i's. (Here "a_i" denotes a scalar, and "x_i" denotes an element of V.)

Example: A linear function in $R \times R$ is described by stating that the linear combination $a_1 x_1 + a_2 x_2$ remains constant (a_0, say) for all $x_1 \in R$ and $x_2 \in R$. In this case,

$$\sum_{i=1}^{2} a_i x_i = a_0$$

graphs as a line in the plane. (In this example, R serves as both the universal class V and the set of scalars S.)

Example: $2x + x^2$ is a linear combination of two functions:

$$f_1 = x \quad \text{and} \quad f_2 = x^2.$$

The scalars in this case are the real numbers $a_1 = 2$ and $a_2 = 1$, so that

$$2x + x^2 = \sum_{i=1}^{2} a_i f_i.$$

(In this example R is the set of scalars and V consists of functions.)

539

Exercises 8.1

1. Let $f_1(x) = \sin(x)$ and $f_2(x) = x$. Graph the functions which are the following linear combinations of f_1 and f_2. (Keep in mind that we have previously defined multiplication of such functions by real numbers, as well as addition of the functions.)

a) $2f_1 + 3f_2$ c) $2f_1 + 5f_2$

b) $(-1)f_1 + 2f_2$ d) $(-3)f_1 + (-2)f_2$

2. Graph the planes in $R \times R \times R$ described by the following linear combinations of x, y, and z. (*Hint:* Plot some critical ordered 3-tuples.)

a) $2x + 3y + z = 1$ c) $-2x - 2y - 2z = -1$

b) $x + (-2)y + 3z = -4$ d) $5x + y - 3z = 0$

When will such a plane be "level" (parallel with the x, y-plane)?

3. a) Show that the set of all linear functions $f: R \to R$ such that $m = b$ is a one-parameter family. (The slope is equal to the y-intercept.)

b) Interpret the family of part a) graphically.

4. Find the equivalence classes of "$\sim$" defined by: $\forall \ell, f \in \mathcal{F}$, $\ell \sim f \Leftrightarrow$ slope of ℓ = slope of f. ($\mathcal{F}$ is the family of all linear functions from R to R.)

5. What is the graph of a hyperplane if $n = 1$?

6. Prove that

a) the inverse of a linear function with nonzero slope exists.

b) the inverse of such a linear function is linear.

c) the composition of linear functions is linear.

7. Show that the condition of Definition 8.1-1 is equivalent to the two conditions of additivity and homogeneity.

8. Find the polar coordinate description of a linear function.

9. Verify that "lim" is a linear function on the class of continuous functions in $R \times R$.

10. Simplify each of the following linear combinations of complex numbers. ($\mathcal{C}$ is the universal class V and R is the set of scalars.)

a) $2(3 + i) + 4(2 - i) + 5(-4 - 2i)$

b) $(-1)(7 - i) + (-3)(5 + 3i) + (-2)(-3 - i)$

c) $5(6 + i) - 3(2 - 3i) + 4(-3 - 6i)$

11. Simplify each of the following linear combinations of complex numbers.

a) $\sum\limits_{k=1}^{3} 2^k(1 + i)^k$ c) $\sum\limits_{m=0}^{5} (1 - 2^m)(2 + i^m)$

b) $\sum\limits_{m=1}^{4} 2(1 - i)^m$ d) $\sum\limits_{k=0}^{3} 3^{k-1}(1 - i)^k$

8.2 Groups, Linear Spaces, and Vectors

Recall that we have in the past designated certain algebraic structures such as number rings and fields and studied their properties abstractly. By doing this we found that a great deal of time could be saved when studying several different examples of the structures. For example, we found that Q, R, and $\mathcal{C}$ were fields; as a result, all have the same elementary algebraic properties.

Using this information we avoided building a completely new list of equation solving rules for $\mathcal{C}$. We merely went ahead and used any of the field properties we had used to solve equations in Q and R.

We wish now to designate two simple abstract structures and give some familiar examples in each case. The first of these is a structure with a single operation.

Groups

8.2-1 Definition: A *commutative group* is a set G along with a binary operation $\oplus$ on G with the following properties:

1) $\forall x, y, z$ $(x \oplus y) \oplus z = x \oplus (y \oplus z)$ *(associative law)*
2) $\forall x, y$ $x \oplus y = y \oplus x$ *(commutative law)*
3) $\exists y \;\; \forall x$ $x \oplus y = x$ *(identity law)*
       (this y is called 0)
4) $\forall x \;\; \exists y$ $x \oplus y = 0$ *(law of inverses)*
       (this y is called $-x$)

You are already familiar with the fact that the rational numbers Q, the real numbers R, and the complex numbers $\mathcal{C}$ are groups under the operation of addition. You are in fact familiar with many simple group results, such as the uniqueness of the identity element and the inverse elements.

Example: Consider $G = \{(x, y, z): x, y, z \in R\}$ (*i.e.,* $G = R \times R \times R$). Define

$$(x, y, z) \oplus (a, b, c) = (x + a, y + b, z + c) \quad \text{(addition by components)}.$$

It is easy to show that $G = R \times R \times R$ is a group under the operation of component-wise addition.

Example: Let $\mathcal{F} = \{f: f: R \to R \text{ and } f(x) = mx + b\}$ be the class of all linear functions in $R \times R$. If we add functions (elements of $\mathcal{F}$) by the point-wise definition for addition of functions,

$$\forall x \in R \quad (f \oplus g)(x) = f(x) + g(x),$$

then $\mathcal{F}$ is a group.

541

We can establish this by showing the following:

    a) If $f, g \in \mathfrak{F}$,   then $f \oplus g \in \mathfrak{F}$.
    b) $\oplus$ is associative and commutative.
    c) 0_f is an identity element for $\oplus$.
    d) $\forall f \in \mathfrak{F}$ $-f \in \mathfrak{F}$ and $f + (-f) = 0_f$.

Example: Let $V_n = \{\omega \in \mathbb{C}: \omega^n = 1\}$ (the set of nth roots of 1, where $n \in N$). V_n is a group under ordinary multiplication of complex numbers. (Verify this.)

Linear Spaces

    Let us now present the second type of abstract space which we promised. A linear space (also called a vector space) involves two kinds of algebraic structures, a field and a group, along with an operation (called scalar multiplication) connecting them in a certain fashion.

8.2-2 Definition: A *linear space* consists of a group V and a field F along with an operation "$\cdot$": $F \times V \to V$ ("$\cdot$" is called scalar multiplication) such that:

1) $\forall x \in V$	$1 \cdot x = x$	(1 is the multiplicative identity element in F)
2) $\forall \alpha \in F$	$\forall x, y \in V$	$\alpha \cdot (x \oplus y) = \alpha \cdot x \oplus \alpha \cdot y$
3) $\forall \alpha, \beta \in F$	$\forall x \in V$	$(\alpha + \beta) \cdot x = \alpha \cdot x \oplus \beta \cdot x$
4) $\forall \alpha, \beta \in F$	$\forall x \in V$	$(\alpha\beta) \cdot x = \alpha \cdot (\beta \cdot x)$

(Note the various kinds of addition and multiplication in this definition. Identify them.)

The elements of V are called *vectors*, and the elements of F are called *scalars*. We say that V is a *vector space over the scalar field F.*
    Although we have four distinct operations in a vector space, we usually use only two symbols to denote them, leaving it for the context to make it clear which is intended; that is, we use the same symbol (usually juxtaposition) to denote both the multiplicative operation in F and scalar multiplication. We use the same sign "$+$" to denote both the additive operation on F and the group operation in V.
    Example: Consider $V = R \times R \times R$ to be the set of vectors using component-wise addition, and let R be the set of scalars where scalar multiplication is defined by

$$\forall \alpha \in R \quad \forall (x, y, z) \in R \times R \times R \quad \alpha(x, y, z) = (\alpha x, \alpha y, \alpha z).$$

It is easy to show that V is a linear space.
    Example: Let $V = \mathbb{C}$ and $F = R$. If $\alpha \in R$ and $x \in \mathbb{C}$, then αx is defined and $\alpha x \in \mathbb{C}$. It is easy to show that we have a vector space. In fact, we have

already seen examples in which elements of $\mathcal{C}$ were viewed graphically as vectors (arrows) to be added to each other and multiplied by real number scalars.

Linear Combinations

One of the basic useful ideas concerning vector spaces is the concept of combining vectors. In a vector space we have the ability to add two vectors or to multiply one vector by a scalar. We can of course extend this to the addition of several vectors which themselves may have been the result of a scalar multiplication.

Example: Let $V = R \times R$ and $F = R$.

Let $\qquad x = (1, 4), \qquad y = (6, 3), \qquad \alpha = 3, \qquad \beta = 2.$

We have here $x, y \in V$ are vectors and $\alpha, \beta \in R$ are scalars.

If $\quad z = \alpha x + \beta y = 3 \cdot (1, 4) + 2 \cdot (6, 3) = (3, 12) + (12, 6) = (15, 18),$

then z is a linear combination of x and y. (See Figure 8.3.)

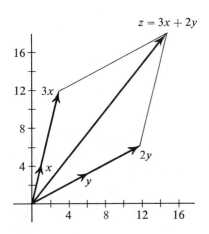

FIG. 8.3 Graphical interpretation of $z = \alpha x + \beta y$.

8.2-3 Definition: Let V be a vector space over the field F.

If $\quad z = \sum_{i=1}^{n} \alpha_i x_i \qquad$ where $\qquad \alpha_i \in F$ and $x_i \in V, i = 1, 2, \ldots, n,$

then we say that z is a *linear combination* of the vectors $x_1, x_2, \ldots, x_n$.

543

The Vector Spaces R^n Over R

In this chapter we shall do considerable work with the linear spaces

$$R \times R = R^2, \; R \times R \times R = R^3, \; \overbrace{R \times R \times R \times \ldots \times R}^{n} = R^n.$$ We shall find it useful to denote the n-tuples in such spaces by a vertical notation rather than horizontal. That is, for example, we shall denote the ordered pair $(2, 4)$ by $\begin{pmatrix} 2 \\ 4 \end{pmatrix}$ and the ordered triple $(4, 1, 7)$ by $\begin{pmatrix} 4 \\ 1 \\ 7 \end{pmatrix}$.

Example: Let $x = \begin{pmatrix} 2 \\ 1 \\ 4 \end{pmatrix}$, $y = \begin{pmatrix} 3 \\ 1 \\ 3 \end{pmatrix}$. Let $\alpha = 4$ and $\beta = 2$.

Then $\qquad \alpha x + \beta y = 4 \begin{pmatrix} 2 \\ 1 \\ 4 \end{pmatrix} + 2 \begin{pmatrix} 3 \\ 1 \\ 3 \end{pmatrix} = \begin{pmatrix} 8 \\ 4 \\ 16 \end{pmatrix} + \begin{pmatrix} 6 \\ 2 \\ 6 \end{pmatrix} = \begin{pmatrix} 14 \\ 6 \\ 22 \end{pmatrix}$.

Exercises 8.2

1. Let $V = R \times R$, $F = R$. Let $x = \begin{pmatrix} 2 \\ 1 \end{pmatrix}$, $y = \begin{pmatrix} 3 \\ 3 \end{pmatrix}$, $z = \begin{pmatrix} 1 \\ 4 \end{pmatrix}$. Find:

   a) $x + y$ c) $2x + y$ e) $2x + 3y - z$

   b) $y + z$ d) $3x - 2y$ f) $3x + 4z$

2. Let $V = R \times R \times R$, $F = R$. Let $x = \begin{pmatrix} 2 \\ 1 \\ 9 \end{pmatrix}$, $y = \begin{pmatrix} 3 \\ 4 \\ 1 \end{pmatrix}$, $z = \begin{pmatrix} 1 \\ 1 \\ 2 \end{pmatrix}$. Find:

   a) $2x + y$ d) $2x + 3y + 2z$

   b) $7x - 4y + z$ e) $\alpha, \beta \in R$ such that $\alpha x + \beta y = z$

   c) $x + 2z$ f) $\alpha, \beta \in R$ such that $\alpha x + \beta z = y$

3. Let $V = R \times R \times R$, $F = R$. Let $x = \begin{pmatrix} 1 \\ 0 \\ 0 \end{pmatrix}$, $y = \begin{pmatrix} 0 \\ 1 \\ 0 \end{pmatrix}$, $z = \begin{pmatrix} 0 \\ 0 \\ 1 \end{pmatrix}$. Find:

   a) $\alpha, \beta, \gamma \in R$ such that $\alpha x + \beta y + \gamma z = \begin{pmatrix} 4 \\ 1 \\ 2 \end{pmatrix}$.

   b) $\alpha, \beta, \gamma \in R$ such that $\alpha x + \beta y + \gamma z = \begin{pmatrix} 1 \\ -2 \\ 4 \end{pmatrix}$.

c) $\alpha, \beta \in R$ such that $\alpha x + \beta y = z$.

d) Show that if $\begin{pmatrix} a \\ b \\ c \end{pmatrix} \in R \times R \times R$, then there exist $\alpha, \beta, \gamma \in R$

where
$$\alpha x + \beta y + \gamma z = \begin{pmatrix} a \\ b \\ c \end{pmatrix}.$$

4. Show that the set $\mathcal{F}$ of all linear functions on R is a linear space over R.

5. Interpret graphically the following points in $R \times R \times R$.

a) $\begin{pmatrix} 1 \\ 4 \\ 7 \end{pmatrix}$ b) $\begin{pmatrix} 2 \\ 3 \\ -4 \end{pmatrix}$ c) $\begin{pmatrix} -2 \\ 1 \\ 1 \end{pmatrix}$

6. a) List some of the elements in the set $S = \left\{ \begin{pmatrix} x \\ y \end{pmatrix} : y = 3x \right\}$.

b) Show that if $A, B \in S$ and $\alpha, \beta \in R$, then $\alpha A + \beta B \in S$.

c) Find some collection of objects in S which can be combined linearly (i.e., multiplied by scalars and then added together), which give $\begin{pmatrix} 4 \\ 1 \end{pmatrix}$ as a result.

7. Investigate (prove or disprove):

a) Any two vectors in $R \times R$ can be expressed as a linear combination of $\begin{pmatrix} 1 \\ 1 \end{pmatrix}$ and $\begin{pmatrix} 1 \\ -1 \end{pmatrix}$.

b) Any two vectors in $R \times R$ can be expressed as a linear combination of $\begin{pmatrix} 1 \\ 1 \end{pmatrix}$ and $\begin{pmatrix} -1 \\ -1 \end{pmatrix}$.

c) If x and y are any two vectors in $R \times R$ which do not lie on the same straight line passing through $\begin{pmatrix} 0 \\ 0 \end{pmatrix}$, then any $z \in R \times R$ can be expressed as

$$z = \alpha x + \beta y \qquad \text{for some} \qquad \alpha, \beta \in R$$

(i.e., any vector in $R \times R$ can be expressed as a linear combination of x and y).

8. Investigate (prove or disprove): Let $V = R \times R \times R$ using the real field R for scalars.

a) If $x \in V$, then x is a linear combination of $\begin{pmatrix} 1 \\ 0 \\ 0 \end{pmatrix}, \begin{pmatrix} 0 \\ 1 \\ 0 \end{pmatrix}$, and $\begin{pmatrix} 0 \\ 0 \\ 1 \end{pmatrix}$.

b) If $x \in V$, then x is some linear combination of $\begin{pmatrix} 2 \\ 1 \\ 1 \end{pmatrix}, \begin{pmatrix} 1 \\ 2 \\ 1 \end{pmatrix}$, and $\begin{pmatrix} 1 \\ 1 \\ 2 \end{pmatrix}$.

c) If $x \in V$, then $x = \alpha \begin{pmatrix} 1 \\ 1 \\ 1 \end{pmatrix} + \beta \begin{pmatrix} 1 \\ -1 \\ 1 \end{pmatrix} + \gamma \begin{pmatrix} 1 \\ 0 \\ 1 \end{pmatrix}$ for some $\alpha, \beta, \gamma \in R$.

8.3　Systems of Linear Equations

The conversion of temperatures from the centigrade scale to the fahrenheit is described by the linear equation

$$F = aC + b, \tag{1}$$

where F represents the Fahrenheit reading and C denotes the centigrade reading. The slope a of this function represents the "expansion" factor between a degree in the centigrade scale and a degree in the fahrenheit scale. The y-intercept b represents the difference in temperature marked by $0°C$ and $0°F$. (Recall that $0°C$ is the same as $32°F$.) In order to determine the parameters a and b in equation (1), we make use of the boundary conditions (under the assumption that the water is pure and is under a standard barometric pressure of 1 atmosphere)

　　a) temperature of freezing water: $0°C$; $32°F$
　　b) temperature of boiling water: $100°C$; $212°F$.

The observation that $0°C$ and $32°F$ are measures of the same temperature implies that

$$32 = a(0) + b, \tag{2}$$

and similarly at the point $(100, 212)$ we must have

$$212 = a(100) + b. \tag{3}$$

Equations (2) and (3) must both be satisfied for the same pair (a, b). We may write

$$0a + b = 32$$
$$100a + b = 212$$

to indicate that we are searching for a common point (α, β) in the linear functions described by (2) and (3). We have what is called a *system* of linear equations, and the process of finding points common to both functions is described as the "simultaneous solution" of the equations in the system.

If we interpret this system graphically, we find that the simultaneous solution of the equations is simply the point of intersection of the graphs of (2) and (3). We can describe this common point in the lines by

$$\{(\alpha, \beta)\} = \{(a, b): 0a + b = 32\} \cap \{(a, b): 100a + b = 212\},$$

so finding the "simultaneous solution" of equations is equivalent to finding the intersection of the relations described by each of the equations. The graphs of (2) and (3) are shown in Figure 8.4.

The problem of finding solutions to systems of linear equations is frequently encountered, and it is of interest to formulate methods of solving

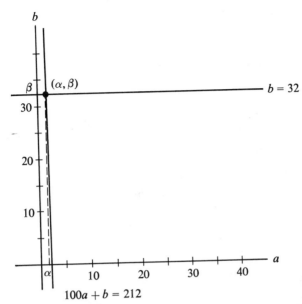

FIG. 8.4   The solution (α, β) of the system is interpreted graphically as the point of intersection of two lines. From the graph it appears that α is about 2 and β is 32.

this problem. When we are dealing with systems of two linear equations in two "unknowns," we could always find an approximate solution graphically (if the system *has* a solution). If the lines do not intersect, there is apparently no solution to the system. Of course, the accuracy of such a solution is dependent upon our ability to read the approximate coordinates of the point of intersection of the lines involved. The graphical solution is not easy, however, when we are dealing with a system of three equations in three unknowns. It is in fact impossible for equations with four or more unknowns.

The problem we intend to face and overcome is that of determining solutions for a given collection of equations of the form

$$\alpha x + \beta y + \gamma z = C.$$

In general we shall call such a collection a *system of linear equations*. (Although we are concentrating on the case in which we seek solutions in $R \times R \times R$ (three space), we could in fact extend this theory to equations in two, four or more variables.)

In particular we would like to know when a system has only one solution and in this case how to find it. Let us notice first, however, that we could impose so many conditions (in the form of equations) that the solution set is empty.

Example: Consider the equations

a) $2x + y + z = 1,$
b) $x + y + z = 1,$
c) $x + y - z = 1,$
d) $x - y + z = 1.$

There is no vector $\begin{pmatrix} a \\ b \\ c \end{pmatrix}$ which satisfies all four conditions. If such a solution exists, then

and
a) $2a + b + c = 1$
b) $a + b + c = 1$

from which

therefore
$2(1 - b - c) + b + c = 1$
$1 - b - c = 0.$

Also we have

and
b) $a + b + c = 1$
c) $a + b - c = 1$

from which
$c = 0.$

Therefore, from above
$b = 1$

and again from a)
$2a + 1 + 0 = 1$

from which
$a = 0.$

However, the vector $\begin{pmatrix} 0 \\ 1 \\ 0 \end{pmatrix}$ does not satisfy d).

We shall now begin to analyze the questions concerning existence and uniqueness for solutions and to develop some sophisticated machinery for determining solutions.

8.3-1 Definition: A system of n linear equations in the n unknowns $x_1, x_2, \ldots, x_n$:

$$\sum_{i=1}^{n} a_{1i} x_i = c_1$$

$$\sum_{i=1}^{n} a_{2i} x_i = c_2$$

$$\cdot$$
$$\cdot$$
$$\cdot$$

$$\sum_{i=1}^{n} a_{ni} x_i = c_n$$

is called *consistent* if there is a unique point (in $\times_{i=1}^{n} R$) of intersection of the hyperplanes associated with the system (*i.e.*, has a unique solution in *n*-space). Otherwise the system is called *dependent* or *inconsistent*, according as whether there are infinitely many points of intersection or no such points, respectively.

Example: The system

$$2x + 3y = 0$$
$$x + y = 1$$

is consistent and has the unique solution $\begin{pmatrix} 3 \\ -2 \end{pmatrix}$.

The system
$$2x + y = 1$$
$$4x + 2y = 2$$

is dependent and has numerous solutions, $\begin{pmatrix} 0 \\ 1 \end{pmatrix}, \begin{pmatrix} 1 \\ -1 \end{pmatrix}, \begin{pmatrix} 2 \\ -3 \end{pmatrix}, \ldots$

The system
$$-2x + y = 3$$
$$-2x + y = 5$$

is inconsistent and has no solution.

The term *dependent* is commonly used in a more general setting. The idea is generalized to arbitrary vectors by the following.

8.3-2 Definition: Suppose $\{x_1, x_2, \ldots, x_n\}$ is a set of *n* vectors. The vectors are called *linearly dependent*, provided there is a linear combination

$$\sum_{i=1}^{n} a_i x_i \qquad \text{(where } a_j \neq 0 \text{ for at least one } j\text{)}$$

of the vectors which is the zero vector. (Note that it is assumed that the a_i's are scalars and the x_i's denote vectors.)

Suppose $\{f_1, f_2, \ldots, f_n\}$ is a set of *n* functions

$$f_i: R \to R.$$

The functions are called linearly dependent provided there is a linear combination

$$\sum_{i=1}^{n} a_i f_i \qquad \text{(where } a_j \neq 0 \text{ for at least one } j \in \{1, 2, \ldots, n\}\text{)}$$

of the functions that is the zero function. Otherwise, the functions $f_1, f_2, \ldots, f_n$ are linearly independent. It follows then that the three functions $\{1_f, \sin^2, \cos^2\}$ are linearly dependent since

$$\forall x \qquad \sin^2 x + \cos^2 x - 1 = 0.$$

On the other hand, the functions x_f and 1_f are independent since

$$ax + b \cdot 1 \equiv 0$$

is impossible no matter which *a* and *b* are chosen (not both zero).

Remark: Note that if 0_f is in a set of functions, then the members of the set are necessarily linearly dependent. (Explain!)

Example: The functions $f_i: R \to R$ described by

$$f_1 = 2 \qquad f_2 = x \qquad f_3 = 19x$$

are linearly dependent, since

$$\sum_{i=1}^{3} a_i f_i = 0_f$$

for $\qquad\qquad a_1 = 0 \qquad a_2 = -19 \qquad a_3 = 1.$

On the other hand, f_1 and f_2 are linearly independent, since

$$a_1 f_1 + a_2 f_2 = 2a_1 + a_2 x = 0 \qquad \forall x \in R \Leftrightarrow a_1 = a_2 = 0.$$

We shall later see how independence of vectors is related to independence of equations.

Solving Systems of Equations

In a later section we will consider several useful methods of solving systems of linear equations. For the present, we shall review two algebraic techniques that can be used to solve such systems. These methods are some-times called "elimination by addition or subtraction" and "elimination by substitution." The following examples show how the techniques are applied.

Example: In order to solve the system

$$5x - 3y + 2z = 5 \qquad (4)$$

$$x - 2y - z = 4 \qquad (5)$$

$$-3x + y + 4z = -1 \qquad (6)$$

we use the method of "elimination by addition or subtraction" as follows:

a) eliminate z between equations (4) and (5) by multiplying both sides of (5) by 2 and adding this to equation (4) to obtain

$$7x - 7y + 0z = 13. \qquad (7)$$

Note: In doing this, we use two facts:

1) Multiplying both sides of (5) by 2 yields an equivalent equation.
2) $\{(x, y, z): 5x - 3y + 2z = 5\} \cap \{(x, y, z): 2x - 4y - 2z = 8\} \subset \{(x, y, z): 7x - 7y = 13\}.$

b) Similarly, eliminate z between equations (5) and (6) by multiplying (5) by 4 and adding to obtain

$$x - 7y = 15. \qquad (8)$$

c) Eliminate x between (7) and (8) by multiplying (8) by 7 and subtract-ing. This yields

$$21y = -46$$

or

$$y = \frac{-46}{21}.$$

d) Substituting this value of *y* in (8), we have

$$x = -\frac{1}{3}$$

e) Finally, substituting $-(1/3)$ and $-(46/21)$ for *x* and *y*, respectively, in equation (5) we have

$$z = \frac{1}{21}.$$

Thus, the unique solution of this (consistent) system of three equations in the three unknowns *x*, *y*, *z* is:

$$x = -\frac{1}{3}, \qquad y = -\frac{46}{21}, \qquad z = \frac{1}{21}.$$

That is,

$$\left\{\left(-\frac{1}{3}, -\frac{46}{21}, \frac{1}{21}\right)\right\} = \{(x, y, z): 5x - 3y + 2z = 5\}$$

$$\cap \{(x, y, z): x - 2y - z = 4\} \cap \{(x, y, z): -3x + y + 4z = -1\}.$$

Example: In order to solve the system

$$\begin{bmatrix} x + y = 5 \\ y - z = 2 \\ 2x + z = -1 \end{bmatrix}$$

we use the method of "elimination by substitution" as follows: From the first equation, we have

$$y = 5 - x.$$

Substituting the quantity $(5 - x)$ for *y* in the second equation yields

$$(5 - x) - z = 2,$$

or

$$z = 3 - x.$$

Substituting the quantity $(3 - x)$ for *z* in the third equation yields

$$2x + (3 - x) = -1.$$

Thus

$$x = -4,$$

$$z = 3 - x = 3 - (-4) = 7,$$

$$y = 5 - x = 5 - (-4) = 9,$$

so that the solution of this system is the point $(-4, 9, 7)$.

Example: The method of elimination by substitution is an efficient way to solve the system relating centigrade and fahrenheit readings, since solving for *b* in the first equation is immediate. We replace *b* in the second equation by 32 and obtain

$$100a + 32 = 212 \Leftrightarrow a = 1.8.$$

551

Thus the conversion formula from centigrade to fahrenheit reading is

$$F = 1.8C + 32.$$

Viewing Solutions of an Equation as Points in a Linear Space

We wish now to consider equations which have as solutions points in some linear space. For example, consider the equation

$$2x + 3y + z = 0.$$

A solution would consist of three components. That is, we need three numbers a, b, c (ordered properly) so that

$$2a + 3b + c = 0.$$

The best way to indicate this fact is to consider the three tuple (vector in $R \times R \times R$) $\begin{pmatrix} a \\ b \\ c \end{pmatrix}$ to be a solution. The solution set for the equation $2x + 3y + z = 0$ then is the set

$$\left\{ \begin{pmatrix} x \\ y \\ z \end{pmatrix} : 2x + 3y + z = 0 \right\}.$$

We see that the solutions for $\alpha x + \beta y + \gamma z = 0$ can be viewed as points in the vector space R^3.

Note in general that an equation $\alpha x + \beta y + \gamma z = 0$ has many solutions. Let us prove the following interesting theorem about solutions of the equation $\alpha x + \beta y + \gamma z = 0$ (which, of course, can be generalized to other spaces as well).

8.3-3 Theorem: If $\begin{pmatrix} a \\ b \\ c \end{pmatrix}$ and $\begin{pmatrix} a' \\ b' \\ c' \end{pmatrix}$ are solutions for the equation $\alpha x + \beta y + \gamma z = 0$, then

$$\forall p, q \in R \qquad p \begin{pmatrix} a \\ b \\ c \end{pmatrix} + q \begin{pmatrix} a' \\ b' \\ c' \end{pmatrix}$$

is also a solution.

Proof: $p \begin{pmatrix} a \\ b \\ c \end{pmatrix} + q \begin{pmatrix} a' \\ b' \\ c' \end{pmatrix} = \begin{pmatrix} pa \\ pb \\ pc \end{pmatrix} + \begin{pmatrix} qa' \\ qb' \\ qc' \end{pmatrix} = \begin{pmatrix} pa + qa' \\ pb + qb' \\ pc + qc' \end{pmatrix}.$

Now

$$\alpha(pa + qa') + \beta(pb + qb') + \gamma(pc + qc')$$
$$= \alpha pa + \alpha qa' + \beta pb + \beta qb' + \gamma pc + \gamma qc'$$
$$= \alpha pa + \beta pb + \gamma pc + \alpha qa' + \beta qb' + \gamma qc'$$
$$= p(\alpha a + \beta b + \gamma c) + q(\alpha a' + \beta b' + \gamma c')$$
$$= p(0) + q(0) = 0$$

since $\begin{pmatrix} a \\ b \\ c \end{pmatrix}$ and $\begin{pmatrix} a' \\ b' \\ c' \end{pmatrix}$ are solutions to the equation $\alpha x + \beta y + \gamma z = 0$. ☐

Example: Consider the equation $x + 2y + 2z = 0$. The point (vector)

$\begin{pmatrix} 2 \\ 1 \\ -2 \end{pmatrix}$ is a solution and hence $3\begin{pmatrix} 2 \\ 1 \\ -2 \end{pmatrix} = \begin{pmatrix} 6 \\ 3 \\ -6 \end{pmatrix}$ also is a solution. Further,

$$\begin{pmatrix} 2 \\ 1 \\ -2 \end{pmatrix} + \begin{pmatrix} 6 \\ 3 \\ -6 \end{pmatrix} = \begin{pmatrix} 8 \\ 4 \\ -8 \end{pmatrix}$$

is a solution.

Notice that if the vector A is a solution, then any scalar times A is a solution. The vector sum of two solutions is in turn a solution.

Question: Are there any solutions for $x + 2y + 2z = 0$ which cannot be obtained from $\begin{pmatrix} 2 \\ 1 \\ -2 \end{pmatrix}$ by scalar multiplication?

The "elimination by addition and subtraction" method we used previously to solve a system of equations was based on successive applications of the following two theorems.

8.3-4 Theorem: If any one of the equations in a system is multiplied by a non-zero scalar, then the resulting system has the same solution set.

Proof: Let $\begin{pmatrix} a \\ b \\ c \end{pmatrix}$ be a solution for

$$\alpha_1 x + \beta_1 y + \gamma_1 z = \delta_1$$
$$\alpha_2 x + \beta_2 y + \gamma_2 z = \delta_2$$
$$\vdots$$
$$\alpha_k x + \beta_k y + \gamma_k z = \delta_k$$
$$\vdots$$
$$\alpha_m x + \beta_m y + \gamma_m z = \delta_m.$$

That is, $\forall p$ $1 \le p \le m$ $\alpha_p a + \beta_p b + \gamma_p c = \delta_p.$

If s is a scalar, then

$$(s\alpha_k)a + (s\beta_k)b + (s\gamma_k)c = s\delta_k$$

and hence $\begin{pmatrix} a \\ b \\ c \end{pmatrix}$ is also a solution for the system

$$\alpha_1 x + \beta_1 y + \gamma_1 z = \delta_1$$

$$\cdot$$

$$\cdot$$

$$\cdot$$

$$(s\alpha_k)x + (s\beta_k)y + (s\gamma_k)z = s\delta_k$$

$$\cdot$$

$$\cdot$$

$$\cdot$$

$$\alpha_m x + \beta_m y + \gamma_m z = \delta_m.$$

The fact that any solution for the latter system is also a solution for the former can be established by using the fact we have just shown and by multiplying the kth equation by $1/s$. ☐

Question: Where would our result fail if we did not insist that s be a *non-zero* scalar?

We proved this only for systems with three variables (*i.e.*, systems whose solutions were vectors with three components). However, it should be clear that this result holds in general.

Let us prove the next theorem for the more general case, in order to illustrate some uses for our $\sum$ notation and to become more familiar with its applications.

8.3-5 Theorem: If any one of the equations in a system of linear equations is replaced by an equation constructed by adding to the given equation another equation in the system, then the new system has the same solution set as the former.

Proof: Consider the following system of equations

$$\sum_{i=1}^{n} \alpha_{1i} x_i = \delta_1$$

$$\sum_{i=1}^{n} \alpha_{2i} x_i = \delta_2$$

$$\cdot$$

$$\cdot$$

$$\cdot$$

$$\sum_{i=1}^{n} \alpha_{ki} x_i = \delta_k$$

$$\cdot$$

$$\cdot$$

$$\cdot$$

$$\sum_{i=1}^{n} \alpha_{mi} x_i = \delta_m$$

with a vector solution $\begin{pmatrix} a_1 \\ a_2 \\ \cdot \\ \cdot \\ \cdot \\ a_n \end{pmatrix}$.

If $$\sum_{i=1}^{n} \alpha_{ki} x_i = \delta_k$$

and $$\sum_{i=1}^{n} \alpha_{pi} x_i = \delta_p$$

are equations in the system, then

$$\sum_{i=1}^{n} \alpha_{ki} a_i = \delta_k \qquad \text{and} \qquad \sum_{i=1}^{n} \alpha_{pi} a_i = \delta_p.$$

It follows that

$$\sum_{i=1}^{n} \alpha_{ki} a_i + \sum_{i=1}^{n} \alpha_{pi} a_i = \delta_k + \delta_p$$

from which

$$\sum_{i=1}^{n} (\alpha_{ki} + \alpha_{pi}) a_i = \delta_k + \delta_p$$

and hence the vector $\begin{pmatrix} a_1 \\ a_2 \\ \cdot \\ \cdot \\ \cdot \\ a_n \end{pmatrix}$ is also a solution for the system

$$\sum_{i=1}^{n} \alpha_{1i} x_i = \delta_1$$

$$\cdot$$
$$\cdot$$
$$\cdot$$

$$\sum_{i=1}^{n} (\alpha_{ki} + \alpha_{pi}) x_i = \delta_k + \delta_p$$

$$\cdot$$
$$\cdot$$
$$\cdot$$

$$\sum_{i=1}^{n} \alpha_{mi} x_i = \delta_m.$$

Again we apply this result "in reverse" to establish the fact that the two systems have exactly the same solutions. □

By successively applying these two theorems we try to reduce the problem to a simpler one whose solutions we can determine by inspection. Sometimes we will discover that the system is inconsistent (has no solution) and other times we may find that the system is dependent (has many solutions).

Later we shall investigate properties of the system which determine existence and uniqueness of solutions. For now we shall practice solving some simple systems.

Example: Solve the following system of equations.

$$6x - 4y - 7z = 17$$
$$9x - 7y - 16z = 29$$
$$10x - 5y - 3z = 23$$

We replace this by the system

$$18x - 12y - 21z = 51 \quad \text{(multiply by 3 from above)}$$
$$18x - 14y - 32z = 58 \quad \text{(multiply by 2 from above)}$$
$$11x - 5y - 3z = 23$$

and then by the system

$$18x - 12y - 21z = 51$$
$$2y + 11z = -7 \quad \text{(replace above by subtracting the second from the first)}$$
$$10x - 5y - 3z = 23,$$

then by

$$180x - 120y - 210z = 510 \quad \text{(multiply by 10)}$$
$$2y + 11z = -7$$
$$180x - 90y - 54z = 414 \quad \text{(multiply by 18),}$$

then by

$$180x - 120y - 210z = 510$$
$$2y + 11z = -7$$
$$-30y - 156z = 96 \quad \text{(subtract third from first),}$$

then

$$18x - 12y - 21z = 51 \quad \text{(divide by 10)}$$
$$2y + 11z = -7$$
$$5y + 26z = -16 \quad \text{(divide by } -6),$$

then

$$18x - 12y - 21z = 51$$
$$12y + 66z = -42 \quad \text{(multiply by 6)}$$
$$5y + 26z = -16,$$

then

$$18x \qquad + 45z = 9 \quad \text{(add 1st and 2nd)}$$
$$2y + 11z = -7 \quad \text{(divide by 6)}$$
$$5y + 26z = -16,$$

then

$$18x \qquad + 45z = 9$$
$$10y + 55z = -35 \quad \text{(multiply by 5)}$$
$$10y + 52z = -32 \quad \text{(multiply by 2),}$$

then

$$2x \qquad + \ 5z = 1 \qquad \text{(divide by 9)}$$
$$2y + 11z = -7 \qquad \text{(divide by 5)}$$
$$3z = -3 \qquad \text{(subtract 3rd from 2nd)},$$

then

$$2x \qquad + \ 5z = 1$$
$$2y + 11z = -7$$
$$5z = -5 \qquad \text{(multiply by 5/3)},$$

then

$$2x \qquad\qquad = 6 \qquad \text{(subtract 3rd from 1st)}$$
$$2y + 11z = -7$$
$$11z = -11 \qquad \text{(multiply by 11/5)},$$

then

$$x \qquad\qquad = 3 \qquad \text{(divide by 2)}$$
$$2y + 11z = -7$$
$$11z = -11,$$

then

$$x \qquad\qquad = 3$$
$$2y \qquad = 4 \qquad \text{(subtract 3rd from 2nd)}$$
$$z = -1 \qquad \text{(divide by 11)},$$

then

$$x \qquad\qquad = 3$$
$$y \qquad = 2 \qquad \text{(divide by 2)}$$
$$z = -1.$$

Hence, by inspection, we see that the system has only the solution $\begin{pmatrix} 3 \\ 2 \\ -1 \end{pmatrix}$.

It should be noted that in our transition from one system to another we often used two or more applications of the above theorems. The rapidity of finding solutions by this method will vary considerably among students, depending on computational ability. It takes a great deal of experimentation and practice to know which step to take next in using this process. Perhaps the following explanation will be of some value.

In applying the reduction method shown above, one should generally follow these major steps:

a) Eliminate "*x*" from the 2nd and 3rd equations.
b) Eliminate "*y*" from the 1st and 3rd equations.
c) Eliminate ' *z*" from the 1st and 2nd equations.

You should now look back over the previous example and see these major steps develop.

557

Exercises 8.3

1. *a*) Find a solution for the following equation, and use Theorem 8.3-3 to develop more solutions.

$$2x + 7y = 4$$

b) Plot these solutions as points in $R \times R$.

2. Show that e^x and e^{-x} are linearly independent functions.

3. Investigate (prove or disprove): Let f and g be functions from R to R. If f is strictly increasing and g is strictly decreasing, then f and g are linearly independent.

4. Find vector solutions for the following systems of equations.

a)
$$3x + 2y \qquad = 13$$
$$3y - 2z = 8$$
$$2x \qquad - 3z = 9$$

b)
$$3x + 4y + 5z = -21$$
$$x + y - z = -11$$
$$y - 8z = -20$$

c)
$$12x - 4y + z = 3$$
$$x - y - 2z = -1$$
$$5x - 2y \qquad = 0$$

d)
$$2x - y + z = -9$$
$$x - 2y + z = 0$$
$$x - y + 2z = -11$$

e)
$$x - y + z = 9$$
$$x - 2y + 3z = 32$$
$$x - 4y + 5z = 62$$

f)
$$2x - 3y - 4z = -10$$
$$3x - 4y + 2z = -5$$
$$4x + 2y + 3z = -21$$

g)
$$9x + 4y = 10z + 11$$
$$12y - 5z = 6x - 9$$
$$15z + 3x = -8y - 16$$

5. If twice the greater of two numbers is divided by the lesser, the quotient is 3 and the remainder 7; and if five times the lesser is divided by the greater, the quotient is 2 and the remainder 23. Find the numbers.

6. A dealer has two kinds of wine, worth 50 and 90 cents a gallon, respectively. How many gallons of each must be taken to make a mixture of 70 gallons, worth 75 cents a gallon?

7. A man invests a certain sum of money in 4 1/2 per cent stock, and a sum $180 greater than the first in 3 1/2 per cent stock. The incomes from the two investments are equal. Find the sums invested.

8. A purse contained $6.55 in quarters, dollars and dimes; after 6 quarters and 8 dimes had been taken out, there remained 3 times as many quarters as dimes. How many were there of each at first?

9. A sum of money is divided equally between a certain number of persons. Had there been m more, each would have received x dollars less; if n less, each would have received y dollars more. How many persons were there, and how much did each receive?

10. For a system of 3 linear functions in $R \times R \times R$, give a graphical interpretation of what it means to say that the system is

    a) independent.   *b*) dependent.   *c*) inconsistent.

11. Suppose $f_1 = \{(x, y): y = 2x - 1\}$, and $f_2 = \{(x, y): 5y = ax + b\}$. Under what circumstances (*i.e.*, what values of a and b) are f_1 and f_2

  a) linearly independent?

  b) linearly dependent?

Investigate: If A is the set of all points (a, b) such that f_1 and f_2 are linearly independent, is $\bar{A} = R \times R - A$ the set of points for which the functions are dependent?

12. Show that the position of any two equations in a system can be interchanged by applying Theorems 8.3-4 and 8.3-5 which we have established for equivalent systems.

13. Show that any linear combination of solutions for $\alpha x + \beta y + \gamma z = 0$ is also a solution.

14. Investigate (prove or disprove):

  a) If $S = \{x_1, \ldots, x_n\}$ is a linearly *dependent* set of vectors, then any vector x_i can be expressed as a linear combination of the remaining $n - 1$ vectors in S.

  b) If $S = \{x_1, \ldots, x_n\}$ is a linearly *independent* set of vectors, and if $\sum_{i=1}^{n} a_i x_i = 0$ for some scalar a_i's, then each scalar $a_i = 0$.

8.4 Introduction to Matrices

The Matrix of Coefficients for a System of Linear Equations

When Glenda Gibson was a junior in high school (the third year she studied freshman algebra), she noticed an interesting and important fact related to the process for finding solutions to a system of linear equations. She noted in the process of successively applying the theorems for obtaining equivalent systems that one need not write the entire equation at each step with unknowns x, y, z. Since she always wrote the equation with the unknown numbers x, y, z in a given order, she found that it was sufficient merely to keep track of the coefficients at each stage. She was unaware that she had rediscovered a popular method for solving systems of linear equations which we shall now examine.

Example: Consider the system of equations

$$2x + 4y = 0$$
$$3x - 2y = 8.$$

We are seeking vector solutions $\begin{pmatrix} x \\ y \end{pmatrix}$. By applying the theorems of the previous section, we find a solution by the following steps.

$$6x + 12y = 0$$
$$6x - 4y = 16$$

$$6x + 12y = 0$$
$$- 16y = 16$$

$$x + 2y = 0$$
$$- 2y = 2$$

$$x \quad = 2$$
$$- 2y = 2$$

$$x \quad = 2$$
$$y = -1$$

If we eliminate the writing of the equal signs, the unknowns, and the addition signs, we might have written instead

$$\begin{bmatrix} 2 & 4 & | & 0 \\ 3 & -2 & | & 8 \end{bmatrix}$$

$$\begin{bmatrix} 6 & 12 & | & 0 \\ 6 & -4 & | & 16 \end{bmatrix}$$

$$\begin{bmatrix} 6 & 12 & | & 0 \\ 0 & -16 & | & 16 \end{bmatrix}$$

$$\begin{bmatrix} 1 & 2 & | & 0 \\ 0 & -2 & | & 2 \end{bmatrix}$$

$$\begin{bmatrix} 1 & 0 & | & 2 \\ 0 & -2 & | & 2 \end{bmatrix}$$

$$\begin{bmatrix} 1 & 0 & | & 2 \\ 0 & 1 & | & -1 \end{bmatrix}$$

from which we could immediately deduce that the only solution to the system is the vector $\begin{pmatrix} 2 \\ -1 \end{pmatrix}$.

Example: Solve the following system by applying the theorems for systems, but keeping track of only the coefficients.

$$x + 2y - z = 6$$
$$2x - y + 3z = -13$$
$$3x - 2y + 3z = -16$$

$$\begin{bmatrix} 1 & 2 & -1 & | & 6 \\ 2 & -1 & 3 & | & -13 \\ 3 & -2 & 3 & | & -16 \end{bmatrix}$$

$$\begin{bmatrix} 2 & 4 & -2 & | & 12 \\ 2 & -1 & 3 & | & -13 \\ 3 & -2 & 3 & | & -16 \end{bmatrix}$$

$$\begin{bmatrix} 2 & 4 & -2 & | & 12 \\ 0 & -5 & 5 & | & -25 \\ 3 & -2 & 3 & | & -16 \end{bmatrix}$$

$$\begin{bmatrix} 3 & 6 & -3 & \bigm| & 18 \\ 0 & 1 & -1 & \bigm| & 5 \\ 3 & -2 & 3 & \bigm| & -16 \end{bmatrix}$$

$$\begin{bmatrix} 3 & 6 & -3 & \bigm| & 18 \\ 0 & 1 & -1 & \bigm| & 5 \\ 0 & 8 & -6 & \bigm| & 34 \end{bmatrix}$$

$$\begin{bmatrix} 1 & 2 & -1 & \bigm| & 6 \\ 0 & 2 & -2 & \bigm| & 10 \\ 0 & 4 & -3 & \bigm| & 17 \end{bmatrix}$$

$$\begin{bmatrix} 1 & 0 & 1 & \bigm| & -4 \\ 0 & 4 & -4 & \bigm| & 20 \\ 0 & 4 & -3 & \bigm| & 17 \end{bmatrix}$$

$$\begin{bmatrix} 1 & 0 & 1 & \bigm| & -4 \\ 0 & 4 & -4 & \bigm| & 20 \\ 0 & 0 & 1 & \bigm| & -3 \end{bmatrix}$$

$$\begin{bmatrix} 1 & 0 & 1 & \bigm| & -4 \\ 0 & 1 & -1 & \bigm| & 5 \\ 0 & 0 & 1 & \bigm| & -3 \end{bmatrix}$$

$$\begin{bmatrix} 1 & 0 & 0 & \bigm| & -1 \\ 0 & 1 & 0 & \bigm| & 2 \\ 0 & 0 & 1 & \bigm| & -3 \end{bmatrix}$$

Hence, the only solution is the vector $\begin{pmatrix} -1 \\ 2 \\ -3 \end{pmatrix}$, since this is the only solution to the system

$$\begin{aligned} x + 0y + 0z &= -1 \\ 0x + y + 0z &= 2 \\ 0x + 0y + z &= -3. \end{aligned}$$

(Explain!)

Matrices and Matrix Multiplication

Let us hesitate here and introduce abstractly the concept of a matrix and matrix multiplication, and then return to where we left off.

8.4-1 Definition: An *m by n matrix* (plural "matrices") over F (usually a field) is a function from $\{1, 2, \ldots, m\} \times \{1, 2, \ldots, n\}$ into F. The values are most conveniently described by a rectangular array with m rows and n columns. (*m* by *n* ($m \times n$) is called the *dimension* of the matrix.)

Example: The following is a 3×4 matrix over the complex field.

561

$$\begin{bmatrix} 2 & 1 & 1+i & 2 \\ 3 & i & i-4 & 1 \\ 2i & 0 & 1 & 3i \end{bmatrix}$$

Example: The following is a 2 × 2 matrix over the real field.

$$\begin{bmatrix} 1 & 2\pi \\ \pi & 3 \end{bmatrix}$$

The values of entries (also sometimes called "images" or "elements") are often denoted by double subscripted symbols, such as a_{23}. Here "a_{23}" means the entry in the 2nd row and the 3rd column. The matrix is sometimes denoted by the symbol $[a_{ij}]$.

Example: Consider the 3 × 4 matrix

$$[a_{ij}] = \begin{bmatrix} 1 & 3 & 4 & 4 \\ 2 & 4 & 7 & 8 \\ 6 & 5 & 1 & 1 \end{bmatrix}.$$

Here, $a_{11} = 1$, $a_{12} = 3$, $a_{31} = 6$, $a_{34} = a_{33} = 1$, etc.

Exercise: Determine a_{22}, a_{23}, a_{32}.

We now give a definition for the multiplication of certain matrices. This multiplication may seem a bit strange at first, but we shall see later that it is useful in simplifying, describing, and solving systems of linear equations.

8.4-2 Definition: If $A = [a_{ij}]$ is an m by n matrix and $B = [b_{ij}]$ is an n by p matrix, then $A \cdot B$ is the m by p matrix $[c_{ij}]$ where

$$c_{ij} = \sum_{k=1}^{n} a_{ik}b_{kj} \quad i = 1, \ldots, m; j = 1, \ldots, p.$$

Example: $\begin{bmatrix} 2 & 1 \\ 3 & 4 \end{bmatrix} \begin{bmatrix} 1 & 2 \\ 2 & 7 \end{bmatrix} = \begin{bmatrix} 2 \cdot 1 + 1 \cdot 2 & 2 \cdot 2 + 1 \cdot 7 \\ 3 \cdot 1 + 4 \cdot 2 & 3 \cdot 2 + 4 \cdot 7 \end{bmatrix}.$

$$= \begin{bmatrix} 4 & 11 \\ 11 & 34 \end{bmatrix}.$$

Example: $\begin{bmatrix} a_{11} & a_{12} \\ a_{21} & a_{22} \\ a_{31} & a_{32} \end{bmatrix} \begin{bmatrix} b_{11} & b_{12} & b_{13} \\ b_{21} & b_{22} & b_{23} \end{bmatrix}$

$$= \begin{bmatrix} a_{11}b_{11} + a_{12}b_{21} & a_{11}b_{12} + a_{12}b_{22} & a_{11}b_{13} + a_{12}b_{23} \\ a_{21}b_{11} + a_{22}b_{21} & a_{21}b_{12} + a_{22}b_{22} & a_{21}b_{13} + a_{22}b_{23} \\ a_{31}b_{11} + a_{32}b_{21} & a_{31}b_{12} + a_{32}b_{22} & a_{31}b_{13} + a_{32}b_{23} \end{bmatrix}.$$

Glenda Gibson describes the multiplication of matrices as a "twitching motion" where she moves her left finger from left to right (along a row of the left matrix) while she moves her right finger from above to below (along a column of the right matrix). The beginner will find some difficulty at first, but should find that this "twitching" habit is not difficult to master.

It should be noted that in order to multiply matrixes $A \cdot B$ it is necessary that the number of columns in A be equal to the number of rows of B. As a result it is immediate that, in general, multiplication of matrices is not commutative. We shall in fact see that matrices where $AB = BA$ are very rare. We will investigate some properties of, and additional operations on, these interesting objects in sections that follow. We conclude this section with a remark on equality of matrices and a useful application of multiplication of matrices.

Remark: Two matrices

$$A = \begin{bmatrix} a_{11} & a_{12} & \cdots & a_{1n} \\ a_{21} & a_{22} & \cdots & a_{2n} \\ \cdot & \cdot & & \cdot \\ \cdot & \cdot & & \cdot \\ \cdot & \cdot & & \cdot \\ a_{m1} & a_{m2} & \cdots & a_{mn} \end{bmatrix} \quad \text{and} \quad B = \begin{bmatrix} b_{11} & b_{12} & \cdots & b_{1k} \\ b_{21} & b_{22} & \cdots & b_{2k} \\ \cdot & \cdot & & \cdot \\ \cdot & \cdot & & \cdot \\ \cdot & \cdot & & \cdot \\ b_{p1} & b_{p2} & \cdots & b_{pk} \end{bmatrix}$$

are equal (written $A = B$) if and only if they have the same dimension $m \times n$ (so that $m = p$ and $n = k$) and the same corresponding elements $(a_{ij} = b_{ij} \;\; \forall i \in \{1, 2, \ldots, m\}$ and $\forall j \in \{1, 2, \ldots, n\})$. Note that this means precisely that the two functions A and B are equal.

Remark: In general, when discussing the dimension of a matrix or an element of a matrix, the information given first is associated with *rows,* and the second number (or subscript) refers to columns. Thus a 5×7 matrix has 5 rows and 7 columns; the element $a_{12,6}$ is the element in the 12th row and 6th column of some matrix with at least 12 rows and 6 columns.

Example: If A is the 2×2 matrix $\begin{bmatrix} 0 & 1 \\ 100 & 1 \end{bmatrix}$ and X is the 2×1 matrix $\begin{bmatrix} a \\ b \end{bmatrix}$, then

$$AX = \begin{bmatrix} 0 & 1 \\ 100 & 1 \end{bmatrix} \begin{bmatrix} a \\ b \end{bmatrix} = \begin{bmatrix} 0a + b \\ 100a + b \end{bmatrix}.$$

If we use this, the linear system for comparing centigrade and fahrenheit temperatures

$$0a + b = 32$$
$$100a + b = 212$$

can be written $AX = C$, where $C = \begin{pmatrix} 32 \\ 212 \end{pmatrix}$.

Remark: It is convenient not to make a distinction between a vector $\begin{pmatrix} x \\ y \\ z \end{pmatrix}$ in three space (more generally, n-space) and the 3×1 matrix $\begin{bmatrix} x \\ y \\ z \end{bmatrix}$ associated with the vector. That is, the system can be written as a matrix equation $AX = C$. (We return to this idea below.)

Example: The linear combination $\sum_{i=1}^{5} a_i f_i$ can be written in matrix notation as

$$[a_1, a_2, a_3, a_4, a_5] \begin{bmatrix} f_1 \\ f_2 \\ f_3 \\ f_4 \\ f_5 \end{bmatrix}.$$

Strictly speaking, the product above of a 1×5 matrix times a 5×1 matrix yields the 1×1 matrix

$$[a_1 f_1 + a_2 f_2 + a_3 f_3 + a_4 f_4 + a_5 f_5] = \left[\sum_{i=1}^{5} a_i f_i \right].$$

However, we shall often not distinguish between the 1×1 matrix $[\sum_{i=1}^{5} a_i f_i]$ and the function $\sum_{i=1}^{5} a_i f_i$. In general, an element $\alpha \in A$ may be considered to be also a 1×1 matrix $[\alpha]$ over A. In order to distinguish between matrices over A and elements of A, we shall refer to the latter as "scalars."

A System of Equations Written as a Matrix Equation

We return to the idea of using matrix multiplication in connection with the "coefficient-only" solution of systems as discussed above.

Example: Consider the system of equations

$$a_{11}x + a_{12}y + a_{13}z = c_1,$$
$$a_{21}x + a_{22}y + a_{23}z = c_2,$$
$$a_{31}x + a_{32}y + a_{33}z = c_3.$$

A vector $\begin{pmatrix} x \\ y \\ z \end{pmatrix}$ is a solution of the system if and only if the matrix $\begin{bmatrix} x \\ y \\ z \end{bmatrix}$ satisfies the matrix equation

$$\begin{bmatrix} a_{11} & a_{12} & a_{13} \\ a_{21} & a_{22} & a_{23} \\ a_{31} & a_{32} & a_{33} \end{bmatrix} \begin{bmatrix} x \\ y \\ z \end{bmatrix} = \begin{bmatrix} c_1 \\ c_2 \\ c_3 \end{bmatrix}.$$

We see that a system of linear equations can be equivalently described by a matrix equation $AX = C$, where A is the matrix of coefficients of the unknowns, X is the matrix (vector) of unknowns, and C is the matrix of "constant coefficient."

Example: Write the following system in matrix form.

$$3x + 2y + z = 4$$
$$x + 3y - z = 0$$
$$2x + 7y \quad\;\; = 0$$

Clearly this is equivalent to the matrix equation

$$\begin{bmatrix} 3 & 2 & 1 \\ 1 & 3 & -1 \\ 2 & 7 & 0 \end{bmatrix} \begin{bmatrix} x \\ y \\ z \end{bmatrix} = \begin{bmatrix} 4 \\ 0 \\ 0 \end{bmatrix}.$$

8.4-3 Definition: If

$$\begin{bmatrix} a_{11} & a_{12} & \ldots & a_{1n} \\ a_{21} & a_{22} & \ldots & a_{2n} \\ & & & \\ \vdots & & \vdots & \\ & & & \\ a_{n1} & a_{n2} & \ldots & a_{nn} \end{bmatrix} \begin{bmatrix} x_1 \\ x_2 \\ \vdots \\ x_n \end{bmatrix} = \begin{bmatrix} c_1 \\ c_2 \\ \vdots \\ c_n \end{bmatrix}$$

is the matrix representation for a system of n equations in n unknowns, then

$$\begin{bmatrix} a_{11} & a_{12} & \ldots & a_{1n} & c_1 \\ a_{21} & a_{22} & \ldots & a_{2n} & c_2 \\ & & & & \\ \vdots & \vdots & & \vdots & \vdots \\ & & & & \\ a_{n1} & a_{n2} & \ldots & a_{nn} & c_n \end{bmatrix}$$

is called the *augmented matrix* for the system.

It is clear that the theorems for transforming a given system of equations into equivalent systems can be immediately restated as theorems for transforming the augmented matrix for a system into an augmented matrix for an equivalent system. Let us state these theorems formally without further proof.

8.4-4 Theorem: If M is the augmented matrix for a system of equations then any of the following operations on M will produce a matrix which is the augmented matrix for an equivalent system:

a) Multiplication of any row by a non-zero number. (By a number we mean a scalar [an element of the field over which we are working].)

b) Replacement of any row by the sum of itself and any other row. (Here we mean the component-wise sum.)

c) Interchange of any two rows.

These operations are called *elementary row operations*.

In solving equations in this fashion, the objective is to transform the augmented matrix to the form

$$\begin{bmatrix} 1 & 0 & 0 & \ldots & 0 & b_1 \\ 0 & 1 & 0 & \ldots & 0 & b_2 \\ \vdots & \vdots & & & & \vdots \\ & & & \ddots & & \\ 0 & 0 & \ldots & 0 & 1 & b_n \end{bmatrix}$$

from which one immediately concludes by inspection that is the

only vector which is a solution. (Why?)

Example: Solve the system of equations given by the matrix equation

$$\begin{bmatrix} 1 & 3 & -4 \\ 2 & -1 & 2 \\ 4 & -6 & 1 \end{bmatrix} \begin{bmatrix} x \\ y \\ z \end{bmatrix} = \begin{bmatrix} -13 \\ 4 \\ -1 \end{bmatrix}.$$

The augmented matrix is

$$\begin{bmatrix} 1 & 3 & -4 & | & -13 \\ 2 & -1 & 2 & | & 4 \\ 4 & -6 & 1 & | & -1 \end{bmatrix}$$

and by the following steps applying the theorems we arrive at a solution.

$$\begin{bmatrix} 2 & 6 & -8 & | & -26 \\ -2 & 1 & -2 & | & -4 \\ 4 & -6 & 1 & | & -1 \end{bmatrix}$$

$$\begin{bmatrix} 2 & 6 & -8 & | & -26 \\ 0 & 7 & -10 & | & -30 \\ 4 & -6 & 1 & | & -1 \end{bmatrix}$$

$$\begin{bmatrix} 4 & 12 & -16 & | & -52 \\ 0 & 7 & -10 & | & -30 \\ -4 & 6 & -1 & | & 1 \end{bmatrix}$$

$$\begin{bmatrix} 4 & 12 & -16 & | & -52 \\ 0 & 7 & -10 & | & -30 \\ 0 & 18 & -17 & | & -51 \end{bmatrix}$$

$$\begin{bmatrix} 1 & 3 & -4 & | & -13 \\ 0 & 7 & -10 & | & -30 \\ 0 & 18 & -17 & | & -51 \end{bmatrix}$$

$$\begin{bmatrix} 7 & 21 & -28 & | & -91 \\ 0 & -21 & 30 & | & 90 \\ 0 & 18 & -17 & | & -51 \end{bmatrix}$$

$$\begin{bmatrix} 7 & 0 & 2 & | & -1 \\ 0 & -7 & 10 & | & 30 \\ 0 & 18 & -17 & | & -51 \end{bmatrix}$$

$$\begin{bmatrix} 7 & 0 & 2 & | & -1 \\ 0 & -7 \cdot 18 & 180 & | & 540 \\ 0 & 18 \cdot 7 & -119 & | & -357 \end{bmatrix}$$

$$\left[\begin{array}{ccc|c} 7 & 0 & 2 & -1 \\ 0 & -7 & 10 & 30 \\ 0 & 0 & 61 & 183 \end{array}\right]$$

$$\left[\begin{array}{ccc|c} 7 & 0 & 2 & -1 \\ 0 & 7 & -10 & -30 \\ 0 & 0 & 1 & 3 \end{array}\right]$$

$$\left[\begin{array}{ccc|c} 7 & 0 & 0 & -7 \\ 0 & 7 & 0 & 0 \\ 0 & 0 & 1 & 3 \end{array}\right]$$

$$\left[\begin{array}{ccc|c} 1 & 0 & 0 & -1 \\ 0 & 1 & 0 & 0 \\ 0 & 0 & 1 & 3 \end{array}\right]$$

It is now obvious that $\begin{pmatrix} -1 \\ 0 \\ 3 \end{pmatrix}$ is the only vector such that

$$\begin{bmatrix} 1 & 0 & 0 \\ 0 & 1 & 0 \\ 0 & 0 & 1 \end{bmatrix} \begin{bmatrix} -1 \\ 0 \\ 3 \end{bmatrix} = \begin{bmatrix} -1 \\ 0 \\ 3 \end{bmatrix}.$$

Since at each step in arriving at this equation we wrote the augmented matrix for a system which has exactly the same solution set as the previous matrix, it follows that $\begin{pmatrix} -1 \\ 0 \\ 3 \end{pmatrix}$ is the only vector $\begin{pmatrix} x \\ y \\ z \end{pmatrix}$ such that

$$\begin{bmatrix} 1 & 3 & -4 \\ 2 & -1 & 2 \\ 4 & -6 & 1 \end{bmatrix} \begin{bmatrix} x \\ y \\ z \end{bmatrix} = \begin{bmatrix} -13 \\ 4 \\ -1 \end{bmatrix}.$$

The three (easily generalized to four or more) major steps in this process are:

a) Arrive at zero's in all except the *first row* of *column one*.

b) Arrive at zero's in all except the *second row* of *column two*.

c) Arrive at zero's in all except the *third row* of *column three*.

In the next section we will establish some formal results which one can use to determine whether a system has a unique solution.

Exercises 8.4

1. Write each of the following systems of equations as a matrix equation.

a) $2x - y + z = 1$
$x - y - z = 2$
$3x - 2y - z = -1$

b) $x - 2y + z = 4$
$2x - 3y + z = 1$
$3x - 2y - z = 2$

c) $3x - 2y \quad = \quad 1$
$\quad x - y - z = \quad 4$
$\quad 3x + y \quad = -4$

2. Write each of the following matrix equations as a system of equations without using matrices.

a) $\begin{bmatrix} 3 & -6 & 5 \\ 2 & -1 & 1 \\ 1 & -2 & 4 \end{bmatrix} \begin{bmatrix} x \\ y \\ z \end{bmatrix} = \begin{bmatrix} 9 \\ -1 \\ 3 \end{bmatrix}$

b) $\begin{bmatrix} 1 & 1 & 1 \\ 1 & -1 & 0 \\ 3 & 1 & 0 \end{bmatrix} \begin{bmatrix} x \\ y \\ z \end{bmatrix} = \begin{bmatrix} 3 \\ 4 \\ 6 \end{bmatrix}$

c) $\begin{bmatrix} 1 & 0 & 1 & -1 \\ 1 & -1 & 1 & 0 \\ 0 & 1 & 1 & 1 \\ 1 & 0 & 2 & 1 \end{bmatrix} \begin{bmatrix} x \\ y \\ z \\ w \end{bmatrix} = \begin{bmatrix} 1 \\ -1 \\ 2 \\ -2 \end{bmatrix}$

3. Write the augmented matrix for each of the equations in (1) and (2) and find a solution for the system by applying the theorems for equivalent equations.

4. Use matrix multiplication and determine AB and BA (whenever possible) where:

a) $A = \begin{bmatrix} 1 & 2 \\ 1 & 1 \end{bmatrix} \quad B = \begin{bmatrix} 2 & 2 \\ 1 & 4 \end{bmatrix}$

b) $A = \begin{bmatrix} 1 & 2 & 2 \end{bmatrix} \quad B = \begin{bmatrix} 2 & 1 \\ 3 & 1 \\ 1 & 1 \end{bmatrix}$

c) $A = \begin{bmatrix} 0 & 1 & 4 \\ 2 & 1 & 1 \\ 4 & 0 & 0 \end{bmatrix} \quad B = \begin{bmatrix} 1 & 4 & 1 \\ 1 & 3 & 6 \end{bmatrix}$

d) $A = \begin{bmatrix} 1 & 0 & 0 \\ 0 & 1 & 0 \\ 0 & 0 & 1 \end{bmatrix} \quad B = \begin{bmatrix} 2 & 4 \\ 1 & 2 \\ 4 & 3 \end{bmatrix}$

e) $A = \begin{bmatrix} 1 & 0 & 0 \\ 0 & 1 & 0 \\ 0 & 0 & 1 \end{bmatrix} \quad B = \begin{bmatrix} 1 & 4 & 7 \\ 9 & 9 & 3 \\ 2 & 8 & 0 \end{bmatrix}$

5. Let
$$[a_{ij}] = \begin{bmatrix} 1 & 2 & 7 & 9 \\ 4 & 8 & 6 & 6 \\ 2 & 1 & 3 & 9 \\ 1 & 0 & 0 & 2 \end{bmatrix}.$$

Determine:

a) a_{14} b) a_{23} c) a_{44} d) a_{32}

Compute:

    a) $a_{13} + a_{22}$ c) $a_{22}a_{31}$

    b) $a_{12} - a_{41}$ d) $a_{41}a_{14}$

6. Show that the sum $\sum_{j=1}^{n} a_j$ can be represented as

    a)

$$
(a_1, a_2, \ldots, a_n)
\begin{pmatrix}
1 \\
1 \\
\cdot \\
\cdot \\
\cdot \\
1
\end{pmatrix}
\quad\text{or}\quad\text{b)}\quad
(1, 1, \ldots, 1)
\begin{pmatrix}
a_1 \\
a_2 \\
\cdot \\
\cdot \\
\cdot \\
a_n
\end{pmatrix}
$$

7. Evaluate whenever possible:

    a)

$$
(1, 2, 3, \ldots, n)
\begin{pmatrix}
1 \\
2 \\
3 \\
\cdot \\
\cdot \\
\cdot \\
n
\end{pmatrix}
\qquad\text{c)}\qquad
\begin{pmatrix}
1 \\
2 \\
3 \\
\cdot \\
\cdot \\
\cdot \\
n
\end{pmatrix}
(1, 2, 3, \ldots, n)
$$

    b)

$$
(1, 2, 3, \ldots, n)
\begin{pmatrix}
n \\
n - 1 \\
\cdot \\
\cdot \\
\cdot \\
2 \\
1
\end{pmatrix}
$$

8. Suppose

$$
A =
\begin{bmatrix}
a & 0 & 0 & 0 \\
0 & a & 0 & 0 \\
0 & 0 & a & 0 \\
0 & 0 & 0 & a
\end{bmatrix}, \text{ where } a > 0.
$$

    a) Compute $AA = A^2$.

    b) Compute

$$
\begin{bmatrix}
1 \\
1 \\
1 \\
1
\end{bmatrix}
(1, 1, 1, 1).
$$

    c) A matrix I_n of dimension $n \times n$ is called an identity matrix if

$$
I_n =
\begin{bmatrix}
1 & 0 & 0 & \ldots & 0 \\
0 & 1 & 0 & \ldots & 0 \\
\cdot & \cdot & \cdot & & \cdot \\
\cdot & \cdot & \cdot & & \cdot \\
\cdot & \cdot & \cdot & & \cdot \\
0 & 0 & 0 & \ldots & 1
\end{bmatrix}
$$

(*i.e.*, I_n has zeros everywhere except down the one diagonal, where it has ones). Show that $CI_4 = C = I_4C$, where C is any 4×4 matrix.

d) Find a 4×4 matrix B such that $AB = I$, where A is the matrix defined above.

8.5   Elementary Linear Algebra

In the preceding section we viewed a matrix A over a set S to be a certain object composed of elements from S. In this section we continue the consideration of matrices. We will see that many of the properties of matrices (and operations on them) are "inherited" from corresponding properties of elements in the set S; in much the same way that properties of operations on functions (such as function addition) were "inherited" from the characteristics of the elements in the domains of the functions. As was seen in the preceding problem section, a very important case in which this does *not* occur for matrices is commutativity of matrix multiplication. Unless otherwise specified, all matrices in this section will be considered to be over the real field R.

In order to ease the burden of writing matrices as arrays of numbers, we shall continue to make use of the following notation:

$$[a_{ij}]_{m \times n} = \begin{bmatrix} a_{11} & a_{12} & \ldots & a_{1n} \\ a_{21} & a_{22} & \ldots & a_{2n} \\ \cdot & \cdot & & \cdot \\ \cdot & \cdot & & \cdot \\ \cdot & \cdot & & \cdot \\ a_{m1} & a_{m2} & \ldots & a_{mn} \end{bmatrix}.$$

Thus $[a_{ij}]_{2 \times 2}$ denotes the 2×2 matrix

$$\begin{bmatrix} a_{11} & a_{12} \\ a_{21} & a_{22} \end{bmatrix}$$

where the a_{ij}'s are assumed to be real numbers. (The $m \times n$ subscript will be omitted if no confusion results by doing so.)

Using this notation, we can restate the definition of matrix multiplication as follows:

Suppose $A = [a_{ij}]_{m \times n}$ and $B = [b_{ij}]_{n \times p}$ are two matrices. The product AB is a matrix $C = [c_{ij}]_{m \times p}$ where $c_{ij} = \sum_{q=1}^{n} a_{iq}b_{qj}$ for all $1 \le i \le m$ and $1 \le j \le p$. That is,

$$[a_{ij}]_{m \times n}[b_{ij}]_{n \times p} = \left[\sum_{q=1}^{n} a_{iq}b_{qj} \right]_{m \times p}.$$

Remark: Note that in order for the product AB of two matrices A and B to be defined, we must have the following conditions satisfied:

a) The number of columns in A is the same as the number of rows in B (with the exception that scalar multiplication may be viewed as multiplication by a 1×1 matrix).

b) It must be possible to form the products $a_{iq}b_{qj}$ of elements in A times elements in B.

c) It must be possible to add these product elements together.

Of course, under the assumption that the elements of A and B are real numbers, conditions (*b*) and (*c*) above are immediately satisfied. However, matrices over other sets are often considered, and these conditions must be investigated before matrix multiplication can be used. In what follows, we will indicate that conditions (*b*) and (*c*) are satisfied by stating that a matrix A is a "matrix over a field."

We can define matrix *addition* in a very straightforward way, simply by adding corresponding elements of the matrices entering into the sum. This necessitates the requirement that the matrices being added be of the same dimension.

8.5-1 Definition: Given two $m \times n$ matrices A and B, $A = [a_{ij}]$ and $B = [b_{ij}]$, the sum $A + B$ of A and B is the $m \times n$ matrix $C = [c_{ij}]$ where

$$c_{ij} = a_{ij} + b_{ij}$$

for all i, $1 \le i \le m$ and all j, $1 \le j \le n$.

Remark: This could be stated

$$[a_{ij}]_{m \times n} + [b_{ij}]_{m \times n} = [a_{ij} + b_{ij}]_{m \times n}.$$

Example: Suppose

$$A = \begin{bmatrix} 1 & -1 & 0 \\ 0 & 1 & 1 \end{bmatrix}, \quad \text{and} \quad B = \begin{bmatrix} 5 & 2 & 7 \\ -1 & -1 & 3 \end{bmatrix}.$$

Then

$$A + B = \begin{bmatrix} 1+5 & -1+2 & 0+7 \\ 0-1 & 1-1 & 1+3 \end{bmatrix} = \begin{bmatrix} 6 & 1 & 7 \\ -1 & 0 & 4 \end{bmatrix}.$$

Since it is now possible to consider the sum of a matrix and itself $(A + A)$ and since we feel that $A + A$ should be $2A$, we might be inclined to define $2A$ to be the matrix

$$[a_{ij} + a_{ij}] = [2a_{ij}].$$

This motivates the following definition of multiplication of a matrix by a scalar.

8.5-2 Definition: $k[a_{ij}] = [ka_{ij}]$ where k is an element of the field over which the matrix $[a_{ij}]$ is taken.

Example: For the matrix A of our first example, we have

$$4A = \begin{bmatrix} 4 & -4 & 0 \\ 0 & 4 & 4 \end{bmatrix}$$

and

$$-1A = \begin{bmatrix} -1 & 1 & 0 \\ 0 & -1 & -1 \end{bmatrix}.$$

Remark: It is natural to define *subtraction* of one matrix B, say, from another, A, as follows:

$$A - B = A + (-1 \cdot B).$$

The reader can easily verify that this amounts to subtracting the corresponding elements of B from those of A.

Example: For the matrices A and B of example one,

$$A - B = \begin{bmatrix} 1-5 & -1-2 & 0-7 \\ 0-(-1) & 1-(-1) & 1-3 \end{bmatrix} = \begin{bmatrix} -4 & -3 & -7 \\ 1 & 2 & -2 \end{bmatrix}.$$

It is easily seen that the operation of matrix addition "inherits" many properties from the ordinary addition of elements in the field over which the matrices are taken. For example, for matrices over R, we have:

8.5-3 Some Matrix Facts: a) $A - A = [0_{ij}]$, where $[0_{ij}]$ is the same dimension as A, but has only zeros as elements.

b) $A + [0_{ij}] = [0_{ij}] + A = A$ for all A and $[0_{ij}]$ of the same dimension. (For this reason, we could call $[0_{ij}]$ the "additive identity matrix.")

c) $A + B = B + A$. (*Commutative property of matrix addition*)

d) $A + (B + C) = (A + B) + C$. (*Associative property of matrix addition*)

e) $k(A + B) = kA + kB$, where $k \in R$. (*Scalar multiplication distributes over matrix addition*)

In order to prove these assertions, it suffices to show that for any pair i, j, the ijth element in the matrix on the left hand side is equal to the ijth element of the matrix on the right hand side.

For example, in order to prove c) above, we proceed as follows:

Proof (of c)): Suppose $A = [a_{ij}]_{m \times n}$ and $B = [b_{ij}]_{m \times n}$.

Then $A + B = [a_{ij} + b_{ij}]_{m \times n} = [b_{ij} + a_{ij}]_{m \times n}$,

since for all i and j, we know that addition of the real numbers a_{ij} and b_{ij} is commutative. That is, since $a_{ij} \in R$ and $b_{ij} \in R$,

$$a_{ij} + b_{ij} = b_{ij} + a_{ij} \quad \forall i, j.$$

But we recognize $[b_{ij} + a_{ij}]_{m \times n}$ as $B + A$. Thus the commutativity of matrix addition follows. ☐

We have seen that matrix addition (and subtraction) is "well behaved" and relatively simple to perform. We have also seen that matrix multiplication is neither as simple, nor as "well behaved." For example we know that

572

AB isn't necessarily the same as BA, even if the dimension of A and B are such that both of the above products are defined. On the other hand, *most* of the properties enjoyed by matrix addition also hold for matrix multiplication. For example, there are *identity* matrices for the operation of matrix multiplication, namely the matrices

$$I_n = [\delta_{ij}]_{n \times n} \quad \text{where} \quad \delta_{ij} = \begin{cases} 1, & \text{if } i = j \\ 0, & \text{if } i \neq j. \end{cases}$$

(The function $\delta\colon Z \times Z \to \{0, 1\}$ defined here is called "Kronecker's delta.") Thus I_n is an $n \times n$ matrix with 1's down the diagonal from upper left to lower right (the so-called main diagonal), and 0's elsewhere. In order to prove that

$$AI_n = I_mA = A, \quad \text{where} \quad A = [a_{ij}]_{m \times n}$$

we proceed as before.

Suppose $AI_n = [b_{ij}]_{m \times n}$. Then b_{ij} is given by

$$b_{ij} = \sum_{q=1}^{n} a_{iq}\delta_{qj}.$$

However, in this sum there is precisely *one* value of q for which the product $a_{iq}\delta_{qj}$ is non-zero: $q = j$, in which case

$$a_{iq}\delta_{qj} = a_{ij}\delta_{jj} = a_{ij}$$

since $\delta_{jj} = 1$. Therefore

$$\sum_{q=1}^{n} a_{iq}\delta_{qj} = a_{ij}\delta_{jj} = a_{ij}.$$

That is, $b_{ij} = a_{ij}.$

Thus $AI_n = [b_{ij}]_{m \times n} = [a_{ij}]_{m \times n} = A.$

Similarly, one can show that $I_mA = A$. $\square$

Example: Suppose A is the 2×3 matrix

$$A = \begin{bmatrix} 1 & 2 & 1 \\ 0 & 3 & -2 \end{bmatrix}.$$

Then

$$AI_3 = \begin{bmatrix} 1 & 2 & 1 \\ 0 & 3 & -2 \end{bmatrix} \begin{bmatrix} 1 & 0 & 0 \\ 0 & 1 & 0 \\ 0 & 0 & 1 \end{bmatrix}$$

$$= \begin{bmatrix} 1 \cdot 1 + 2 \cdot 0 + 1 \cdot 0 & 1 \cdot 0 + 2 \cdot 1 + 1 \cdot 0 & 1 \cdot 0 + 2 \cdot 0 + 1 \cdot 1 \\ 0 \cdot 1 + 3 \cdot 0 - 2 \cdot 0 & 0 \cdot 0 + 3 \cdot 1 - 2 \cdot 0 & 0 \cdot 0 + 3 \cdot 0 - 2 \cdot 1 \end{bmatrix}$$

$$= \begin{bmatrix} 1 & 2 & 1 \\ 0 & 3 & -2 \end{bmatrix} = A.$$

Also,

$$I_2 A = \begin{bmatrix} 1 & 0 \\ 0 & 1 \end{bmatrix} \begin{bmatrix} 1 & 2 & 1 \\ 0 & 3 & -2 \end{bmatrix} = \begin{bmatrix} 1 \cdot 1 + 0 \cdot 0 & 1 \cdot 2 + 0 \cdot 3 & 1 \cdot 1 + 0 \cdot (-2) \\ 0 \cdot 1 + 1 \cdot 0 & 0 \cdot 2 + 1 \cdot 3 & 0 \cdot 1 + 1 \cdot (-2) \end{bmatrix}$$

$$= \begin{bmatrix} 1 & 2 & 1 \\ 0 & 3 & -2 \end{bmatrix} = A.$$

In our work involving matrices in this book, we will be primarily concerned with matrices with the same number of rows as columns. Such a matrix is called a *square* matrix. It is interesting and useful to determine whether certain square matrices A are such that there is a multiplicative inverse A^{-1}. That is, given an $n \times n$ matrix $A = [a_{ij}]$, is there a matrix $B = [b_{ij}]$ such that $AB = I$ (multiplied on the *right*)? The answer to this question is, "Not always." However, some matrices have inverses, as is seen in the following examples.

Example: Suppose

$$A = \begin{bmatrix} 2 & 3 & -1 \\ 1 & 2 & 1 \\ 3 & 5 & 1 \end{bmatrix} \quad \text{and} \quad B = \begin{bmatrix} -3 & -8 & 5 \\ 2 & 5 & -3 \\ -1 & -1 & 1 \end{bmatrix}.$$

Then $AB = I$, so that $A^{-1} = B$. (Note also in this case that $BA = I$, so that $B^{-1} = A$ (i.e., $(A^{-1})^{-1} = A$).)

Example: For any $n \in N$, $I_n^{-1} = I_n$. (That is, $I_n I_n = I_n$.) The problem of determining whether a given square matrix has an inverse is easily solved using the *determinant* function introduced later. Of course, knowing that A^{-1} *exists*, and actually *finding* A^{-1} are two very different problems. We will discuss methods of constructing and approximating A^{-1} (when it exists) from A in following sections. In general, finding A^{-1} is not easy, especially when the dimension of A is large. A great deal of research has been done (and is currently being done) on finding ways to "speed up" (reduce the amount of computation required for) the determination of A^{-1}, given A. Much of this work is associated with the use of computers to do the computations involved. We will limit much of our consideration to 2×2 and 3×3 matrices, since the computational difficulty becomes significant for larger matrices (certainly not *impossible*, however).

It is interesting that we can say a great deal about multiplicative inverses of matrices, even though we as yet have no systematic procedure for finding them. Some properties of inverses are given in the following theorem. (A square matrix A is called *nonsingular* if it has an inverse; otherwise it is called *singular*.)

8.5-4 Theorem: Suppose A and B are $n \times n$ nonsingular matrices, and $k \in R$. Then

    a) $(A^{-1})^{-1} = A$ (provided $(A^{-1})^{-1}$ exists)

    b) $(kA)^{-1} = (1/k)A^{-1}$, where $k \neq 0$

c) The product AB has an inverse, and moreover

$$(AB)^{-1} = B^{-1}A^{-1}.$$

Proof: Part a). We need only show that

$$(A^{-1})A = I.$$

We need only show this since by definition, if $A^{-1}B = I$, then B is the inverse of the matrix A^{-1}. Note, however, that at this stage we cannot assume that $(A^{-1})A$ is the same as $A(A^{-1})$, since, in general, matrix multiplication fails to be commutative. Now

$$A^{-1} = A^{-1}I = A^{-1}(AA^{-1}) = (A^{-1}A)A^{-1}$$

since matrix multiplication is associative (see Problem 8). But this equation shows that

$$(A^{-1}A)A^{-1} = A^{-1} = IA^{-1}.$$

Therefore $A^{-1}A = I$

provided it is true that $JA^{-1} = A^{-1} \Rightarrow J = I.$

In order to see this, note that

$$J = JI = J(A^{-1}(A^{-1})^{-1}) = (JA^{-1})(A^{-1})^{-1} = A^{-1}(A^{-1})^{-1} = I.$$

We were careful *not* to assume that $(A^{-1})^{-1} = A$ (why?). (Where did we assume that $(A^{-1})^{-1}$ exists?)

Part b). Let a_{ij}^* denote the ijth entry in A^{-1}. Since

$$(kA)\left(\frac{1}{k}A^{-1}\right) = \left[\sum_{q=1}^{n} ka_{iq}\frac{1}{k}a_{qj}^*\right]$$

$$= \left[\sum_{q=1}^{n} a_{iq}a_{qj}^*\right]$$

$$= AA^{-1}$$

where $A = [a_{ij}]$ and $A^{-1} = [a_{ij}^*]$, it follows that

$$(kA)\left(\frac{1}{k}A^{-1}\right) = I$$

which (by definition) implies that

$$(kA)^{-1} = \frac{1}{k}A^{-1}.$$

Part c). In this part we need to show that

$$(AB)(B^{-1}A^{-1}) = I. \tag{1}$$

(This will automatically imply that (AB) has an inverse.) By the associative property of matrix multiplication, the matrix on the left hand side of equation (1) can be written

$$A(BB^{-1})A^{-1} = AIA^{-1} = AA^{-1} = I. \;\square$$

In summary, it appears that the operations of matrix addition and multiplication have properties similar to those enjoyed by ordinary addition and multiplication of scalars, the major exception being the non-commutativity of matrix multiplication. In order to reinforce this feeling, the reader is asked to prove several of the following facts in the problems that follow:

$$kA + kB = k(A + B) \quad \text{(Scalar multiplication distributes over matrix addition)}$$

$$CA + CB = C(A + B) \quad \text{(Matrix multiplication distributes over matrix addition)}$$

$$(AB)C = A(BC)$$

$$A + B = B + A$$

A^{-1} is unique (if it exists)

$$A + (B + C) = (A + B) + C$$

Note: We did not show that the existence of A^{-1} guaranteed the existence of $(A^{-1})^{-1}$. We did, however, show that if it does exist, then it should be A. (Anticipating, of course, the uniqueness of inverses.) Be sure to keep us honest on this point.

Exercises 8.5

1. Let

$$A = \begin{bmatrix} 1 & 3 \\ 0 & -2 \end{bmatrix} \quad \text{and} \quad B = \begin{bmatrix} -2 & 5 \\ -1 & 0 \end{bmatrix}.$$

Compute:

a) $A + B$ and $B + A$ c) $6A + 3B$

b) $A - B$ and $B - A$ d) $-5B + 2A$

2. Suppose $A = [a_{ij}]_{3\times3}$, where $a_{ij} = i + j$, and $B = [b_{ij}]_{3\times3}$, where $b_{ij} = i \cdot j$.

a) Compute $A + B$ and $A - B$. (First determine explicit descriptions for A and B.)

b) Compute AB.

c) Compute BA.

d) Compute $(-A)B$.

3. Suppose $A = [a_{ij}]_{4\times4}$ and $B = [b_{ij}]_{4\times4}$ such that

$$a_{ij} = (i + 1)j \quad \text{and} \quad b_{ij} = 2i(j - 1).$$

Denote $\qquad AB = [c_{ij}] \quad \text{and} \quad BA = [d_{ij}].$

Determine:

a) a_{24}, b_{31}, a_{33}, b_{42}

b) $a_{24} \cdot b_{33}$, $b_{31} \cdot a_{42}$, $a_{11} \cdot b_{23}$

    c) c_{24}, c_{33}, c_{41}, c_{31}

    d) d_{21}, d_{33}, d_{13}, d_{44}

4. Prove Facts 8.5-3.

5. Show that if AB and BA are both defined, then A and B are square matrices. (Discount the fact that scalar multiplication may be viewed as multiplication by a 1×1 matrix.)

6. *a)* Prove that if A, B, C are nonsingular $n \times n$ matrices, then $(ABC)^{-1} = C^{-1}B^{-1}A^{-1}$.

    b) Generalize this to the inverse of a product of k, $n \times n$ nonsingular matrices.

7. Show that the set of all $m \times m$ matrices over R is a linear space over R. (*Hint:* First list the things you need to show.)

8. Prove that $(AB)C = A(BC)$, where A, B, C are matrices with dimensions $n \times n$. (*Hint:* Denote the ijth component of a matrix M by M_{ij}. Hence

$$((AB)C)_{ij} = \sum_{p=1}^{n} ((AB)_{ip} \cdot C_{pj}) = \sum_{p=1}^{n} \left(\left(\sum_{k=1}^{n} A_{ik}B_{kp} \right) C_{pj} \right)$$

$$= \ldots \text{(for you to complete using certain}$$
$$\text{facts concerning double summations)}$$

$$= \sum_{k=1}^{n} \left(A_{ik} \sum_{p=1}^{n} B_{kp}C_{pj} \right) = \sum_{k=1}^{n} (A_{ik} \cdot (BC)_{kj})$$

$$= (A(BC))_{ij}.)$$

"Actually when we write $A = [a_{ij}]$ we mean that a_{ij} is the ijth component of the function A. Logically it would be more accurate to use the notation A_{ij}, but for psychological convenience the "small" letters are used as a reminder that the entries are scalars. This has another useful facet in that we later use the notation A_{ij} for a particular matrix."

9. Show that the inverse of a matrix (if one exists) is unique. (*Hint:* Assume that $AB = I$ and that $AA^{-1} = A^{-1}A = I$, and show that B must be A^{-1}.)

10. Investigate (prove or disprove):

    a) If M is an $n \times n$ matrix such that $MM = M$, then M is the identity matrix (*i.e.*, $M^2 = M \Rightarrow M = I$).

    b) If $M = I$, then $M^2 = M$.

11. Prove that $A(B + C) = AB + AC$, where A, B, C are $n \times n$ matrices.

12. Find a matrix $A \neq [0_{ij}]$ such that $A^2 = [0_{ij}]$.

    Note: This example shows that it is quite possible that the product of "non-zero" matrices is the zero matrix $[0_{ij}]$. Thus the argument

$$AB = 0 \Rightarrow A = 0 \quad \text{or} \quad B = 0$$

fails to be valid in the case of matrices.

13. Find $\begin{bmatrix} 1 & 0 \\ 0 & -1 \end{bmatrix}^{-1} \cdot \left(Hint: \text{Compute } \begin{bmatrix} 1 & 0 \\ 0 & -1 \end{bmatrix}^2 \cdot \right)$

14. Suppose $A = [a_{ij}]$ and $B = [b_{ij}]$ are $m \times n$ matrices.

Define $\qquad A \leq B \qquad$ iff $\qquad a_{ij} \leq b_{ij}$ for all i, j.

Investigate (prove or disprove):
  a) If $A \leq B$ and $B \leq A$, then $A = B$.
  b) $A \leq B$ and $B \leq C \Rightarrow A \leq C$.
  c) $A \leq B \Rightarrow -B \leq -A$.

15. Show that the statements made in this section concerning matrix addition and multiplication, additive and multiplicative inverses, and identities all hold in particular for 1×1 matrices (scalars).

8.6 Interpretation of Matrix Operations as Transformations on a Linear Space

We pause briefly here to consider a "graphical" interpretation of the matrix, operations that so far have been discussed from a purely algebraic point of view. We shall restrict ourselves here to the linear space R^2, and 2×2 matrices over R, although the ideas involved carry over without difficulty to other linear spaces and associated matrices. In particular, we want to see how multiplication by, and addition of, matrices to vectors "transform" these vectors.

Suppose $\begin{pmatrix} x \\ y \end{pmatrix}$ is a vector in R^2, and $A = [a_{ij}]$ is a 2×2 matrix over R. Then

$$A \begin{pmatrix} x \\ y \end{pmatrix} = \begin{pmatrix} a_{11}x + a_{12}y \\ a_{21}x + a_{22}y \end{pmatrix}$$

is again a vector in R^2. It appears, then, that A can be viewed as a transformation (function)

$$A: R^2 \to R^2.$$

8.6-1 Theorem: Under the conditions described above, A is a linear function.

Proof: We need only show that for $\begin{pmatrix} x \\ y \end{pmatrix}$ and $\begin{pmatrix} x' \\ y' \end{pmatrix}$, any two points in R^2, and any scalar b,

$$A \left(b \begin{pmatrix} x \\ y \end{pmatrix} + \begin{pmatrix} x' \\ y' \end{pmatrix} \right) = bA \begin{pmatrix} x \\ y \end{pmatrix} + A \begin{pmatrix} x' \\ y' \end{pmatrix}.$$

Now $A \left(b \begin{pmatrix} x \\ y \end{pmatrix} + \begin{pmatrix} x' \\ y' \end{pmatrix} \right) = A \begin{pmatrix} bx + x' \\ by + y' \end{pmatrix} = \begin{pmatrix} a_{11}(bx + x') + a_{12}(by + y') \\ a_{21}(bx + x') + a_{22}(by + y') \end{pmatrix}$, whereas $bA \begin{pmatrix} x \\ y \end{pmatrix} + A \begin{pmatrix} x' \\ y' \end{pmatrix} = \begin{bmatrix} ba_{11} & ba_{12} \\ ba_{21} & ba_{22} \end{bmatrix} \begin{pmatrix} x \\ y \end{pmatrix} + \begin{bmatrix} a_{11} & a_{12} \\ a_{21} & a_{22} \end{bmatrix} \begin{pmatrix} x' \\ y' \end{pmatrix}$

$$= \begin{pmatrix} ba_{11}x + ba_{12}y \\ ba_{21}x + ba_{22}y \end{pmatrix} + \begin{pmatrix} a_{11}x' + a_{12}y' \\ a_{21}x' + a_{22}y' \end{pmatrix}$$

$$= \begin{pmatrix} ba_{11}x + ba_{12}y + a_{11}x' + a_{12}y' \\ ba_{21}x + ba_{22}y + a_{21}x' + a_{22}y' \end{pmatrix}$$

$$= \begin{pmatrix} a_{11}(bx + x') + a_{12}(by + y') \\ a_{21}(bx + x') + a_{22}(by + y') \end{pmatrix}. \quad \square$$

Similarly, note that adding a vector $\begin{pmatrix} a \\ b \end{pmatrix}$ to a point $\begin{pmatrix} x \\ y \end{pmatrix}$ in R^2 yields

$$\begin{pmatrix} x \\ y \end{pmatrix} + \begin{pmatrix} a \\ b \end{pmatrix} = \begin{pmatrix} x + a \\ y + b \end{pmatrix}.$$

We recognize this as a *translation* of the original point $\begin{pmatrix} x \\ y \end{pmatrix}$ (see Figure 8.5).

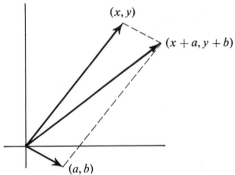

FIG. 8.5 Addition of $\begin{pmatrix} a \\ b \end{pmatrix}$ to $\begin{pmatrix} x \\ y \end{pmatrix}$ results in translating $\begin{pmatrix} x \\ y \end{pmatrix}$ to the new point $\begin{pmatrix} x + a \\ y + b \end{pmatrix}.$

You should note that this is equivalent to the "vector addition" discussed in connection with adding complex numbers by the "parallelogram law."

Example: Suppose $A = \begin{bmatrix} \sqrt{2} & -\sqrt{2} \\ \sqrt{2} & \sqrt{2} \end{bmatrix}$. Then

$$A \begin{pmatrix} x \\ y \end{pmatrix} = \begin{pmatrix} \sqrt{2}x & -\sqrt{2}y \\ \sqrt{2}x & +\sqrt{2}y \end{pmatrix}$$

is a vector in R^2 which has the same length as $\begin{pmatrix} x \\ y \end{pmatrix}$, but which has been rotated $\pi/4$. (See Figure 8.6.)

579

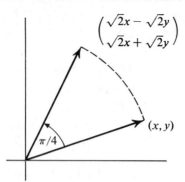

FIG. 8.6 Multiplication of $\begin{pmatrix} x \\ y \end{pmatrix}$ by A results in a rotation to $\begin{pmatrix} \sqrt{2}x - \sqrt{2}y \\ \sqrt{2}x + \sqrt{2}y \end{pmatrix}$.

(You are asked to verify this in Problem 1.)

In general, multiplication of a vector by a matrix results in a rotation and an "expansion." We shall see later that the amount of this "expansion" is related to the so-called "determinant" of the matrix involved.

You recall the "rotation of coordinates" transformation:

$$\Theta: R \times R \to R \times R$$

defined by

$$(x', y') = \Theta(x, y) = (x \cos \theta + y \sin \theta, \ -x \sin \theta + y \cos \theta),$$

results in a rotation of the point (x, y) (in Cartesian coordinate) to the new point (x', y'). This rotation is through an angle of θ. It is interesting to note that this can be written as

$$\begin{pmatrix} x' \\ y' \end{pmatrix} = \begin{bmatrix} \cos \theta & \sin \theta \\ -\sin \theta & \cos \theta \end{bmatrix} \begin{pmatrix} x \\ y \end{pmatrix}.$$

Thus rotation of coordinates can be viewed as a transformation by matrix multiplication.

Exercises 8.6

1. Verify that upon rotating $\begin{pmatrix} x \\ y \end{pmatrix}$ by $\pi/4$, one obtains $\begin{pmatrix} \sqrt{2}x - \sqrt{2}y \\ \sqrt{2}x + \sqrt{2}y \end{pmatrix}$.

2. Graph the point $\begin{pmatrix} x \\ y \end{pmatrix}$ in $R \times R$ and the point $\begin{bmatrix} 2 & 1 \\ 3 & -1 \end{bmatrix} \begin{pmatrix} x \\ y \end{pmatrix}$ where $\begin{pmatrix} x \\ y \end{pmatrix}$ is

given by

a) $\begin{pmatrix} 1 \\ 2 \end{pmatrix}$.

c) $\begin{pmatrix} 1 \\ 3 \end{pmatrix}$.

b) $\begin{pmatrix} -1 \\ -2 \end{pmatrix}$.

d) $\begin{pmatrix} -4 \\ 6 \end{pmatrix}$.

3. Let a transformation $T: R \times R \to R \times R$ be defined by the matrix $\begin{bmatrix} 1 & 2 \\ 3 & 2 \end{bmatrix}$. Determine the image of the unit square $[0, 1] \times [0, 1]$ under T. (*Hint:* Plot some critical functional values.)

4. Determine a matrix $\begin{bmatrix} a_{11} & a_{12} \\ a_{21} & a_{22} \end{bmatrix}$ which doubles every vector distance from the origin but does not rotate it. (*Hint:* Find a_{ij} so that

$$\begin{bmatrix} a_{11} & a_{12} \\ a_{21} & a_{22} \end{bmatrix} \begin{pmatrix} x \\ y \end{pmatrix} = \begin{pmatrix} 2x \\ 2y \end{pmatrix}.)$$

5. Describe the effect on $R \times R$ of the transformation determined by the matrix

a) $\begin{bmatrix} 2 & 0 \\ 0 & 3 \end{bmatrix}$ b) $\begin{bmatrix} 5 & 0 \\ 0 & 4 \end{bmatrix}$ c) $\begin{bmatrix} -1 & 0 \\ 0 & -2 \end{bmatrix}$ d) $\begin{bmatrix} -2 & 0 \\ 0 & 3 \end{bmatrix}$

6. a) Find a matrix A that, upon multiplication, results in a rotation of coordinates of amount $\pi/3$.

    b) Find a second matrix, B, that results in a rotation of $-\pi/3$.

    c) Observe that $AB = BA = I$. Explain what this means in terms of inverses of rotations.

7. a) Let $\tau = \left\{ \begin{bmatrix} \cos\theta & -\sin\theta \\ \sin\theta & \cos\theta \end{bmatrix} : \theta \in [0, \pi) \right\}$. Show that τ forms a commutative group under the operation of matrix multiplication.

    b) Explain what this multiplication does in terms of rotation transformations.

8. Recall that we have identified $\mathbb{C}$ and $R \times R$. Hence $x + iy$ may also be denoted by $\begin{pmatrix} x \\ y \end{pmatrix}$. Determine the 2×2 matrix which has the same effect on $\begin{pmatrix} x \\ y \end{pmatrix} = x + iy$ as does multiplying $x + iy$ by the number $a + bi$.

8.7 Systems with Nonsquare Coefficient Matrix, Solutions and Inverses

Up to this point we have looked only at systems in which there were n equations and n unknowns. These systems could be represented by the matrix $AX = C$ where A was an n by n (square) matrix. There is no reason to restrict our study to these special systems. We shall examine systems where there are more equations than unknowns and also systems with more unknowns than equations. We will first look at a system which has no solution and then a system with more than one solution. We will then try to determine what characteristics of a system determine the number of solutions.

Example: Consider the following system which gives four conditions and three unknowns.

$$\begin{aligned} x + y + z &= 1 \\ 3x - 2y + z &= 0 \\ 2x + y - z &= 2 \\ x - 2y - z &= 0 \end{aligned}$$

We can represent this system by the matrix equation

$$\begin{bmatrix} 1 & 1 & 1 \\ 3 & -2 & 1 \\ 2 & 1 & -1 \\ 1 & -2 & -1 \end{bmatrix} \begin{pmatrix} x \\ y \\ z \end{pmatrix} = \begin{pmatrix} 1 \\ 0 \\ 2 \\ 0 \end{pmatrix}.$$

Recall that we do not distinguish between a vector $\begin{pmatrix} x_1 \\ \cdot \\ \cdot \\ x_n \end{pmatrix}$ and the associated

$n \times 1$ matrix $\begin{bmatrix} x_1 \\ \cdot \\ \cdot \\ x_n \end{bmatrix}$. The augmented matrix for this system is

$$\begin{bmatrix} 1 & 1 & 1 & | & 1 \\ 3 & -2 & 1 & | & 0 \\ 2 & 1 & -1 & | & 2 \\ 1 & -2 & -1 & | & 0 \end{bmatrix}.$$

The elementary row operations described previously for producing equivalent systems were independent of the number of equations and variables and hence we can reduce this system as follows.

$$\begin{bmatrix} 1 & 1 & 1 & | & 1 \\ 0 & 5 & 2 & | & 3 \\ 0 & 1 & 3 & | & 0 \\ 0 & 3 & 2 & | & 1 \end{bmatrix} \leftrightarrow \begin{bmatrix} 5 & 0 & 3 & | & 2 \\ 0 & 5 & 2 & | & 3 \\ 0 & 0 & -13 & | & 3 \\ 0 & 0 & -4 & | & 4 \end{bmatrix}$$

$$\leftrightarrow \begin{bmatrix} 65 & 0 & 0 & | & 35 \\ 0 & 65 & 0 & | & 45 \\ 0 & 0 & -13 & | & 3 \\ 0 & 0 & 0 & | & 40 \end{bmatrix} \leftrightarrow \begin{bmatrix} 13 & 0 & 0 & | & 7 \\ 0 & 13 & 0 & | & 9 \\ 0 & 0 & -13 & | & 3 \\ 0 & 0 & 0 & | & 1 \end{bmatrix}$$

We see now that a vector $\begin{pmatrix} x \\ y \\ z \end{pmatrix}$ which satisfies the system must be such that

$$\begin{bmatrix} 13 & 0 & 0 \\ 0 & 13 & 0 \\ 0 & 0 & -13 \\ 0 & 0 & 0 \end{bmatrix}\begin{bmatrix} x \\ y \\ z \end{bmatrix} = \begin{bmatrix} 7 \\ 9 \\ 3 \\ 1 \end{bmatrix}$$

and hence must satisfy the following system

$$\begin{aligned} 13x + 0y + 0z &= 7 \\ 0x + 13y + 0z &= 9 \\ 0x + 0y - 13z &= 3 \\ 0x + 0y + 0z &= 1. \end{aligned}$$

It is clear, however, that no vector will satisfy the last equation and therefore there is no solution.

Example: Consider the following system

$$\begin{aligned} x + y + z &= 0 \\ 2x + 2y + 2z &= 0 \\ x - 2y - z &= 1 \\ 3x - 6y - 3z &= 3. \end{aligned}$$

$$\begin{bmatrix} 1 & 1 & 1 \\ 2 & 2 & 2 \\ 1 & -2 & -1 \\ 3 & -6 & -3 \end{bmatrix}\begin{bmatrix} x \\ y \\ z \end{bmatrix} = \begin{bmatrix} 0 \\ 0 \\ 1 \\ 3 \end{bmatrix}$$

which can be put into augmented form and reduced by row operations as follows:

$$\left[\begin{array}{ccc|c} 1 & 1 & 1 & 0 \\ 2 & 2 & 2 & 0 \\ 1 & -2 & -1 & 1 \\ 3 & -6 & -3 & 3 \end{array}\right] \leftrightarrow \left[\begin{array}{ccc|c} 1 & 1 & 1 & 0 \\ 1 & 1 & 1 & 0 \\ 1 & -2 & -1 & 1 \\ 1 & -2 & -1 & 1 \end{array}\right] \leftrightarrow \left[\begin{array}{ccc|c} 1 & 1 & 1 & 0 \\ 0 & 0 & 0 & 0 \\ 1 & -2 & -1 & 1 \\ 0 & 0 & 0 & 0 \end{array}\right]$$

$$\leftrightarrow \left[\begin{array}{ccc|c} 1 & 1 & 1 & 0 \\ 0 & 3 & 2 & -1 \\ 0 & 0 & 0 & 0 \\ 0 & 0 & 0 & 0 \end{array}\right] \leftrightarrow \left[\begin{array}{ccc|c} 3 & 0 & 1 & 1 \\ 0 & 3 & 2 & -1 \\ 0 & 0 & 0 & 0 \\ 0 & 0 & 0 & 0 \end{array}\right]$$

Although we have not formally discussed a procedure to follow in finding a solution by repeated use of the row operations, it seems clear at this stage that one cannot reduce this matrix to the desired form from which one can immediately determine a unique solution. We do know however that a solution to the original equation must also satisfy the following equation.

$$\begin{bmatrix} 3 & 0 & 1 \\ 0 & 3 & 2 \\ 0 & 0 & 0 \\ 0 & 0 & 0 \end{bmatrix}\begin{bmatrix} x \\ y \\ z \end{bmatrix} = \begin{bmatrix} 1 \\ -1 \\ 0 \\ 0 \end{bmatrix}$$

From this we know that it is both necessary and sufficient that x, y, and z satisfy the following two equations

$$3x + z = 1$$
$$3y + 2z = -1. \quad \text{(Explain!)}$$

By selecting any arbitrary z then, we can determine a solution. For example, by letting $z = 0$ we have $\begin{pmatrix} 1/3 \\ -1/3 \\ 0 \end{pmatrix}$ as a solution. By letting $z = 1$ we have $\begin{pmatrix} 0 \\ -1 \\ 1 \end{pmatrix}$ as a solution. It is clear then, that this system has as many different solutions as there are ways to select z. That is all vectors $\begin{pmatrix} \dfrac{1-z}{3} \\ \dfrac{-1-2z}{3} \\ z \end{pmatrix}$ are solutions.

Any System Expressed as a Matrix Equation $MX = C$ where M is a Square Matrix

Before we proceed, let us comment here that the solution for any system of equations can be reduced to an equivalent problem in finding vectors (sometimes of a special form) which are solutions to a matrix equation $MX = C$ where M is a square matrix. Due to the excessive notation required to make this rigorous, we include only some examples, but it should be clear that this result is general.

Example: Consider the following system of equations

$$2x + y + z + w = 1$$
$$x + y + 2z + 2w = 0$$
$$x - y + z - w = 2.$$

It is clear that a vector $\begin{pmatrix} x \\ y \\ z \\ w \end{pmatrix}$ satisfies this equation if and only if it satisfies the following:

$$2x + y + z + w = 1$$
$$x + y + 2z + 2w = 0$$
$$x - y + z - w = 2$$
$$0x + 0y + 0z + 0w = 0$$

That is, the vector $\begin{pmatrix} x \\ y \\ z \\ w \end{pmatrix}$ satisfies the matrix equation

$$\begin{bmatrix} 2 & 1 & 1 & 1 \\ 1 & 1 & 2 & 2 \\ 1 & -1 & 1 & -1 \end{bmatrix} \begin{bmatrix} x \\ y \\ z \\ w \end{bmatrix} = \begin{bmatrix} 1 \\ 0 \\ 2 \end{bmatrix}$$

if and only if it satisfies

$$\begin{bmatrix} 2 & 1 & 1 & 1 \\ 1 & 1 & 2 & 2 \\ 1 & -1 & 1 & -1 \\ 0 & 0 & 0 & 0 \end{bmatrix} \begin{bmatrix} x \\ y \\ z \\ w \end{bmatrix} = \begin{bmatrix} 1 \\ 0 \\ 2 \\ 0 \end{bmatrix}.$$

Example: Consider the equations

$$\begin{aligned} 2x + y + z &= 1 \\ x - y - z &= 0 \\ 2x + y + 2z &= 2 \\ 4x + 5y - 3z &= 3. \end{aligned}$$

A vector $\begin{pmatrix} x \\ y \\ z \end{pmatrix}$ satisfies the above system if and only if

$$\begin{aligned} 2x + y + z + 1 \cdot 0 &= 1 \\ x - y - z + 1 \cdot 0 &= 0 \\ 2x + y + 2z + 1 \cdot 0 &= 2 \\ 4x + 5y - 3z + 1 \cdot 0 &= 3. \end{aligned}$$

That is, the vector $\begin{pmatrix} x \\ y \\ z \end{pmatrix}$ satisfies the matrix equation

$$\begin{bmatrix} 2 & 1 & 1 \\ 1 & -1 & -1 \\ 2 & 1 & 2 \\ 4 & 5 & -3 \end{bmatrix} \begin{bmatrix} x \\ y \\ z \end{bmatrix} = \begin{bmatrix} 1 \\ 0 \\ 2 \\ 3 \end{bmatrix}$$

if and only if the vector $\begin{pmatrix} x \\ y \\ z \\ 0 \end{pmatrix}$ satisfies the matrix equation

$$\begin{bmatrix} 2 & 1 & 1 & 1 \\ 1 & -1 & -1 & 1 \\ 2 & 1 & 2 & 1 \\ 4 & 5 & -3 & 1 \end{bmatrix} \begin{bmatrix} x \\ y \\ z \\ 0 \end{bmatrix} = \begin{bmatrix} 1 \\ 0 \\ 2 \\ 3 \end{bmatrix}.$$

We proceed now to concentrate on vector equations $MX = C$ where M is a square matrix.

The Solutions of a System Using the Inverse of a Matrix

In the matrix equation $AX = C$ (having unique solutions) which we have solved thus far, we reduced the equation by row operations to an equation $IX = C'$. It seems natural to wonder whether this could have been solved by first finding a matrix B such that $BA = I$, and then multiplying both sides of the equation on the left by B. That is, $B(AX) = BC$. Since multiplication of matrices is associative, we have $(BA)X = BC$, $IX = BC$, from which we could immediately determine the solution by looking at BC.

Example: Suppose that we are asked to solve the system

$$\begin{bmatrix} 2x + 3y = 2 \\ x + 2y = 1 \end{bmatrix}.$$

This can be written in matrix form as

$$\begin{bmatrix} 2 & 3 \\ 1 & 2 \end{bmatrix}\begin{pmatrix} x \\ y \end{pmatrix} = \begin{pmatrix} 2 \\ 1 \end{pmatrix}$$

or $AX = C$, where

$$A = \begin{bmatrix} 2 & 3 \\ 1 & 2 \end{bmatrix}, \quad X = \begin{pmatrix} x \\ y \end{pmatrix}, \quad C = \begin{pmatrix} 2 \\ 1 \end{pmatrix}.$$

Note that $A^{-1} = \begin{bmatrix} 2 & -3 \\ -1 & 2 \end{bmatrix}$, since

$$\begin{bmatrix} 2 & 3 \\ 1 & 2 \end{bmatrix}\begin{bmatrix} 2 & -3 \\ -1 & 2 \end{bmatrix} = \begin{bmatrix} 1 & 0 \\ 0 & 1 \end{bmatrix} = I_2$$

(although the method used to *find* A^{-1} remains rather mysterious at this point). The solution to the system is thus given by

$$A^{-1}AX = \begin{bmatrix} 2 & -3 \\ -1 & 2 \end{bmatrix}\begin{bmatrix} 2 & 3 \\ 1 & 2 \end{bmatrix}\begin{pmatrix} x \\ y \end{pmatrix} = A^{-1}C = \begin{bmatrix} 2 & -3 \\ -1 & 2 \end{bmatrix}\begin{pmatrix} 2 \\ 1 \end{pmatrix} = \begin{pmatrix} 1 \\ 0 \end{pmatrix},$$

that is, the unique solution of the system is $x = 1$ and $y = 0$. Of course, the solution could also be found by the methods discussed earlier (elimination by substitution or addition-subtraction). We will investigate later how these methods of "elimination" are interpreted in matrix notation.

Example: Consider the equation

$$\begin{bmatrix} 1 & 1 & 1 \\ 1 & 2 & 1 \\ 1 & 1 & 2 \end{bmatrix}\begin{bmatrix} x \\ y \\ z \end{bmatrix} = \begin{bmatrix} 1 \\ 1 \\ 1 \end{bmatrix}.$$

Note that

$$\begin{bmatrix} 3 & -1 & -1 \\ -1 & 1 & 0 \\ -1 & 0 & 1 \end{bmatrix}\begin{bmatrix} 1 & 1 & 1 \\ 1 & 2 & 1 \\ 1 & 1 & 2 \end{bmatrix} = \begin{bmatrix} 1 & 0 & 0 \\ 0 & 1 & 0 \\ 0 & 0 & 1 \end{bmatrix}.$$

Recalling that associativity holds, let us see what happens if we multiply both sides by the given matrix.

$$\begin{bmatrix} 3 & -1 & -1 \\ -1 & 1 & 0 \\ -1 & 0 & 1 \end{bmatrix}\begin{bmatrix} 1 & 1 & 1 \\ 1 & 2 & 1 \\ 1 & 1 & 2 \end{bmatrix}\begin{bmatrix} x \\ y \\ z \end{bmatrix} = \begin{bmatrix} 3 & -1 & -1 \\ -1 & 1 & 0 \\ -1 & 0 & 1 \end{bmatrix}\begin{bmatrix} 1 \\ 1 \\ 1 \end{bmatrix}$$

From here we have

$$\begin{bmatrix} 1 & 0 & 0 \\ 0 & 1 & 0 \\ 0 & 0 & 1 \end{bmatrix}\begin{bmatrix} x \\ y \\ z \end{bmatrix} = \begin{bmatrix} 1 \\ 0 \\ 0 \end{bmatrix}$$

or simply

$$\begin{bmatrix} x \\ y \\ z \end{bmatrix} = \begin{bmatrix} 1 \\ 0 \\ 0 \end{bmatrix}.$$

We thus see that the only solution for our system is the vector $\begin{pmatrix} 1 \\ 0 \\ 0 \end{pmatrix}$. If we solve the system as before using row operations on the augmented matrix, we arrive at the same answer. (Verify this.)

Computing the Inverse of a Matrix by Row Operations

To point out the very strong connection between the inverse of the coefficient matrix and the existence of a solution, let us investigate a method for computing the inverse. This method is identical to solving the equation by reducing it by row operations to the form $IX = C'$.

Example: Find an inverse for

$$\begin{bmatrix} 1 & 2 & 1 \\ 3 & 1 & 1 \\ 1 & 4 & 1 \end{bmatrix}.$$

If we reduce this matrix to the identity matrix by row operations and at each step perform the same operation on I as follows, then we will have transformed I into the inverse we are seeking.

$$\begin{bmatrix} 1 & 2 & 1 \\ 3 & 1 & 1 \\ 1 & 4 & 1 \end{bmatrix} \vdots \begin{bmatrix} 1 & 0 & 0 \\ 0 & 1 & 0 \\ 0 & 0 & 1 \end{bmatrix}$$

$$\begin{bmatrix} 1 & 2 & 1 \\ 0 & 5 & 2 \\ 0 & -2 & 0 \end{bmatrix} \vdots \begin{bmatrix} 1 & 0 & 0 \\ 3 & -1 & 0 \\ 1 & 0 & -1 \end{bmatrix}$$

$$\begin{bmatrix} 5 & 10 & 5 \\ 0 & 10 & 4 \\ 0 & -10 & 0 \end{bmatrix} \vdots \begin{bmatrix} 5 & 0 & 0 \\ 6 & -2 & 0 \\ 5 & 0 & -5 \end{bmatrix}$$

$$\begin{bmatrix} 5 & 0 & 1 \\ 0 & 5 & 2 \\ 0 & 0 & 4 \end{bmatrix} \cdot \begin{bmatrix} -1 & 2 & 0 \\ 3 & -1 & 0 \\ 11 & -2 & -5 \end{bmatrix}$$

$$\begin{bmatrix} 20 & 0 & 0 \\ 0 & 10 & 0 \\ 0 & 0 & 4 \end{bmatrix} \cdot \begin{bmatrix} -15 & 10 & 5 \\ -5 & 0 & 5 \\ 11 & -2 & -5 \end{bmatrix}$$

$$\begin{bmatrix} 1 & 0 & 0 \\ 0 & 1 & 0 \\ 0 & 0 & 1 \end{bmatrix} \cdot \begin{bmatrix} -3/4 & 1/2 & 1/4 \\ -1/2 & 0 & 1/2 \\ 11/4 & -1/2 & -5/4 \end{bmatrix}$$

Hence, it should be that

$$\begin{bmatrix} -3/4 & 1/2 & 1/4 \\ -1/2 & 0 & 1/2 \\ 11/4 & -1/2 & -5/4 \end{bmatrix} \begin{bmatrix} 1 & 2 & 1 \\ 3 & 1 & 1 \\ 1 & 4 & 1 \end{bmatrix} = \begin{bmatrix} 1 & 0 & 0 \\ 0 & 1 & 0 \\ 0 & 0 & 1 \end{bmatrix}.$$

Exercise: Verify the claim above and also show that

$$\begin{bmatrix} 1 & 2 & 1 \\ 3 & 1 & 1 \\ 1 & 4 & 1 \end{bmatrix} \begin{bmatrix} -3/4 & 1/2 & 1/4 \\ -1/2 & 0 & 1/2 \\ 11/4 & -1/2 & -5/4 \end{bmatrix} = \begin{bmatrix} 1 & 0 & 0 \\ 0 & 1 & 0 \\ 0 & 0 & 1 \end{bmatrix}.$$

Example: Compute the inverse of

$$\begin{bmatrix} 1 & 0 & 2 \\ 1 & 2 & 1 \\ 0 & 1 & 3 \end{bmatrix}$$

$$\begin{bmatrix} 1 & 0 & 2 \\ 1 & 2 & 1 \\ 0 & 1 & 3 \end{bmatrix} \cdot \begin{bmatrix} 1 & 0 & 0 \\ 0 & 1 & 0 \\ 0 & 0 & 1 \end{bmatrix}$$

$$\begin{bmatrix} 1 & 0 & 2 \\ 0 & 2 & -1 \\ 0 & 1 & 3 \end{bmatrix} \cdot \begin{bmatrix} 1 & 0 & 0 \\ -1 & 1 & 0 \\ 0 & 0 & 1 \end{bmatrix}$$

$$\begin{bmatrix} 1 & 0 & 2 \\ 0 & 2 & -1 \\ 0 & 0 & -7 \end{bmatrix} \cdot \begin{bmatrix} 1 & 0 & 0 \\ -1 & 1 & 0 \\ -1 & 1 & -2 \end{bmatrix}$$

$$\begin{bmatrix} 7 & 0 & 14 \\ 0 & 28 & -14 \\ 0 & 0 & -14 \end{bmatrix} \cdot \begin{bmatrix} 7 & 0 & 0 \\ -14 & 14 & 0 \\ -2 & 2 & -4 \end{bmatrix}$$

$$\begin{bmatrix} 7 & 0 & 0 \\ 0 & 28 & 0 \\ 0 & 0 & -14 \end{bmatrix} \cdot \begin{bmatrix} 5 & 2 & -4 \\ -12 & 12 & 4 \\ -2 & 2 & -4 \end{bmatrix}$$

$$\begin{bmatrix} 1 & 0 & 0 \\ 0 & 1 & 0 \\ 0 & 0 & 1 \end{bmatrix} \cdot \begin{bmatrix} 5/7 & 2/7 & -4/7 \\ -3/7 & 3/7 & 1/7 \\ 1/7 & -1/7 & 2/7 \end{bmatrix}.$$

And hence

$$\begin{bmatrix} 5/7 & 2/7 & -4/7 \\ -3/7 & 3/7 & 1/7 \\ 1/7 & -1/7 & 2/7 \end{bmatrix} \begin{bmatrix} 1 & 0 & 2 \\ 1 & 2 & 1 \\ 0 & 1 & 3 \end{bmatrix} = \begin{bmatrix} 1 & 0 & 0 \\ 0 & 1 & 0 \\ 0 & 0 & 1 \end{bmatrix}.$$

Question: Can you justify this method for finding inverses?

Exercises 8.7

1. Show that the following system of equations has no solution.

$$\begin{aligned} x + y + z &= 0 \\ 2x + 2y + 2z &= 1 \\ x + 2y - z &= 2 \\ x + 2y - z &= 0 \end{aligned}$$

2. Describe the set of solutions for the following system.

$$\begin{aligned} 2x + y + z &= 0 \\ x - y + 2z &= 3 \end{aligned}$$

3. Express each of the following as matrix equations $MX = C$ with M a square matrix.

a) $\begin{bmatrix} 2 & 3 & 1 \\ 1 & 4 & 1 \end{bmatrix} \begin{bmatrix} x \\ y \\ z \end{bmatrix} = \begin{bmatrix} 1 \\ 2 \end{bmatrix}$

c) $\begin{aligned} x + 2y &= 7 \\ 3x - 4y &= 2 \\ 5x + y &= 7 \end{aligned}$

b) $\begin{bmatrix} 2 & 3 \\ 2 & 8 \\ 1 & 6 \end{bmatrix} \begin{bmatrix} x \\ y \end{bmatrix} = \begin{bmatrix} 4 \\ 9 \\ 1 \end{bmatrix}$

d) $\begin{aligned} 7x + y + z &= 2 \\ x - y + 2z &= 0 \end{aligned}$

4. Find an inverse for each matrix by the method described in this section.

a) $\begin{bmatrix} 1 & 2 & 0 \\ 0 & 1 & 1 \\ 0 & 2 & 1 \end{bmatrix}$

d) $\begin{bmatrix} 2 & 2 & 1 \\ 1 & -4 & 1 \\ 2 & 1 & 1 \end{bmatrix}$

b) $\begin{bmatrix} 2 & 3 & -1 \\ 1 & -1 & 2 \\ 1 & 2 & 1 \end{bmatrix}$

e) $\begin{bmatrix} -1 & 6 & 4 \\ 3 & 1 & 7 \\ 4 & 2 & -3 \end{bmatrix}$

c) $\begin{bmatrix} 1 & 2 & 3 \\ 1 & 1 & 2 \\ 2 & 3 & -1 \end{bmatrix}$

5. Consider the matrix $A = \begin{bmatrix} 2 & 1 & 1 \\ 3 & 1 & 4 \\ 1 & 2 & -1 \end{bmatrix}$.

a) Find a matrix B such that $BA = \begin{bmatrix} 2 & 1 & 1 \\ 1 & 2 & -1 \\ 3 & 1 & 4 \end{bmatrix}$ (*i.e.*, interchanges the last two rows of A). (*Hint:* Try the identity matrix with the last two rows interchanged.)

b) Find a matrix B such that $BA = \begin{bmatrix} 2 & 1 & 1 \\ 3 & 1 & 4 \\ 2 & 4 & -2 \end{bmatrix}$.

589

c) Find a matrix B such that $BA = \begin{bmatrix} 6 & 3 & 3 \\ 3 & 1 & 4 \\ 2 & 4 & -2 \end{bmatrix}$.

d) Find a matrix B such that $BA = \begin{bmatrix} 2 & 1 & 1 \\ 6 & 2 & 8 \\ 2 & 4 & -2 \end{bmatrix}$.

e) Find a matrix B such that $BA = \begin{bmatrix} 2 & 1 & 1 \\ 6 & 2 & 8 \\ 2 & -1 & 5 \end{bmatrix}$.

6. Justify the method for finding inverses described in this section.

7. Solve the following equations by first finding an inverse matrix and then multiplying it on both sides.

a) $\begin{bmatrix} 2 & 3 & 1 \\ 4 & 1 & -1 \\ 2 & -1 & 3 \end{bmatrix} \begin{bmatrix} x \\ y \\ z \end{bmatrix} = \begin{bmatrix} 1 \\ 2 \\ 0 \end{bmatrix}$

c) $2x + 4y = 0$
$\quad 3x - 2y = 8$

b) $\begin{bmatrix} -1 & 3 & -4 \\ 2 & -1 & 2 \\ 3 & -2 & 6 \end{bmatrix} \begin{bmatrix} x \\ y \\ z \end{bmatrix} = \begin{bmatrix} 0 \\ 1 \\ -2 \end{bmatrix}$

d) $\quad x + 3y - 4z = 0$
$\quad 2x - y + 2z = 0$
$\quad 4x - 6y + z = 0$

8. Consider how three planes in space can intersect (or fail to intersect). From these geometric considerations, what can you conclude about the possible solution of a system of three linear equations in three unknowns?

9. Investigate (prove or disprove): Any system of two homogeneous (right-hand side is 0) linear equations in three unknowns always has solutions other than the "trivial" solution $\begin{pmatrix} 0 \\ 0 \\ 0 \end{pmatrix}$.

10. The sum of the digits of a three-digit number is 14 and the middle digit is the sum of the other two digits. If the last two digits are interchanged, the number obtained is 27 less than the original number. Find the number.

11. Investigate (prove or disprove):
   a) Given the matrix equation $AB = AC$, then it follows that $B = C$.
   b) If the matrix equations

$$AX = I \quad \text{and} \quad XA = I$$

have a solution X, then there is only one solution.

8.8 The Determinant Function

In this section we define and investigate properties of a function (denoted "det") whose domain is the class S of square matrices over a field F and whose range is contained in the field F. As in the last section, we will usually assume that the field F over which the matrices are taken is the real field R. Our study of the determinant function will enable us to determine when an element of S has an inverse, and to state another method of computing the inverse if it exists. Keep in mind that one of the advantages in being able to compute A^{-1}, given the matrix A, is that it leads to the solution of the system of linear equations

$$AX = C,$$

where A is the $n \times n$ "coefficient matrix," X is the $n \times 1$ matrix of "unknowns," and C is the $n \times 1$ matrix of constants. If A^{-1} can be found, the equation can be written in equivalent form as

$$A^{-1}(AX) = A^{-1}C,$$

or equivalently

$$X = A^{-1}C.$$

(Provided, of course, that $AX = C \Rightarrow A^{-1}(AX) = A^{-1}C$. The reader is asked to prove that this is indeed the case (see Exercise 3).) The solution to the system is therefore given by identifying each unknown in X as the corresponding constant in the $n \times 1$ matrix $A^{-1}C$.

Before we formally define the determinant function, we would like to provide some motivation in the simple case of a 2×2 matrix.

Determinant of a 2 × 2 Matrix

Let us investigate some two by two matrices and try to determine conditions under which a matrix will be nonsingular. Consider the matrix $A = \begin{bmatrix} a & b \\ c & d \end{bmatrix}$. We wish to find a matrix $B = \begin{bmatrix} x & y \\ z & w \end{bmatrix}$ such that

$$\begin{bmatrix} x & y \\ z & w \end{bmatrix} \begin{bmatrix} a & b \\ c & d \end{bmatrix} = \begin{bmatrix} 1 & 0 \\ 0 & 1 \end{bmatrix}.$$

That is,

$$\begin{bmatrix} xa + yc & xb + yd \\ az + wc & zb + wd \end{bmatrix} = \begin{bmatrix} 1 & 0 \\ 0 & 1 \end{bmatrix}$$

or equivalently we wish to find solutions for the following equations.

$$xa + yc = 1$$
$$xb + yd = 0$$
$$za + wc = 0$$
$$zb + wd = 1$$

This requirement can also be expressed by requiring solutions for the following two matrix equations.

$$\begin{bmatrix} a & c \\ b & d \end{bmatrix} \begin{bmatrix} x \\ y \end{bmatrix} = \begin{bmatrix} 1 \\ 0 \end{bmatrix}$$

$$\begin{bmatrix} a & c \\ b & d \end{bmatrix} \begin{bmatrix} z \\ w \end{bmatrix} = \begin{bmatrix} 0 \\ 1 \end{bmatrix}$$

From these we can deduce that the only possible solutions are given by

$$x = \frac{d}{ad - bc} \qquad y = \frac{-b}{ad - bc}$$

$$z = \frac{-c}{ad - bc} \qquad w = \frac{a}{ad - bc} \qquad \text{(verify this!).}$$

Notice that it must be assumed that $ad - bc \neq 0$. If $ad - bc = 0$, then there is no solution, and hence no inverse for the matrix. The number $ad - bc$ is called the *determinant* of the matrix $A = \begin{bmatrix} a & b \\ c & d \end{bmatrix}$ denoted by det A.

We have established that the inverse of a 2×2 matrix exists if and only if det $A \neq 0$. If possible, we would like to define the determinant of arbitrary $n \times n$ matrices so that the result holds in general. This definition is not very well motivated, since the theorems which follow are not at all obvious. In a case like this it is best not to seek immediate motivations but to appreciate the research which has been done and to try to develop insight by working problems and reading proofs. First, we shall state some needed preliminary definitions.

The General Determinant

The definition of the determinant function is essentially a "recursive" definition. Hence, as the reader might suspect, this means that the proofs tend to rely heavily upon mathematical induction. We shall first define the numbers (images) mapped to by det when 1×1 and 2×2 pre-images (matrices) in S are considered. (Keep in mind that S denotes the class of all square matrices over R.) We shall notice an inductive step between the determinants of 1×1 and 2×2 matrices which we use to extend to the arbitrary $n \times n$ case.

8.8-1 Definitions: a) det $[a]_{1 \times 1} = a \qquad \forall a \in R$.

b) det $[a_{ij}]_{2 \times 2} = a_{11}a_{22} - a_{12}a_{21}$.

Example: det $[1] = 1$.

$$\det \begin{bmatrix} 1 & 3 \\ -2 & -7 \end{bmatrix} = -7 + 6 = -1.$$

$$\det \begin{bmatrix} 5 & 1 \\ 4 & 6 \end{bmatrix} = 26.$$

det $[-2] = -2$.

$$\det \begin{bmatrix} 1 & 1 \\ 2 & 2 \end{bmatrix} = 0.$$

Note that determinants of 1×1 and 2×2 matrices may be positive, negative, or zero. We shall define det $[a_{ij}]_{n \times n}$ in terms of a certain linear combination of determinants of $(n - 1) \times (n - 1)$ matrices. These square matrices of smaller dimension are called *minors*, and are obtained from $[a_{ij}]_{n \times m}$ as follows.

8.8-2 Definition: The $(n - 1) \times (n - 1)$ matrix obtained from the matrix $A = [a_{ij}]_{n \times n}$ by deleting the ith row and jth column of A is called the ijth *minor* of A and is denoted by A_{ij}. (We assume, of course, that $n > 1$.)

Example: Given the matrix

$$A = \begin{bmatrix} 1 & 2 & 2 \\ -1 & 0 & 7 \\ 5 & 1 & 6 \end{bmatrix},$$

we have (upon deleting the first (top) row and first (left most) column)

$$A_{11} = \begin{bmatrix} 0 & 7 \\ 1 & 6 \end{bmatrix}.$$

Similarly,

$$A_{12} = \begin{bmatrix} -1 & 7 \\ 5 & 6 \end{bmatrix}, \qquad A_{13} = \begin{bmatrix} -1 & 0 \\ 5 & 1 \end{bmatrix}, \qquad A_{32} = \begin{bmatrix} 1 & 2 \\ -1 & 7 \end{bmatrix}.$$

Remark: Notice that the minors of

$$A = \begin{bmatrix} a_{11} & a_{12} \\ a_{21} & a_{22} \end{bmatrix}$$

are

$$A_{11} = [a_{22}], \qquad A_{12} = [a_{21}], \qquad A_{21} = [a_{12}], \qquad A_{22} = [a_{11}].$$

Further, the determinant of A can be given in terms of the determinants of its minors as follows:

$$\det A = a_{11} \det A_{11} - a_{12} \det A_{12}.$$

Question: When does a non-homogeneous matrix equation in 1×1 matrices have a solution? That is, when does the equation

$$[a][x] = [c] \qquad c \neq 0$$

have a solution x?

The determinant of $A = [a_{ij}]_{n \times n}$ is defined to be a linear combination of determinants of minors of elements in the first row of A as follows:

8.8-3 Definition: $\det [a_{ij}]_{n \times n} = \sum\limits_{j=1}^{n} (-1)^{i+1} a_{1j} \det A_{1j}$, where $n \geq 2$.

Example: For the 3×3 matrix of the previous example, we have

$$\det A = \sum_{j=1}^{3} (-1)^{i+1} a_{1j} \det A_{1j}$$

$$= (-1)^{1+1} \cdot 1 \cdot \det \begin{bmatrix} 0 & 7 \\ 1 & 6 \end{bmatrix} + (-1)^{2+1} \cdot 2 \cdot \det \begin{bmatrix} -1 & 7 \\ 5 & 6 \end{bmatrix}$$

$$+ (-1)^{3+1} \cdot 2 \cdot \det \begin{bmatrix} -1 & 0 \\ 5 & 1 \end{bmatrix}$$

$$= (-1)^2 \cdot 1 \cdot (0 \cdot 6 - 7 \cdot 1) + (-1)^3 \cdot 2 \cdot (-1 \cdot 6 - 7 \cdot 5) + (-1)^4 \cdot 2 \cdot (-1 \cdot 1 - 0 \cdot 5)$$

$$= -7 + 82 - 2 = 73.$$

Thus
$$\det \begin{bmatrix} 1 & 2 & 2 \\ -1 & 0 & 7 \\ 5 & 1 & 6 \end{bmatrix} = 73.$$

Remark: Note that the effect of multiplying each term in the linear combination by $(-1)^{j+1}$ is to introduce "alternating signs" in the combination. Thus the determinant of a 3×3 matrix A could be written

$$\det A = a_{11} \det A_{11} - a_{12} \det A_{12} + a_{13} \det A_{13}.$$

Remark: In the calculation of the determinant of a 4×4 matrix, we must first obtain a linear combination of 3×3 determinants, then in turn evaluate each of these in terms of linear combinations of 2×2 matrices. It is not difficult to imagine that in order to calculate the determinant of, say a 10×10 matrix (a relatively "small" matrix in many problems where matrices are used), the process of obtaining a linear combination of ten 9×9 determinants; then each of these in turn as a combination of nine 8×8 determinants; etc., down to all 2×2 determinants is very tedious. The methodical "wearing down" of the dimension of the determinants, fortunately, is well suited to machine computation. However, even though computers can do these operations very rapidly (tens, hundreds, thousands, or more per second), the tremendous increase in the number of computational operations required as the dimension increases makes this method of calculating $\det A$ very time consuming, even by computers, for matrices with dimension on the order of 50×50 or more. Therefore, in applications where such determinants must be calculated, the technique introduced in our definition is replaced by "faster" methods (that is, methods that require fewer calculations). Another extremely important reason to search for methods requiring fewer calculations is the reduction of possible computational error. The computer necessarily "rounds off" and "truncates" decimals to limit the numbers in the machine to manageable length. Thus, as more and more computations are performed with numbers obtained from previous computations (with a possible "rounding error" at each stage), the total error may have a "snowballing" effect. That is to say, if at each stage an error of 10^{-10} is introduced, and if 10^{20} stages are involved, it is not difficult to see that the total error involved may add up to a very serious one, even though the error at each computation is quite small in itself.

Remark: If we apply Definition 8.8-3 to the calculation of the determinant of a 2×2 matrix, we have

$$\det [a_{ij}]_{2\times 2} = \sum_{j=1}^{2} (-1)^{j+1} a_{1j} \det A_{1j}$$

$$= a_{11} \det A_{11} - a_{12} \det A_{12}$$

$$= a_{11}a_{22} - a_{12}a_{21}$$

since $A_{11} = [a_{22}]$ and $A_{12} = [a_{21}]$ in this case. Note that this is the same value that is introduced in Definition 8.8-1, so that Definition 8.8-1 can be applied to 2×2 matrices as well as matrices of higher dimension.

The Transpose of a Matrix

In our analysis involving existence of inverses we shall find it useful to consider a matrix B obtained from a given matrix A by interchanging the rows and columns of A. That is, each row of A is written as a column in the new matrix B. In this case the matrix B is called the *transpose* of A, denoted by A^T.

8.8-4 Definition: $[a_{ij}]_{n\times m}^T = [a_{ji}]_{m\times n}$. (This operation need not be restricted to square matrices although we are interested primarily in this special case.)

Example: $\begin{bmatrix} 2 & -2 & 3 \\ 0 & 1 & 0 \\ -1 & 8 & 5 \end{bmatrix}^T = \begin{bmatrix} 2 & 0 & -1 \\ -2 & 1 & 8 \\ 3 & 0 & 5 \end{bmatrix}$.

Example: $\begin{bmatrix} 1 & 2 & 3 \\ 5 & 0 & 4 \end{bmatrix}^T = \begin{bmatrix} 1 & 5 \\ 2 & 0 \\ 3 & 4 \end{bmatrix}$.

8.8-5 Theorem: a) $(A^T)^T = A$ for all $A \in S$.

b) $(A + B)^T = A^T + B^T$.

c) $(AB)^T = B^T A^T$.

d) If A is nonsingular (has an inverse), then so is A^T, and moreover $(A^{-1})^T = (A^T)^{-1}$.

Proof: a) $(A^T)^T = [a_{ji}]^T = [a_{ij}] = A$.

b) The proof of this part is left as an exercise.

c) Suppose $A = [a_{ij}]$ and $B = [b_{ij}]$. Then

$$(AB)^T = \left[\sum_{q=1}^{n} a_{iq}b_{qj} \right]^T = \left[\sum_{q=1}^{n} a_{jq}b_{qi} \right]$$

$$= \left[\sum_{q=1}^{n} b_{qi}a_{jq} \right]$$

$$= \left[\sum_{q=1}^{n} b_{iq}^* a_{qj}^* \right]$$

where b_{iq}^* denotes the iqth element of B^T and a_{qj}^* the qjth element of A^T. But then by definition $b_{iq}^* = b_{qi}$ and $a_{qj}^* = a_{jq}$, hence the latter matrix is $B^T A^T$.

d) In order to show that

$$A \text{ nonsingular} \Rightarrow A^T \text{ nonsingular}$$

we need only show that $A^T(A^{-1})^T = I$. (Why?) But by part *c)*,

$$A^T(A^{-1})^T = (A^{-1}A)^T = I^T = I.$$

Note that we have also shown that

$$(A^T)^{-1} = (A^{-1})^T. \quad \square$$

595

Some Determinant Theorems

As was mentioned previously, we shall concentrate upon determinants of 1×1, 2×2, and 3×3 matrices, although the theorems and results we discuss for these cases are true for $n \times n$ matrices for any $n \in N$. In order to indicate this fact, the theorems are stated in general form although many of the proofs are given only for 1×1, 2×2, and 3×3 matrices. Such proofs are signaled by writing "proof" in quotation marks. We shall devote the remainder of the section to stating and proving several theorems about the det function.

8.8-6 Theorem: Suppose A is an $n \times n$ matrix in S. Then

$$\det (kA) = k^n \det A.$$

As an example of how induction can be used to obtain a proof for matrices of any dimension $n \times n$ ($n \in N$), we proceed to an inductive argument.

Proof: i) If A is 1×1, $kA = [kA]$ where $A = [a]$, so that

$$\det kA = k \det A.$$

If A is 2×2, $kA = [ka_{ij}]$, so

$$\det kA = (ka_{11}ka_{22} - ka_{12}ka_{21}).$$

Thus in this case

$$\det kA = k^2(a_{11}a_{22} - a_{12}a_{21}) = k^2 \det A.$$

We have now shown that

$$\det k[a_{ij}]_{n \times n} = k^n \det [a_{ij}]_{n \times n} \qquad \text{for } n = 1, 2.$$

ii) Suppose the result holds for $n = t$ for some $t \in N$. Then it also holds for $n' = t + 1$, since

$$\det kA = \det [ka_{ij}]_{(t+1) \times (t+1)} = \sum_{j=1}^{t+1} (-1)^{i+1} ka_{1j} \det kA_{1j}$$

where A_{ij} is the ijth minor of A, and is thus a $t \times t$ matrix. But by the inductive hypothesis,

$$\det kA_{ij} = k^t \det A_{ij},$$

and the right hand side of our equation can be written

$$\sum_{j=1}^{t+1} (-1)^{i+1} k^{t+1} \cdot a_{1j} \det A_{1j} = k^{t+1} \sum_{j=1}^{t+1} (-1)^{i+1} a_{1j} \det A_{1j} = k^{t+1} \det A. \quad \square$$

8.8-7 Theorem: $\det AB = \det A \det B$, where A and B are $n \times n$ matrices.

Proof: This is obvious if A and B are 1×1. If they are 2×2,

$$\det AB = \det \left[\sum_{q=1}^{2} a_{iq}b_{qj} \right]$$

$$= (a_{11}b_{11} + a_{12}b_{21})(a_{21}b_{12} + a_{22}b_{22}) - (a_{11}b_{12} + a_{12}b_{22})(a_{21}b_{11} + a_{22}b_{21})$$

which, after simplification, can be written

$$(a_{11}a_{22} - a_{12}a_{21})(b_{11}b_{22} - b_{12}b_{21}) = \det A \det B.$$

The proof for 3×3 matrices can similarly be reduced to algebraic verification that both sides of an equation are the same. □

Example: Let

$$A = \begin{bmatrix} 1 & 1 & 2 \\ -1 & 1 & 1 \\ 0 & 1 & 3 \end{bmatrix} \quad B = \begin{bmatrix} -1 & 1 & 0 \\ 2 & 0 & 3 \\ -2 & 1 & 1 \end{bmatrix}.$$

Then

$$AB = \begin{bmatrix} -3 & 3 & 5 \\ 1 & 0 & 4 \\ -4 & 3 & 6 \end{bmatrix}.$$

$$\det A = 1 \cdot \det \begin{bmatrix} 1 & 1 \\ 1 & 3 \end{bmatrix} - 1 \cdot \det \begin{bmatrix} -1 & 1 \\ 0 & 3 \end{bmatrix} + 2 \cdot \det \begin{bmatrix} -1 & 1 \\ 0 & 1 \end{bmatrix}$$

$$= 2 - (-3) + 2 \cdot (-1) = 3.$$

$$\det B = -1 \cdot \det \begin{bmatrix} 0 & 3 \\ 1 & 1 \end{bmatrix} - 1 \cdot \det \begin{bmatrix} 2 & 3 \\ -2 & 1 \end{bmatrix} + 0 \cdot \det \begin{bmatrix} 2 & 0 \\ -2 & 1 \end{bmatrix}$$

$$= (-1)(-3) - 1(8) = -5.$$

$$\det AB = -3 \cdot \det \begin{bmatrix} 0 & 4 \\ 3 & 6 \end{bmatrix} - 3 \cdot \det \begin{bmatrix} 1 & 4 \\ -4 & 6 \end{bmatrix} + 5 \cdot \det \begin{bmatrix} 1 & 0 \\ -4 & 3 \end{bmatrix}$$

$$= (-3)(-12) - 3(22) + 5(3) = 36 - 66 + 15$$

$$= -15 = 3(-5) = \det A \det B.$$

8.8-8 Theorem: $\det A^{-1} = 1/\det A$.

Proof: This is easily seen by noting that

$$\det A^{-1}A = \det A^{-1} \det A$$
$$= \det I = 1 \quad \text{(why?)}.$$

Thus $\det A^{-1} = 1/\det A$, provided that $\det A \neq 0$. □

This could not be the case if A^{-1} did not exist. However, we will show in the next section that A^{-1} exists only when $\det A$ is non-zero.

8.8-9 Theorem: $\det A^T = \det A$.

Proof: If A is 1×1, then $A = A^T$, and the result is trivial. If A is 2×2, then

$$\det \begin{bmatrix} a_{11} & a_{21} \\ a_{12} & a_{22} \end{bmatrix} = a_{11}a_{22} - a_{21}a_{12} = \det \begin{bmatrix} a_{11} & a_{12} \\ a_{21} & a_{22} \end{bmatrix}.$$

If A is 3×3, a computational argument easily yields the result. □

8.8-10 Theorem: Suppose $A \in S$, and A^* is obtained from A by interchanging two adjacent rows of A. Then $\det A = -\det A^*$.

Proof: If $A = \begin{bmatrix} a_{11} & a_{12} \\ a_{21} & a_{22} \end{bmatrix}$, then $A^* = \begin{bmatrix} a_{21} & a_{22} \\ a_{11} & a_{12} \end{bmatrix}$ and

$$-\det A^* = -(a_{21}a_{12} - a_{22}a_{11}) = \det A.$$

A similar argument can be used in case A is 3×3. ⬜

8.8-11 Theorem: Suppose $A \in S$, and A^* is obtained from A by multiplying each element in a row of A by a scalar α. Then $\det A^* = \alpha \det A$.

Proof left as an exercise.

8.8-12 Theorem: A matrix $A \in S$ with two identical rows has zero determinant.

Proof: Suppose $A = [a_{ij}]$ where $a_{tj} = a_{kj}$ for some $t < k$ and all j. We may form the matrix A^* from A by writing the kth row of A as the last row of A^* (involving the interchange of adjacent rows $n - k$ times) and the tth row of A as the $n - 1$st row of A^* (by $n - 1 - t$ interchanges), leaving all other rows in the same relative position. That is,

$$A^* = [a_{ij}^*], \quad \text{where} \quad a_{ij}^* = \begin{cases} a_{ij} & \text{for } i < t \\ a_{i+1,j} & \text{for } t \le i < k \\ a_{i+2,j} & \text{for } k \le i < n - 2 \\ a_{kj} & \text{for } i = n - 1 \text{ and } i = n. \end{cases}$$

The value of $\det A$ can be obtained by the computation of $\det A^*$, since

$$\det A = (-1)^{(n-k)+(n-1-t)} \det A^*.$$

By Definition 8.8-3, the value of $\det A^*$ is eventually "worked down" to a linear combination of determinants of 2×2 matrices, each obtained from the last two rows of A^*. That is, for some p,

$$\det A^* = \sum_{m=1}^{p} c_m \det A_m^*,$$

where for each m,

$$A_m^* = \begin{bmatrix} a_{n-1,q}^* & a_{n-1,r}^* \\ a_{nq}^* & a_{nr}^* \end{bmatrix}$$

for some q and r, and c_m is some constant. However, since the $n - 1$st and nth rows of A^* are identical, we see that

$$\det A_m^* = \det \begin{bmatrix} a_{nq}^* & a_{nr}^* \\ a_{nq}^* & a_{nr}^* \end{bmatrix} = a_{nq}^* a_{nr}^* - a_{nr}^* a_{nq}^* = 0.$$

It follows that the linear combination $\det A^*$ is also zero, and hence that $\det A = 0$. ⬜

Exercise: Determine the p mentioned in this proof.

8.8-13 Theorem: Suppose $A \in S$, and A^* is obtained from A by adding to the elements of the tth row of A a scalar multiple, α, of the corresponding elements in the kth row of A. That is, if $A = [a_{ij}]$ and $A^* = [a_{ij}^*]$, where

$$a_{ij}^* = \begin{cases} a_{ij} & \text{if } i \neq t, \\ a_{tj} + \alpha a_{kj} & \text{if } i = t. \end{cases}$$

Then $\det A = \det A^*$.

Proof left as an exercise.

8.8-14 Theorem: Theorems 8.8-10, 8.8-11, 8.8-12, and 8.8-13 remain true if the word "row" is replaced by the word "column" throughout.

Proof: Operations on columns of a matrix A result in corresponding operations on the rows of A^T. Since $\det A^T = \det A$ (Theorem 8.8-9), it follows that "column operations" on A have the same effect as "row operations," as far as the function det is concerned. ☐

In summary, we have seen that replacing a row (or column) of a matrix A by the row (column) *plus* a linear combination of the other rows (columns) does not alter the image $\det A$. These theorems are of great interest for two reasons. They will enable us to easily examine the "elimination by substitution and addition-subtraction" techniques of solving systems of linear equations in terms of operations on matrices; and they will allow us to prove in the next section that a matrix is singular if its rows (or columns) form linearly dependent vectors, in which case its determinant is zero.

Exercises 8.8

1. Compute $\det A$ where:

   a) $A = \begin{bmatrix} 1 & 2 \\ 4 & 1 \end{bmatrix}$

   b) $A = \begin{bmatrix} -1 & -3 \\ 2 & 0 \end{bmatrix}$

   c) $A = \begin{bmatrix} 1 & 2 \\ 1 & 2 \end{bmatrix}$

   d) $A = \begin{bmatrix} -1 & 6 \\ 2 & -3 \end{bmatrix}$

2. Find A^T (A-transpose) where:

   a) $A = \begin{bmatrix} 1 & 2 & 4 \\ 6 & 1 & 7 \end{bmatrix}$

   b) $A = \begin{bmatrix} 1 & 2 & 4 \\ 1 & 0 & 8 \\ 0 & 3 & -7 \end{bmatrix}$

   c) $A = \begin{bmatrix} i & 2+i & 3i \\ 1 & 5 & i \end{bmatrix}$

   d) $A = \begin{bmatrix} 1 & 4 \\ 1 & 2i \\ 2 & 1 \end{bmatrix}$

3. *a)* Prove that $A = B \Rightarrow CA = CB$ for any matrix C with dimensions such that these products are defined.

   b) Conclude that if C is nonsingular, the converse also holds. (*Hint:* Use part *a)* to obtain

   $$CA = CB \Rightarrow C^{-1}CA = C^{-1}CB.)$$

4. Let

$$A = \begin{bmatrix} 2 & 3 & 1 & 4 \\ 2 & 0 & 1 & -3 \\ 1 & -4 & 0 & -2 \end{bmatrix}.$$

Find the 2 × 3 matrix

    a) A_{11} *b)* A_{23} *c)* A_{33} *d)* A_{21} *e)* A_{22}

5. Compute det A where:

    a)
$$A = \begin{bmatrix} -1 & 2 & 3 \\ 0 & 4 & -2 \\ 1 & 2 & 3 \end{bmatrix}$$
    c)
$$A = \begin{bmatrix} -4 & 1 & -2 \\ 2 & 2 & 1 \\ 1 & -6 & 3 \end{bmatrix}$$

    b)
$$A = \begin{bmatrix} 0 & 1 & -2 \\ 2 & 0 & 4 \\ 0 & 0 & 1 \end{bmatrix}$$
    d)
$$A = \begin{bmatrix} 1 & 2 & 0 & -3 \\ 0 & 1 & 4 & -2 \\ -2 & -1 & 2 & 1 \\ 8 & 4 & -5 & 3 \end{bmatrix}$$

6. Find A^{-1} where:

    a)
$$A = \begin{bmatrix} 2 & 1 \\ 1 & 3 \end{bmatrix}$$
    b)
$$A = \begin{bmatrix} 2i & -i \\ 4 & 1 \end{bmatrix}$$
    c)
$$A = \begin{bmatrix} 2+3i & 2i \\ 0 & 4i \end{bmatrix}$$

7. Investigate (prove or disprove):
    a) $\det (A + B) = \det A + \det B$
    b) $\det (-A) = (-1)^n \det A$ (A is $n \times n$)
    c) $(A + B)^T = A^T + B^T$

8. Show that a matrix with a row (column) of zeros is singular. (*Hint:* There is no loss of generality in assuming that the zeros occur in the first row. (Why not?))

9. Let
$$A = \begin{bmatrix} a & b & c & d \\ a' & b' & c' & d' \\ a'' & b'' & c'' & d'' \\ a''' & b''' & c''' & d''' \end{bmatrix}.$$

Let H be the result of interchanging the 2nd and 3rd rows of I_4

(*i.e.,*).
$$H = \begin{bmatrix} 1 & 0 & 0 & 0 \\ 0 & 0 & 1 & 0 \\ 0 & 1 & 0 & 0 \\ 0 & 0 & 0 & 1 \end{bmatrix}$$

    a) Determine the effect of multiplying A on the left by H (*i.e.*, compute HA).
    b) Determine the effect of multiplying A on the right by H (*i.e.*, compute AH).

10. Show that det $I_n = 1$ for all n.

11. Let
$$A = \begin{bmatrix} a & b & c \\ a' & b' & c' \\ a'' & b'' & c'' \end{bmatrix}.$$

Let H be the matrix formed from I_3 by replacing the first row by the sum of itself and k times the second row

$$\left(i.e., \ H = \begin{bmatrix} 1 & k & 0 \\ 0 & 1 & 0 \\ 0 & 0 & 1 \end{bmatrix} \right).$$

    a) Compute HA and AH.

    b) Find det H.

    c) What can you say about det (HA)?

12. For a 4×4 matrix A, let A^* be obtained from A by multiplying each element in the 3rd row by a scalar k.

Let H be the 4×4 matrix obtained from I_4 by multiplying each element in the 3rd row by a scalar k.

    a) Show that $HA = A.^*$

    b) Compute det H.

    c) Compute det A^* in terms of det A. (Recall that det $AB =$ det A det B.)

    d) Prove Theorem 8.8-11.

13. For a 4×4 matrix A, let A^* be obtained from A by adding to the elements of the 2nd row of A a scalar multiple (α) of the corresponding elements in the 4th row.

Let H be similarly obtained from I_4.

    a) Show that $A^* = HA$.

    b) Compute det H.

    c) Compute det A^* in terms of det A.

    d) Prove Theorem 8.8-13.

    e) Improve the "proof" of Theorem 8.8-10.

14. Show an alternate proof of det $kA = k^n$ det A (where A is $n \times n$) can be obtained by using the fact that det $AB =$ det A det B, and the fact that $kA = (kI)A$.

15. Suppose $A = [a_{ij}]_{3\times3}$.

    a) Show that det A
$$= (a_{11}a_{22}a_{33} + a_{12}a_{23}a_{31} + a_{13}a_{21}a_{32}) - (a_{11}a_{23}a_{32} + a_{12}a_{21}a_{33} + a_{13}a_{22}a_{31}).$$

    b) Show that this is also det A^T.

    c) Show that det $AB =$ det A det B for 3×3 matrices A and B.

16. Define a relation D on the set of square matrices as follows

$$(A, B) \in D \qquad \text{iff} \qquad \det A = \det B.$$

    a) Show that D is an equivalence relation.

    b) Describe the equivalence classes.

8.9 More on Inverses

    We are now in a position to make use of the function *det* in connection with the determination of the multiplicative inverse of a matrix in S (if the inverse exists (*i.e.*, if the matrix is *nonsingular*).) Recall that multiplying a row (or column) of a matrix by a scalar has the effect of multiplying the image det A by that scalar, while adding a scalar times a row (or column) to another row (or column, respectively) of A does not change the image. (Note that a "scalar times a row of A" is interpreted as the scalar times each element of the row in question, and that "adding one row of A to another row" means adding the corresponding elements of one row to those in the other.) We shall put these facts together to relate the linear independence of the rows (or columns) of a matrix A to the image det A.

Example: Let

$$A = \begin{bmatrix} 1 & 2 & 3 \\ 0 & 1 & 1 \\ 1 & 3 & 4 \end{bmatrix}.$$

Here the third row vector $(1, 3, 4)$ is the component-wise sum of the first two row vectors $(1, 2, 3)$ and $(0, 1, 1)$.

$$\det A = 1 \cdot \det \begin{bmatrix} 1 & 1 \\ 3 & 4 \end{bmatrix} - 2 \cdot \det \begin{bmatrix} 0 & 1 \\ 1 & 4 \end{bmatrix} + 3 \cdot \det \begin{bmatrix} 0 & 1 \\ 1 & 3 \end{bmatrix}$$

$$= 1 - 2(-1) + 3(-1) = 0$$

Example: Let

$$A = \begin{bmatrix} 2 & 0 & 2 \\ 1 & 2 & 5 \\ 3 & 1 & 5 \end{bmatrix}.$$

The third column vector $\begin{pmatrix} 2 \\ 5 \\ 5 \end{pmatrix}$ is a linear combination of the other two column vectors.

$$\begin{pmatrix} 2 \\ 5 \\ 5 \end{pmatrix} = \begin{pmatrix} 2 \\ 1 \\ 3 \end{pmatrix} + 2 \begin{pmatrix} 0 \\ 2 \\ 1 \end{pmatrix}$$

$$\det A = 2 \cdot \det \begin{bmatrix} 2 & 5 \\ 1 & 5 \end{bmatrix} + 2 \cdot \det \begin{bmatrix} 1 & 2 \\ 3 & 1 \end{bmatrix}$$

$$= 2 \cdot 5 + 2(-5) = 0$$

We have seen here two examples of a general result, concerning the relationship between column and row vectors and the determinant function.

8.9-1 Lemma: If the rows (columns) of a square matrix A are linearly dependent, then

$$\det A = 0.$$

Proof: Suppose $A = [a_{ij}]$, and suppose $\bar{a}_i = (a_{i1}, a_{i2}, \ldots, a_{in})$ is the ith row of A. The rows of A are linearly dependent, provided there are n scalars, $\alpha_1, \alpha_2, \ldots, \alpha_n$, not all zero such that

$$\sum_{i=1}^{n} \alpha_i \bar{a}_i = (0, 0, \ldots, 0). \tag{1}$$

Suppose that $\alpha_t \neq 0$. Then multiplying the tth row $\bar{a}_t$ of A by α_t to obtain A^* gives us

$$\det A^* = \alpha_t \det A.$$

Now suppose we add to the tth row of A^*

$$\sum_{\substack{i=1 \\ i \neq t}}^{n} \alpha_i \bar{a}_i.$$

(*i.e.*, add to $\alpha_t \bar{a}_t$ all other rows after being multiplied by a scalar.) We know that each of these additions (for example, adding $\alpha_1 \bar{a}_1$ (if $t \neq 1$) to the tth row of A^*) does not change det A^*. Let us denote the matrix obtained by these additions to the tth row of A^* by B, so that

$$\det B = \det A^* = \alpha_t \det A.$$

By equation (1), the tth row of B is a row of zeros. But this implies that

$$\det B = 0. \quad \square$$

The proof for linearly dependent columns is not necessary since we can consider that case to be reduced to the present one by considering the transpose.

8.9-2 Lemma: Suppose A is a square matrix, and that det $A \neq 0$. Then the rows and columns of A are linearly independent.

Proof: If the rows or columns of A were not linearly independent, then we could not have det $A \neq 0$ by Lemma 8.9-1. (Note that Lemma 8.9-2 is simply the contrapositive of Lemma 8.9-1.) $\square$

Let us consider some examples which illustrate further the idea of column and row vectors being linearly dependent and independent.

Example: Let

$$A = \begin{bmatrix} 1 & 2 & 1 \\ 2 & 1 & 0 \\ 3 & 3 & 2 \end{bmatrix}.$$

If the three column vectors

$$\begin{pmatrix} 1 \\ 2 \\ 3 \end{pmatrix}, \quad \begin{pmatrix} 2 \\ 1 \\ 3 \end{pmatrix}, \quad \begin{pmatrix} 1 \\ 0 \\ 2 \end{pmatrix}$$

are independent, then there are no real numbers a, b, c (not all zero) such that

$$a \begin{pmatrix} 1 \\ 2 \\ 3 \end{pmatrix} + b \begin{pmatrix} 2 \\ 1 \\ 3 \end{pmatrix} + c \begin{pmatrix} 1 \\ 0 \\ 2 \end{pmatrix} = \begin{pmatrix} 0 \\ 0 \\ 0 \end{pmatrix}.$$

Equivalently, there are no real numbers a, b, c (not all zero) such that

$$\begin{pmatrix} a + 2b + c \\ 2a + b + 0c \\ 3a + 3b + 2c \end{pmatrix} = \begin{pmatrix} 0 \\ 0 \\ 0 \end{pmatrix}$$

which can be written as the following matrix equation

$$\begin{bmatrix} 1 & 2 & 1 \\ 2 & 1 & 0 \\ 3 & 3 & 2 \end{bmatrix} \begin{pmatrix} a \\ b \\ c \end{pmatrix} = \begin{pmatrix} 0 \\ 0 \\ 0 \end{pmatrix}.$$

Thus we see that the answer to the question concerning linear independence of the column vectors for a square matrix A depends on whether the equation

$$AX = [0]$$

(meaning by $[0]$ the $n \times 1$ column matrix with all zeros) has solutions other than the trivial solution $X = [0]$.

Example: Let

$$A = \begin{bmatrix} 1 & 1 & 2 \\ 2 & 3 & 0 \\ 3 & 4 & 3 \end{bmatrix}.$$

If the three row vectors

$$(1, 1, 2), \qquad (2, 3, 0), \qquad (3, 4, 3)$$

are linearly independent, then there are no scalars a, b, c (not all zero) such that

$$a(1, 1, 2) + b(2, 3, 0) + c(3, 4, 3) = (0, 0, 0).$$

Equivalently, there are no scalars a, b, c (not all zero) such that

$$(a + 2b + 3c, a + 3b + 4c, 2a + 0b + 3c) = (0, 0, 0).$$

This can be written as the system

$$\begin{aligned} a + 2b + 3c &= 0 \\ a + 3b + 4c &= 0 \\ 2a + 0b + 3c &= 0 \end{aligned}$$

or as the matrix equation

$$\begin{bmatrix} 1 & 2 & 3 \\ 1 & 3 & 4 \\ 2 & 0 & 3 \end{bmatrix} \begin{pmatrix} a \\ b \\ c \end{pmatrix} = \begin{pmatrix} 0 \\ 0 \\ 0 \end{pmatrix}.$$

Thus we see that linear independence of the row vectors for a square matrix A depends on whether the equation

$$A^T X = [0]$$

has solutions other than the trivial solution $X = [0]$.

These examples should, in some sense, indicate the connection between solutions for linear systems (which are related to inverses of matrices) and the idea of row and column vectors being independent. Let us now proceed with the development.

8.9-3 Theorem: The rows and columns of a square matrix A are linearly independent iff $\det A \neq 0$.

Proof: In view of Lemma 8.9-2, we need only prove the "only if" part. That is, we must show that:

(all rows and columns of A linearly independent) $\Rightarrow \det A \neq 0$.

We prove the contrapositive as follows:

Suppose $\det A = 0$, and that $A = [a_{ij}]$. Then

$$\sum_{j=1}^{n} (-1)^{j+1} a_{1j} \det A_{1j} = 0 \qquad (2)$$

by definition. But also

$$\sum_{j=1}^{n} (-1)^{j+1} a_{kj} \det A_{1j} = 0 \qquad \text{for } k \in \{2, 3, \ldots, n\} \qquad (3)$$

since for each k this expression may be viewed as

$$\pm\det A^* = [a_{ij}^*] \qquad \text{where} \qquad a_{ij}^* = \begin{cases} a_{kj} & \text{for } i = 1 \\ a_{ij} & \text{for } i \in \{2, 3, \ldots, n\}, \end{cases}$$

and since A^* has repeated rows (the first and k^{th}), thus making $\det A^* = 0$. If $\det A_{1j} \neq 0$ for some j, then equations (2) and (3) together imply that the columns of A are linearly dependent, since they could be written

$$\sum_{j=1}^{n} \alpha_j \bar{a}_j = [0],$$

where $\alpha_j = (-1)^{j+1} \det A_{1j}$ (a scalar) and $\bar{a}_j$ is the jth column of A. On the other hand, if $\det A_{1j} = 0$ for $j = 1, 2, \ldots, n$, then the 2nd, 3rd, $\ldots$, nth rows of A are linearly dependent, which in turn implies that the rows of A are linearly dependent. ☐

Note: The student should satisfy himself that the details of the above argument holds. It would not be surprising, however, if the argument seems difficult at this stage. It would perhaps be advisable to return to this proof after having done the exercises at the close of the section.

The student should recall that he was earlier asked to show that a square matrix with a row or column of zeros is singular. It is easy to see that the determinant of such a matrix is zero. We next show that the value $\det A$ can always be used in this way to determine whether A is singular.

8.9-4 Theorem: A square matrix A is nonsingular iff $\det A \neq 0$.

Proof: a) Suppose that A is a nonsingular matrix. We must show that $\det A \neq 0$. Since A is nonsingular there is a matrix A^{-1} such that

$$I = AA^{-1}.$$

This implies that

$$1 = \det I = \det AA^{-1}$$
$$= \det A \det A^{-1}$$
$$\Rightarrow \det A \neq 0 \qquad \text{and} \qquad \det A^{-1} \neq 0.$$

b) Assume on the other hand that A is a square matrix such that $\det A \neq 0$. We must show that there is a matrix $B \in S$ such that $AB = I$. That is, we want to prove that

$$\det A \neq 0 \Rightarrow A \text{ nonsingular}.$$

605

We shall give a very useful "constructive proof" of this fact as follows:

Let $$B = [(-1)^{i+j} \det A_{ij}]^T.$$

Then $$(1/\det A)B = A^{-1},$$

that is, $$AB = (\det A)I.$$

Note that the equivalence of these two equations requires the assumption that $\det A \neq 0$.

Let $A = [a_{ij}]$ and $B = [b_{ij}]$ be defined as above. We must show that

$$\begin{bmatrix} a_{11} & a_{12} & \ldots & a_{1n} \\ a_{21} & a_{22} & \ldots & a_{2n} \\ \cdot & \cdot & & \cdot \\ \cdot & \cdot & & \cdot \\ \cdot & \cdot & & \cdot \\ a_{n1} & a_{n2} & \ldots & a_{nn} \end{bmatrix}$$

$$\begin{bmatrix} \det A_{11} & -\det A_{21} & \ldots & (-1)^{n+1}\det A_{n1} \\ -\det A_{12} & \det A_{22} & \ldots & (-1)^{n+2}\det A_{n2} \\ \cdot & \cdot & & \cdot \\ \cdot & \cdot & & \cdot \\ \cdot & \cdot & & \cdot \\ (-1)^{n+1}\det A_{1n} & (-1)^{n+2}\det A_{2n} & \ldots & \det A_{nn} \end{bmatrix}$$

$$= \begin{bmatrix} \det A & 0 & \ldots & 0 \\ 0 & \det A & \ldots & 0 \\ \cdot & \cdot & & \cdot \\ \cdot & \cdot & & \cdot \\ \cdot & \cdot & & \cdot \\ 0 & 0 & \ldots & \det A \end{bmatrix} = (\det A)I.$$

Suppose we denote AB by $C = [c_{ij}]$. To show that

$$c_{ij} = \begin{cases} \det A & \text{if } i = j \\ 0 & \text{if } i \neq j, \end{cases}$$

consider first the computation of a diagonal element of C, say c_{qq}. Note that

$$c_{qq} = \sum_{t=1}^{n} a_{qt}b_{tq}$$

$$= \sum_{t=1}^{n} a_{qt}(-1)^{t+q} \det A_{qt}.$$

But we recognize this as $\det A$, since by $q - 1$ interchanges of adjacent rows in A, we can obtain the matrix A^* whose first row is composed of the elements $a_{q1}, a_{q2}, \ldots, a_{qn}$, and since

$$(-1)^{q-1} \det A = \det A^* = \sum_{t=1}^{n} (-1)^{t+1}a_{qt} \det A_{qt}$$

which implies that

$$\det A = (-1)^{q-1} \sum_{t=1}^{n} (-1)^{t+1} a_{qt} \det A_{qt}$$

$$= \sum_{t=1}^{n} (-1)^{t+q} a_{qt} \det A_{qt} = c_{qq}.$$

To show that the off diagonal elements of C are zero, consider the element c_{kr} with $k \neq r$. Now

$$c_{kr} = \sum_{t=1}^{n} a_{kt} b_{tr}$$

$$= \sum_{t=1}^{n} a_{kt} (-1)^{t+r} \det A_{rt}$$

$$= (-1)^{r-1} \sum_{t=2}^{n} (-1)^{t+1} a_{kt} \det A_{rt}.$$

But $(-1)^{r-1} \sum_{t=2}^{n} (-1)^{t+1} a_{kt} \det A_{rt}$ is the determinant of a matrix D obtained from A as follows:

a) write the rth row of A as the first row (by $r - 1$ interchanges of adjacent rows of A), then

b) replace this top row by the kth row of A. Thus

$$D = \begin{bmatrix} a_{k1} & a_{k2} & \cdots & a_{kn} \\ a_{11} & a_{12} & \cdots & a_{1n} \\ \cdot & \cdot & & \cdot \\ \cdot & \cdot & & \cdot \\ a_{k1} & a_{k2} & \cdots & a_{kn} \\ \cdot & \cdot & & \cdot \\ \cdot & \cdot & & \cdot \\ \cdot & \cdot & & \cdot \\ a_{n1} & a_{n2} & \cdots & a_{nn} \end{bmatrix}$$

and $\det D = 0$ since D has repeated rows. Since $c_{kr} = \det D$, we have $c_{kr} = 0 \quad \forall k \neq r$. $\square$

Remark: The matrix B defined in this proof furnishes us with a way of actually constructing A^{-1} from A whenever $\det A \neq 0$. But we have also seen that $\det A \neq 0$ is a necessary and sufficient condition for A^{-1} to exist.

Example: Determine whether $A = \begin{bmatrix} 1 & 2 \\ 3 & 4 \end{bmatrix}$ is nonsingular, and if so, find A^{-1}.

Solution: Since $\det A = 4 - 6 = -2$, we know that A^{-1} exists. Using the matrix B defined in the proof of 8.9-4, we have

$$B = \begin{bmatrix} \det A_{11} & -\det A_{21} \\ -\det A_{12} & \det A_{22} \end{bmatrix} = \begin{bmatrix} 4 & -2 \\ -3 & 1 \end{bmatrix},$$

so that $A^{-1} = (1/\det A)B = -1/2 \begin{bmatrix} 4 & -2 \\ -3 & 1 \end{bmatrix} = \begin{bmatrix} -2 & 1 \\ 3/2 & -1/2 \end{bmatrix}.$

Check: $A(1/\det A)B = \begin{bmatrix} 1 & 2 \\ 3 & 4 \end{bmatrix}\begin{bmatrix} -2 & 1 \\ 3/2 & -1/2 \end{bmatrix} = \begin{bmatrix} 1 & 0 \\ 0 & 1 \end{bmatrix}.$

The reader can also readily see that $(1/\det A)BA = I$.

Example: If

$$A = \begin{bmatrix} -2 & 0 & 4 \\ 5 & 2 & 1 \\ -3 & 2 & -1 \end{bmatrix}$$

we compute $\det A = 72$, so A^{-1} exists. In fact A^{-1} is obtained by

$$\frac{1}{\det A} B = \frac{1}{72}\begin{bmatrix} \det A_{11} & -\det A_{21} & \det A_{31} \\ -\det A_{12} & \det A_{22} & -\det A_{32} \\ \det A_{13} & -\det A_{23} & \det A_{33} \end{bmatrix}$$

$$= \frac{1}{72}\begin{bmatrix} -4 & 8 & -8 \\ 2 & 14 & 22 \\ 16 & 4 & -4 \end{bmatrix}$$

$$= \begin{bmatrix} -4/72 & 8/72 & -8/72 \\ 2/72 & 14/72 & 22/72 \\ 16/72 & 4/72 & -4/72 \end{bmatrix}.$$

Example: Find the solution to the system

$$\begin{aligned} -2x \qquad + 4z &= 72 \\ 5x + 2y + z &= 144 \\ -3x + 2y - z &= 24. \end{aligned}$$

Solution: We observe this system can be written in matrix form by $AX = C$, where the coefficient matrix A is the 3×3 matrix A of the preceding example.

$$X = \begin{pmatrix} x \\ y \\ z \end{pmatrix} \qquad \text{and} \qquad C = \begin{pmatrix} 72 \\ 144 \\ 24 \end{pmatrix}.$$

Thus the solution is obtained by

$$\begin{pmatrix} x \\ y \\ z \end{pmatrix} = X = A^{-1}AX = A^{-1}C$$

$$\begin{bmatrix} -4/72 & 8/72 & -8/72 \\ 2/72 & 14/72 & 22/72 \\ 16/72 & 4/72 & -4/72 \end{bmatrix}\begin{pmatrix} 72 \\ 144 \\ 24 \end{pmatrix} = \begin{pmatrix} 28/3 \\ 112/3 \\ 68/3 \end{pmatrix},$$

so

$$x = \frac{28}{3}, \qquad y = \frac{112}{3}, \qquad z = \frac{68}{3},$$

is the solution.

Although this may not be the most efficient method for solving systems with two or three unknowns, it can be useful. Further, it gives us a general method for computing specific components of the inverse of a matrix.

Exercises 8.9

1. Let
$$A = \begin{bmatrix} 1 & -1 & 4 \\ -1 & 2 & 0 \\ 0 & 1 & 1 \end{bmatrix}.$$

a) List the column vectors of A.
b) List the row vectors.
c) Are the column vectors independent?
d) Are the row vectors independent?

2. Let A be a 4×4 matrix.

a) Show that the column vectors of A are linearly independent iff the equation $AX = [0]$ has only the trivial solution $X = [0]$.

b) Show a similar fact for the row vectors with respect to the equation $A^T X = [0]$.

3. Use the construction used in the proof of Theorem 8.9-4 to compute inverses for each of the following. (If the inverse exists.)

a) $\begin{bmatrix} 1 & 2 & 1 \\ 1 & 1 & 1 \\ 2 & 3 & 0 \end{bmatrix}$

c) $\begin{bmatrix} 1 & 4 & -6 \\ 2 & 0 & 0 \\ -1 & 2 & -2 \end{bmatrix}$

b) $\begin{bmatrix} 2 & 0 & 1 \\ 4 & -1 & 0 \\ 1 & 1 & -1 \end{bmatrix}$

d) $\begin{bmatrix} -1 & -1 & -2 \\ 0 & 0 & -3 \\ 4 & -1 & 0 \end{bmatrix}$

4. Show that the determinant of a square matrix with a column or row of zeros has determinant 0.

5. Argue that the homogeneous equation $AX = [0]$ has only the trivial solution iff det $A \neq 0$.

6. Solve the following systems of equations by first computing inverse matrices using the method of Theorem 8.9-4.

a) $2x + y - z = 2$
$4x - y + 2z = 0$
$x + 2y + z = 1$

b) $x + y + z - w = 2$
$x + y + z - w = 1$
$x + y - z + w = 3$
$x - y + z + w = -1$

7. Show that computing $A^{-1} = B$ using Theorem 8.9-4 yields a matrix such that $BA = I$. (We showed that $AB = I$.)

8. Show that an $n \times n$ matrix is nonsingular iff all row vectors are linearly independent and all column vectors are linearly independent.

9. Investigate (prove or disprove):

a) If the rows of a square matrix are linearly dependent, then so are the columns.

609

b) If the columns of a square matrix are linearly independent, then so are the rows.

c) Consider questions *a)* and *b)* for non-square matrices.

10. Suppose A is a $n \times n$ matrix, and A^* is a $n - 1 \times n$ matrix formed by deleting the kth row of A. Show that if the rows of A^* are linearly dependent, then the rows of A are also linearly dependent.

11. Show that A is nonsingular iff A^{-1} is nonsingular.

8.10 Methods of Solving Systems of Linear Equations

We have discussed the solution of the system

$$AX = C$$

by multiplying both sides by A^{-1}, provided that A is a nonsingular matrix. The solution obtained in this case is

$$X = A^{-1}C.$$

However several questions remain, such as, "How is this solution related to the 'elimination' methods used earlier?" and, "What happens if $C = [0]$ as compared with $C \neq [0]$?" In this section we want to investigate these questions and to describe two additional techniques for solving the system. One of these, *Cramer's Rule*, is primarily of "theoretical" use, while the other, *Relaxation*, may be used in connection with a "computer solution."

If the constants in the matrix C are all zero, the system is called a *homogeneous system*, otherwise it is called *non-homogeneous*. Of course, the solution $X = A^{-1}C$ is valid for a homogeneous system, provided the coefficient matrix A is nonsingular. However, in this case,

$$A^{-1}C = [0]$$

and the solution is the *zero* solution. *Every* homogeneous system has the zero solution, and this solution is called the trivial solution. It is of interest to determine when a homogeneous system also has a *non-trivial* solution. In view of the solution $X = A^{-1}C$, we see that if the coefficient matrix of a homogeneous system is nonsingular, then the system admits only the trivial solution. Thus it follows that a necessary condition that a homogeneous system have a non-trivial solution is that its coefficient matrix be singular.

Example: The homogeneous system

$$x + y = 0$$
$$2x + 3y = 0$$

has only the trivial solution $x = y = 0$. (Note that $\det \begin{pmatrix} 1 & 1 \\ 2 & 3 \end{pmatrix} = 1$, so the coefficient matrix is nonsingular in this case.)

Example: The homogeneous system

$$\begin{bmatrix} 1 & 1 & 1 \\ 2 & 2 & -1 \\ -1 & -1 & -1 \end{bmatrix} \begin{pmatrix} x \\ y \\ z \end{pmatrix} = \begin{pmatrix} 0 \\ 0 \\ 0 \end{pmatrix}$$

has infinitely many solutions; namely any ordered triple satisfying the equations

$$x = -y \quad \text{and} \quad z = 0.$$

Note that these equations describe a solution set which has as its graph a line in the x, y-plane passing through the origin $(0, 0, 0)$. Thus the trivial solution $x = y = z = 0$ corresponds to only one point on the "solution line." The reader should verify that the coefficient matrix in this system is singular.

8.10-1 Theorem: A homogeneous system of linear equations

$$AX = [0] \quad \text{where} \quad A = [a_{ij}]$$

has non-trivial solutions iff $\det A = 0$.

Proof: Let us prove the contrapositive (for both implications) (*i.e.*, we shall deduce that the equation $AX = [0]$ has only the trivial solution iff $\det A \neq 0$). If $\det A \neq 0$, then A has a unique inverse and hence

$$X = A^{-1}[0] = [0]$$

is the only solution.

If $AX = [0]$ has only the trivial solution, then both the rows and the columns are linearly independent, hence $\det A \neq 0$. Let us work through the details of showing that the columns are independent.

If the columns are dependent, then there exist constants (not all zero) such that

$$\sum_{j=1}^{n} c_j \begin{pmatrix} a_{1j} \\ a_{2j} \\ \vdots \\ \vdots \\ a_{nj} \end{pmatrix} = \begin{pmatrix} 0 \\ 0 \\ \vdots \\ \vdots \\ 0 \end{pmatrix}.$$

This can be expressed equivalently as the matrix equation

$$\begin{bmatrix} a_{11} & a_{12} & \cdots & a_{1n} \\ a_{21} & a_{22} & \cdots & a_{2n} \\ \vdots & \vdots & & \vdots \\ \vdots & \vdots & & \vdots \\ a_{n1} & a_{n2} & \cdots & a_{nn} \end{bmatrix} \begin{pmatrix} c_1 \\ c_2 \\ \vdots \\ \vdots \\ c_n \end{pmatrix} = \begin{pmatrix} 0 \\ 0 \\ \vdots \\ \vdots \\ 0 \end{pmatrix}$$

611

thus giving $AX = [0]$ a non-trivial solution. A similar argument for the rows would yield a non-trivial solution for $A^T X = [0]$. (Can you show that if $AX = [0]$ has only the trivial solution, then $A^T X = [0]$ also has only the trivial solution?) ☐

We shall not discuss a general approach to finding the non-trivial solutions of a homogeneous system, although such techniques exist and are of great interest.* Instead we shall concentrate upon a few representative results for non-homogeneous systems in the remainder of this section. We have seen that a system has a unique solution if the coefficient matrix is nonsingular. (This statement is true for both homogeneous and non-homogeneous systems.) However, the condition of a singular coefficient matrix does not guarantee the existence of more than one solution for the non-homogeneous case.

Example: Consider the system

$$\begin{bmatrix} 2 & -1 \\ 4 & -2 \end{bmatrix} \begin{pmatrix} x \\ y \end{pmatrix} = \begin{pmatrix} 1 \\ 1 \end{pmatrix}.$$

This system has *no* solutions, since the solution points (x, y) would have to be in the set

$$\{(x, y): 2x - y = 1\} \cap \{(x, y): 2x - y = 1/2\} = \{(x, y): 0 = 1/2\} = \varnothing.$$

(This system is thus *inconsistent.*)

On the other hand, the system

$$\begin{bmatrix} 2 & -1 \\ 4 & -2 \end{bmatrix} \begin{pmatrix} x \\ y \end{pmatrix} = \begin{pmatrix} 1 \\ 2 \end{pmatrix}$$

has infinitely many solutions; namely, any point in $\{(x, y): 2x - y = 1\}$, since the two equations in this system are equivalent. (This system is *dependent.*)

Geometrically, an inconsistent system is one in which the hyperplanes (in this case lines) represented by the equations do not intersect. A dependent system is one in which the hyperplanes intersect in several places.

Example: Suppose the coefficient matrix is

$$A = \begin{bmatrix} 1 & 1 & 1 \\ 2 & 2 & -1 \\ -1 & -1 & -1 \end{bmatrix}$$

and the matrix C is

$$C = \begin{pmatrix} 2 \\ 4 \\ -2 \end{pmatrix}.$$

In this case $\det A = 0$. This system has a solution set given by

$$\{(x, y, z): x + y = 2 \quad \text{and} \quad z = 0\}. \quad \text{(Why?)}$$

---

* This is discussed in most elementary *Linear Algebra* books. See for example, "Linear Algebra," G. Hadley, Addison-Wesley Publishing Company, Inc., 1961, pp. 173–82.

(The student should graph the planes described by $x + y + z = 2$ and $2x + 2y - z = 4$ and satisfy himself that they do indeed intersect in the line $x + y = 2$ in the x, y plane.)

Row Operations on the Augmented Matrix and Matrix Multiplication

Recall that earlier we developed a method for solving linear systems by performing a series of elementary operations on the augmented matrix of coefficients. We also noted that by performing the same series of operations on the identity matrix we could arrive at an inverse for the matrix of coefficients. We would now like to examine this procedure in light of matrix multiplication.

Example: Consider the system

$$2x + y - z = 1$$
$$x - y + z = -1$$
$$-x + 2y + z = 2$$

which can be written

$$AX = C \quad \text{where} \quad A = \begin{bmatrix} 2 & 1 & -1 \\ 1 & -1 & 1 \\ -1 & 2 & 1 \end{bmatrix}, \quad X = \begin{pmatrix} x \\ y \\ z \end{pmatrix}, \quad C = \begin{pmatrix} 1 \\ -1 \\ 2 \end{pmatrix}.$$

The augmented matrix is the 3×4 matrix

$$\begin{bmatrix} 2 & 1 & -1 & 1 \\ 1 & -1 & 1 & -1 \\ -1 & 2 & 1 & 2 \end{bmatrix}.$$

We can solve this system by row operations where every operation on rows of the coefficient matrix is also performed on the matrix C of constants. Thus the transition may be viewed as

$$AX = C \leftrightarrow \begin{bmatrix} 2 & 1 & -1 \\ 1 & -1 & 1 \\ -1 & 2 & 1 \end{bmatrix} X = \begin{pmatrix} 1 \\ -1 \\ 2 \end{pmatrix}$$

$$\rightarrow \begin{bmatrix} 3 & 0 & 0 \\ 1 & -1 & 1 \\ -1 & 2 & 1 \end{bmatrix} X = \begin{pmatrix} 0 \\ -1 \\ 2 \end{pmatrix}$$

$$\rightarrow \begin{bmatrix} 1 & 0 & 0 \\ 1 & -1 & 1 \\ -1 & 2 & 1 \end{bmatrix} X = \begin{pmatrix} 0 \\ -1 \\ 2 \end{pmatrix}$$

$$\rightarrow \begin{bmatrix} 1 & 0 & 0 \\ 0 & 1 & -1 \\ 0 & 2 & 1 \end{bmatrix} X = \begin{pmatrix} 0 \\ 1 \\ 2 \end{pmatrix}$$

613

$$\rightarrow \begin{bmatrix} 1 & 0 & 0 \\ 0 & 1 & -1 \\ 0 & 0 & -3 \end{bmatrix} X = \begin{pmatrix} 0 \\ 1 \\ 0 \end{pmatrix}$$

$$\rightarrow \begin{bmatrix} 1 & 0 & 0 \\ 0 & 3 & 0 \\ 0 & 0 & -3 \end{bmatrix} X = \begin{pmatrix} 0 \\ 3 \\ 0 \end{pmatrix}$$

$$\rightarrow \begin{bmatrix} 1 & 0 & 0 \\ 0 & 1 & 0 \\ 0 & 0 & 1 \end{bmatrix} X = \begin{pmatrix} 0 \\ 1 \\ 0 \end{pmatrix}$$

or, in terms of the augmented matrix

$$\begin{bmatrix} 2 & 1 & -1 & 1 \\ 1 & -1 & 1 & -1 \\ -1 & 2 & 1 & 2 \end{bmatrix} \rightarrow \begin{bmatrix} 3 & 0 & 0 & 0 \\ 1 & -1 & 1 & -1 \\ -1 & 2 & 1 & 2 \end{bmatrix}$$

$$\rightarrow \begin{bmatrix} 1 & 0 & 0 & 0 \\ 1 & -1 & 1 & -1 \\ -1 & 2 & 1 & 2 \end{bmatrix} \rightarrow \cdots$$

$$\rightarrow \begin{bmatrix} 1 & 0 & 0 & 0 \\ 0 & 1 & 0 & 1 \\ 0 & 0 & 1 & 0 \end{bmatrix}.$$

Our claim that the systems are equivalent is based on the fact that such row operations on the matrices A and C leave the solution the same. (Or for convenience of notation, that these operations on the "augmented matrix" leave the solution to the corresponding systems the same.)

Our first operation was that of replacing the first row by the sum of the first and second row. Consider the matrix M_1 obtained by performing this operation on I.

$$M_1 = \begin{bmatrix} 1 & 1 & 0 \\ 0 & 1 & 0 \\ 0 & 0 & 1 \end{bmatrix}$$

Now consider the effect of multiplying both sides of our equation by M_1.

$$M_1 A X = M_1 C$$

We obtain

$$\begin{bmatrix} 1 & 1 & 0 \\ 0 & 1 & 0 \\ 0 & 0 & 1 \end{bmatrix} \begin{bmatrix} 2 & 1 & -1 \\ 1 & -1 & 1 \\ -1 & 2 & 1 \end{bmatrix} X = \begin{bmatrix} 1 & 1 & 0 \\ 0 & 1 & 0 \\ 0 & 0 & 1 \end{bmatrix} \begin{pmatrix} 1 \\ -1 \\ 2 \end{pmatrix}$$

which simplifies to

$$\begin{bmatrix} 3 & 0 & 0 \\ 1 & -1 & 1 \\ -1 & 2 & 1 \end{bmatrix} X = \begin{pmatrix} 0 \\ -1 \\ 2 \end{pmatrix}$$

(the result of the first step in the previous computation). Note also that one can multiply the 3 × 4 augmented matrix on the left by the 3 × 3 matrix M_1 and obtain the augmented matrix in the second step.

Similarly, one can determine a matrix M_2 which performs the second step, and so on for all six steps.

Thus our solution amounts to multiplying six matrices together to obtain a matrix M in such a way that

$$(M_6 M_5 M_4 M_3 M_2 M_1 A)X = MC.$$

Our final stage was

$$IX = MC,$$

thus

$$MA = I.$$

This example points out that there is no essential difference between solving a system by a series of row reductions and solving it by multiplying by the inverse matrix.

Cramer's Rule

We next discuss a technique of solving a consistent system of non-homogeneous linear equations using the determinant function.

8.10-2 Theorem: (Cramer's Rule) Given the system $AX = C$, where $A = [a_{ij}]_{n \times n}$ is nonsingular,

$$X = \begin{pmatrix} x_1 \\ x_2 \\ \cdot \\ \cdot \\ x_n \end{pmatrix} \quad \text{and} \quad C = \begin{pmatrix} c_1 \\ c_2 \\ \cdot \\ \cdot \\ c_n \end{pmatrix},$$

the solution is given by

$$X = A^{-1}C = \begin{vmatrix} \dfrac{\det A_1}{\det A} \\[2mm] \dfrac{\det A_2}{\det A} \\[2mm] \cdot \\ \cdot \\ \cdot \\[2mm] \dfrac{\det A_n}{\det A} \end{vmatrix},$$

where A_j denotes the $n \times n$ matrix formed by replacing the jth column of A by the column C.

Remark: Note that if the system is homogeneous (so that $c_i = 0 \ \forall_i$), then each of the matrices A_j has a column of zeros, so that $\det A_j / \det A = 0$ $\forall_j$ which is the trivial solution (and the only solution in this case).

615

Proof (of Theorem 8.10-2): If A is a 2×2 matrix, we have

$$\begin{bmatrix} a_{11} & a_{12} \\ a_{21} & a_{22} \end{bmatrix} \begin{pmatrix} x_1 \\ x_2 \end{pmatrix} = \begin{pmatrix} c_1 \\ c_2 \end{pmatrix}$$

iff

$$\begin{pmatrix} x_1 \\ x_2 \end{pmatrix} = \begin{bmatrix} a_{11} & a_{12} \\ a_{21} & a_{22} \end{bmatrix}^{-1} \begin{pmatrix} c_1 \\ c_2 \end{pmatrix} = \frac{1}{\det A} \begin{bmatrix} a_{22} & -a_{12} \\ -a_{21} & a_{11} \end{bmatrix} \begin{pmatrix} c_1 \\ c_2 \end{pmatrix}$$

by the construction of A^{-1} in the proof of Theorem 8.9-4. But this implies that

$$\begin{pmatrix} x_1 \\ x_2 \end{pmatrix} = \frac{1}{\det A} \begin{pmatrix} a_{22}c_1 - a_{12}c_2 \\ -a_{21}c_1 + a_{11}c_2 \end{pmatrix} = \begin{pmatrix} \det A_1/\det A \\ \det A_2/\det A \end{pmatrix}$$

since, for example,

$$\det A_1 = \det \begin{bmatrix} c_1 & a_{12} \\ c_2 & a_{22} \end{bmatrix} = a_{22}c_1 - a_{12}c_2.$$

The same argument applied to 3×3 coefficient matrices yields

$$\begin{pmatrix} x_1 \\ x_2 \\ x_3 \end{pmatrix} = A^{-1} \begin{pmatrix} c_1 \\ c_2 \\ c_3 \end{pmatrix} = \frac{1}{\det A} \begin{bmatrix} \det A_{11} & -\det A_{21} & \det A_{31} \\ -\det A_{12} & \det A_{22} & -\det A_{32} \\ \det A_{13} & -\det A_{23} & \det A_{33} \end{bmatrix} \begin{pmatrix} c_1 \\ c_2 \\ c_3 \end{pmatrix}$$

$$= \frac{1}{\det A} \begin{pmatrix} c_1 \det A_{11} - c_2 \det A_{21} + c_3 \det A_{31} \\ -c_1 \det A_{12} + c_2 \det A_{22} - c_3 \det A_{32} \\ c_1 \det A_{13} - c_2 \det A_{23} + c_3 \det A_{33} \end{pmatrix}.$$

By evaluating the respective determinants involved, the latter matrix may be recognized to be

$$\frac{1}{\det A} \begin{pmatrix} \det A_1 \\ \det A_2 \\ \det A_3 \end{pmatrix}. \quad \square$$

Example: In order to solve the system

$$\begin{bmatrix} 0 & 1 & 1 \\ 1 & 0 & 1 \\ 2 & -1 & 0 \end{bmatrix} \begin{pmatrix} x \\ y \\ z \end{pmatrix} = \begin{pmatrix} 2 \\ 1 \\ -1 \end{pmatrix}$$

we can write the solution set as

$$\left\{ \left(\frac{\det A_1}{\det A}, \frac{\det A_2}{\det A}, \frac{\det A_3}{\det A} \right) \right\}$$

$$= \left\{ \left(\frac{\det \begin{bmatrix} 2 & 1 & 1 \\ 1 & 0 & 1 \\ -1 & -1 & 0 \end{bmatrix}}{\det A}, \frac{\det \begin{bmatrix} 0 & 2 & 1 \\ 1 & 1 & 1 \\ 2 & -1 & 0 \end{bmatrix}}{\det A}, \frac{\det \begin{bmatrix} 0 & 1 & 2 \\ 1 & 0 & 1 \\ 2 & -1 & -1 \end{bmatrix}}{\det A} \right) \right\}$$

$$= \left\{ \left(\frac{2-1-1}{1}, \frac{4-3}{1}, \frac{3-2}{1} \right) \right\} = \{(0, 1, 1)\}.$$

(The student should verify these steps!)

Example: Use Cramer's Rule to solve the following system of equations

$$x - y + 2z = 1$$
$$3x + 2y - z = 2$$
$$x + y + 2z = -1$$

that is

$$AX = \begin{pmatrix} 1 \\ 2 \\ -1 \end{pmatrix}.$$

We have

$$A = \begin{bmatrix} 1 & -1 & 2 \\ 3 & 2 & -1 \\ 1 & 1 & 2 \end{bmatrix} \quad \text{and} \quad \det A = 14,$$

$$A_1 = \begin{bmatrix} 1 & -1 & 2 \\ 2 & 2 & -1 \\ -1 & 1 & 2 \end{bmatrix} \quad \text{and} \quad \det A_1 = 16,$$

$$A_2 = \begin{bmatrix} 1 & 1 & 2 \\ 3 & 2 & -1 \\ 1 & -1 & 2 \end{bmatrix} \quad \text{and} \quad \det A_2 = -14,$$

$$A_3 = \begin{bmatrix} 1 & -1 & 1 \\ 3 & 2 & 2 \\ 1 & 1 & -1 \end{bmatrix} \quad \text{and} \quad \det A_3 = -8.$$

Hence we have the solution

$$x = \frac{16}{14} = \frac{8}{7} \qquad y = \frac{-14}{14} = -1 \qquad z = \frac{-8}{14} = -\frac{4}{7}.$$

Relaxation

Finally, we discuss briefly a method of solving systems of linear equations which is well suited to computer use under certain conditions. This method is called "relaxation." † The main feature of the relaxation method is the use of successive approximations of the solution, starting from some initial "guess," or "initial solution." The initial solution can be taken to be any choice of values for the unknown, although in general "poor guesses" necessitate more steps in the process. The correction to be added to the initial solution is determined by applying corrections at the various stages, in accordance with an "operations table," in such a manner that at each stage the largest "residual" is reduced in magnitude. Let us illustrate the method with an example.

† The interested reader can find an elementary treatment of "computer techniques" in L. D. Kovach, *Computer Oriented Mathematics*, Holden-Day, Inc., 1964. For a discussion of the relaxation method, see pp. 60–8.

Suppose we are asked to solve the system

$$2x - y = 38$$
$$-x + 3y = 6.$$

This problem can be viewed as that of finding values of x and y which make the "residuals" R_1 and R_2 both zero, where

$$R_1 = 38 - 2x + y$$
$$R_2 = 6 + x - 3y.$$

In order to find such values, we start with an "initial solution," say $x = 0$ and $y = 0$. We note that the initial solution yields $R_1 = 38$, $R_2 = 6$. We wish to change the initial solution by some amount which reduces the largest residual, R_1. In order to see how this is done, we may construct an "operations table" which shows how R_1 and R_2 are affected by unit changes in the initial x and the initial y.

Suppose we let "Δx" denote a change in x (from the value of x at a previous stage) and similarly for Δy. Let ΔR_1 and ΔR_2 denote the corresponding changes in the residuals. Then we may summarize the effect of unit changes in x and y by the following *operations table:*

Δx	Δy	ΔR_1	ΔR_2
1	0	-2	1
0	1	1	-3

Thus, a change of 1 in x ($\Delta x = 1$, $\Delta y = 0$) results in a decrease of 2 in R_1 ($\Delta R_1 = -2$) and unit increase in R_2 ($\Delta R_2 = 1$). The second row of the operations table indicates that a unit increase in y results in $\Delta R_1 = 1$ and $\Delta R_2 = -3$.

We may tabulate the first stages of the relaxation solution as follows:

	x	y	R_1	R_2
initial solution →	0	0	38	6
1st stage ———→	$\Delta x = 19$	$\Delta y = 0$	0	25

Here we have increased x by 19 to reduce the largest residual to zero. We note that in doing so, the residual R_2 is increased to 25. In view of the operations table, we can best reduce R_2 by changing y ($\Delta y = 8$ is a convenient change). But the change $\Delta y = 8$ increases R_1 to 8, so at the 4th stage we take $\Delta x = 4$ to reduce R_1, and so on. This process is continued until R_1 and R_2 are both zero. The complete process may be tabulated as in the following table.

stage	x	y	R_1	R_2
initial	0	0	38	6
1	$\Delta x = 19$	$\Delta y = 0$	0	25
2	$\Delta x = 0$	$\Delta y = 8$	8	1
3	$\Delta x = 4$	$\Delta y = 0$	0	5
4	$\Delta x = 0$	$\Delta y = 2$	2	-1
5	$\Delta x = 1$	$\Delta y = 0$	0	0
solution	$\Sigma \Delta x = 24$	$\Sigma \Delta y = 10$		

The solution to the system is given by the initial values plus all the changes in these values, which yields the solution (24, 10) in this example. (Verify that (24,10) is the solution.)

This process has several desirable features (such as being easy to program on a computer), and some undesirable ones. For example, there is some question as to whether this process will always "converge," or whether in some cases we might continue indefinitely without getting $R_1 = R_2 = 0$. The interested reader is urged to review some of the references given by Kovach (see previous footnote), where sufficient conditions for convergence of the process are given.

We conclude this section with another example of the solution of a system by the relaxation method.

Example: For the system

$$3x + y = 7$$
$$x - 2y = -49$$

the residuals are

$$R_1 = 7 - 3x - y$$
$$R_2 = -49 - x + 2y$$

so that the corresponding operations table is as follows:

Δx	Δy	ΔR_1	ΔR_2
1	0	-3	-1
0	1	-1	2

Starting from the initial solution (1, 4), we proceed to the final solution $(-5, 22)$ of the system as below.

	x	y	R_1	R_2
initial solution →	1	4	0	-42
		$\Delta y = 21$	-21	0
$\Delta x = -7$			0	7
		$\Delta y = -3$	3	1
$\Delta x = 1$			0	0
final solution →	-5	22		

Exercises 8.10

1. Show that a system of equations

$$AX = C, \qquad C \neq [0]$$

such that $\det A = 0$, has either no solutions or else an infinite number. What does this mean geometrically?

2. *a)* Draw the three hyperplanes in three space given by the following three constraining equations.

$$2x - 3y + z = 0$$
$$x + y + z = 1$$
$$3x - 2y + 2z = 1$$

b) Write the system of equations in *a)* in the form $AX = C$ and show that det $A = 0$.

c) Graph in $R \times R \times R$ the solution set for the equation in *b)*.

3. *a)* Prove that if the rows of a square matrix A are linearly independent, then so are its columns. (*Hint:* Recall that det $A = $ det A^T.)

b) Use this to complete the proof of Theorem 8.10-1.

4. Let A be a 4×4 matrix. Find a matrix B such that BA is found from A by

a) replacing the 2nd row with the sum of itself and twice the 4th row.

b) replacing the 3rd row by the sum of twice itself and -4 times the 2nd row.

c) replacing the 4th row by the sum of 3 times itself and twice the 2nd and 3rd rows.

5. Use Cramer's Rule to solve the following systems of equations.

a)
$$\begin{bmatrix} -2 & 1 & 0 \\ 1 & -2 & 1 \\ 0 & 1 & -2 \end{bmatrix} \begin{pmatrix} x \\ y \\ z \end{pmatrix} = \begin{pmatrix} 1 \\ -1 \\ 2 \end{pmatrix}$$

b)
$$\begin{bmatrix} 8 & 0 & 0 \\ 0 & -7 & 0 \\ 0 & 0 & 3 \end{bmatrix} \begin{pmatrix} x \\ y \\ z \end{pmatrix} = \begin{pmatrix} 2 \\ -2 \\ 0 \end{pmatrix}$$

c)
$$\begin{bmatrix} 0 & 1 & -2 \\ -1 & 1 & 3 \\ 2 & -3 & 0 \end{bmatrix} \begin{pmatrix} x \\ y \\ z \end{pmatrix} = \begin{pmatrix} 1 \\ 1 \\ 1 \end{pmatrix}$$

d)
$$\begin{bmatrix} 1 & 2 & -1 & 3 \\ 2 & 5 & 0 & 7 \\ 1 & 2 & 0 & 2 \\ 2 & 3 & -4 & 6 \end{bmatrix} \begin{pmatrix} x \\ y \\ z \\ w \end{pmatrix} = \begin{pmatrix} 1 \\ -1 \\ 0 \\ 2 \end{pmatrix}$$

6. *a)* Show that the solution set to a homogeneous system is closed under scalar multiplication. That is, for any solution $(x_1, x_2, \ldots, x_n)$ the n-tuple $(\alpha x_1, \alpha x_2, \ldots, \alpha x_n)$ is also a solution for all $\alpha \in R$.

b) Show that any linear combination of solutions for a homogeneous system is a solution.

7. Use the relaxation method to solve the following systems of equations.

a) $4x + y = 3$
    $x - y = 2$

c) $3x + y \quad\quad = 0$
    $\quad\quad y + z = 1$
    $3x + y + z = 4$

b) $-2x + 3y = 1$
    $x + y = 2$

8. Prove Cramer's Rule for the 4×4 case.

8.11 Convex Sets

We have previously considered universal classes of sets *closed* under certain operations. For example, recall that an event space is a class of subsets of a sample space closed under complementation and countable intersections. In the present section we shall consider another class of sets which is closed under intersections—the class of *convex* sets. We shall make use of convex sets in connection with the "linear programming" techniques introduced at the end of this chapter.

In what follows we shall restrict ourselves to universal sets of the form

$$R^2 = R \times R, \qquad R^3 = R \times R \times R, \qquad \text{or} \qquad R^n = \underset{i=1}{\overset{n}{\times}} R.$$

For convenience, we refer to such product universes as "Euclidean spaces," and denote them by R^n where "n" denotes the number of components in the elements (n-tuples) of R^n. Thus, for example, "R^3" (read "R-three" or "Euclidean three-space") denotes the set $R \times R \times R$ of all ordered triples of real numbers.

Suppose $\bar{x}$ and $\bar{y}$ are two points in R^n. That is,

$$\bar{x} = (x_1, x_2, x_3, \ldots, x_n) \qquad \text{and} \qquad \bar{y} = (y_1, y_2, y_3, \ldots, y_n).$$

A common alternate notation associated with points in R^n involves double subscripts. We might for example consider points $\bar{x}_1$ and $\bar{x}_2$ in R^n, where

$$\bar{x}_1 = (x_{11}, x_{12}, \ldots, x_{1n}) \qquad \text{and} \qquad \bar{x}_2 = (x_{21}, x_{22}, \ldots, x_{2n}).$$

In this notation, the first subscript of x_{ij} indicates the "point" or element of R^n (x_i in this case); the second subscript, j, indicates the component of that point. Thus if the universe is R^3, we might consider a point $\bar{x}_5 \in R^3$ with components $x_{51}, x_{52},$ and x_{53}, so that

$$\bar{x}_5 = (x_{51}, x_{52}, x_{53}) \in R \times R \times R.$$

The "bar" is not really needed here, but it is useful as a reminder that a point in n-space is intended rather than a scalar in R. Now two distinct points $\bar{x}$ and $\bar{y}$ in R^n determine a line in R^n: the line containing the points $\bar{x}$ and $\bar{y}$. The following theorem defines this line in terms of the given points.

8.11-1 Theorem: The line L containing the points $\bar{x}$ and $\bar{y}$ is the set described by

$$L = \{\bar{z} : \bar{z} = \lambda\bar{x} + (1 - \lambda)\bar{y} \text{ for some } \lambda \in R\}.$$

Proof (of R^2): We must show that for any real λ, $\lambda\bar{x} + (1 - \lambda)\bar{y}$ is on the line, and, conversely, that any point on the line can be given as $\lambda\bar{x} + (1 - \lambda)\bar{y}$

for some real number λ. Let L denote the line containing $\bar{x}$ and $\bar{y}$ and let A denote the set

$$A = \{\bar{z} : \bar{z} = \lambda\bar{x} + (1 - \lambda)\bar{y}, \lambda \in R\}.$$

Note that $\bar{x} \in A$ and $\bar{y} \in A$, since $\bar{z} = \bar{x}\lambda + (1 - \lambda)\bar{y}$ is $\bar{x}$ when $\lambda = 1$ and is $\bar{y}$ when $\lambda = 0$. Note also that the description of the set A can be stated equivalently by

$$A = \{(z_1, z_2) : z_1 = \lambda x_1 + (1 - \lambda)y_1 \text{ and}$$
$$z_2 = \lambda x_2 + (1 - \lambda)y_2 \text{ for some } \lambda \in R\} \quad (1)$$

where $\bar{z} = (z_1, z_2)$, $\bar{x} = (x_1, x_2)$, $\bar{y} = (y_1, y_2)$.
It is easy to see that

$$\bar{z} \in A \Leftrightarrow \bar{z} \in L$$

if L is a vertical or horizontal line. For example, if L has zero slope, we must have $x_2 = y_2$ (why?), and the second equation in description (1) reduces to

$$z_2 = \lambda x_2 + (1 - \lambda)x_2 = x_2.$$

The first equation in (1) is satisfied (for some λ) for each $\bar{z}$ on the horizontal line (see Figure 8.7), so that in this case A describes the horizontal line

$$L = \{(z_1, z_2) : z_2 = x_2\}.$$

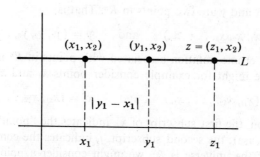

FIG. 8.7 If the line L is horizontal, the equation $\bar{z} = \bar{y} + \lambda(\bar{x} - \bar{y})$, is certainly satisfied for some λ, since this is equivalent to $z_1 = y_1 + \lambda(x_1 - y_1)$. In fact the number λ can be given by

$$\lambda = \frac{z_1 - y_1}{x_1 - y_1},$$

since $x_1 \neq y_1$ (why?).

Suppose, then, that L has some non-zero slope m. Note that

$$m = \frac{x_2 - y_2}{x_1 - y_1} = \frac{z_2 - y_2}{z_1 - y_1} \quad (2)$$

iff $(z_1, z_2) \in L$. Since $x_2 - y_2 \neq 0$, we can write the second equation in (2) equivalently as

$$\frac{z_2 - y_2}{x_2 - y_2} = \frac{z_1 - y_1}{x_1 - y_1} = \lambda.$$

But the latter equations imply that $\bar{z} \in L$ iff

$$z_2 - y_2 = \lambda(x_2 - y_2) \qquad \text{and} \qquad z_1 - y_1 = \lambda(x_1 - y_1),$$

that is, iff

$$z_2 = \lambda x_2 + (1 - \lambda)y_2 \qquad \text{and} \qquad z_1 = \lambda x_1 + (1 - \lambda)y_1,$$

thus

$$\bar{z} \in L \Leftrightarrow \bar{z} \in A. \;\square$$

Remark: If we restrict λ to the interval $[0, 1]$ we obtain only the segment of the line lying between the points $\bar{x}$ and $\bar{y}$. (See Figure 8.8.) The theorem is true for any Euclidean space R^n, although our proof is given only for the special case $n = 2$. We shall not prove the theorem for R^3 or higher dimensional spaces. The student is encouraged to devise a proof for R^3.

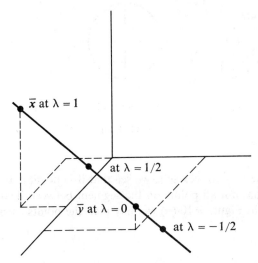

FIG. 8.8 The points $\bar{x}$ and $\bar{y}$ are in R^3. The point $\bar{z} = \lambda\bar{x} + (1 - \lambda)\bar{y}$ on the line is between $\bar{x}$ and $\bar{y}$ for λ's between 0 and 1. For λ's greater than 1, the point lies on the end of the line away from $\bar{y}$; for negative λ's, $\bar{z}$ lies on the line to the right of $\bar{y}$.

8.11-2 Definition: A subset C of R^n is *convex* iff it contains the line segment between any two of its points.

Example: Each of the graphs in Figure 8.9 correspond to convex sets in R^2.

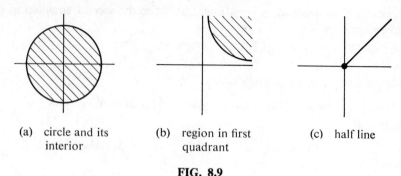

(a) circle and its interior (b) region in first quadrant (c) half line

FIG. 8.9

The sets graphed in Figure 8.10 are *not* convex.

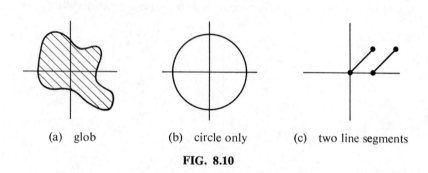

(a) glob (b) circle only (c) two line segments

FIG. 8.10

For each of the non-convex sets, we see that it is possible to find two points in the set so that not all points on the segment between them are in the set. For example, in Figure 8.10 (*a*) we may pick the points as shown in Figure 8.11.

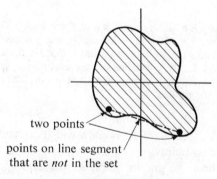

two points
points on line segment
that are *not* in the set

FIG. 8.11

Some convex sets contain points which are not strictly between any other points of the set. Such points are called "extreme points."

8.11.3 Definition: A point $\bar{z}$ in a convex set C is called an *extreme point* of C iff there do not exist points $\bar{x}_1$ and $\bar{x}_2$ in C such that

$$\bar{z} = \lambda\bar{x}_1 + (1 - \lambda)\bar{x}_2, \qquad \lambda \in (0, 1).$$

Remark: Note that in requiring λ to be in the *open* interval we impose the condition that neither of the points $\bar{x}_1$ and $\bar{x}_2$ can be $\bar{z}$.

Example: In the example above, every point on the "boundary" (the circle, for example) is an extreme point. The convex set graphed in Figure 8.9 (c) has only the point $(0, 0)$ as an extreme point.

We shall now prove the main result of this section: the intersection of convex sets is a convex set. This means, among other things, that the class of all convex subsets of R^n is closed under the intersection operation. This fact will be useful to us later.

8.11-4 Theorem: Suppose $\mathfrak{F} = \{T_\alpha : \alpha \in \Gamma\}$ is a class of convex sets T_α indexed by Γ. Then

$$T = \bigcap_{\alpha \in \Gamma} T_\alpha \qquad \text{is convex.}$$

Proof: We need only show that if $\bar{\imath}_1$ and $\bar{\imath}_2$ are two points in T, then

$$\{\bar{\imath} : \bar{\imath} = \lambda\bar{\imath}_1 + (1 - \lambda)\bar{\imath}_2, \lambda \in [0, 1]\} \subset T. \qquad \text{(Explain!)}$$

If $\bar{\imath}_1$ and $\bar{\imath}_2$ are in T, then

$$\forall \alpha \in \Gamma, \qquad \bar{\imath}_1 \in T_\alpha \qquad \text{and} \qquad \bar{\imath}_2 \in T_\alpha$$

by the definition of intersection. Since all of the T_α's are convex, it follows that

$$\forall \alpha \in \Gamma, \qquad \{\bar{\imath} : \bar{\imath} = \lambda\bar{\imath}_1 + (1 - \lambda)\bar{\imath}_2, \lambda \in [0, 1]\} \subset T_\alpha.$$

But this in turn implies that

$$\{\bar{\imath} : \bar{\imath} = \lambda\bar{\imath}_1 + (1 - \lambda)\bar{\imath}_2, \lambda \in [0, 1]\} \subset \bigcap_{\alpha \in \Gamma} T_\alpha. \; \square$$

Example: The intersection T of the convex sets described by $T_1 = \{(x, y): 1/2\, x + y \leq 2\}$, $T_2 = \{(x, y): x \geq 0\}$, $T_3 = \{(x, y): y > |x|\}$ is graphed in Figure 8.12. Note that $T_1 \cap T_2 \cap T_3$ is a convex set, as are $T_1 \cap T_2$, $T_1 \cap T_3$, and $T_2 \cap T_3$.

Note also that one "boundary" of T is not in T (dotted line segment), and that T has only one extreme point (the point $(0, 2)$).

Finally, we make the remark that every subset A of R^n is contained in a unique "smallest" convex subset of R^n. Such a set is called the "*hull*" of A and is denoted by $[A]$. The hull of a set is defined to be the intersection of all the convex sets containing the set. (Will there always be convex sets containing a given set?) Note that

$$A \subset [A]$$

and that

$$[A] \subset C$$

for any convex set C such that $A \subset C$ (why?). Thus the hull of a set is the *smallest* convex set containing it in the same sense that we used in discussing a *minimal* extension of a class so that it would be closed, namely, smallest in the sense of set inclusion.

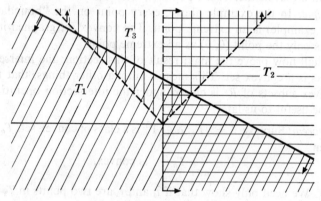

FIG. 8.12

Example: The convex hulls of the three non-convex sets graphed in Figure 8.10 are shown in Figure 8.13.

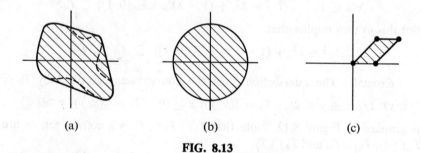

(a)   (b)   (c)

FIG. 8.13

The convex hull of the set $\{(0, 0), (1, 2), (3, -4), (-2, -2), (1, 0)\}$ is shown in Figure 8.14.

Note that

$$[\{(0, 0), (1, 2), (3, -4), (-2, -2), (1, 0)\}] = [\{(1, 2), (3, -4), (-2, -2)\}],$$

and that $(1, 2), (3, -4), (-2, -2)$ are all extreme points of this convex hull.

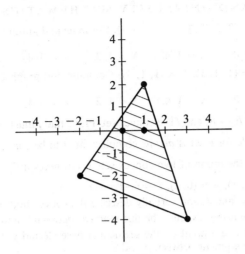

FIG. 8.14

Exercises 8.11

1. Identify each of the following as either convex or not.

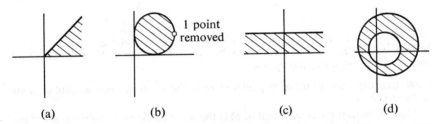

(a)   (b)   (c)   (d)

FIG. 8.15

e) $\{(x, y): x^2 + y^2 > 1\}$ h) $\{(x, y): x^2 + y^2 < 1\}$

f) $\{(x, y): y = 0\}$ i) 1st quadrant

g) $\{(x, y): x^2 + y^2 = 1\}$ j) $\{(x, y): ax + by < c\}$

k) $\varnothing$ (Is the definition vacuously satisfied?)

l) R^n

2. Give examples of convex sets such that
    a) every one of its points is an extreme point.
    b) none of its points are extreme points.

3. a) Let $\bar{x} = (1, 2), \bar{y} = (-1, -1)$. Compute and graph some values of $\bar{z} = \lambda\bar{x} + (1 - \lambda)\bar{y}$ for $\lambda \in [0, 1]$.

     b) Let $\bar{x} = (2, 1), \bar{y} = (0, -1)$. Compute and graph some values of $\bar{z} = \lambda\bar{x} + (1 - \lambda)\bar{y}$ for $\lambda \in [0, 1]$.

627

4. *a)* Let $\bar{x} = (2, 2, 3)$, $\bar{y} = (1, 2, -1)$. Compute and graph $\bar{z} = \lambda\bar{x} + (1 - \lambda)\bar{y}$ where

$$\lambda = 0, \qquad \lambda = 1/4, \qquad \lambda = 1/2, \qquad \lambda = 3/4, \qquad \lambda = 1.$$

b) Let $\bar{x} = (1, 1, 1)$, $\bar{y} = (1, 1, 2)$. Compute and graph $\bar{z} = \lambda\bar{x} + (1 - \lambda)\bar{y}$ where

$$\lambda = 0, \qquad \lambda = 1/4, \qquad \lambda = 1/2, \qquad \lambda = 3/4, \qquad \lambda = 1.$$

5. Suppose $f: R \to R$, and f is a convex set. Prove that f must be a linear function.

6. Is it possible for a set A *and* its complement $\bar{A}$ to be convex?

7. Prove that the union of two convex sets is not necessarily convex.

8. Let $\bar{x} = (1, 1)$, $\bar{y} = (0, 2)$, $\bar{z} = (-1, -1)$.

a) Plot $\bar{x}$, $\bar{y}$, and $\bar{z}$, and verbally describe the convex hull of $\{\bar{x}, \bar{y}, \bar{z}\}$.

b) Describe using λ's, etc., the line segment between $\bar{x}$ and $\bar{y}$.

c) Let $\bar{p}$ denote a point on the segment between $\bar{x}$ and $\bar{y}$. Use λ's to describe all points on the segment between $\bar{p}$ and $\bar{z}$.

d) Can you now describe the convex hull of $\{\bar{x}, \bar{y}, \bar{z}\}$ using λ_1's, λ_2's, etc.?

9. *a)* Show that

$$[\{\bar{x}, \bar{y}, \bar{w}\}] = \{\bar{z}: \bar{z} = \lambda_1\bar{x} + \lambda_2\bar{y} + \lambda_3\bar{w}; \lambda_1 \geq 0, \lambda_2 \geq 0, \lambda_3 \geq 0, \lambda_1 + \lambda_2 + \lambda_3 = 1\}.$$

b) The linear combination $KX = (k_1, k_2, \ldots, k_n) \begin{pmatrix} \bar{x}_1 \\ \bar{x}_2 \\ \cdot \\ \cdot \\ \cdot \\ \bar{x}_n \end{pmatrix} = \sum_{i=1}^{n} k_1 \cdot \bar{x}_i$ is

called a *convex combination* if all the k_i's are non-negative and $\sum_{i=1}^{n} k_i = 1$. Thus in part *a)* you showed that the convex hull of three points in R^2 is the set of all convex combinations of the points.

Show that the convex hull of m points in E^2 is the set of all convex combinations of these points.

c) Show that the convex hull of *b)* is the set of all convex combinations of the extreme points of the hull.

10. Show that the convex hull of a set consisting of a finite number of points in R^n is the convex hull of its extreme points.

8.12 Systems of Linear Inequalities

Earlier we discussed functions in $R \times R$ described by setting linear combinations of the form $\sum_{i=1}^{2} a_i x_i$ equal to a constant, say a_0. Of course, this defines the linear function described by

$$\{(x_1, x_2): a_1 x_1 + a_2 x_2 = a_0\} \tag{1}$$

where the linear equation involved is in the "general form." Reducing the linear equation in (1) to the slope-intercept form, we have the equivalent description

$$x_2 = \frac{-a_1}{a_2} x_1 + \frac{a_0}{a_2}.$$

It is interesting to note that the constant a_0 enters into this equation only in the y intercept term: $\frac{a_0}{a_2}$. Thus the slope of the linear function is completely determined by the constants in the linear combination $\sum_{i=1}^{2} a_i x_i$. For example, suppose $a_1 = 1$ and $a_2 = -2$. By setting the linear combination, $(1, -2) \begin{pmatrix} x_1 \\ x_2 \end{pmatrix}$, equal to various constants, we obtain lines in the plane that have the same slope $(1/2)$ and which are therefore parallel. (See Figure 8.16.)

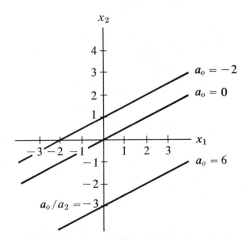

FIG. 8.16 By setting the linear combination $(1, -2) \begin{pmatrix} x_1 \\ x_2 \end{pmatrix}$ equal to various constants a_0 we obtain linear functions whose graphs are parallel. The effect of changing a_0 in the description $(1, -2) \begin{pmatrix} x_1 \\ x_2 \end{pmatrix} = a_0$ is to "move" the line parallel to itself upward or downward. Here three such lines are shown, corresponding to a_0 values of -2 (top line), 0, and 6 (bottom line).

This property carries over to higher dimensional spaces as well. For example, in R^3 the linear combination

$$(a_1, a_2, a_3) \begin{pmatrix} x_1 \\ x_2 \\ x_3 \end{pmatrix}$$

629

defines a plane if set equal to a constant. By varying this constant, other planes, parallel to each other are obtained. This is easily seen by considering the intercepts of the plane. The x_1 intercept is given by a_0/a_1 (setting $x_2 = x_3 = 0$) and similarly, the other intercepts are a_0/a_2 and a_0/a_3. The intercepts are always in the same ratio, however, which implies that the planes are parallel for the various values of a_0. Graph such planes in R^3 and use similar triangles to deduce that this is indeed the case. (See Figure 8.17.)

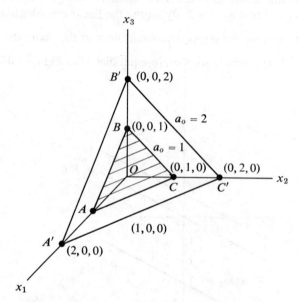

FIG. 8.17 Here we have portions of planes which are defined by

$$(1, 1, 1) \begin{pmatrix} x_1 \\ x_2 \\ x_3 \end{pmatrix} = a_0$$

in the first octant. The plane nearest the origin is associated with $a_0 = 1$, the other with $a_0 = 2$. By setting $x_2 = 0$ we obtain the lines AB and $A'B'$ in the x_1, x_3 plane. Note that these lines are parallel, and that triangles AOB and $A'OB'$ are similar.

Recall that, in general, sets in R^n described by setting linear combinations of variables equal to a constant are called "hyperplanes."

If $A = (a_1, a_2, \ldots, a_n)$ is a $1 \times n$ matrix of constants and $X^T = (x_1, x_2, \ldots, x_n)$ is a matrix of variables, the hyperplanes

$$AX = 5, \qquad AX = -7$$

and in general $$AX = a_0$$

are *parallel hyperplanes.*

Recall also that if the equal sign in the description of a hyperplane is replaced by an inequality, we obtain the description of a *half space* or *open half space,* depending upon whether the inequality is strict. Graphically, a half space consists of the points on the hyperplane together with all points on one side of it.

Example: The half space in R^3 defined by

$$AX \geq 0 \quad \text{where} \quad A = (0, 0, 1)$$

is the set of points on or above the x_1, x_2 plane. That is,

$$(0, 0, 1) \begin{pmatrix} x_1 \\ x_2 \\ x_3 \end{pmatrix} = 0x_1 + 0x_2 + x_3 = x_3.$$

Therefore, $AX \geq 0$ iff $x_3 \geq 0$. (See Figure 8.18.)

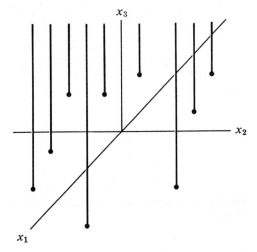

FIG. 8.18

Now suppose we consider taking the intersection of several half spaces. For example, consider in R^2 the half spaces

$$AX \leq 2 \quad \text{and} \quad BX \geq 1, \tag{1}$$

where $A = (1, 2)$ and $B = (-2, 5)$. Finding the intersection

$$\{X: AX \leq 2\} \cap \{X: BX \geq 1\}$$

can be viewed as finding the "simultaneous" solution of the inequalities

$$x_1 + 2x_2 \leq 2$$
$$2x_1 - 5x_2 \leq -1, \tag{2}$$

631

which may be written in matrix notation as

$$\begin{bmatrix} 1 & 2 \\ 2 & -5 \end{bmatrix} \begin{pmatrix} x_1 \\ x_2 \end{pmatrix} \leq \begin{pmatrix} 2 \\ -1 \end{pmatrix}.$$

The solution set for this system of two inequalities in the two unknowns x_1 and x_2 is graphed in Figure 8.19.

Remark: When we write "$A \leq B$" for $n \times m$ matrices $A = [a_{ij}]$ and $B = [b_{ij}]$, we shall mean that $a_{ij} \leq b_{ij}$ for every i and j. Note that in order to use this notation, we must write the inequalities in (1) with all the inequalities in the same direction as in (2). This can always be done with appropriate multiplications by -1.

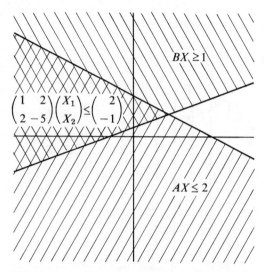

FIG. 8.19 Solution set is intersection of two half spaces.

A system of linear inequalities of the form

$$AX \leq C,$$

where $A = [a_{ij}]_{m \times n}$, $X^T = (x_1, x_2, \ldots, x_n)$, and $C^T = (c_1, c_2, \ldots, c_m)$ may have an empty solution set, a solution set with only one point, or as was seen in the example above, infinitely many points in its solution set.

Example: Consider the system

$$\begin{bmatrix} 1 & 3 & -2 \\ -1 & -3 & 2 \end{bmatrix} \begin{pmatrix} x_1 \\ x_2 \\ x_3 \end{pmatrix} \leq \begin{pmatrix} 6 \\ -8 \end{pmatrix}.$$

The two bounding hyperplanes involved are parallel, and the corresponding half spaces have empty intersection.

Example: The system

$$IX \geq [0]$$

where I is the usual $n \times n$ identity matrix and $[0]^T = (0, 0, \ldots, 0)$ has as its solution set the *positive orthant.* If $n = 2$, the system may be written

$$x_1 \geq 0 \quad \text{and} \quad x_2 \geq 0$$

which describes the 1st quadrant. For R^3 the positive orthant is seen to be the set of points we have called the "positive octant." In general, the positive orthant of R^n consists of all points $(x_1, x_2, \ldots, x_n)$ with nonnegative components x_i.

Example: To see that the solution set of a system can be a singleton set, consider the system

$$\begin{bmatrix} 1 & 0 \\ 0 & 1 \\ -1 & -1 \end{bmatrix} \begin{pmatrix} x \\ y \end{pmatrix} \geq \begin{pmatrix} 0 \\ 0 \\ 0 \end{pmatrix},$$

which graphically is the intersection of the positive orthant of R^2 with the relation in $R \times R$ described by $y \leq -x$. The single point in this intersection is the origin $(0, 0)$.

8.12-1 Theorem: The solution set of a system of linear inequalities is convex.

Proof: We could construct a proof using the definition of convexity, showing that a convex combination of any two points in the solution set S is also in S. (You should try to do this.) Instead, however, we shall make use of Theorem 8.11-4 proved in the preceding section. We shall show that a half space is a convex set, from which it follows that the intersection of half spaces is convex. But this means that the solution set of a system of inequalities is convex. Suppose we consider two points,

$$\bar{y} = (y_1, y_2, \ldots, y_n) \quad \text{and} \quad \bar{z} = (z_1, z_2, \ldots, z_n)$$

in the half space defined by

$$\sum_{i=1}^{n} a_i x_i \leq a_0. \tag{1}$$

Then we must have

$$\sum_{i=1}^{n} a_i y_i \leq a_0 \quad \text{and} \quad \sum_{i=1}^{n} a_i z_i \leq a_0. \tag{2}$$

Any convex combination $\lambda \bar{y} + (1 - \lambda)\bar{z}$ $(0 \leq \lambda \leq 1)$ of $\bar{y}$ and $\bar{z}$ must also satisfy inequality (1), since

$$\sum_{i=1}^{n} a_i(\lambda y_i + (1 - \lambda)z_i) = \lambda \sum_{i=1}^{n} a_i y_i + (1 - \lambda) \sum_{i=1}^{n} a_i z_i$$

$$\leq \lambda a_0 + (1 - \lambda)a_0 = a_0$$

by inequalities (2). (Where do we use the assumption that $\lambda \in [0, 1]$?) But

633

$$\sum_{i=1}^{n} a_i(\lambda y_i + (1 - \lambda)z_i) \le a_0$$

implies that the point $\lambda \bar{y} + (1 - \lambda)\bar{z}$ is the half space described by (1). □

We have mentioned that an easy way to graph relations defined by inequalities is to first graph the boundary of the region. This is done by imagining an equality to hold in place of the inequality. In order to complete the graph, we need only find which "side" (*i.e.*, top or bottom, inside or outside, etc.) must also be included in the graph because of the inequality involved. This can be done in most cases by considering a "test point" on one side. If the defining inequality holds for the test point, then *all* points on the same side must be included; if not, then include points on the opposite side. Finally, the student should decide whether the boundary itself must be included in the graph. This will depend upon whether the defining inequality is strict.

Remark: It may be the case in some problems that there is no "boundary," and hence no analysis of one "side" or the other can be made. Two examples of this are the (trivial) relations in $R \times R$ defined by

$$\{(x, y): x^2 + 1 < 0\} \quad \text{and} \quad \{(x, y): x^2 + y^2 \ge -1\}.$$

In most cases of interest, however, the process of graphing relations described by inequalities can be carried out as described above.

In the particular case of half spaces, the boundaries are lines, planes, or hyperplanes, and the "side analysis" for graphing them works quite well. We have seen that the solution set of a system of the form $AX \le C$ of linear inequalities is a convex set (the intersection of the corresponding half spaces). The extreme points of such sets occur at the "corners" formed where two or more boundary hyperplanes intersect. Thus one can systematically find the extreme points of these sets by finding solutions to associated systems of linear *equations*. In general not all intersections of the boundary hyperplanes will be extreme points, since these points may not be in the convex set. At any rate, the set of all of these boundary intersections will *contain* all extreme points. We can check each point in the set of boundary intersections to determine whether it is also an extreme point of the convex solution set by determining whether the point is in the solution set. We illustrate this by an example.

Example: Consider the relation S in R^2 which is the solution set of the system

$$\begin{bmatrix} 1 & 0 \\ 0 & 1 \\ -1 & -1 \\ -2 & 1 \end{bmatrix} \begin{pmatrix} x \\ y \end{pmatrix} \ge \begin{pmatrix} 0 \\ 0 \\ -3 \\ -2 \end{pmatrix}.$$

Note that the top two inequalities

$$\begin{bmatrix} 1 & 0 \\ 0 & 1 \end{bmatrix} \begin{pmatrix} x \\ y \end{pmatrix} \ge \begin{pmatrix} 0 \\ 0 \end{pmatrix}$$

in this system restrict the solution set to the positive orthant of R^2. We graph the four boundary lines and indicate the side included by the inequalities as is shown in Figure 8.20.

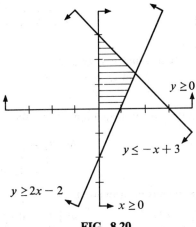

FIG. 8.20

The (convex) intersection of these half spaces is the shaded region. The extreme points of this solution set are found by finding the intersection of each pair of lines. There are six such points: $(0, -2)$, $(0, 0)$, $(0, 3)$, $(1, 0)$, $(3, 0)$, and $(5/3, 4/3)$. For example, the point $(5/3, 4/3)$ is found by solving the system

$$y = 2x - 2$$
$$y = -x + 3$$

and is thus the intersection point of the corresponding boundary lines of the solution set. Of these six points, only four are elements of S (which ones?) so that the four extreme points of S are easily determined.

Exercises 8.12

1. Sketch the graph of each inequality, and then shade the intersection of all of the graphs:

$$x \geq 0, \qquad y \geq 0, \qquad x \geq 4, \qquad y \geq 3, \qquad x + y \geq 8.$$

2. a) Graph the convex region determined by the inequalities:

$$x \geq 0, \qquad y \geq 0, \qquad 3x + 12y \leq 36, \qquad 4x + 3y \leq 12.$$

b) Plot the graph of $4x + 8y = a_0$ for $a_0 = 0, 1, 2, 3, \ldots$, and find which

635

members of this family of lines passes through an extreme point of the convex region of part a).

3. Graph the solution set of each inequality.

a) $x + 2y > 3$
b) $-4x + y \leq 3$
c) $-2x - 3y < 24$
d) $9x - 2y < 0$
e) $9x + 2y \geq 3$
f) $4x + 2y > 1$

4. Graph the set S where

a) $S = \{(x, y): 3x + 2y > 5 \text{ and } x + 4y > 2\}$.
b) $S = \{(x, y): 3x - 2y > 6 \text{ and } 2x + y/2 < 5\}$.
c) $S = \{(x, y): 3x < 10 \text{ and } -2x > 4\}$.

5. Graph the following systems of inequations. Write the system as a matrix inequation.

a) $y - 3x \leq 2$
$\quad y + 4x \leq 7$

b) $2y - 2x \leq 2$
$\quad y + 5x \leq 7$
$\quad -y - 7x \leq 3$

6. Graph the following systems of inequations.

a) $\begin{bmatrix} 1 & -1 \\ 1 & 2 \\ -1 & -1 \end{bmatrix} \begin{pmatrix} x \\ y \end{pmatrix} \leq \begin{pmatrix} 2 \\ 5 \\ 0 \end{pmatrix}$

b) $\begin{bmatrix} 1 & 0 \\ 0 & 1 \\ 1 & 3 \\ 3 & 2 \\ 2 & -1 \end{bmatrix} \begin{pmatrix} x \\ y \end{pmatrix} \geq \begin{pmatrix} 0 \\ 0 \\ 6 \\ 11 \\ -2 \end{pmatrix}$

7. Find a matrix inequality which has as a solution set

a) the interior and boundary of the triangle in R^2 with vertices $(0, 0)$, $(1, 1)$, $(1, 3)$.

b) the complement of the triangle in a).

c) the interior (not including the boundary) of the quadrilateral with vertices at $(1, 2)$, $(0, 4)$, $(-1, -1)$, $(0, -5)$.

d) the complement of the quadrilateral in c).

8. Graph each of the following systems of inequalities and list all vertices (extreme points).

a) $\begin{bmatrix} 2 & -3 \\ -11 & 3 \\ 1 & 3 \\ 5 & -3 \end{bmatrix} \begin{pmatrix} x \\ y \end{pmatrix} \leq \begin{pmatrix} 10 \\ -1 \\ 23 \\ 25 \end{pmatrix}$

b) $\begin{bmatrix} 2 & -1 \\ -1 & 3 \\ 1 & 0 \\ 0 & 1 \end{bmatrix} \begin{pmatrix} x \\ y \end{pmatrix} \geq \begin{pmatrix} -5 \\ -11 \\ 1 \\ -2 \end{pmatrix}$

9. Determine the region in $R \times R \times R$ with solution set

a) $\begin{bmatrix} 1 & 0 & 0 \\ 0 & 1 & 0 \\ 0 & 0 & 1 \\ -1 & -1 & -1 \end{bmatrix} \begin{pmatrix} x \\ y \\ z \end{pmatrix} \geq \begin{pmatrix} 0 \\ 0 \\ 0 \\ -2 \end{pmatrix}$.

b) $\begin{bmatrix} 1 & 1 & 0 \\ 0 & 0 & 1 \\ -1 & 0 & 0 \\ -1 & 0 & 0 \end{bmatrix} \begin{pmatrix} x \\ y \\ z \end{pmatrix} \leq \begin{pmatrix} 1 \\ 5 \\ 0 \\ 0 \end{pmatrix}$.

8.13   Optimization Problems and Linear Programming

A great deal of the work of mathematicians and others is concerned with trying to find "optimal" ways of performing certain tasks. For example, in the manufacture of a product, the manufacturer wants to find the most economical way of producing his product—consistent with other considerations such as the quality of the product and the volume in which it must be produced. In everyday life we usually try to attack a given job in such a way as to complete it with a minimal amount of work, expense, or time. One large class of such problems can be formulated in mathematical terms as the problem of finding the "maximum" of a function, subject to certain conditions, or "constraints."

There are a great many ways to try to solve a problem of maximization or minimization. One way is by "physical analogy." This amounts to trial and error using some kind of model of the process involved. We have discussed previously the use of *Mathematical Models* to answer questions about some physical phenomenon under observation. The "physical analogy" differs from the mathematical one only in the tools used. The philosophy is the same in either case.

Consider, for example, the problem of finding the shape of a container which holds a given volume V, and which requires the least amount of material for its manufacture. We interpret this problem in more precise terms as follows: Find the shape of the solid of volume V with minimal surface area. We might attack this problem by considering various geometrical solids, trying to select the "best" of these. Thus we find that, of a right circular cylinder of radius r and height r, and a cube of side s, the cube has larger area for the same volume V. On the other hand, a sphere of volume V has even smaller surface area than the cylinder. Of course, we can never exhaust all the possible shapes using this trial and error approach, and thus will never be sure that using it we will find the "optimal" shape we are seeking. In fact it is not entirely clear that there *is* an optimal shape! We *may* be dealing with a problem for which there is no solution.

We can find the optimal solution, however, if we consider an analogous system, the soap bubble. Here we conjecture that the surface tension of the soap film will cause a bubble of a certain volume to form in a shape so that the surface area is minimized. We observe that the bubbles form in spherical shapes, and hence conjecture that the spherical shape is optimal. (The spherical shape *is* optimal, but it is fairly difficult to prove this analytically.)

Let us return to the problem of maximization and minimization from a mathematical point of view. As was mentioned above, we can often interpret

637

the maximization problem in terms of trying to find the point, or points (if any) in the domain of a function at which the graph of the function is at its "highest" value.

8.13-1 Definition: Given a function $f: A \rightarrow B$ in $R \times R$, the *maximum* of the function f over A is the point $f(a)$, $a \in A$, such that $\forall x \in A, f(x) \leq f(a)$. (If such a point exists.) Graphically, the maximum value of a function over a set A is the largest value in the range of the function, *if there is such a value.*

Example: The maximum of the function x over $[0, 1]$ is 1. The function x has no maximum over the set $[0, 1)$, since there is no value $a \in [0, 1)$ such that $f(x) \leq f(a)$ for *all* $x \in [0, 1)$. The minimum of this function over both sets exists and is 0.

Example: The maximum of the sine function

$$\sin: R \rightarrow R$$

is 1 and the minimum is -1, since 1 and -1 are in the range of sine and

$$\forall x, \qquad -1 \leq \sin x \leq 1.$$

Example: The linear function in $R \times R$ described by $y = mx + b$ has no maximum or minimum over R unless $m = 0$, in which case the maximum and minimum coincide (both are b).

In summary, we see that a function may have a maximum but no minimum, or vice-versa. It may have neither, or both. The maximum may be attained at many points in the function's domain (as in the case of the sine function), or at only one. The existence of a maximum (or minimum) depends both upon the function f and the set A over which the maximum is sought.

In order to see how the maximization of functions is associated with optimal solution problems, consider the following example.

Example: A farmer has 800 yards of wire with which to enclose a pasture bordering a river. (See Figure 8.21.) He wishes to use the wire to form three

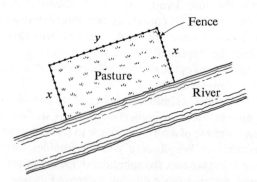

FIG. 8.21 The rectangular pasture of dimension x by y is to be constructed to contain maximal area subject to the condition that 800 yards of fence are used (i.e., $2x + y = 800$).

sides of a rectangular plot, the river forming the fourth side. What dimensions should he use in order to obtain a plot of maximal area?

Solution: We may start by labeling the unknown dimensions of the pasture x and y. (Note that we must not assume at the outset that the pasture of maximal area will be *square*—that is, we do not label the length and width of the pasture both by x.) The area of the pasture is thus given by $A = xy$. Even though we are careful not to assume that x and y are the same, we notice that one dimension *determines* the other by the assumption that 800 yards of fence are used. Thus $2x + y = 800$, or equivalently

$$y = 800 - 2x.$$

Thus the area can be expressed as a function of x only, replacing y by its given value. Thus we have

$$A(x) = x(800 - 2x).$$

We wish to find the value of x (if any) for which the area $A(x)$ is maximized. In order to find the maximum of the function $A(x)$ over the set $[0, 400]$ (do you agree that x must be in this interval?), we may sketch its graph. This is done in Figure 8.22. The symmetry of this graph leads us to the conclusion that the function does indeed have a maximum over $[0, 400]$, and that the maximum is $A(200)$. Thus for $x = 200$ (and therefore $y = 400$), the area of the pasture is maximized. The optimal shape is thus to make the side parallel to the river be twice as long as the other two sides.

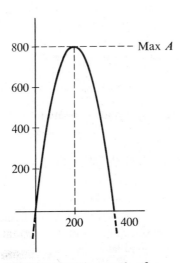

FIG. 8.22 The graph of $y = A(x)$ is a parabola. The solid portion represents the restriction of x to the interval $[0, 400]$. By symmetry, we see that the maximum of $A(x)$ over $[0, 400]$ is $A(200)$.

Many optimization problems can be solved using intuitive techniques similar to that used in the example above. A systematic approach to solving such problems is developed in the calculus. Using the calculus methods, one can avoid the difficulty of using intuitive notions such as symmetry in finding maximums and minimums of certain functions. The calculus methods are not always applicable, however. We now wish to discuss one such general type of optimization problem, and give the solution to Gilbert Gibson's problem. (You should review Gilbert's problem. It is posed in the introduction to this chapter.)

Linear Programming

We now aim to interpret a certain type of maximization problem graphically and to use this interpretation to develop a method of solution. We have discussed the problem of maximizing a function subject to certain *constraints*. For example, in the fence problem we wanted to maximize the area function $A = xy$ subject to the constraints

$$2x + y = 800 \qquad x \geq 0, \qquad y \geq 0.$$

(The latter two inequalities express the fact that the pasture must have non-negative dimensions.)

In this section the functions to be maximized, the so-called *object functions*, are linear, and the constraints will be in the form of linear inequalities. The linear programming problem can thus be stated as follows:

Find X which maximizes the object function

$$AX = \sum_{i=1}^{n} a_i x_i \tag{1}$$

subject to constraints given by a matrix inequation

$$BX \geq C. \tag{2}$$

In this statement we assume that $A = (a_1, a_2, \ldots, a_n)$,

$$B = [b_{ij}]_{m \times n}, \qquad X^T = (x_1, x_2, \ldots, x_n), \qquad \text{and} \qquad C^T = (c_1, c_2, \ldots, c_m).$$

The solution set of the system (2) is called the set of *feasible solutions* for the problem, since each point X in this set satisfies all the constraints and hence is a candidate for the solution. Using this terminology, the linear programming problem can be stated as:

Find the feasible solution X for which the linear combination $(a_1, a_2, \ldots, a_n)X$ is the largest.

Remark: In a given problem, there may be no feasible solution X which makes AX largest. On the other hand, there may be a unique X, or there may be infinitely many such points. In the event that there are none, the problem

640

has no solution. If there are infinitely many, we shall agree that any one may be taken as the solution to the problem.

Example: Solve the linear programming problem for the case in which the object function is

$$AX = (2, 1) \begin{pmatrix} x \\ y \end{pmatrix},$$

and the set of feasible solutions is described by

$$\begin{bmatrix} 1 & 0 \\ 0 & 1 \\ -1 & -1 \\ -3 & -1 \end{bmatrix} \begin{pmatrix} x \\ y \end{pmatrix} \geq \begin{pmatrix} 0 \\ 0 \\ -2 \\ -4 \end{pmatrix}.$$

Solution: We note first of all that the set of feasible solutions is the set of points in the positive orthant of R^2 for which

$$x + y \leq 2 \qquad \text{and} \qquad 3x + y \leq 4.$$

These half spaces are graphed in Figure 8.23 together with the set of feasible solutions.

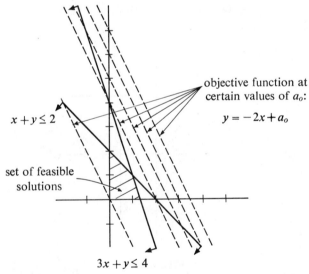

$x + y \leq 2$

objective function at certain values of a_o:

$$y = -2x + a_o$$

set of feasible solutions

$3x + y \leq 4$

FIG. 8.23 The set of feasible solutions together with several hyperplanes obtained by setting the objective function equal to some constant a_0.

We next observe that each value a_0 of the objective function is attained along the line $AX = a_0$, and that the problem of maximizing AX is equivalent to finding the line associated with the largest a_0. However we must also insist that x be in the set of feasible solutions, so we must choose a_0 so that the line intersects the set of feasible solutions. Now increasing a_0 in the expression

$$2x + y = a_0$$

simply yields lines further in the right, while decreasing a_0 "moves" the line to the left. We want the largest a_0 for which the line passes through the set of feasible solutions, so we want to "move" the lines in from the right until it first touches the set of feasible solutions. In view of Figure 8.23, it appears that the line will first touch at the extreme point $(1, 1)$, so that the maximum of the function $2x + y$ subject to the condition that (x, y) be in the set of feasible solutions is $a_0 = 3$, and is attained at $x = 1$ and $y = 1$. Hence the solution to our problem is,

$$\text{"}AX \text{ is maximal for the feasible solution } X = \begin{pmatrix} 1 \\ 1 \end{pmatrix}.\text{"}$$

Example: Find x and y which will maximize p where $p = 2x + y$ where x and y are subject to the constraints

$$x \leq 2 \quad \text{and} \quad y \leq 3.$$

First observe the graph of

$$S = \{(x, y): x \leq 2 \quad \text{and} \quad y \leq 3\}.$$

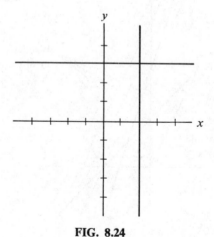

FIG. 8.24

Hence any feasible point (x, y) must lie in the double hashed section of the plane. We wish then to choose (x, y) from S in a way which will make p as large as possible. For some fixed p_0, the set of all points (x, y) such that

$$p_0 \geq 2x + y$$

(*i.e.*, $y \leq -2x + p_0$) is shown in Figure 8.25.

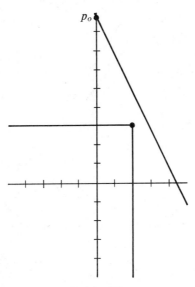

FIG. 8.25

We see then that by increasing p_0 the line $y = -2x + p_0$ rises and that the feasible point which allows the largest value for p is the point $(2, 3)$ in the upper right hand corner of S. We conclude that the maximum value of p (subject to the given constraints) is 7.

Example: Gurney Gibson pastures both sheep and hogs on his 40 acres of rough pasture by the river. He knows that over the summer he can pasture 5 hogs per acre, or 6 sheep, and that his profit from the fall sale will be $5 on a sheep and $7 on a hog. However, due to federal regulations, he must raise at least as many sheep as he does hogs. How many hogs and how many sheep should Gurney pasture in order to maximize his profits?

Solution: Let x denote the number of hogs and y the number of sheep. We wish to maximize p, where

$$p = 7x + 5y, \quad \text{(profit on sales of } x \text{ hogs and } y \text{ sheep)}$$

subject to the constraints

$$x \geq 0, y \geq 0 \quad \text{(Gurney cannot pasture "negative" hogs or sheep)}$$
$$x/5 + y/6 \leq 40 \quad \text{(the animals must have enough to eat)}$$
$$x \leq y \quad \text{(federal regulations)}$$

Figure 8.26 is the graph of the set of feasible solutions. Hence, to maximize p, we choose x and y to be the solution of the equations

$$x = y \quad \text{and} \quad y = -(6/5)x + 240,$$

that is, the point $\left(109\frac{1}{11}, 109\frac{1}{11}\right)$. However, since we can use only integral

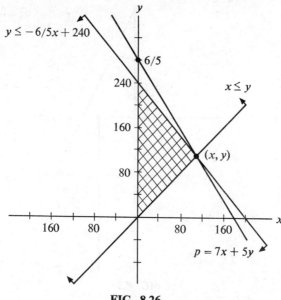

FIG. 8.26

solutions, we take (109, 109). That is, Gurney had best pasture 109 sheep and 109 hogs.

Question: Do you agree with the way in which the constraint "only integral solutions" was handled in this problem?

In the above examples, we saw that in moving the line associated with values of the object function, the line will first come in contact with the set of feasible solutions on the sets boundary, if it has one. In fact, the largest value of the object function (if there is a largest) will always be attained at an extreme point of the set of feasible solutions. This is the fundamental result of linear programming. We shall restate it as a theorem without giving a proof.‡

8.13-2 Theorem: Given the object function AX, the set F of feasible solutions described by the constraints $BX \geq C$, where A, X, B, and C are as described above, then

a) the linear programming problem has a solution provided that $F \neq \emptyset$ and $F \subset \{X: |X| \leq k\}$ for some $k \in N$.

b) if the linear programming problem has a solution, it can be taken to be an extreme point of the set of feasible solutions.

Serious interest in linear programming is a relatively new thing in mathematics. The discipline got its biggest impetus when a computing algorithm

‡ A very good and fairly detailed development of linear programming is given in *Linear Programming*, G. Hadley, Addison-Wesley (1962).

for the method invented by George Dantzig was published§ in 1951. The problem of actually computing the solution to a linear programming problem becomes very great if the number n of variables x_i is large. It is not uncommon in some industries to encounter linear programming problems with hundreds of variables. Note that simple graphical solutions that we used are not available in, say, R^{300}. Hence Dantzig's method, called the *simplex* method, had a great impact upon the usefulness of linear programming.

We shall not develop the simplex method here, but will describe roughly what it does. First of all, note that the solution to a linear programming problem occurs at an extreme point of the set of feasible solutions. Recall that these extreme points may be found by solving associated systems of linear equations. (These points may be found by using a computer routine for solving systems of linear equations, for example.) Now, we could use trial and error with the set of extreme points to find one which gives the maximum value of the object function. There is a tremendous difficulty with this scheme, however. If there are hundreds of constraints, that is, if the constraint inequality $BX \geq C$ involves a $m \times n$ matrix B with large m, there may be millions of extreme points! Hence, even if we have a large (fast) computer, it may not be feasible to find all the extreme points, and to check them one by one to find the optimal one. Herein lies the value of the simplex method.

In the simplex method, extreme points are calculated as they are needed. The method starts with some "initial guess," and proceeds one step at a time, an extreme point being computed at each stage. At each stage, the method indicates whether the extreme point involved is the solution, and if not, *how to compute a better one.* Thus we are not usually required to compute *all* of the extreme points, but rather in a sequence of stages get only extreme points that lie closer and closer to the optimal one. Moreover, the simplex method and modifications of it are readily programmed on a computer, so that the solution of large linear programming problems becomes economically feasible to perform.

We end this section and the chapter with two more examples, one of which is the "Gibson" problem stated at the beginning of the chapter.

Example: Mr. I. M. Atree plans an orchard in which he will raise apples, cherries, and peaches. The land area available to him will support a total of 3,000 trees. The number of cherry trees cannot exceed 500, and at least 1000 peach trees must be grown. The profit on each apple tree is estimated to be $15 per year, on each cherry tree $25 per year, and on each peach $10 per year. How many of each should he raise to maximize his estimated yearly profit?

Solution: Suppose we let "a" denote the number of apple trees and "c" denote the number of cherry trees that should be planted. Then 3000 —

§ T. Koopmans (ed.), *Acitivity Analysis of Production and Allocation*, Cowles Commission Monograph No. 13, John Wiley and Sons (1951).

$(a + c)$ peach trees are to be planted. The object function—the thing that we wish to maximize—is in this case profit. The estimated profit on a apple trees, c cherry trees, and $3000 - (a + c)$ peach trees is given by

$$P = 15a + 25c + 10(3000 - (a + c))$$
$$= 5a + 15c + 30,000.$$

Of course if we maximize $5a + 15c$ we will also maximize $5a + 15c + 30,000$, so we may consider the object function to be

$$AX = 5a + 15c.$$

The constraints are

$$a \geq 0, \quad c \geq 0, \quad c \leq 500, \quad \text{and} \quad 3000 - (a + c) \geq 1000,$$

given in matrix form by

$$\begin{bmatrix} 1 & 0 \\ 0 & 1 \\ 0 & -1 \\ -1 & -1 \end{bmatrix} \begin{pmatrix} a \\ c \end{pmatrix} \geq \begin{pmatrix} 0 \\ 0 \\ -500 \\ -2000 \end{pmatrix}.$$

(We naturally must require that the number of peach trees is non-negative [that is, that $3000 - (a + c) \geq 0$], but this is implied by the constraint that at least 1000 peach trees are grown ($3000 - (a + c) \geq 1000$).) The set of feasible solutions is graphed in Figure 8.27 together with lines representing various values a_0 of the objective function. We see that the line farthermost to the right but still touching the set of feasible solutions will correspond to the maximal value of the object function. This value is associated with the extreme point $(1500, 500)$, so we see that the estimated profit will be maxi-

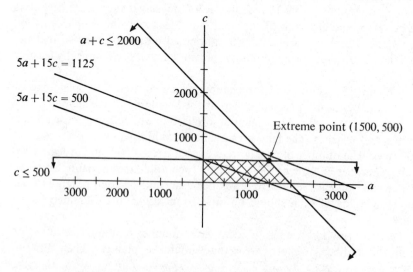

FIG. 8.27 Graph of linear programming problem.

mized if Mr. Atree plants 1500 apple trees, 500 cherry trees, and 1000 peach trees.

Example: In the introduction to this chapter a problem confronting Gilbert Gibson, of the Gibson Grain Elevator Company was presented. Mr. Gibson can store up to 100,000 bushels of wheat consisting of various grades: plump, medium, and scrawny kernel. The problem is to determine the amounts of each grade which should be purchased so as to maximize his profit. The profit per bushel for each grade of wheat depends, however, upon whether more or less than 50,000 bu. of that grade are sold. Thus the problem may be broken down into several cases, one for each possible form of the object (profit) function. Let us denote the number of bushels of plump, medium, and scrawny kernel wheat to be purchased by p, m, and s, respectively. The constraints are

$$p \geq 0, \quad m \geq 0, \quad s \geq 0, \tag{1}$$

$$p + m + s \leq 100,000, \tag{2}$$

$$s \geq p, \tag{3}$$

$$m \leq 50,000. \tag{4}$$

We can now make the following observations regarding the problem:

a) Since the profit per bushel is positive for all grades regardless of the amounts sold, it is obvious that a full 100,000 bu. should be purchased so as to maximize the profit. This allows us to rewrite constraint (2) as

$$p + m + s = 100,000$$

or equivalently as

$$m = 100,000 - (p + s). \tag{5}$$

This, of course, is important since it allows us to reduce the problem to one involving only the two variables p and s (replacing m by $100,000 - (p + s)$ throughout), so that we need only consider a graph in R^2. This is much simpler than a graph involving the three variables p, s, and m in R^3.

b) Since the amount of medium kernel wheat cannot exceed 50,000 bu. (constraint (4)), we will not be required to consider the profit of storing large lots of it. Also by constraint (3) we see that if either of the other grades of wheat exceeds 50,000 bu., it must be the scrawny kernel. Thus we shall consider two profit functions:

$$P_1 = 7p + 5m + 4s \quad \text{if} \quad p \leq 50,000 \quad \text{and} \quad s \leq 50,000,$$

or

$$P_2 = 5p + 4m + 2s \quad \text{if} \quad p \leq 50,000 \quad \text{and} \quad s \geq 50,000.$$

Case 1. $p \leq 50,000$ and $s \leq 50,000$. In this case, the object function P_1 can be written (using Equation 5)

$$P_1 = 7p + 5(100,000 - (p + s)) + 4s$$
$$= 2p - s + 500,000.$$

Again, it is sufficient to maximize $2p - s$ in order to maximize the profit in this case (why?). The constraints in this case can be written as

$$p \leq 50,000, \quad s \leq 50,000 \quad \text{(under the assumption of Case 1)}$$
$$p \geq 0, \quad s \geq 0, \quad p + s \leq 100,000 \quad \text{(from (1))}$$
$$s \geq p \quad \text{(from (3))}$$
$$p + s \geq 50,000 \quad \text{(from (4))}.$$

The set of feasible solutions is shown in Figure 8.28 together with lines obtained by setting the object function $2p - s$ equal to several constants.

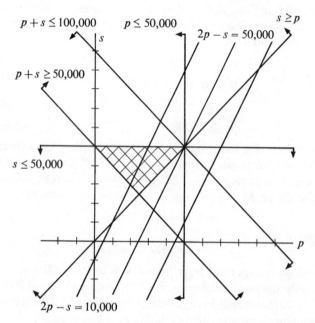

FIG. 8.28 Set of feasible solutions for Case 1 and some profit lines.

Note that several of the constraints, such as $p \leq 50,000$, are implied by the other constraints. The value of $2p - s$ is larger for lines lying more to the right, so we see that in Case 1, the optimal solution is

$$s = p = 50,000, \quad m = 0,$$

and that the profit for this purchase will be

$$P_1 = 7p + 5m + 4s = 550,000 \text{ cents.}$$

Case 2. $p \leq 50,000$ and $s \geq 50,000$. We shall leave it for the reader to determine the maximum for this profit function. Figure 8.29 shows a graph of the set of feasible solutions. It is clear from the profit function $P_2 = 5p + 4m +$ 2s and the constraint $p + m + s \le 100{,}000$, that P_2 cannot exceed 500,000. (Why?)

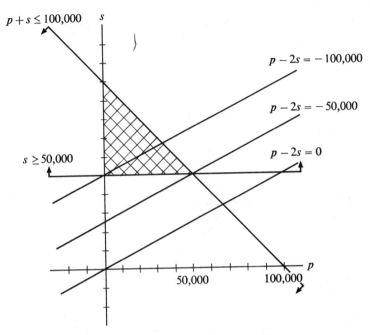

FIG. 8.29 Set of feasible solutions for Case 2.

Since this maximal value of P_2 is less than that of P_1, it follows that the optimal solution is for Mr. Gibson to buy 50,000 bushels each of scrawny and plump kernel wheat and no medium kernel wheat.

Exercises 8.13

1. *a)* Why do you think bees build honey combs that consist of cells which appear *hexagonal* in cross section? That is, do you think the hexagonal shape is accidental, are the bees esthetically pleased with hexagons, or is this shape optimal in some sense?

   b) In what sense do you think the hexagonal shape optimal?

2. Suppose $f: A \to B$. Show that the minimum of f over A is $-b$, where b is the maximum of $-f$ over A.

   Note: This shows that one may concentrate on maximization only, since the minimum of a function can be expressed in terms of the maximum of another function.

3. What is the largest rectangular pasture along the river which can be fenced with 800 yards of wire where

  a) 100 yards of existing fence perpendicular to the river may be utilized.

  b) an unlimited amount of existing fence perpendicular to the river may be utilized.

4. a) Maximize $p = x + y$ subject to the following constraints:

$$5x + 10y \leq 50$$
$$x + y \geq 1$$
$$y \leq 4$$
$$x \geq 0$$
$$y \geq 0$$

  b) Minimize $p = 2x + y$ subject to the same constraints.

5. Maximize $p = x + y$ subject to the following constraints:

$$x \geq 0, \qquad y \geq 0$$
$$x + 3y \leq 9$$
$$2x + y \leq 8$$

6. Minimize $p = 3x + 2y$ subject to:

$$x \geq 0, \qquad y \geq 0$$
$$3x + 7y \geq 7$$
$$2x \leq 5$$

7. The perimeter of a garden is 60 ft. If the garden were 20 ft. longer, the perimeter would be 100 ft. What are the dimensions of the garden? (Assume the garden is rectangular.)

8. A manufacturer makes two types of slide rules, the Standard and the Deluxe. Each slide rule must be processed by two machines, A and B. In order to manufacture one Standard rule, machine A must work 2 hours and machine B must work 4 hours. To make one Deluxe rule, machine A must work 4 hours and machine B must work 2 hours. How many of each type should he make per day to maximize his profit, if his profit is $3.00 on each Standard and $5.00 on each Deluxe? Assume a 24-hour working day.

9. A certain type of humming-bird seed is sold in 150-lb. sacks. It is prepared by mixing two feeds, one of which costs $2 per 5-lb. package and the other $8 per 10-lb. package. It is required that at least 10 packages of the more expensive feed be used in each sack, and that no more than 20 packages of the less expensive feed be used. How many of each type of feed should be used in order to minimize the cost?

10. A company manufactures two kinds of dog food, brands "Arf" and "Urp." The dog foods are a mixture of meat and cereal. Due to shipping difficulties, the company may not use more than 2400 lbs. of meat nor more than 2400 lbs. of cereal a day. The dog food is sold in six-lb. packages; brand Arf contains 4 lbs. of meat and 2 lbs. of cereal per package, while brand Urp contains 2 lbs. of meat and 4 lbs. of cereal per package. The company makes a $.50 profit on a package of Arf and a $.30 profit on a package of Urp. How many packages of each brand should the company make per day for a maximum profit?

11. Suppose that, of each of two foods supplies, three required vitamins. Each pound of "Zip" (costing $4) gives two units of vitamin A, four units of vitamin B,

and one unit of vitamin C. Each pound of "Go" (costing $6) gives three units of vitamin A, one of vitamin B, and two of vitamin C. If a person's diet requires two units of each vitamin, how many pounds of each food should he eat to achieve a full diet at minimum cost?

12.   Determine the maximum profit for Case 2 of Gurney's problem.

9

Polynomial Functions

9.1   Introduction

In the early part of this chapter, we intend to study polynomial functions and to consider certain properties of these functions which are inherited from the structure of the "underlying set." We also wish to make it clear that many standard results about polynomial functions over the real field R also hold elsewhere and in particular over the complex field $\mathcal{C}$. In addition, we wish to emphasize the fact that linear independence of the functions $1, x, x^2, \ldots, x^n$ is not an inherent property of polynomial functions in general but rather one that depends upon properties of the underlying set. We then develop some theory of polynomial functions over the complex numbers and subrings of the complex numbers, establishing common results usually associated with the name "theory of equations." In the latter part of the chapter, we study the analytic nature of polynomials and introduce the Weierstrass Theorem.

Polynomials Over a Ring D

9.1-1 Definition: If D is a number ring,* then $D[x]$ is the set of all functions $f: D \to D$ which can be described as follows:

$$\forall x \in D, \quad f(x) = a_0 + a_1 x + \ldots + a_n x^n$$

$$= \sum_{i=0}^{n} a_i x^i \quad \text{for some } n \in N_0$$

* See 3.5-8 (Axioms for a Number Ring).

where $\forall i$, $a_i \in D$. The a_i's are called *coefficients*, and in particular a_i is called the coefficient of the ith term. The elements (functions) in $D[x]$ are called *polynomials* over D.

Remark: Note that it is not implied above that a polynomial function has a *unique* description. We know only that for each element in $D[x]$ there exists at least one description of the form $\sum_{i=0}^{n} a_i x^i$.

Example: Let $D = Z_3$ (mod 3 arithmetic). Let

$$f(x) = 2 + x + x^2 \qquad \text{and} \qquad g(x) = 2 + x + x^4.$$

(Do you agree that $f \in D[x]$ and $g \in D[x]$?) Then

$$f(\bar{0}) = \bar{2} + \bar{0} + \bar{0}^2 = \bar{2}$$
$$f(\bar{1}) = \bar{2} + \bar{1} + \bar{1}^2 = \bar{4} = \bar{1} \qquad \text{(recall that } \bar{4} = \bar{1} \text{ in } Z_3\text{)}$$
$$f(\bar{2}) = \bar{2} + \bar{2} + \bar{2}^2 = \bar{4} + \bar{4} = \bar{2}$$
$$g(\bar{0}) = \bar{2} + \bar{0} + \bar{0}^4 = \bar{2}$$
$$g(\bar{1}) = \bar{2} + \bar{1} + \bar{1}^4 = \bar{1}$$
$$g(\bar{2}) = \bar{2} + \bar{2} + \bar{2}^4 = \bar{4} + \overline{16} = \overline{20} = \bar{2}.$$

Hence we have $f = g$.

Note: In the remaining text and in the exercises we omit the bar ("$-$") over a number in the modular arithmetics.

Let us now consider some examples involving addition and multiplication of polynomial functions.

Example: Let $f, g \in Z[x]$ be defined as follows:

$$\forall x, \quad f(x) = 3 + 2x + x^2 \qquad \text{and} \qquad \forall x, \quad g(x) = 1 - x + 2x^2 + x^3.$$

Then for all elements x in Z,

$$\begin{aligned}
(f + g)(x) &= f(x) + g(x) \\
&= (3 + 2x + x^2) + (1 - x + 2x^2 + x^3) \\
&= (3 + 1) + (2 - 1)x + (1 + 2)x^2 + x^3 \\
&= 4 + x + 3x^2 + x^3,
\end{aligned}$$

and

$$\begin{aligned}
f \cdot g(x) &= f(x)g(x) \\
&= (3 + 2x + x^2)(1 - x + 2x^2 + x^3) \\
&= 3 \cdot 1 + (-3 + 2)x + (6 - 2 + 1)x^2 + (3 + 4 - 1)x^3 \\
&\quad + (2 + 2)x^4 + 1 \cdot x^5 \\
&= 3 - x + 5x^2 + 6x^3 + 4x^4 + x^5.
\end{aligned}$$

Example: Let $f, g \in Z_3[x]$ be defined as follows:

$$f(x) = 2 + x^2 \qquad \text{and} \qquad g(x) = 1 + 2x + 2x^2.$$

Then for all $x \in Z_3$,

$$\begin{aligned}
(f + g)(x) &= f(x) + g(x) = (2 + x^2) + (1 + 2x + 2x^2) \\
&= (2 + 1) + 2x + (1 + 2)x^2 \\
&= 0 + 2x + 0x^2 \qquad \text{(in } Z_3, 0 = 3\text{)} \\
&= 2x,
\end{aligned}$$

and

$$f \cdot g(x) = f(x)g(x) = (2 + x^2)(1 + 2x + 2x^2)$$
$$= 2 \cdot 1 + 2 \cdot 2x + (2 \cdot 2 + 1)x^2 + 2x^3 + 2x^4$$
$$= 2 + 4x + 5x^2 + 2x^3 + 2x^4$$
$$= 2 + x + 2x^2 + 2x^3 + 2x^4.$$

We notice in these examples that $f + g$ and $f \cdot g$ are also polynomial functions. Being curious budding mathematicians, we should ask ourselves whether this is an accident of the particular examples or if this will always be the case.

Closure of $D[x]$

As you recall, in Chapter 3 we showed that the space of all functions over a number ring D had inherited certain algebraic properties from D. Namely that it too is a number ring. We would like to establish the same result for $D[x]$. All that remains in order to do this is to show that $D[x]$ is closed under addition and multiplication. (Why?)

9.1-2 Theorem: If $f, g \in D[x]$, then $f + g$ and $f \cdot g$ are in $D[x]$. (That is, $D[x]$ is closed under function addition and function multiplication.)

Proof: Let $f(x) = a_0 + a_1 x + \ldots + a_n x^n$ and $g(x) = b_0 + b_1 x + \ldots + b_m x^m$ for some $n, m \in N$, and elements a_i and b_i in D. We may assume that $m \geq n$. (Why?) Now $\forall x \in D$,

$$(f + g)(x) = f(x) + g(x)$$
$$= (a_0 + a_1 x + \ldots + a_n x^n) + (b_0 + b_1 x + \ldots + b_m x^m)$$
$$= (a_0 + b_0) + (a_1 + b_1)x + \ldots + (a_n + b_n)x^n + b_{n+1} x^{n+1} + \ldots + b_m x^m$$

which is a function in $D[x]$. Similarly,

$$f \cdot g(x) = f(x)g(x)$$
$$= (a_0 + a_1 x + \ldots + a_n x^n)(b_0 + b_1 x + \ldots + b_m x^m)$$
$$= a_0 b_0 + (a_0 b_1 + a_1 b_0)x + \ldots + (a_0 b_n + a_1 b_{n-1} + \ldots + a_n b_0)x^n$$
$$+ (a_0 b_{n+1} + a_1 b_n + \ldots + a_n b_1)x^{n+1} + \ldots$$
$$+ (a_0 b_m + a_1 b_{m-1} + \ldots + a_n b_{m-n})x^m + \ldots + a_n b_m x^{m+n},$$

again an element of $D[x]$. □

Although this "proof" cannot be considered to be a careful rigorous proof, it does serve as a convincing illustration, and we shall not go into more detail. We leave it to the reader to be convinced that the theorem is true as a result of massive experience in performing multiplication and addition of polynomial functions.

It is especially useful in working with polynomial functions to employ the "slightly sloppy" language convention introduced in Chapter 3, Section 16. That is, we use as a name for the function a formula which determines the functional values. Occasionally to avoid confusion we use the identically equal sign "$\equiv$" to emphasize the fact that we mean equality of functions rather than equality of points in D.

Example: Evaluate the polynomial $3x^2 + 2x^3 \in Z_4[x]$ at $x = 1$. What is meant here is "Find $f(1)$ where

$$\forall x \in Z_4, \qquad f(x) = 3x^2 + 2x^3."$$

We see that $\qquad f(1) = 3(1)^2 + 2(1)^3 = 1 \in Z_4.$

Exercises 9.1

1. Let $f, g, h \in Z[x]$, where

$$f(x) = 3 + 2x + x^2, \qquad g(x) = 5x + 2x^2 + x^3, \qquad \text{and} \qquad h(x) = 3x.$$

a) Write explicit polynomial descriptions for

$$(f + g)(x), \qquad f \cdot g(x) \quad ((f + g) + h)(x), \qquad \text{and} \qquad ((f \cdot g) \cdot h)(x).$$

b) Does $f + g = g + f$? Does $f \cdot g = g \cdot f$? Does $(f \cdot g) \cdot h = f \cdot (g \cdot h)$? Does $(f + g) + h = f + (g + h)$? Why?

2. Consider the following functions in $Z_4[x]$.

$$f(x) = 1 + 3x + x^2, \qquad g(x) = 2x^2 + x^3, \qquad h(x) = 2x + x^2, \qquad \varphi(x) = x^4.$$

a) Do the same as Part *a*) Exercise 1.
b) Do the same as Part *b*) Exercise 1.
c) Simplify $(f - \varphi)(x)$.
d) Show that $\forall x \in Z_4, (f - \varphi)(x) = 1 + 3x$.

3. Show that if f, g, and h are polynomial functions over some number ring D, then $f \cdot (g + h) = f \cdot g + f \cdot h$.

4. Find some modular arithmetic Z_n over which the function $f(x) = 2x^3 + x^5$ is the zero function.

5. Let $f \in \mathbb{C}[x]$ such that $f(x) = 2i + 3x + ix^2$. Compute:

a) $f(i)$ b) $f(1)$ c) $f\left(\dfrac{\sqrt{17} - 3}{2i}\right)$

6. If $f(x) = c + \pi x - 5x^4$ is a polynomial over the real numbers, then find a polynomial $g \in R[x]$ such that $f + g = 0$.

In Problems 7, 8, and 9, all functions are over the modular arithmetic number ring Z_3.

7. a) If $f(x) = 2x^2 + x + 1$, then find $f(0), f(1), f(2)$.
b) Do the same for f and g where

$$f(x) = x^3 + x + 2 \qquad \text{and} \qquad g(x) = 2x^4 + x.$$

8. a) If $f(x) = 2x^3$, if possible find $a, b, c \in Z_3$ such that

$$f(x) = ax^2 + bx + c.$$

b) Do the same for $f(x) = x^4 + x$.

9. If $f(x) = 2x$, if possible find $a, b, c \in Z_3$ such that

$$f(x) = ax^2 + bx + c \quad \text{where } b \neq 2.$$

10. Let $f \in Z[x]$ such that $f(x) = 2x^3$. If possible, find numbers $a, b, c \in Z$ such that $f(x) = ax^2 + bx + c$.

11. Justify the assertions made in the proof of Theorem 9.1-2

that $(a_0 + b_0) + (a_1 + b_1)x + \ldots + b_m x^m \in D[x]$

and $a_0 b_0 + (a_0 b_1 + a_1 b_0)x + \ldots + a_n b_m x^{m+n} \in D[x]$.

12. Why do we insist that polynomials be defined over a ring rather than an arbitrary set?

13. Argue that $a \in D, f \in D[x] \Rightarrow f(a) \in D$.

14. Show that $D[x]$ is closed under composition. (That is, prove that $f \in D[x]$ and $g \in D[x]$ implies that $f \circ g \in D[x]$, where $\forall x \in D, f \circ g(x) = f(g(x))$.)

15. Consider the following polynomials over the complex field.

$$f(x) = 2ix^3 - 3x + (4 + i) \qquad g(x) = (3 - i)x^2 + ix - 3$$

a) Compute: $f(2i), f(i - 1), g(i + 1), g(2i + 2)$.
b) Express $f + g, f \cdot g, f \circ g$, and $g \circ f$ in standard polynomial form.

16. Recall "Checkerboard Jimmy," the robot who lives on an infinitely large checkerboard and can make the 5 moves S-top, L-eft, R-ight, F-orward, B-ack. (See Section 3.1, Exercise 7.) Jimmy has been programmed to take instructions via polynomial functions in $Z_5[x]$, where

$$\bar{0} = S, \qquad \bar{1} = L, \qquad \bar{2} = R, \qquad \bar{3} = F, \qquad \bar{4} = B.$$

That is, $\forall n \in N$ Jimmy's instruction is $\bar{n}$. For example, the polynomial $f(x) = \bar{1} + x^2$ would instruct Jimmy to repeat in succession the moves

$$\bar{1} + \bar{0}^2 = \bar{1} = L, \qquad \bar{1} + \bar{1}^2 = \bar{2} = R, \qquad \bar{1} + \bar{2}^2 = \bar{0} = S,$$
$$\bar{1} + \bar{3}^2 = \bar{0} = S, \qquad \bar{1} + \bar{4}^2 = \bar{2} = R.$$

Hence Jimmy would go $L, R, S, S, R, L, R, S, S, R, \ldots$ under the polynomial program $\bar{1} + x^2$.

Determine Jimmy's course when programmed by the polynomial (we eliminate the "bars" here)

a) $2x + x^3$.

d) $x^4 + x^5$.

b) $2 + 3x + x^2$.

e) $x + 2x^2 + x^4$.

c) x^4.

f) x^3.

If possible, find a polynomial in $Z_5[x]$ that would instruct Jimmy to make the following repeated move.

g) $L, L, R, R, B, \ldots$

j) $F, B, F, B, S, \ldots$

h) $L, R, R, L, S, \ldots$

k) $F, F, F, F, F, \ldots$

i) $L, L, L, L, F, \ldots$

l) $S, S, S, S, B, \ldots$

17. How would you use polynomials in some $Z_n[x]$ to give Jimmy instructions of "length" seven?

9.2 Degrees of Polynomials

9.2-1 Definition: If $f \in D[x]$, then the *degree of f* ("$\deg f$") is the smallest non-negative integer n such that $f(x) = \sum_{i=0}^{n} a_i x^i$ for some $a_0, a_1, \ldots, a_n \in D$, where $a_n \neq 0$. (In this case, a_n is called the *leading coefficient of f.*)

Remark: We assign no degree to the zero function. If $\deg f = 0$ or if f is the zero function, then we say f is a constant function, or simply that f is a constant. (Do you agree that $D[x]$ contains the constant functions?)

As we noticed previously, a polynomial function over a ring D may possibly be described in more than one way. Thus in the example referred to above, we saw a ring Z_3 where a function had two descriptions:

$$2 + x + x^2 \equiv 2 + x + x^4.$$

We see then that the degree of the function is not four since we could express it as $2 + x + x^2$, but still we cannot be certain without further examination that the function has degree two. (Why?) We do know, however, that it has degree less than or equal to two. (Why?) In general all we know if

$$f(x) = a + ax_1 + \ldots + a_n x^n$$

is that $\deg f \leq n$. Another thing we can conclude is contained in the following.

9.2-2 Theorem: If $f(x) = a_0 + a_1 x$ and $a_1 \neq 0$, then $\deg f = 1$.

Proof: We know $\deg f \leq 1$, so let us assume that for some $a \in D$, $f(x) = a$. Therefore $f(0) = a$ and $f(1) = a$; but also

$$f(0) = a_0 + a_1(0) = a_0, \quad \text{and} \quad f(1) = a_0 + a_1(1) = a_0 + a_1.$$

Therefore $a_0 = a_0 + a_1$ from which it follows that $a_1 = 0$. This contradicts the hypothesis and hence the assumption that $f(x) = a$, leaving only the possibility that $\deg f = 1$. ∎

Factors of Polynomials

9.2-3 Definition: If $f = g \cdot h$, then we say that g is a *factor* of f or that g *divides f*. (We say also that h is a factor of f.)

9.2-4 Theorem: If $(x - a)$ is a factor of f, then a is a zero of f.

Proof: Assume that $f(x) = (x - a) \cdot h(x)$ for some h. Then

$$f(a) = (a - a)h(a) = 0 \cdot h(a) = 0. \ ∎$$

The question which naturally arises at this point is whether the converse of the preceding theorem is true. That is, if $f(a) = 0$, then is $(x - a)$ necessarily a factor of f? We now establish some results which will allow us to answer this question.

9.2-5 Lemma: If $a_0 + a_1x + \ldots + a_nx^n$ is a polynomial over some number ring D and $b \in D$, then for some $q \in D[x]$ and some $r \in D[x]$,

$$f(x) = (x - b)\cdot q(x) + r(x),$$

where deg $r < \max\{1, n\}$ or $r \equiv 0$ (if $r(x)$ doesn't have a degree).

Proof: Case 1. $(n = 0)$. Let $q(x) = 0$ and $r(x) = f(x)$. Then

$$f(x) = 0\cdot(x - b) + f(x),$$

and we know that $f \equiv 0$ or deg $f = 0$. Since $n = 0$, $n < 1 \leq \max\{1, n\} = 1$.

Case 2. $(n \geq 1)$. In this case we may write f in the form

$$f(x) = a_nx^{n-1}(x - b) + (a_{n-1} + ba_n)x^{n-1} + a_{n-2}x^{n-2} + \ldots + a_0$$

in which case

$$q(x) = a_nx^{n-1}$$

and $\qquad r(x) = (a_{n-1} + ba_n)x^{n-1} + a_{n-2}x^{n-2} + \ldots + a_0.$

Thus we see that deg $r \leq n - 1$ or $r \equiv 0$. Hence in either case,

$$\deg r \leq \max\{n, 1\} \qquad \text{or} \qquad r \equiv 0. \quad \square$$

9.2-6 Theorem: If $a_0 + a_1x + \ldots + a_nx^n$ is a polynomial over some number ring D and $b \in D$, then for some q and some r in $D[x]$,

$$f(x) = (x - b)q(x) + r(x)$$

where deg $r < 1$ or $r \equiv 0$.

Proof: If $n = 0$, then take $q \equiv 0$ and $r \equiv f$. If $n \geq 1$, then by Lemma 9.2-5 there is a q_1 and an r_1 such that

$$f(x) = (x - b)q_1(x) + r_1(x)$$

where deg $r_1 < \max\{1, n\}$ or $r_1 \equiv 0$. Now we can write r_1 as

$$r_1(x) = b_0 + b_1x + \ldots + b_{n-1}n^{n-1}.$$

If $n - 1 = 0$ we are done (why?), otherwise apply the lemma again to r_1 and we have

$$r_1(x) = (x - b)q_2(x) + r_2(x)$$

where deg $r_2 < \max\{1, n - 1\}$. Clearly we can continue this process on our remainder r_k until for some k deg $r_k < \max\{1, 0\}$ or $r_k \equiv 0$. (A more rigorous argument requires the well ordering principle.) Hence

$$\begin{aligned} f(x) &= (x - b)q_1(x) + (x - b)q_2(x) + \ldots + (x - b)q_k(x) + r_k(x) \\ &= (x - b)(q_1(x) + q_2(x) + \ldots + q_k(x)) + r_k(x). \end{aligned}$$

We then take

$$q = q_1 + q_2 + \ldots + q_k \qquad \text{and} \qquad r = r_k.$$

Note that deg $r < \max\{1, 0\} = 1$ or $r \equiv 0$, so the theorem follows.

We are now in a position to prove the converse of Theorem 9.2-4.

9.2-7 Corollary: (The Factor Theorem) If $f(a) = 0$, then $x - a$ is a factor of f. The proof is left as an exercise.

9.2-8 Corollary: If $f(x) = a_0 + a_1x + \ldots + a_nx^n$ and $n \geq 1$ and $f(a) = 0$ for some $a \in D$, then

$$f(x) = (x - a)q(x) \quad \text{where} \quad q(x) = b_0 + b_1x + \ldots + b_{n-2}x^{n-2} + a_nx^{n-1}$$

for some $b_0, b_1, \ldots, b_{n-2} \in D$. (That is, the $(n - 1)$th coefficient on the description of q is the same as the nth coefficient on f.)

Proof: By examining the form of the equations in the proof of Lemma 9.2-5 (keeping in mind that $f(a) = 0$), it is easily verified that this holds. ▯

9.2-9 Corollary: (The Remainder Theorem) If $f \in D[x]$ and $a \in D$, then for some $r \in D$ and some $q \in D[x]$,

$$f(x) = (x - a)q(x) + r \quad \text{and} \quad f(a) = r.$$

Remark: A common way to state the remainder theorem is: *If f is divided by $x - a$, then $f(a)$ is the remainder r.*

Example: Let $f(x) = 2x + 3x^3 + x^4$ be a polynomial over Z. Find $q, r \in Z[x]$ such that

$$f(x) = (x - 3)q(x) + r(x)$$

and deg $r < 1$, or $r = 0$.

Solution: The method for doing this is the familiar process of "long division." A careful analysis of the process and a comparison with the above lemma and theorem will reveal that they essentially describe this division process. We may carry out the division process as follows:

$$
\begin{array}{r}
x^3 + 6x^2 + 18x + 56 \\
x - 3\overline{)x^4 + 3x^3 + 2x} \\
\underline{x^4 - 3x^3} \\
6x^3 \qquad\qquad + 2x \\
\underline{6x^3 - 18x^2} \\
18x^2 + 2x \\
\underline{18x^2 - 54x} \\
56x \\
\underline{56x - 168} \\
168
\end{array}
$$

Hence

$$f(x) = (x - 3)(x^3 + 6x^2 + 18x + 56) + 168 \quad \text{(where deg } 168 < 1).$$

Exercises 9.2

1. Let $f(x) = 1 + x + 2x^2$, where $f \in Z_2[x]$. Determine deg f.

2. How many functions from $Z_3 \xrightarrow{\text{into}} Z_3$ are there?

3. What is $\deg f$ if $f \in Z_3[x]$ where:
    a) $f(x) = x^3$ b) $f(x) = 2x^2$ c) $f(x) = x^4 + 2x$

4. Show that every function from $Z_3 \xrightarrow{\text{into}} Z_3$ is a polynomial function. (*Hint:*
    a) Show that if $ax^2 + bx + c = 0$, then $a = b = c = 0$.
    b) Show that if $a_1x^2 + b_1x + c_1 = a_2x^2 + b_2x + c_2$, then $a_1 = a_2$, $b_1 = b_2$,
    $c_1 = c_2$.
    c) Count the number of distinct polynomial functions $ax^2 + bx + c$.
    d) Compare your result with the result in Exercise 2.)

5. a) If $f \in Z_3[x]$, then what can you say about $\deg f$? Explain. (*Hint:* See Exercise 4.)
    b) If $f(x) = x^2 + 1$, what is $\deg f$?

6. If $f \in Z_4[x]$, what can you say about $\deg f$?

7. a) If $\deg f = m$ and $\deg g = n$, show that $\deg (f + g) \leq \max \{m, n\}$.
    b) What about $f \cdot g$ and $f \circ g$?

8. Consider the function $f: Z_4 \to Z_4$ given by

$$f(0) = f(1) = f(2) = 0 \qquad \text{and} \qquad f(3) = 1.$$

Show that $f \notin Z_4[x]$.

9. We have seen that all functions on Z_3 can be expressed as polynomial functions, while in Z_4 this is not true. For which modular arithmetics Z_n will all functions f: $Z_n \to Z_n$ be expressible as polynomials?[†]

10. Show that $f(x) = 1/x$ is not a polynomial function in $R[x]$. (*Hint:* Examine $\lim_{x \to 0} 1/x$ and compare this with $\lim_{x \to 0} g(x)$ where $g \in R[x]$.)

11. Let $f \in Z[x]$ where $f(x) = x^4 - 2x^3 + 2x^2 - 3x - 2$.
    a) Show that $f(2) = 0$ and then find $q \in Z[x]$ such that $f(x) = (x - 2)q(x)$.
    b) Does there exist an $h \in Z[x]$ such that $f(x) = (x - 3)h(x)$? Why?

12. Let $f \in Z_4[x]$ where $f(x) = 2x^3 - 3x^2 + 1$. Does there exist a $q \in Z_4[x]$ such that $f(x) = (x - 1)q(x)$? Why? If so, find one such q.

13. a) Let $2x^2 + 3x + 1$ be a polynomial over the integers. Does there exist an integer $a > 0$ such that $2a^2 + 3a + 1 = 0$?
    b) For some $a < 0$?

14. Prove the factor theorem. (*Hint:* Apply Theorem 9.2-6 and show that $r = 0$.)

15. Verify the statement made in the proof of Corollary 9.2-8.

16. Prove the remainder theorem.

17. Let $f(x) = 2x^3 + 2x^2 + x + 2, f \in Q[x]$. Use the remainder theorem to find:
    a) $f(3)$ b) $f(4)$ c) $f(2)$ d) $f(6)$

[†] See "A Characterization of Finite Fields" by Brother Joseph Heisler, C.S.C., St. Edward's University, Austin, Texas. The American Mathematical Monthly, Volume 74, Number 5, May, 1967.

18. Let $f(x) = 5x^4 + x^3 + x^2 - x - 4, f \in Q[x]$. Use the remainder theorem to find:

a) $f(2)$ b) $f(-3)$ c) $f(-4)$ d) $f(5)$

19. Write the polynomial $a_0 + a_1x + \ldots + a_nx^n = \sum_{i=1}^{n} a_i x^i$ as the product of a $1 \times n$ matrix and a $n \times 1$ matrix.

9.3 Polynomials Over a Field

At this point let us turn our attention to polynomial functions over the slightly more sophisticated field structure. (Fields are discussed in Chapter 3.) Let us keep in mind that everything we have proved about polynomials over an arbitrary number ring will also hold where our functions are taken over a field.

The new and very important fact that is added when we have a field rather than a number ring is the knowledge that we have a multiplicative inverse for each non-zero element. That is, if $a \neq 0$, then for some b, $ab = 1$.

9.3-1 Lemma: Let F be a field and let $f, g \in F[x]$ where

$$f(x) = a_nx^n + \ldots + a_1x + a_0,$$

and $\qquad g(x) = b_mx^m + \ldots + b_1x + b_0, \qquad$ where $b_m \neq 0$.

Then for some $q \in F[x]$ and $r \in F[x]$

$$f = gq + r \qquad \text{where} \qquad \deg r < \max \{m, n\} \qquad \text{or} \qquad r \equiv 0.$$

Proof: Case 1. Suppose $m > n$. Take $q = 0$ and $r = f$, so that $f = g \cdot 0 + f$. We know that $\deg f \leq n < m = \max \{m, n\}$.

Case 2. Suppose $m \leq n$. Then

$$f(x) = \frac{a_n}{b_m} x^{n-m} (b_mx^m + b_{m-1}x^{m-1} + \ldots + b_0) + \left(a_{n-1} - \frac{a_n}{b_m} b_{m-1}\right) x^{n-1}$$

$$+ \left(a_{n-2} - \frac{a_n}{b_m} b_{m-2}\right) x^{n-2} + \ldots + \left(a_{n-m} - \frac{a_n}{b_m} b_{m-m}\right) x^{n-m} + a_{n-m-1}x^{n-m-1}$$

$$+ \ldots + a_1x + a_0. \qquad \text{(Verify this!)}$$

Here we have

$$q(x) = \frac{a_n}{b_m} x^{n-m}$$

and $\qquad r(x) = \left(a_{n-1} - \frac{a_n}{b_m} b_{m-1}\right) x^{n-1} + \ldots + a_1x + a_0,$

of course keeping in mind the slight changes in the expression depending on the size of $n - m$. We see, however, that such a q and r exist and that $\deg r \leq n - 1 < n = \max \{m, n\}$. $\square$

9.3-2 Theorem: (*The Euclidean Algorithm for polynomial functions over a field*)
Let F be a field and let f, $g \in F[x]$ such that

$$f(x) = a_n x^n + \ldots + a_1 x + a_0$$

and $g(x) = b_m x^m + \ldots + b_1 x + b_0,$ where $b_m \neq 0.$

Then for some q, $r \in F[x]$, $f = gq + r$, where $\deg r < m$ or $r \equiv 0$.

Proof: Applying Lemma 9.3-1 to f and successively to r a finite number
(k) of times until max $\{m, n - k\} = m$ and we have

$$f = gq_0 + gq_1 + \ldots + gq_k + r_k = g(q_0 + q_1 + \ldots + q_k) + r_k,$$

where $\deg r_k < $ max $\{m, n - k\} = m$. $\square$

Question: What induction type principle do we employ in this proof?

Zeros of Polynomials

We have seen in various number rings and fields that if $f(x) = a_0 +$
$a_1 x + \ldots + a_n x^n$ (where $a_n \neq 0$), we could not be sure that $\deg f = n$. We
have seen that a function $f \in D[x]$ has in general no unique representation
of the form $a_0 + a_1 x + \ldots + a_n x^n$. As was pointed out in the exercises however, the functions in $Z_3[x]$ do indeed have unique representations of the form
$a_0 + a_1 x + a_2 x^2$. You may have suspected that each polynomial function over
$\mathbb{C}$, R, Q, or Z can be represented in only one way. Let us now substantiate
these suspicions.

Recall that a number ring D is said to be integral if and only if

$$\forall a, b \in D, \qquad ab = 0 \Rightarrow a = 0 \text{ or } b = 0.$$

In particular, Z is an integral number ring and so are the fields Q, R, and $\mathbb{C}$
as are all fields.

Example: In Z_3 we have three numbers: 0, 1, 2. Since $1 \times 2 = 2$, Z_3 is an
integral number ring. (Why?)

Example: In Z_6, $2 \neq 0$ and $3 \neq 0$, but $2 \times 3 = 0$. Hence Z_6 is not an
integral number ring.

9.3-3 Theorem: Assume that D is an integral number ring and $f \in D[x]$,
where for some $a_0, \ldots, a_n \in D$, $a_n \neq 0$, f can be expressed in the form

$$f(x) = a_0 + a_1 x + \ldots + a_n x^n.$$

Then f has no more than n zeros in D.

Proof: Let us use the principle of mathematical induction in the form
called "Strong Induction."

i) If $n = 0$, then f has no zeros.

If $n = 1$, then $f(x) = a_0 + a_1 x.$

663

If we assume that

$$a_0 + a_1\alpha = 0 = a_0 + a_1\beta$$

then we deduce that

$$a_1(\alpha - \beta) = 0$$

and since $a_1 \neq 0$, it follows that

$$\alpha - \beta = 0. \quad \text{(Why?)}$$

That is, $\alpha = \beta$ and so we can have no more than one zero.

ii) Now let $k \geq 1$ and assume that for every integer between 1 and k inclusive the theorem holds. If

$$f(x) = a_{k+1}x^{k+1} + \ldots + a_0 \quad \text{where} \quad a_{k+1} \neq 0,$$

then either f has no zeros or there is a number $c \in D$ such that $f(c) = 0$. If $f(c) = 0$, then by Theorem 9.2-6 and Corollary 9.2-7 (the factor theorem),

$$f(x) = (x - c)(a_{k+1}x^k + b_{k+1}x^{k-1} + \ldots + b_0) = (x - c)q(x).$$

By the inductive hypothesis, $q(x)$ can have no more than k zeros and $x - c$ has only one. Since D is integral, $f(\alpha)$ cannot be zero unless $\alpha - c$ or $q(\alpha)$ is zero; hence f can have no more than $k + 1$ zeros.

We have now established the two necessary steps for an induction proof and hence we conclude that the theorem is true. □

Question: Did we begin this induction at 0 or at 1?

9.3-4 Corollary: If f is a polynomial of degree n over an integral number ring, then f has no more than n zeros.

9.3-5 Corollary: If D is an infinite integral number ring, then

$$f(x) = a_0 + \ldots + a_nx^n \quad \text{where} \quad a_n \neq 0$$

cannot be the zero function. (Explain!)

Although we used the integral property of D in the proofs, we might wonder whether or not we really needed it. The following example will show that the assumption is necessary.

Example: Let $f \in Z_{24}[x]$ where f is described by

$$f(x) = (x - 19)(x - 17)(x - 14) = x^3 + 22x^2 + 11x + 14.$$

Note that $\deg f \leq 3$ (why?). However 19, 17, 14, 23, 22, and 1 are zeros of f. (Verify this!) Also note that $f(x) \neq 0$ since $f(0) \neq 0$.

Linear Independence and Degree

Recall in Chapter 8 we defined what was meant by linear independence of functions. Thus, the functions $f_1, f_2, \ldots, f_n$ over some number ring D are said to be linearly independent if and only if

$$a_1f_1 + a_2f_2 + \ldots + a_nf_n = 0 \Rightarrow a_1 = a_2 = \ldots = a_n = 0.$$

The functions f_i are said to be linearly dependent if they are not linearly independent.

Example: The polynomial functions x^2, x^3, x^4 over Z_4 are linearly dependent since $f(x) = x^2 + 2x^3 + x^4 \equiv 0$.

We are now ready to establish a very interesting and important fact about the linear independence of polynomials over an infinite number ring.

9.3-6 Theorem: If D is an integral number ring with an infinite number of elements, then $\forall n \in N$ the functions $1, x, \ldots, x^n$ are linearly independent.

Proof: Assume that $a_0 + a_1x + \ldots + a_nx^n \equiv 0$. Either

$$a_0 = a_1 = \ldots = a_n = 0,$$

or for some largest k, $n \geq k \geq 0$, $a_k \neq 0$. But

$$f(x) = a_0 + \ldots + a_kx^k$$

cannot be the zero function by virtue of Corollary 9.3-5. Hence $a_0 = \ldots = a_n = 0$. ☐

9.3-7 Corollary: If $f(x) = a_0 + a_1x + \ldots + a_nx^n$,

and $\qquad\qquad f(x) = b_0 + b_1x + \ldots + b_nx^n$,

is a polynomial over an integral number ring with an infinite number of points, then

$$a_0 = b_0, \qquad a = b_1, \ldots, a_n = b_n.$$

Proof: Left as an exercise.

Remark: We now see that for any integral number ring D with an infinite number of elements, and in particular for Z, Q, R, and C, a polynomial function over D has a unique expression of the form

$$f(x) = a_0 + a_1x + \ldots + a_nx^n \qquad \text{where} \qquad a_n \neq 0.$$

There are many useful applications of this result.

We can now strengthen some of our previous results concerning polynomials which in particular hold if we are taking them to be functions over Z, Q, R, or C.

9.3-8 Theorem: If $f \in D[x]$, where D is an infinite integral number ring, and if

$$f(x) = a_0 + a_1x + \ldots + a_nx^n \qquad \text{where} \qquad a_n \neq 0.$$

then $\deg f = n$.

Proof: Assume $\deg f < n$. Then for some $m < n$, f can be written in the form

$$f(x) = b_0 + b_1x + \ldots + b_mx^m + \ldots + 0x^n.$$

But by Corollary 9.3-7

$$a_0 = b_0, \ldots, a_m = b_m \qquad \text{and} \qquad a_n = 0,$$

a contradiction. ☐

9.3-9 Corollary: If $f, g \in D[x]$, where D is an infinite integral number ring, and if $\deg f = m$, and $\deg g = n$, then $\deg f \cdot g = m + n$.

Proof: Let $f(x) = a_0 + a_1 x + \ldots + a_m x^m \ (a_m \neq 0)$,

and $g(x) = b_0 + b_1 x + \ldots + b_n x^n \ (b_n \neq 0)$.

Then $f \cdot g$ is of the form

$$f \cdot g(x) = a_0 b_0 + \ldots + a_m b_n x^{m+n}$$

(where the terms in between are more complicated, of course). Since $a_m \neq 0$ and $b_n \neq 0$, it follows that $a_m b_n \neq 0$. (Why?) Therefore, $\deg f \cdot g = m + n$. $\square$

9.3-10 Theorem: Let $f, g \neq 0$ be polynomials over an infinite field F. Then there exist unique polynomials $q, r \in F[x]$ such that

$$f = g \cdot q + r \quad \text{where} \quad \deg r < \deg g \quad \text{or} \quad r \equiv 0.$$

Proof: The existence follows directly from Theorem 9.3-2. Let us then prove uniqueness. Let

$$f = g \cdot q_1 + r_1 = g \cdot q_2 + r_2,$$

where $\deg r_1 < \deg g$ or $r_1 = 0$ and $\deg r_2 < \deg g$ or $r_2 = 0$. We wish to show that $q_1 = q_2$ and $r_1 = r_2$. Immediately we have

$$g \cdot (q_1 - q_2) + (r_1 - r_2) = 0$$

and it clearly suffices to show that $q_1 = q_2$ or $r_1 = r_2$. We know that $\deg g$ exists and if $q_1 - q_2 \neq 0$, then $\deg g \cdot (q_1 - q_2)$ exists. (Why?) Since $g \cdot (q_1 - q_2) = r_2 - r_1$, we have

$$\deg g \cdot (q_1 - q_2) = \deg g + \deg (q_1 - q_2) = \deg (r_2 - r_1). \quad \text{(Why?)}$$

Hence

$$\deg (r_2 - r_1) \geq \deg g,$$

but

$$\deg (r_2 - r_1) \leq \max \{\deg r_2, \deg r_1\} < \deg g$$

a contradiction. Hence $q_1 - q_2 = 0$, and therefore

$$q_1 = q_2 \quad \text{and} \quad r_1 = r_2.$$

Exercises 9.3

1. Let $f(x) = 3x^4 - 2x^2 + 1$ and $g(x) = 2x^2 - 3$ be polynomials over Q. Then find q and $r \in Q[x]$ such that $f = gq + r$, where $\deg r < 2$ or $r \equiv 0$.

2. Let $f, g \in Z_3[x]$ such that $f(x) = 2x^3 - 2x + 1$ and $g(x) = 2x^2 - 1$. Find q, $r \in Z_3[x]$ such that $f = gq + r$, where $\deg r < 2$ or $r \equiv 0$.

3. Explain why it follows that everything we have proved about polynomials over an arbitrary number ring will also hold concerning polynomial functions over a field.

4. What crucial role did the assumption that $b_m \neq 0$ play in the proof of Lemma 9.3-1?

5. Follow the argument outlined in the proof of Theorem 9.3-2 and construct a detailed proof of the theorem.

6. Show with an example that the Euclidean Algorithm is not valid for polynomial functions over Z.

7. Investigate (prove or disprove): A slight variation of the Euclidean Algorithm for polynomials over an arbitrary number ring holds if

$$g(x) = 1 \cdot x^m + \ldots + b_1 x + b_0$$

(*i.e.*, if $b_m = 1$).

8. Let f and g be polynomials in $Z[x]$ as follows and divide f by g (*i.e.*, find (if possible) $q, r \in Z[x]$ such that $f = gq + r$ where $\deg r < \deg g$ or $r = 0$).

   a) $f(x) = 5x^2 + 3x - 2$, $g(x) = x + 3$
   b) $f(x) = 7x^3 - 3x^2 + x - 2$, $g(x) = x^2 + 3x + 4$
   c) $f(x) = 3x^2 - 2x + 1$, $g(x) = x^3 + x - 2$
   d) $f(x) = x^4 + 3x^2 + 2$, $g(x) = 2x^2 - 3$

9. Prove Corollaries 9.3-4 and 9.3-5.

10. Let $f \in Z[x]$ be given by $f(x) = 3x^4 + 2x^3 + 3$. Is it possible to find $a_0, a, b, c, d \in Z$ where:

   a) $f(x) = ax^3 + bx^2 + cx + d$
   b) $f(x) = 5x^4 + ax^3 + bx^2 + cx + d$
   c) $f(x) = x^5 + ax^4 + bx^3 + cx^2 + dx + a_0$

Explain your answer in each case.

11. Assume that $f(x) = ax^4 + bx^3 + cx^2 + dx + a_0$ and $g(x) = 3x^3 + 2x + 4$ $f, g \in R[x]$. If $\forall x$ $f(x) = g(x)$, find a, b, c, d, a_0.

12. a) Show that if $f_1, f_2, \ldots, f_n$ are n linearly independent functions in $D \times D$ (where D is an integral number ring), then

$$\left(\sum_{i=1}^{n} a_i f_i = \sum_{i=1}^{n} b_i f_i \right) \Leftrightarrow \forall i, \quad a_i = b_i.$$

Note: We do not assume that the f_i's are necessarily polynomials although they might be in a particular case.

   b) Use part a) to prove Corollary 9.3-7.
   (*Hint:* $(a_0 - b_0) + (a_1 - b_1)x + \ldots + (a_n - b_n)x^n = 0$.)

13. a) Interpret graphically the zeros of a polynomial $f \in R[x]$.

   b) What conditions on $\deg f$ will ensure the existence of at least 1 *real* zero of f?

14. a) Suppose f and g are two functions in $R \times R$ such that $f \cdot g = 0$. Does it necessarily follow that $f = 0$ or $g = 0$?

   b) Repeat part a) under the added assumption that f and g are linearly independent.

15. Can a non-zero polynomial function in $R[x]$ be 0 on a very small interval $(a, b) \subset R$? Explain.

16. If f is a non-zero polynomial in $R[x]$ and $f(a) = 0$, then argue that for some positive ε (perhaps very small) f has only one zero in $(a - \varepsilon, a + \varepsilon)$.

17.　*a)* Can you find a function $f \in R[x]$ such that $f(\pi) = 0$?

　　b) Can you find a function $f \in Q[x]$ such that $f(\pi) = 0$?

　　c) Can you find a function $f \in Q[x]$ such that $f(\sqrt{2}) = 0$?

18.　*a)* How many functions are there in $Q[x]$ (*i.e.*, what is the cardinality of $Q[x]$)?

　　b) What is the cardinality of $R[x]$?

　　c) What is the cardinality of $\mathbb{C}[x]$?

19.　Show that $R[x]$ forms a linear space over the field R.

9.4　The Fundamental Theorem of Algebra

In the extension of our number system from the natural numbers to the complex numbers, we could have taken the following point of view: in the consideration of polynomial functions over the non-negative integers, we become interested in the idea of zeros of a function and decide to extend our number system in such a way that any polynomial function over the new system of degree 1 or greater will have zeros.

The first thing we note is that $(x + 1) \in N[x]$ has no zero. If we extend our numbering system now to include -1 and then even further to include all the numbers we now call the integers, we have a system in which many more polynomials have zeros. For example,

$$f(x) = x^2 + x - 2 \in Z[x]$$

has a zero at 1 and

$$g(x) = x + 4 \in Z[x]$$

has a zero at -4. The question again is whether *all* polynomials in $Z[x]$ have zeros (in Z of course). We discover rather quickly that the answer is negative. For example, note that $f(x) = 2x - 1$ does not have a zero in Z. We then extend our number system to include all the numbers we have called the rational numbers (positive, negative, and zero), and as a result many more polynomial functions have zeros. For example,

$$f(x) = 6x + 2 \quad \text{and} \quad g(x) = 2x - 5$$

have zeros, whereas, their restrictions to Z do not. We continue in this manner and again ask the question, "Does each polynomial function over the set of rational numbers have a zero?" Once again we need not look far to notice that many polynomials, for example,

$$f(x) = x^2 - 2 \quad \text{and} \quad g(x) = x^2 - 3,$$

do not have zeros in Q. If we then extend our number system to include the real numbers, we will have zeros for the extended functions. However, again we ask the same question, and to our alarm we once again see that many very simple polynomials, such as $f(x) = x^2 + 1$, have no zeros.

At this stage we perhaps are a little disgusted with the game, but nevertheless continue. If we extend our numbers to include the complex numbers, we find that we have a number in $\mathbb{C}$ which is a zero of $x^2 + 1$, thus

$$f(i) = i^2 + 1 = -1 + 1 = 0.$$

In fact if we look further, we notice many functions now have zeros that had none before our extension to $\mathbb{C}$.

Let us continue with our game and once again ask if the polynomials of degree 1 or more all have zeros (as functions from $\mathbb{C}$ to $\mathbb{C}$). At this point, strangely enough, in spite of the ease with which we found polynomials with no zeros in the preceding situations, we cannot find non-constant polynomials in $\mathbb{C}[x]$ with no zeros. We thus decide the answer to the question is affirmative. That is, any polynomial function f over $\mathbb{C}$ of degree one or greater has a zero in $\mathbb{C}$.

This is a very important fundamental result, and we state it here formally without proof. It is commonly called the "fundamental theorem of algebra," although there has been some argument as to whether it is either fundamental or a theorem of algebra. The first satisfactory proof of this theorem was presented by Gauss.‡

9.4-1 Theorem: (Fundamental Theorem of Algebra) If $f(x) = \sum_{j=0}^{n} a_j x^j$ for some $n \in N$, $a_n \neq 0$, where $\forall i, a_i \in \mathbb{C}$, then for some $z \in \mathbb{C}, f(z) = 0$.

From this fundamental theorem and our previous results, we can develop many interesting and useful properties concerning polynomial functions over the complex numbers and the various number rings contained in the complex numbers. Some of the most interesting and useful results concern factorization of the polynomials into products of other polynomials in the same function space. Recall in the natural number set N, any number can be factored into a product of prime positive integers in a unique way (discounting changes that can be made using commutativity).

We wish to establish some similar results pertaining to the number rings $\mathbb{C}[x]$, $R[x]$, $Q[x]$, $Z[x]$. To facilitate our discussions along this line, let us introduce some language via the following definitions and remarks.

9.4-2 Definition: Let D be a number ring. Then $f \in D[x]$ is said to be a *prime* element or an *irreducible* element of $D[x]$ iff f is not constant and

$$f = g \cdot h \quad \Rightarrow \quad \deg h = 0 \quad \text{or} \quad \deg g = 0$$

(*i.e.,* $f = g \cdot h \Rightarrow$ either h or g is a constant).

9.4-3 Definition: If $f \in D[x]$ and $\deg f = n$ where

$$f(x) = a_0 + a_1 x + \ldots + 1 \cdot x^n,$$

‡ See "History of Mathematics" by D. E. Smith, p. 474, Dover, 1958.

then f is said to be *monic* (*i.e.*, a monic polynomial is one in which the leading coefficient is 1).

Remark: Assume D and D' are number rings such that $D \subset D'$ and the operations on D' are extensions of those on D. If $f \in D[x]$, then f *induces* a polynomial in $D'[x]$ since the coefficients on the description of f are also elements in D'. It is common to call both functions by the same name although they are not the same.

Example: Let $f \in Z[x]$ be described by $f(x) = 2x + 3x^2$. Since $2, 3 \in Q$, it follows that $g(x) = 2x + 3x^2$ describes a function in $Q[x]$. The distinction is clear since $(1/3, 2 \cdot 1/3 + 3(1/3)^2) \in g$ but is not in f. That is, $g|_Z = f$.

There is no need to use two names for f in a discussion as long as it is clear from the context which function space is being discussed. It is important, however, to understand the distinction even though a certain amount of imprecise language is acceptable (and desirable).

Example: If $f \in Z[x]$ is described by $f(x) = x^2 - 2$, then f induces $g \in R[x]$ where $\forall x \in R$, $g(x) = x^2 - 2$. The distinction is clear since g as an element in $R[x]$ can be expressed as the product $(x - \sqrt{2})(x + \sqrt{2})$, but f as an element in $Z[x]$ cannot.

Remark: In connection with the phenomenon of a polynomial function over D' being induced from a polynomial over D where $D \subset D'$, we employ such expressions as "f is reducible over D' but not over D" which means "f is a prime in $D[x]$ but the induced function also called f is not prime in $D'[x]$."

Example: $f(x) = x^2 + 1$ is irreducible over Z, Q, and R, but can be reduced over $\mathbb{C}$. (Verify this!)

Factoring Polynomials in R

We shall now investigate ways in which the process of factoring polynomials into a product of primes is effected by the underlying universal set. As we shall see, it turns out that the larger the domain D over which the polynomials are taken, the "finer" one can factor the polynomials. All primes in $\mathbb{C}[x]$ can be expressed as functions of degree one, whereas $Q[x]$ contains primes of arbitrary large degree.

9.4-4 Lemma: Let $f \in \mathbb{C}[x]$ be a monic polynomial of degree $n \geq 1$. Then f can be factored into n monic linear factors.

Proof: We use the principle of mathematical induction.

i) If $\deg f = 1$, then f is trivially factored into n monic linear factors.

ii) Assume that for $k \geq 1$ any monic polynomial of deg k can be factored into k monic linear factors. Now suppose

$$f(x) = a_0 + a_1 x + \ldots + a_k x^k + x^{k+1}$$

is a monic polynomial of degree $k + 1$. By the fundamental theorem of algebra, $f(c) = 0$ for some $c \in \mathcal{C}$, and by Corollary 9.2-8,

$$f(x) = (x - c)\cdot(x^k + b_{k-1}x^{k-1} + \ldots + b_0) = (x - c)\cdot(q(x)).$$

Now $\deg q = k$ and k is monic. Hence by the induction hypothesis, q can be factored into k monic linear factors. It is then immediate that f can be factored into $k + 1$ monic linear factors. ☐

9.4-5 Lemma: If $f \in \mathcal{C}[x]$ is a monic polynomial of degree $n \geq 1$ and

$$f(x) = (x - c_1)(x - c_2) \ldots (x - c_n) = \prod_{i=1}^{n} (x - c_i),$$

and if f can also be written

$$f(x) = (x - b_1)(x - b_2) \ldots (x - b_n) = \prod_{j=1}^{n} (x - b_j),$$

then for each i, $1 \leq i \leq n$, there exists some j, $1 \leq j \leq n$, such that

$$c_i = b_j.$$

Proof: $f(c_i) = 0$ so that

$$(c_i - b_1)(c_i - b_2) \ldots (c_i - b_n) = 0. \qquad \text{(Why?)}$$

Since $\mathcal{C}$ is an integral number ring, the only way a product of complex numbers can be zero is for some factor to be 0. Thus $c_i - b_j = 0$ for some j. ☐

Upon combining these two lemmas, we have a theorem which concerns the function space $\mathcal{C}[x]$ in very much the same way as "the fundamental theorem of arithmetic" concerns the positive integers. Recall that the fundamental theorem of arithmetic asserts that any positive integer n can be factored into prime factors in exactly one way (if possible changes by commutativity are discounted). Thus in $\mathcal{C}[x]$, we find that our prime factors (the irreducible elements) are the first degree polynomials.

The following theorem is useful in various theoretical and applied problems.

9.4-6 Theorem: If $f \in \mathcal{C}[x]$ and $\deg f = n$, $n \geq 1$, then f can be factored uniquely into a product of n monic linear factors and a constant.

Proof: If $\qquad f(x) = c_0 + c_1x + \ldots + c_nx^n$,

then $c_n \neq 0$, since $\deg f = n$. Thus

$$f(x) = c_n\left(\frac{c_0}{c_n} + \frac{c_1}{c_n}x + \ldots + x^n\right),$$

and we see $f(x) = c_n g(x)$ where g is monic. Applying Lemma 9.4-4 to the monic polynomial g we obtain a factorization of f, and applying Lemma 9.4-5 we conclude that the factorization is unique. ☐

Let us consider a similar question concerning the factorization of the elements in $R[x]$, the polynomial functions over the real field. The following lemma will help us answer this question.

9.4-7 Lemma: If $f \in \mathbb{C}[x]$ with coefficients in R, then non-real zeros of f occur in conjugate pairs. More formally:

If $\qquad f(x) = a_0 + a_1 x + \ldots + a_n x^n \qquad$ where $\qquad \forall i, \quad a_i \in R$,

then $\qquad\qquad\qquad f(z) = 0 \implies f(\bar{z}) = 0$.

(Recall that if $z = x + iy$, then $\bar{z} = x - iy$.)

Proof: If $f(z) = 0$, then

$$a_0 + a_1 z + \ldots + a_n z^n = 0.$$

Since $\qquad\qquad \overline{a_0 + a_1 z + \ldots + a_n z^n} = \bar{0} = 0,$

and since $\qquad\qquad \overline{\alpha + \beta} = \bar{\alpha} + \bar{\beta} \qquad \forall \alpha, \quad \beta \in \mathbb{C},$

$$\overline{a_0} + \overline{a_1 z} + \ldots + \overline{a_n z^n} = 0.$$

Also, since $\qquad\qquad\qquad \overline{\alpha\beta} = \bar{\alpha}\bar{\beta},$

we have $\qquad\qquad \bar{a}_0 + \bar{a}_1 \bar{z} + \ldots + \bar{a}_n \bar{z}^n = 0.$

Now $\bar{a}_i = a_i$ since $a_i \in R$, hence

$$a_0 + a_1 \bar{z} + \ldots + a_n \bar{z}^n = 0.$$

That is, $\qquad\qquad\qquad f(\bar{z}) = 0. \quad \square$

9.4-8 Theorem: If $f \in R[x]$, then f can be factored uniquely into the product of monic linear and quadratic factors and a constant.

$\qquad$ *Proof:* If $\qquad f(x) = a_0 + a_1 x + \ldots + a_n x^n \quad (a_n \neq 0),$

then $\quad f(x) = (b_0 + b_1 x + \ldots + x^n)a_n = g(x)a_n, \qquad$ where $\qquad b_i = \dfrac{a_i}{a_n}.$

The monic polynomial g can be factored into linear factors $(x - c_i)$ as an element of $\mathbb{C}[x]$. However if $c_i \notin R$, then $(x - \bar{c}_i)$ is also a factor. Now

$$(x - c_i)(x - \bar{c}_i) = x^2 - (c_i + \bar{c}_i)x + c_i\bar{c}_i.$$

Recall that $\quad \forall \alpha \in \mathbb{C}, \quad \alpha + \bar{\alpha} \in R, \quad$ and $\quad \alpha\bar{\alpha} \in R.$

Hence the pairs of linear factors which are not in $R[x]$ can be combined by multiplication, each such pair resulting in a quadratic factor which is in $R[x]$. We leave the uniqueness as an exercise. $\square$

$\qquad$ *Exercise:* Verify that the quadratic factors discussed in this proof are irreducible in $R[x]$.

$\qquad$ *Remark:* By the preceding theorem, it follows that the prime or irreducible elements in $R[x]$ are of no higher degree than two.

$\qquad$ It seems reasonable to hope that we can make a similar assertion concerning the factorization of elements in $Q[x]$. That is, perhaps any element in $Q[x]$ can be factored into factors of degree no higher than some given n. We find, however, that this cannot be done. To establish this result, let us state without proof a well known theorem of algebra.

9.4-9 Eisenstein's Theorem: Let $f(x) = a_0 + a_1x + \ldots + a_nx^n$ be a polynomial of degree $n \geq 1$ over Z. Suppose there is a prime integer p such that

  a) p divides a_i, $i = 0, 1, \ldots, n - 1$
  b) p does not divide a_n
  c) p^2 does not divide a_0.

Then f is irreducible over Q.

9.4-10 Corollary: For any $n \geq 1$ there exist polynomials of degree n over Q that are prime in $Q[x]$. (Explain!)
   Example: Let $f(x) = 3 + 3x + 3x^3 + 3x^4 + 5x^5$. Now take $p = 3$. We have $3|3$ but $3\!\!\not|5$ and $3^2\!\!\not|3$. Therefore f is irreducible over Q. Does f have any zeros in Q?
   Let us conclude this section with a theorem which is useful in finding zeros of polynomials in $Q[x]$.

9.4-11 Theorem: If $f \in R[x]$ with integral coefficients a_i,

$$f(x) = a_0 + a_1x + \ldots + a_nx^n \quad (a_n \neq 0),$$

and if $f(k/m) = 0$ for some $k, m \in Z$ where k and m are relatively prime (i.e., k/m is reduced to "lowest terms"), then k divides a_0 and m divides a_n.

   Proof: Assume that

$$a_0 + a_1\left(\frac{k}{m}\right) + a_2\left(\frac{k}{m}\right) + \ldots + a_n\left(\frac{k}{m}\right)^n = 0.$$

Now upon multiplication by m^n we have

$$m^na_0 + a_1m^{n-1}k + a_2m^{n-2}k^2 + \ldots + a_nk^n = 0. \tag{1}$$

Therefore $-m^na_0 = k(a_1m^{n-1} + a_2m^{n-2}k + \ldots + a_nk^{n-1}),$

so that k is a divisor of m^na_0. But since k and m are relatively prime, k and m^n are also relatively prime and hence k divides a_0. Next from (1),

$$m(m^{n-1}a_0 + a_1m^{n-2}k + \ldots + a_{n-1}k^{n-1}) = -a_nk^n$$

and thus m is a divisor of a_nk^n and hence m divides a_n. $\square$

Corollary: If $f \in Z[x]$ is monic described by $f(x) = a_0 + a_1x + \ldots + x^n$, then $f(q) = 0$ for some $q \in R \Rightarrow q \in Z$ and $q|a_0$.

Exercises 9.4

1. Find four polynomials which are irreducible (prime) in $D[x]$ but not in $D'[x]$ where:

  a) $D = Z$, $D' = Q$ c) $D = R$, $D' = \mathbb{C}$
  b) $D = Q$, $D' = R$ d) $D = Q$, $D' = \mathbb{C}$

2. Factor each of the following polynomials in $R[x]$ into a product of prime monic polynomials and a constant. (*Hint:* Use the quadratic formula and the factor theorem.)

a) $f(x) = 2x^2 - 3x + 1$

b) $f(x) = -3x^2 + x + 2$

c) $f(x) = (x^2 - 2)(3x^2 + 4)$

d) $f(x) = (5x^2 + 1)(2x - 3)$

3. Factor each of the following polynomials in $\mathbb{C}[x]$ into a product of prime monic polynomials and a constant.

a) $f(x) = 2x^2 - ix + 2$

b) $f(x) = -ix^2 + 2x - i$

c) $f(x) = (2 - i)x^2 - 4x + (2 + i)$

d) $f(x) = 3x^2 + 2x + 1$

4. a) Show that if f is prime in $D'[x]$ and if $D \subset D'$, then f is prime in $D[x]$. In other words, if f is irreducible in $D'[x]$, then f is irreducible in $D[x]$.

b) Derive an inequality between the number n of zeros of f in $D'[x]$ and the number m of zeros of f in $D[x]$.

5. Look up a reference which discusses the Greek society of mathematicians called the "Pythagoreans." In particular, find out how they reacted upon finding that the polynomial $x^2 - 2$ had no zeros in Q. (*Hint:* Try the library!)

6. Let $f(x) = 2x^2 - 3x$ be an element of $Z[x]$. Then f induces polynomials in:

a) $Q[x]$

b) $R[x]$

c) $\mathbb{C}[x]$

List three ordered pairs in the induced functions (also called f) in each case that are not in f as given.

7. Verify the statement made in the proof of Lemma 9.4-4 that $f(x)$ can be written in the form

$$f(x) = (x - c)(x^k + b_{k-1}x^{k-1} + \ldots + b_0).$$

8. a) Describe the difference between elements of $Z[x]$ and $R[x]$ with respect to coefficients involved.

b) Do you think Eisenstein's Theorem would be true if "Z" is replaced by "R"?

9. Use Eisenstein's Theorem to list a prime polynomial in $Q[x]$ of degree:

a) 5

b) 7

c) 8

d) 9

10. Use Theorem 9.4-11 to find all rational roots of the following equations.

a) $x^3 + 2x^2 - 5x - 6 = 0$

b) $x^4 - 20x^2 + 4 = 0$

c) $x^4 - 2x^3 - 16x^2 + 12x + 12 = 0$

d) $12x^3 - 4x^2 - 3x + 1 = 0$

e) $2x^3 - x^2 - 2x + 1 = 0$

f) $x^5 + 3x^3 + 2x = 0$

g) $4x^3 + 2x^2 - 4x + 1 = 0$

11. Investigate (prove or disprove):

a) An odd degree polynomial in $R[x]$ must have at least one real zero.

b) An even degree polynomial in $R[x]$ has an even number of zeros.

12. Why can't we use Corollary 9.4-11 to prove Theorem 9.4-10? Or *can* we?

9.5   Rational Functions, Decomposition into Partial Fractions

We have now encountered some very interesting function spaces $R[x]$ and $C[x]$ which behave a great deal like the familiar number system Z. The objects in these spaces obey all of the algebraic properties ascribed to a number ring under the operations of function addition and multiplication. We found it useful to consider the functions involved as being objects in some sort of number system, and in doing so, answered some very important questions concerning solutions of equations.

The algebra which governs $R[x]$ and $C[x]$ parallels the algebra of Z in many ways. There are prime elements, and a theorem which says that every object in the space can be factored into primes in essentially one way. If we wished, we could further parallel this number theoretic development by defining greatest common divisors, relative prime factors, etc. Let us consider the possibility of imbedding such a number ring ($R[x]$ or $C[x]$) in a larger set of functions allowing the existence of multiplicative inverses (reciprocals), thus developing a field. The immediate place to look for such reciprocals would be in the collection of functions of the form $1/f(x)$ where f is a polynomial. If f has no zeros, we would have a multiplicative inverse $1/f$. We run into difficulty however, if f has zeros. (Why?) Let us then abandon the hope of constructing a genuine field, but nevertheless consider some useful algebraic results concerning these functions. These functions are very often encountered in calculus and its applications.

9.5-1 Definition: Let F be a field. The set

$$\left\{ \frac{f(x)}{g(x)} : f(x), g(x) \in F[x] \right\}$$

is called the set of *rational functions over F*. (We use the convention of maximal domain.)

Example: The function

$$h(x) = \frac{2x^2 + x + 1}{x^4 + 2}$$

is a rational function over R. $h(1) = 4/3$, $h(0) = 1/2$, etc.

Remark: A rational function is not uniquely expressible in the form $f(x)/g(x)$. For example,

$$\frac{(x - 1)(x^3 + 3x + 2)}{(x - 1)^2} = \frac{x^3 + 3x + 2}{(x - 1)}.$$

Notice how this resembles representation of fractions in Q.

The algebra of rational functions over a field is essentially a field algebra.

675

The only thing that prevents us from having a genuine field is the fact that the domain of $f(x)/g(x)$ must exclude all points α such that $g(\alpha) = 0$.

Example: $\dfrac{2x^2 + 1}{(x - 1)(x^2 + 1)} + \dfrac{3x}{3x^2 - 2}$

$$= \frac{(3x^2 - 2)(2x^2 + 1) + 3x(x - 1)(x^2 + 1)}{(3x^2 - 2)(x - 1)(x^2 + 1)}.$$

That is, addition of rational fractions is accomplished by the same process as adding rational numbers. This, of course, is due to the fact that our addition and multiplication of functions is "pointwise" addition and multiplication. Hence, for any $\alpha \in R$,

$$\frac{f}{g}(\alpha) = \frac{f(\alpha)}{g(\alpha)}.$$

Partial Fractions

The major point of this section is the development of a theorem by which we can in a sense "undo" the process of adding rational fractions. This process is commonly known as decomposition by *partial fractions*, and is a very important process when working in the area of integral calculus. When given a fraction $f(x)/g(x)$, we wish to find "simpler" fractions $f_i(x)/g_i(x)$ such that

$$\frac{f(x)}{g(x)} = \frac{f_1(x)}{g_1(x)} + \frac{f_2(x)}{g_2(x)} + \ldots + \frac{f_n(x)}{g_n(x)}.$$

By simpler, we mean that we would like the f_i and g_i to have as low a degree as possible.

Remark: Throughout our development, we will assume that $\deg f < \deg g$ since by the Euclidean Algorithm for polynomials, we can express

$$\frac{f(x)}{g(x)} = h(x) + \frac{f_1(x)}{g(x)} \qquad \text{where } \deg f_1 < \deg g.$$

It seems reasonable that we could express $f(x)/g(x)$ as a sum in which the denominators are irreducible factors or powers of irreducible factors of $g(x)$. Recall that in $R[x]$, the irreducible factors are either linear or quadratic.

Linear Factors

Consider the following lemma.

9.5-2 Lemma: Assume that $f, h \in R[x]$, $r \in R$, such that

$$\deg f(x) < \deg ((x - r)^n h(x)) \quad (n \in N)$$

and $f(r) \neq 0$ and $h(r) \neq 0$ (*i.e.*, neither f nor h contains the factor $(x - r)$). Then for some $A \in R$, $A \neq 0$ and some $f_1 \in R[x]$,

$$\frac{f(x)}{(x - r)^n h(x)} = \frac{A}{(x - r)^n} + \frac{f_1(x)}{(x - r)^{n-1} h(x)},$$

where
$$\deg f_1(x) < \deg ((x - r)^{n-1} h(x)).$$

Proof: We wish to find A and f_1 such that

$$\frac{f(x)}{(x - r)^n h(x)} - \frac{A}{(x - r)^n} = \frac{(x - r)f_1(x)}{(x - r)^n h(x)} = \frac{f_1(x)}{(x - r)^{n-1} h(x)}.$$

Since
$$\frac{f(x)}{(x - r)^n h(x)} - \frac{A}{(x - r)^n} = \frac{f(x) - Ah(x)}{(x - r)^n h(x)}$$

it is sufficient to find A such that $(x - r)$ is a factor of $f(x) - Ah(x)$. Now $(x - r)$ is a factor of the polynomial $f(x) - Ah(x)$ if and only if

$$f(r) - Ah(r) = 0.$$

That is, we take A to be $f(r)/h(r)$ which exists and is non-zero since $f(r) \neq 0$ and $h(r) \neq 0$. Hence for some $f_1 \in R[x]$,

$$f(x) - Ah(x) = (x - r)f_1(x).$$

Further, $\deg f_1(x) = \deg (f(x) - Ah(x)) - 1,$

but $\deg (f(x) - Ah(x)) \leq \max \{\deg f(x), \deg Ah(x)\}.$

Hence $\deg f_1 < \deg ((x - r)^{n-1} h(x))$ (Consider two cases.)

since $\deg f < \deg ((x - r)^n h(x)).$ (Explain!)

This completes the proof. $\square$

9.5-3 Theorem: If f, $g \in R[x]$, $\deg f < \deg g$, and g can be factored into monic linear factors

$$g(x) = (x - r_1)^{n_1} \cdot (x - r_2)^{n_2} \ldots (x - r_m)^{n_m}$$

(*WLOG* we may assume that any constant factor is part of f), then there exist constants

$$A_{11}, A_{12}, \ldots, A_{1n_1}, \qquad A_{21}, \ldots, A_{2n_2}, \ldots, \text{etc.},$$

(how many constants in all?) such that

$$\frac{f(x)}{g(x)} = \frac{A_{11}}{(x - r_1)^{n_1}} + \frac{A_{12}}{(x - r_1)^{n_1-1}} + \ldots + \frac{A_{1n_1}}{(x - r_1)^1}$$

$$+ \frac{A_{21}}{(x - r_2)^{n_2}} + \ldots + \frac{A_{mn_m}}{(x - r_m)^1}.$$

Proof: This follows inductively from the above lemma. ∎

Remark: It might at first appear that all A_{ij}'s will be non-zero. This does not follow, since for example, in the second inductive step using the lemma, there is no guarantee that f_1 does not contain the factor $(x - r)$. If f_1 contains $(x - r)$ as a factor k times, then k constants will be zero.

Example: Decompose

$$\frac{x^2 + x + 29}{(x - 4)(x + 3)^2}$$

into partial fractions. By the theorem, we know there exist A, B, and C such that

$$\frac{x^2 + x + 29}{(x - 4)(x + 3)^2} = \frac{A}{x - 4} + \frac{B}{(x + 3)^2} + \frac{C}{x + 3}.$$

Multiplying both sides by the denominator on the left, we have

$$x^2 + x + 29 = A(x + 3)^2 + B(x - 4) + C(x - 4)(x + 3).$$

Putting the right hand side in standard polynomial form we have,

$$x^2 + x + 29 = (A + C)x^2 + (6A + B - C)x + (9A - 4B - 12C).$$

Since the functions 1, x, x^2, x^3, $\ldots$, etc., are linearly independent, we can equate coefficients and thus obtain the system of linear equations

$$\begin{aligned}
A \quad\quad\quad + \quad C &= 1 \\
6A + B - \quad C &= 1 \\
9A - 4B - 12C &= 29.
\end{aligned}$$

Solving the system we obtain

$$A = 1, \quad\quad B = -5, \quad\quad C = 0$$

and hence

$$\frac{x^2 + x + 29}{(x - 4)(x + 3)^2} = \frac{1}{x - 4} - \frac{5}{(x + 3)^2}.$$

Quadratic Factors

If we wished only to deal with decomposition of rational fractions over $\mathbb{C}$, we would need only Theorem 9.5-3 (stated in terms of $\mathbb{C}[x]$ of course) since all irreducible elements of $\mathbb{C}[x]$ are linear. The major application of partial fractions however, deals with real valued functions in which quadratic factors are sometimes irreducible. We wish now to deal with this case. Notice, in the proof of the following lemma, how we conveniently consider information dealing with $\mathbb{C}[x]$ in spite of the fact that our result is concerned only with real valued functions. This is a common procedure in certain more advanced areas of mathematics such as Differential Equations and Analysis.

9.5-4 Lemma: Let $q(x) \in R[x]$ be an irreducible monic quadratic function. Let $f, h \in R[x]$ such that

$$\deg f(x) < \deg (q(x)^n h(x))$$

and assume that q is neither a factor of f nor of h. Then there exist real numbers A and B (not both zero) and some $f_1 \in R[x]$ such that

678

$$\frac{f(x)}{q(x)^n h(x)} = \frac{Ax + B}{q(x)^n} + \frac{f_1(x)}{q(x)^{n-1}h(x)}$$

where $\deg f_1(x) < \deg ((q(x)^{n-1}h(x)))$.

Proof: The basic argument is very similar to Lemma 9.5-2. We desire to find A and B such that

$$\frac{f(x)}{q(x)^n h(x)} - \frac{Ax + B}{q(x)^n} = \frac{q(x)f_1(x)}{q(x)^n h(x)} = \frac{f_1(x)}{q(x)^{n-1}h(x)}.$$

At this point, we assume that we can factor $q(x)$ in $\mathbb{C}[x]$ in the form

$$q(x) = (x - r)(x - \bar{r}) \qquad \text{where } r \in \mathbb{C} - R.$$

(Explain why this can be done!) Under this assumption we have

$$\frac{f(x)}{q(x)^n h(x)} - \frac{Ax + B}{q(x)^n} = \frac{f(x) - (Ax + B)h(x)}{(x - r)^n(x - \bar{r})^n h(x)},$$

and we wish to assert the existence of real numbers A and B (not both zero), such that $(x - r)(x - \bar{r}) = q(x)$ is a factor of

$$f(x) - (Ax + B)h(x).$$

This will be true if and only if we can find satisfactory solutions for the equations

$$f(r) - (Ar + B)h(r) = 0$$

and $f(\bar{r}) - (A\bar{r} + B)h(\bar{r}) = 0$

or equivalently to the system

$$\begin{bmatrix} r & 1 \\ \bar{r} & 1 \end{bmatrix} \begin{pmatrix} A \\ B \end{pmatrix} = \begin{pmatrix} \dfrac{f(r)}{h(r)} \\ \dfrac{f(\bar{r})}{h(\bar{r})} \end{pmatrix}.$$

(Explain why both $f(r)/h(r)$ and $f(\bar{r})/h(\bar{r})$ exist and are non-zero.) This system has a unique solution since

$$\det \begin{bmatrix} r & 1 \\ \bar{r} & 1 \end{bmatrix} = r - \bar{r} \neq 0 \qquad (r \in \mathbb{C} - R).$$

Clearly this is not the solution $\begin{pmatrix} A \\ B \end{pmatrix} = \begin{pmatrix} 0 \\ 0 \end{pmatrix}$. We leave it as an exercise to verify that an equation

$$\begin{bmatrix} r & 1 \\ \bar{r} & 1 \end{bmatrix} \begin{pmatrix} A \\ B \end{pmatrix} = \begin{pmatrix} z \\ \bar{z} \end{pmatrix}$$

has solution $\begin{pmatrix} A \\ B \end{pmatrix}$ such that $A, B \in R$. Note that

$$\overline{\left(\frac{f(r)}{h(r)}\right)} = \frac{\overline{f(r)}}{h(r)} = \frac{f(\bar{r})}{h(\bar{r})}.$$

The fact that f_1 has degree as claimed is similar to the argument given in Lemma 9.5-2. ☐

We can now put all this information together in a general result concerning decomposition of real valued rational fractions.

9.5-5 Theorem: (The Partial Fraction Theorem)

Assume $f, g \in R[x]$ are such that $\deg f < \deg g$ and
$$g(x) = q_1(x)^{n_1} q_2(x)^{n_2} \ldots q_m(x)^{n_m}(x - a_1)^{k_1} \ldots (x - a_p)^{k_p}$$
where the q_i's are irreducible monic quadratic elements in $R[x]$. Then
$$\frac{f(x)}{g(x)} = \frac{A_{1n_1}x + B_{1n_1}}{q_1(x)^{n_1}} + \frac{A_{2n_1}x + B_{2n_1}}{q_1(x)^{n_1-1}} + \cdots + \frac{C_{1k_p}}{(x - a_p)^{k_p}} + \cdots + \frac{C_{pk_p}}{(x - a_p)}.$$
(How many constants A_{ij}, B_{ij}, C_{ij} in all?)

Proof: This follows inductively from Lemmas 9.5-4 and 9.5-2. ☐

Example: Decompose
$$\frac{x^2 - 6x + 2}{(x - 1)(x^2 + x + 1)}.$$
By the theorem,
$$\frac{x^2 - 6x + 2}{(x - 1)(x^2 + x + 1)} = \frac{A}{x - 1} + \frac{Bx + C}{x^2 + x + 1}$$
since $x^2 + x + 1$ is irreducible in $R[x]$. Hence we have
$$x^2 - 6x + 2 = A(x^2 + x + 1) + (Bx + C)(x - 1)$$
$$= (A + B)x^2 + (A - B + C)x + (A - C).$$

Hence
$$A + B \quad = \quad 1$$
$$A - B + C = -6$$
$$A \quad - C = \quad 2. \quad \text{(Why?)}$$

Upon solving this system we have
$$A = -1, \quad B = 2, \quad C = -3.$$

Hence
$$\frac{x^2 - 6x + 2}{(x - 1)(x^2 + x + 1)} = \frac{-1}{x - 1} + \frac{2x - 3}{x^2 + x + 1}.$$

Example: Decompose
$$\frac{3x^4 + 15x^2 + 3x + 18}{x(x^2 + 3)^2}$$
into partial fractions. Now by the theorem,
$$\frac{3x^4 + 15x^2 + 3x + 18}{x(x^2 + 3)^2} = \frac{A}{x} + \frac{Bx + C}{(x^2 + 3)^2} + \frac{Dx + E}{x^2 + 3}.$$

Hence
$$3x^4 + 15x^2 + 3x + 18 = (x^2 + 3)^2 A + (Bx + C)x + x(x^2 + 3)(Dx + E)$$
$$= (A + D)x^4 + Ex^3 + (6A + B + 3D)x^2$$
$$+ (C + E)x + (9A)$$

from which

$$A + D = 3$$
$$E = 0$$
$$6A + B + 3D = 15$$
$$C + E = 3$$
$$9A = 18.$$

Upon solving we have

$$A = 2, \quad B = 0, \quad C = 3, \quad D = 1, \quad E = 0$$

and hence the decomposition is

$$\frac{2}{x} + \frac{3}{(x^2 + 3)^2} + \frac{x}{x^2 + 3}.$$

Exercises 9.5

1. *a)* Show that the equation

$$\begin{bmatrix} r & 1 \\ \bar{r} & 1 \end{bmatrix} \begin{pmatrix} x \\ y \end{pmatrix} = \begin{pmatrix} z \\ \bar{z} \end{pmatrix}$$

has a solution $\begin{pmatrix} A \\ B \end{pmatrix}$ such that $A, B \in R$ (assuming that $r \in \mathcal{C} - R$).

b) Use the Euclidean Algorithm for polynomials to show that any rational fraction $f(x)/g(x)$ can be written in the form

$$h(x) + \frac{f_1(x)}{g(x)} \quad \text{where } \deg f_1 < \deg g.$$

2. Decompose into partial fractions.

a) $\dfrac{7x^2 - 22}{(2x - 3)(x - 2)(x + 1)}$

d) $\dfrac{2x - 21}{2x^2 - 3x - 20}$

b) $\dfrac{2x^2 + 10x + 2}{(x + 1)(x - 2)(x + 3)}$

e) $\dfrac{x^2 + 9x - 4}{x(x - 2)(x + 1)}$

c) $\dfrac{10x + 1}{(x - 2)(2x + 3)}$

f) $\dfrac{5x + 5}{(x + 3)(x^2 + 1)}$

3. Decompose into partial fractions.

a) $\dfrac{8x^2 - 5x + 6}{(3x - 2)(x^2 + x + 2)}$

d) $\dfrac{3x^2 + 4}{(x + 1)^2(3x - 1)^2}$

b) $\dfrac{5x^2 - 6x}{x^3 - 27}$

e) $\dfrac{-2x^3 + 2x^2 + 9x + 7}{(x + 1)^2(x^2 + x + 1)}$

c) $\dfrac{3x^2 - 2x + 5}{(x^2 + 1)(2x^2 - x + 3)}$

4. Decompose into partial fractions.

a) $\dfrac{3x + 5}{(x + 1)^2}$

d) $\dfrac{4x^4 + 3x^3 + 6x^2 + 5x}{(x - 1)(x^2 + x + 1)^2}$

b) $\dfrac{5x^2 - 25x + 8}{(3x + 2)(x - 3)^2}$

e) $\dfrac{5x - 2}{(x - 1)^2}$

c) $\dfrac{x^5 + x^4 + 4x^3 + 7x^2 - 2x + 19}{(x^2 + 3)(x^2 - x + 2)}$

f) $\dfrac{-5x^2 + 27x + 42}{(3x + 2)(x - 4)^2}$

5. Decompose into partial fractions.

a) $\dfrac{9x^2 + x + 3}{2x^3 + x^2 + x}$

c) $\dfrac{2x^3 + x + 9}{x(2x^2 + 3)^2}$

b) $\dfrac{14x^3 - 17x^2 + 11x + 5}{(2x + 1)^2(x^2 - 2x + 2)}$

d) $\dfrac{x^4 - 4x^2 - 3x + 1}{3x(x^2 + 3x + 1)^2}$

9.6 Graphing Polynomials f: R → R

In this section we discuss some of the interesting graphical properties of functions of the form $\sum_{i=0}^{n} a_i x^i$ in $R \times R$. We shall see that many of the results of the preceding sections can be applied to help us in graphing polynomials. We begin by investigating a polynomials' behavior in the large.

9.6-1 Theorem: Suppose $f \in R[x]$, then

$$\deg f = n \Rightarrow f(x) = 0(a_n x^n) \qquad \text{as } x \to \pm\infty,$$

where a_n is the leading coefficient of f.

Proof: We must show that

$$\lim_{x \to \infty} \frac{f(x)}{a_n x^n} = 1 \tag{1}$$

and similarly as $x \to -\infty$. Since $\deg f = n$, f may be described in the form

$$f(x) = a_n x^n + a_{n-1} x^{n-1} + \ldots + a_0 \qquad \text{(where } a_n \neq 0\text{),}$$

so that $\dfrac{f(x)}{a_n x^n}$ is of the form

$$\sum_{i=0}^{n} \frac{a_i}{a_n} x^{i-n} = \frac{a_n}{a_n} + \frac{a_{n-1}}{a_n x} + \ldots + \frac{a_0}{a_n x^n}. \tag{2}$$

However, by the limit theorem

$$\lim_{x \to \infty} \sum_{i=0}^{n} \frac{a_i}{a_n} x^{i-n} = \sum_{i=0}^{n} \lim_{x \to \infty} \frac{a_i}{a_n} x^{i-n}, \tag{3}$$

and we know that

$$\forall k \geq 1 \qquad \lim_{x \to \infty} \frac{a_{n-k}}{a_n x^k} = 0.$$

Thus only one of the limits in (2) is non-zero, that corresponding to the last term a_n/a_n on the right side. But $a_n/a_n \to 1$ as $x \to \pm\infty$, and (1) follows. ∎

Remark: The preceding theorem shows that in the large, a polynomial function behaves as its highest degree term. Thus in graphing f, we may in effect sketch the graph of the simpler function $a_n x^n$ for x values far from zero.

Example: In order to graph $f(x) = x^3 + 2x^2 - 3x + 1$, we note that $f(x) = 0(x^3)$ as $x \to \pm\infty$. The simple cubic polynomial is a familiar function whose graph we know. Graphing the behavior of f for "small" x values can be accomplished by tabulating some ordered pairs in f.

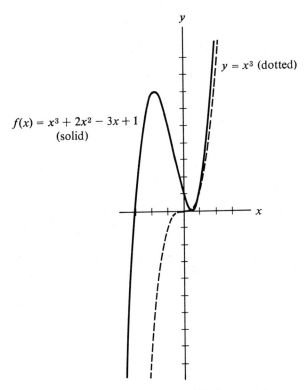

FIG. 9.1 The behavior of f in the large is essentially like that of the function x^3.

9.6-2 Theorem: If $f \in R[x]$ has odd degree, then $f: R \xrightarrow{\text{onto}} R$.

Proof: We need to show that any real number $b \in R$ is the image of at least one point in R. That is, given

$$f(x) = \sum_{i=0}^{n} a_i x^i,$$

there is a point a such that

$$f(a) = b.$$

This equation is satisfied for any real root of the equation $f(x) - b = 0$. Since $f(x) - b$ is a polynomial in $R[x]$ of odd degree, it has at least one real zero. (This is true since the complex zeros of $f(x) - b$ occur in conjugate pairs.) []

This theorem shows that an odd degree polynomial must have a graph that extends into quadrants I and III if $a_n > 0$, or into quadrants II and IV if $a_n < 0$. The reader is asked to determine the possibilities for even degree polynomials in Exercise 1. Note that the polynomial graphed in Figure 9.1 is of odd degree and has leading coefficient $a_n = 1 > 0$. Thus we know that, in the large, the graph will be in quadrants I and III, as shown.

9.6-3 Theorem: Polynomials in $R[x]$ are continuous.

Proof: By the limit theorem, $\forall \alpha \in R$,

$$\lim_{x \to \alpha} f(x) = \lim_{x \to \alpha} \sum_{i=0}^{n} a_i x^i = \sum_{i=0}^{n} a_i \left(\lim_{x \to \alpha} x^i \right)$$

$$= \sum_{i=0}^{n} a_i \left(\lim_{x \to \alpha} x \right)^i = \sum_{i=0}^{n} a_i \alpha^i = f(\alpha). \; []$$

Remark: This means that the graph of any polynomial does not have "jumps" or "holes." Moreover, it is proved in calculus that polynomials have graphs that must be *smooth* (no sharp corners). Thus it appears that polynomials are very "nice" functions, with graphs that are relatively simple to sketch.

Another interesting thing about the graphs of polynomials is their "high" and "low" points. We call these "relative maximums and minimums."

9.6-4 Definition: A function $f: R \to R$ has a *relative maximum* at a point $a \in R$ iff

$$f(a) \geq f(x)$$

for all x in some interval (c, d) containing a. f has a *relative minimum* at a if the inequality is reversed. In these cases, $f(a)$ is called a relative maximum or relative minimum of f. A *relative extremum* of f is a relative maximum or relative minimum.

Example: The function shown in Figure 9.1 has a relative maximum at $x = 2/3$ and a relative minimum at $x = 3$. These are the only relative extrema of the function.

9.6-5 Theorem: A non-constant polynomial of degree n has at most $n - 1$ relative extrema. (See Exercise 7.)

Remark: Note that a polynomial may have *fewer* than $n - 1$ relative extrema. Thus, the function x^3 has no relative extremum, whereas the third degree function f graphed in Figure 9.1 has two. These examples show that the upperbound $n - 1$ cannot in general be reduced; on the other hand it may not be attained for certain polynomials.

The zeros of polynomials have an interesting graphical interpretation. Note that if $f(x)$ is zero for $x = a$, then the graph of f crosses or touches the x-axis at $x = a$. (Why?) It follows that the graph of an nth degree polynomial crosses the x-axis at most n times. Of course, the graph crosses the y-axis exactly once (why?), at the point $(0, f(0))$.

In general, the *intercepts* of the graphs are good points to plot (among others) in constructing the graph of a polynomial, provided the computation of its zeros is not too difficult. Recall that for 1st degree polynomials of the form $mx + b$, the zero is $x = -b/m$. For 2nd degree polynomials of the form $ax^2 + bx + c$, the quadratic formula can be used to find the zeros:

$$\frac{-b + \sqrt{b^2 - 4ac}}{2a} \quad \text{and} \quad \frac{-b - \sqrt{b^2 - 4ac}}{2a}.$$

Of course if the discriminant $b^2 - 4ac$ is *negative*, the zeros are not real, but occur as a complex conjugate pair. Thus if $b^2 - 4ac < 0$, the graph of $ax^2 + bx + c$ does not cross the x-axis. (Why not?) There are "formulas" of the "quadratic equation" type for finding zeros of general third and fourth degree polynomials, although they are rather involved. It is a very interesting fact that there is no such formula in general for polynomials of fifth degree or higher. This very significant result was first proved by the French mathematician Evereste Galois at the age of 20! §

Using the graphical interpretation of real zeros of polynomials, one can approximate these zeros by first graphing the function and then "reading off" the points at which the graph intersects the x-axis. There are other approximation techniques for finding the zeros of polynomials, some of which are well suited to computer use. In the calculus, the reader may study some simple computation schemes for approximating zeros using ideas developed there.

Finally, we mention two types of symmetry that some polynomials exhibit.

9.6-6 Theorem: Suppose $f \in R[x]$. Then

    i) f is an odd function if it contains only odd powers of x.

    ii) f is an even function if it contains only even powers of x.

Proof: Recall that a function is odd if $f(-x) = -f(x)$, and it is even if $f(-x) = f(x)$. Under the assumption *i)* f has the form

$$f(x) = a_1x + a_3x^3 + \ldots + a_nx^n$$

§ See "Men of Mathematics" by E. T. Bell, Chapter 20, "Genius and Stupidity." Simon and Schuster, Inc., 1965.

685

for some odd integer n. But then

$$f(-x) = a_1(-x) + a_3(-x)^3 + \ldots + a_n(-x)^n$$
$$= -a_1x - a_3x^3 - \ldots - a_nx^n \quad \text{(Why?)}$$
$$= -f(x).$$

The proof of ii) is similar, and is left as an exercise. $\square$

Remark: It is the above fact that leads to the "even" and "odd" terminology. The graphical interpretation of even and odd functions has been discussed previously.

Now let us examine one final example which shows how the ideas of this section can be applied to a given graphing problem.

Example: Consider the function $f(x) = x^4 - 5x^2 + 4$. We note that f has the following properties:

$a)$ f is an even function (symmetry about the y-axis).

$b)$ $f = 0(x^4)$ as $x \to \pm\infty$ (graph approaches the function x^4 for large $|x|$).

$c)$ leading coefficient $1 > 0$ (graph trails into quadrants I and II for large $|x|$).

$d)$ f has at most 3 relative extrema (at most 3 "high" or "low" points on the graph).

$e)$ f has y intercept 4 (the point $(0, 4)$ is on the graph).

$f)$ f has four real zeros obtained as follows:

$$x^4 - 5x^2 + 4 = (x^2 - 1)(x^2 - 4) = 0$$
$$\Rightarrow (x^2 - 1) = 0 \quad \text{or} \quad (x^2 - 4) = 0$$
$$\Rightarrow x \in \{1, -1, 2, -2\}$$

(graph crosses x-axis at the four points ± 1, ± 2).

Using these facts and facts about continuity, the student can (and should!) verify that the graph of f is as shown in Figure 9.2.

Note that f attains its minimum value at two points, one in $(-2, -1)$ and the other in $(1, 2)$. Note that f has a relative maximum at 0, but has no maximum value. Further, it is neither *onto* nor *1-1*.

Exercises 9.6

1. Determine the quadrants that contain the graph of $f(x)$ for $|x|$ large when $\deg f$ is even. (*Hint:* Consider two cases: $a_n > 0$ and $a_n < 0$. (Why don't you have to consider also the case $a_n = 0$?))

2. $a)$ Is it possible for a function to have a relative maximum at α *and* a relative minimum also at α?

$b)$ Answer $a)$ if the function is assumed to be a polynomial.

3. Find the relative extrema of x^4.

4. $a)$ Recall that earlier we discussed the maximum of a function over a set A. What is the difference between a maximum and a relative maximum?

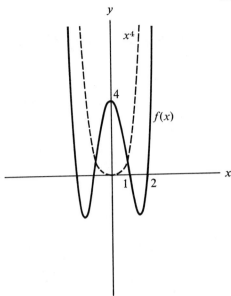

FIG. 9.2 Graph of $x^4 - 5x^2 + 4$. (Note the symmetry.)

b) Is it possible for a non-constant polynomial to have a maximum or minimum? (*Hint:* Consider two cases: deg f odd and deg f even.)

5. Prove that if the discriminant of the function $ax^2 + bx + c$ is negative, the function has one relative extremum, and this is a maximum if $a < 0$; otherwise it is a minimum.

6. Graph each of the following polynomials in $R[x]$ "in the large." Use any additional knowledge available to you to approximate the remainder of the graph.

a) $3x^3 - x + 1$

b) $x^5 + x^3 + x$

c) $3x^4 + 2x^2 - 1$

d) $2x^2 - 3x + 1$

e) $x^6 + x^7 + x^5 + x^3$

7. Prove Theorem 9.6-5 by the following steps.

a) Use the limit formula for finding the slope of a function at a point α (see Section 5.7) to describe a function f' which gives the slope of f at each $\alpha \in R$.

b) Show that f' is a polynomial with degree $n - 1$.

c) Argue that relative extrema occur only at the zeros of f'.

d) Maximize the number of zeros of f'.

8. Use symmetry of even functions to show that an even polynomial has an even number of zeros, provided $f(0) \neq 0$.

9. Use any information and knowledge available to graph the following functions.

a) $f(x) = -2x^4 - 3x + 1$

b) $f(x) = -3x^5 + 1$

c) $f(x) = 2x^4 - x^2 + 2$

d) $f(x) = 2(x^2 + 1)^2 + 3(x^2 + 1) - 1$

e) $f(x) = x^5 - x^3 - x + 2$

9.7   The Weierstrass Theorem, Curve Fitting

Recall that in the first part of this chapter you proved a very interesting fact: any function $f: Z_3 \to Z_3$ is a polynomial in $Z_3[x]$. (This result generalizes to $Z_n[x]$ if n is prime, in which case Z_n is a field.) You used an interesting argument for this—a "counting argument." You first counted the number of possible functions $f: Z_3 \to Z_3$, 3^3, and then found $\#[Z_3[x]] = 3^3$. The conclusion is, of course, that each function in $Z_3 \times Z_3$ with domain Z_3 is a polynomial (an element of $Z_3[x]$).

It may not appear too surprising to find that in a certain sense this idea carries over to functions over non-finite fields as well. This is the content of the famous Weierstrass Theorem, which we state without proof.

9.7-1 Theorem: (*The Weierstrass Approximation Theorem*)

Given a continuous function $f: [a, b] \to R$, and any tolerance $\varepsilon > 0$, there is a polynomial $p(x)$ in $R[x]$ such that

$$\forall x \in [a, b], \qquad |f(x) - p(x)| < \varepsilon.$$

Remark: This shows that while a continuous function with domain $[a, b]$ may not *be* a polynomial, it does not differ significantly from some polynomial. Thus we would say that the polynomial can be used as an *approximation* of the given function.

The fact that continuous functions are essentially polynomials (in the sense of the Weierstrass Theorem) has a host of applications. For one thing, we can use an approximating polynomial to calculate various function values. For example, you may have wondered how the values for the "trig tables," or the "tables of logarithms" are found. One way is to find a polynomial which approximates the function under consideration and use the polynomial values (which are relatively easy to compute) as the values of the original function.

Example: Suppose we want values for $f(x) = \cos x$ over $[-.1, .1]$. The polynomial

$$p(x) = 1 - \frac{x^2}{2} + \frac{x^4}{24}$$

can be used to approximate $\cos x$ for all $x \in [-.1, .1]$ to within an error of at most 10^{-8}. Thus to compute $\cos .01$ we compute

$$1 - \frac{(.01)^2}{2} + \frac{(.01)^4}{24} = .99995,$$

and claim that $\cos .01$ is approximated very well by $.99995$. (Is it?)‖

‖ This approximation is discussed by E. R Heineman in "Geometric Interpretations of Polynomial Approximations of the Cosine Function," *The American Mathematical Monthly*, Volume 73, Number 6, 1966, p. 648.

We have not given the reader any idea as to how to actually *find* a polynomial to approximate a given function—nor does the Weierstrass Theorem. All that is known by the Weierstrass Theorem is that there is such a polynomial. In the calculus, methods are developed for actually finding approximating polynomials for certain functions.

Example: The exponential function e^x is approximated over any interval $[a, b]$ by the polynomial

$$p(x) = \sum_{i=0}^{n} \frac{x^i}{i!}. \tag{1}$$

In general, the "closeness" of the approximation over $[a, b]$ improves with larger n. Thus, suppose we are interested in the interval $[0, 1]$. Denote by $p_n(x)$ the nth degree polynomial $p_n(x) = \sum_{i=0}^{n} \frac{x^i}{i!}$. Now

$$p_0(x) = 1, \qquad\qquad p_1(x) = 1 + x,$$

$$p_2(x) = 1 + x + \frac{x^2}{2}, \quad p_3(x) = 1 + x + \frac{x^2}{2} + \frac{x^3}{6},$$

etc., are successively better approximations of e^x over $[0, 1]$, as may be verified by graphing the p_i's along with e^x (see Figure 9.3). As a matter of fact, it turns out that $\lim_{n \to \infty} p_n(x)$ *is* e^x for all x.

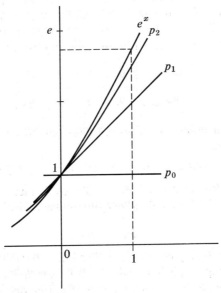

FIG. 9.3 $p_n(x)$ becomes a better approximation of e^x over $[0, 1]$ as n gets large.

Remark: The use of polynomials to approximate continuous functions is very much like using rational numbers to approximate real numbers. Thus any "point" (number) $\alpha \in R$ is approximated to within any preselected tolerance $\varepsilon > 0$ by some rational number. Similarly, any "point" (function) in the set of continuous functions is approximated to within a tolerance by some $p \in R[x]$. The analogy carries further. For example, we know that any $\alpha \in R$ can be expressed as the limit of a sequence of points in Q. Also a function in the class of functions continuous over an interval $[a, b]$ is the limit of a sequence of points (functions) in $R[x]$.

Curve Fitting

Another application of the Weierstrass Theorem is made in the area of "curve fitting." It frequently happens that we desire a mathematical model which we can use to explain some phenomenon we observe. One way to approach this is to make repeated observations of the phenomena at various times or under various conditions and to graph these observations as points on the plane. Then we "fit" a *polynomial* function to these observed points. The fact that we needn't use more exotic functions than polynomials is due to the Weierstrass Theorem, since *any* continuous function containing the observed points is, in effect, a polynomial.

Example: Suppose that we wish to find a function $s(t)$ that expresses the distance s an object falls in t seconds when dropped from a tower. We conduct an experiment in which we measure the distance for some specific t's. Suppose the results are as shown in the table below:

Time	0	1	2	3
Distance	0	16	64	144

We graph the four points as shown in Figure 9.4. Now we search for a polynomial of the form

$$s(x) = a_0 + a_1 x + a_2 x^2 + \ldots + a_n x^n$$

which has a graph containing the observed points. Since $s(0) = 0$ and $s(1) = 16$, a second degree polynomial containing the points $(0, 0)$ and $(1, 16)$ is given by

$$s(x) = 16x^2.$$

We note that (by happy coincidence) that the other points are also in this function, so we might conclude that $16x^2$ is a reasonable model for a falling body. There is some danger in this, however. For one thing, the observed distances and times are only *approximations*, since we obtain these numbers by reading measuring devices, and we are not really able to read them *exactly*. (Was $s(1)$ really 16, or was it 15.999?) For another, we must be very

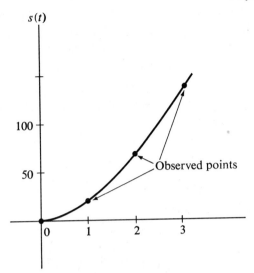

FIG. 9.4 $s(x) = 16x^2$.

careful not to extrapolate our model to times far out of the range of observation. It would be risky to predict that in 100 seconds the object would
fall $16(100)^2 = 160,000$ feet (why?). However, we might be fairly confident
that the polynomial "fitted" to the four observed points is a good model
for all t's between 0 and 4 seconds.

In connection with the problem of finding polynomials that contain
certain points, the following theorem is of interest.

9.7-2 Theorem: Given n points $(x_1, y_1), (x_2, y_2), \ldots, (x_n, y_n)$ such that $x_i \neq x_j$
for all $i \neq j$, there is a polynomial in $R[x]$ of degree at most $n - 1$ containing
these points.

Proof: Take $\qquad p_{n-1}(x) = \sum_{i=0}^{n-1} a_i x^i,$

where each a_i is determined as follows. Form the system

$$Y = \begin{pmatrix} y_1 \\ y_2 \\ \vdots \\ y_n \end{pmatrix} = \begin{pmatrix} p_{n-1}(x_1) \\ p_{n-1}(x_2) \\ \vdots \\ p_{n-1}(x_n) \end{pmatrix} = \begin{pmatrix} a_0 + a_1 x_1 + a_2 x_1^2 + \ldots + a_{n-1} x_1^{n-1} \\ \vdots \\ a_0 + a_1 x_n + a_2 x_n^2 + \ldots + a_{n-1} x_n^{n-1} \end{pmatrix}$$

$$= \begin{bmatrix} 1 & x_1 & x_1^2 & \ldots & x_1^{n-1} \\ 1 & x_2 & x_2^2 & \ldots & x_2^{n-1} \\ \vdots & & & & \vdots \\ 1 & x_n & x_n^2 & \ldots & x_n^{n-1} \end{bmatrix} \begin{pmatrix} a_0 \\ a_1 \\ \vdots \\ a_{n-1} \end{pmatrix} = XA.$$

Note that Y and X are known so we wish to solve for the unknown a_i's in A. Now if $x_i \neq x_j$ for all $i \neq j$, X is nonsingular (see Exercise 1) and $XA = Y$ has the unique solution $A = X^{-1}Y$. The polynomial

$$p_{n-1} = (1, x, x^2, \ldots, x^{n-1})A$$

is of degree no larger than $n - 1$ and contains the given n points. []

Example: Suppose we are given the three points $(0, 1)$, $(1, 3)$, and $(-1, -2)$. We find p_2 as follows: Let

$$p_2(x) = a_0 + a_1x + a_1x^2.$$

Now at $(0, 1)$, $\quad p_2(0) = a_0 = 1$;

at $(1, 3)$, $\quad p_2(1) = a_0 + a_1 + a_2 = 3$;

at $(-1, -2)$, $\quad p_2(-1) = a_0 - a_1 + a_2 = -2$.

We can easily solve the system

$$\begin{bmatrix} 1 & 0 & 0 \\ 1 & 1 & 1 \\ 1 & -1 & 1 \end{bmatrix} \begin{pmatrix} a_0 \\ a_1 \\ a_2 \end{pmatrix} = \begin{pmatrix} 1 \\ 3 \\ -2 \end{pmatrix}$$

by various techniques discussed in Chapter 8, obtaining the solution

$$\begin{pmatrix} a_0 \\ a_1 \\ a_2 \end{pmatrix} = \begin{pmatrix} 1 \\ 5/2 \\ -1/2 \end{pmatrix}.$$

Thus the polynomial $1 + 5/2\,x - 1/2\,x^2$ is the polynomial of degree 2 containing the three given points.

9.7-3 Remark: As a matter of fact, we have proved a slightly stronger statement above than that claimed in Theorem 9.7-2. Actually, it follows that under the assumptions stated, there is a *unique* polynomial of degree $n - 1$ or less containing the given points. Of course, there may be polynomials of higher degrees also containing the points.

We have discussed how one might "fit" polynomials to observed data to try to formulate a model for the phenomenon being observed. We can always find a polynomial containing the observed points, as long as the requirement $x_i \neq x_j$ is met. However, if we make repeated observations on y for some fixed x value, say x_j, then we will have several points of the form

$$(x_j, y_{j1}), (x_j, y_{j2}), \ldots, (x_j, y_{jn})$$

among other points. We can no longer find a polynomial containing all the points (Why?), so we must approximate the observations somehow. There are many ways to do this. Several of the popular methods (such as "least squares" and "minimum maximal deviation") are based upon statistical methods. Others rely on numerical approximations or just plain "eye-balling" a curve that looks like it approximates the data.

A polynomial model of degree $n - 1$ fitting the n observed points exactly may not be considered very reliable, since it has not been "tested."

Thus it is considered very desirable to find polynomials of smaller degree
that fit the data—or at least approximate it. In this case, the additional
points serve to "test" the model for its ability to predict what will happen
when more points are observed. Thus, in our falling body example we found
a polynomial of degree 2 that fitted *four* observed points. This seems very
promising, inasmuch as it isn't often possible to find a polynomial of degree 2 that fits 4 observations. We could get excited about our second degree
model, while a third degree model would have been routine and probably
not as good a predictor.

Exercises 9.7

1. Show that if $x_1, x_2, \ldots, x_n$ are distinct real numbers, the matrix

$$X = \begin{bmatrix} 1 & x_1 & x_1^2 & \cdots & x_1^{n-1} \\ 1 & x_2 & x_2^2 & \cdots & x_2^{n-1} \\ \cdot & \cdot & \cdot & & \cdot \\ \cdot & \cdot & \cdot & & \cdot \\ \cdot & \cdot & \cdot & & \cdot \\ 1 & x_n & x_n^2 & \cdots & x_n^{n-1} \end{bmatrix}$$

is nonsingular. (*Hint:* Show that det $X \neq 0$, using induction on n. It is easier to
work with X^T.)

2. Verify the uniqueness statement made in Remark 9.7-3.

3. Find a polynomial passing through the points:
    a) $(1, 1), (-1, 0), (2, 1)$ *c)* $(-1, 2), (0, 4), (1, 0)$
    b) $(-2, 3), (1, 4), (5, 0)$ *d)* $(1, 1), (2, 2), (3, 3)$

4. Find two polynomials fitting the points $(1, 0), (2, 0), (-5, 0)$.

5. Find a polynomial fitting the points (if possible):
    a) $(1, 0), (1, 1), (-1, 2), (2, 2)$
    b) $(0, 1), (0, 2), (0, 3), (0, -1)$
    c) $(2, 1), (1, 2), (-1, 3), (-2, 5)$

6. Find a polynomial approximation of the sine function over the interval
    $[-.1, .1]$. (*Hint:* The sine function is an odd function. We have seen an approxima-
    tion for the even function cosine.)

7. *a)* Find a second degree polynomial approximation of $f(x) = \dfrac{1}{1 + x}$ over the
    interval $[0, 1]$. (*Hint:* Try dividing $1 + x$ into 1.)
    b) Graph $\dfrac{1}{1 + x}$ and your approximation on the same coordinate system. What
    do you conclude?

TABLE I.   Logarithms to Base 10

N	0	1	2	3	4	5	6	7	8	9
1.0	.0000	.0043	.0086	.0128	.0170	.0212	.0253	.0294	.0334	.0374
1.1	.0414	.0453	.0492	.0531	.0569	.0607	.0645	.0682	.0719	.0755
1.2	.0792	.0828	.0864	.0899	.0934	.0969	.1004	.1038	.1072	.1106
1.3	.1139	.1173	.1206	.1239	.1271	.1303	.1335	.1367	.1399	.1430
1.4	.1461	.1492	.1523	.1553	.1584	.1614	.1644	.1673	.1703	.1732
1.5	.1761	.1790	.1818	.1847	.1875	.1903	.1931	.1959	.1987	.2014
1.6	.2041	.2068	.2095	.2122	.2148	.2175	.2201	.2227	.2253	.2279
1.7	.2304	.2330	.2355	.2380	.2405	.2430	.2455	.2480	.2504	.2529
1.8	.2553	.2577	.2601	.2625	.2648	.2672	.2695	.2718	.2742	.2765
1.9	.2788	.2810	.2833	.2856	.2878	.2900	.2923	.2945	.2967	.2989
2.0	.3010	.3032	.3054	.3075	.3096	.3118	.3139	.3160	.3181	.3201
2.1	.3222	.3243	.3263	.3284	.3304	.3324	.3345	.3365	.3385	.3404
2.2	.3424	.3444	.3464	.3483	.3502	.3522	.3541	.3560	.3579	.3598
2.3	.3617	.3636	.3655	.3674	.3692	.3711	.3729	.3747	.3766	.3784
2.4	.3802	.3820	.3838	.3856	.3874	.3892	.3909	.3927	.3945	.3962
2.5	.3979	.3997	.4014	.4031	.4048	.4065	.4082	.4099	.4116	.4133
2.6	.4150	.4166	.4183	.4200	.4216	.4232	.4249	.4265	.4281	.4298
2.7	.4314	.4330	.4346	.4362	.4378	.4393	.4409	.4425	.4440	.4456
2.8	.4472	.4487	.4502	.4518	.4533	.4548	.4564	.4579	.4594	.4609
2.9	.4624	.4639	.4654	.4669	.4683	.4698	.4713	.4728	.4742	.4757
3.0	.4771	.4786	.4800	.4814	.4829	.4843	.4857	.4871	.4886	.4900
3.1	.4914	.4928	.4942	.4955	.4969	.4983	.4997	.5011	.5024	.5038
3.2	.5051	.5065	.5079	.5092	.5105	.5119	.5132	.5145	.5159	.5172
3.3	.5185	.5198	.5211	.5224	.5237	.5250	.5263	.5276	.5289	.5302
3.4	.5315	.5328	.5340	.5353	.5366	.5378	.5391	.5403	.5416	.5428
3.5	.5441	.5453	.5465	.5478	.5490	.5502	.5514	.5527	.5539	.5551
3.6	.5563	.5575	.5587	.5599	.5611	.5623	.5635	.5647	.5658	.5670
3.7	.5682	.5694	.5705	.5717	.5729	.5740	.5752	.5763	.5775	.5786
3.8	.5798	.5809	.5821	.5832	.5843	.5855	.5866	.5877	.5888	.5899
3.9	.5911	.5922	.5933	.5944	.5955	.5966	.5977	.5988	.5999	.6010
4.0	.6021	.6031	.6042	.6053	.6064	.6075	.6085	.6096	.6107	.6117
4.1	.6128	.6138	.6149	.6160	.6170	.6180	.6191	.6201	.6212	.6222
4.2	.6232	.6243	.6253	.6263	.6274	.6284	.6294	.6304	.6314	.6325
4.3	.6335	.6345	.6355	.6365	.6375	.6385	.6395	.6405	.6415	.6425
4.4	.6435	.6444	.6454	.6464	.6474	.6484	.6493	.6503	.6513	.6522
4.5	.6532	.6542	.6551	.6561	.6571	.6580	.6590	.6599	.6609	.6618
4.6	.6628	.6637	.6646	.6656	.6665	.6675	.6684	.6693	.6702	.6712
4.7	.6721	.6730	.6739	.6749	.6758	.6767	.6776	.6785	.6794	.6803
4.8	.6812	.6821	.6830	.6839	.6848	.6857	.6866	.6875	.6884	.6893
4.9	.6902	.6911	.6920	.6928	.6937	.6946	.6955	.6964	.6972	.6981
5.0	.6990	.6998	.7007	.7016	.7024	.7033	.7042	.7050	.7059	.7067
5.1	.7076	.7084	.7093	.7101	.7110	.7118	.7126	.7135	.7143	.7152
5.2	.7160	.7168	.7177	.7185	.7193	.7202	.7210	.7218	.7226	.7235
5.3	.7243	.7251	.7259	.7267	.7275	.7284	.7292	.7300	.7308	.7316
5.4	.7324	.7332	.7340	.7348	.7356	.7364	.7372	.7380	.7388	.7396
N	0	1	2	3	4	5	6	7	8	9

TABLE I. Logarithms to Base 10 (*continued*)

N	0	1	2	3	4	5	6	7	8	9
5.5	.7404	.7412	.7419	.7427	.7435	.7443	.7451	.7459	.7466	.7474
5.6	.7482	.7490	.7497	.7505	.7513	.7520	.7528	.7536	.7543	.7551
5.7	.7559	.7566	.7574	.7582	.7589	.7597	.7604	.7612	.7619	.7627
5.8	.7634	.7642	.7649	.7657	.7664	.7672	.7679	.7689	.7694	.7701
5.9	.7709	.7716	.7723	.7731	.7738	.7745	.7752	.7760	.7767	.7774
6.0	.7782	.7789	.7796	.7803	.7810	.7818	.7825	.7832	.7839	.7846
6.1	.7853	.7860	.7868	.7875	.7882	.7889	7896	.7903	.7910	.7917
6.2	.7924	.7931	.7938	.7945	.7952	.7959	.7966	.7973	.7980	.7987
6.3	.7993	.8000	.8007	.8014	.8021	.8028	.8035	.8041	.8048	.8055
6.4	.8062	.8069	.8075	.8082	.8089	.8096	.8102	.8109	.8116	.8122
6.5	.8129	.8136	.8142	.8149	.8156	.8162	.8169	.8176	.8182	.8189
6.6	.8195	.8202	.8209	.8215	.8222	.8228	.8235	.8241	.8248	.8254
6.7	.8261	.8267	.8274	.8280	.8287	.8293	.8299	.8306	.8312	.8319
6.8	.8325	.8331	.8338	.8344	.8351	.8357	.8363	.8370	.8376	.8382
6.9	.8388	.8395	.8401	.8407	.8414	.8420	.8426	.8432	.8439	.8445
7.0	.8451	.8457	.8463	.8470	.8476	.8482	.8488	.8494	.8500	.8506
7.1	.8513	.8519	.8525	.8531	.8537	.8543	.8549	.8555	.8561	.8567
7.2	.8573	.8579	.8585	.8591	.8597	.8603	.8609	.8615	.8621	.8627
7.3	.8633	.8639	.8645	.8651	.8657	.8663	.8669	.8675	.8681	.8686
7.4	.8692	.8698	.8704	.8710	.8716	.8722	.8727	.8733	.8739	.8745
7.5	.8751	.8756	.8762	.8768	.8774	.8779	.8785	.8791	.8797	.8802
7.6	.8808	.8814	.8820	.8825	.8831	.8837	.8842	.8848	.8854	.8859
7.7	.8865	.8871	.8876	.8882	.8887	.8893	.8899	.8904	.8910	.8915
7.8	.8921	.8927	.8932	.8938	.8943	.8949	.8954	.8960	.8965	.8971
7.9	.8976	.8982	.8987	.8993	.8998	.9004	.9009	.9015	.9020	.9025
8.0	.9031	.9036	.9042	.9047	.9053	.9058	.9063	.9069	.9074	.9079
8.1	.9085	.9090	.9096	.9101	.9106	.9112	.9117	.9122	.9128	.9133
8.2	.9138	.9143	.9149	.9154	.9159	.9165	.9170	.9175	.9180	.9186
8.3	.9191	.9196	.9201	.9206	.9212	.9217	.9222	.9227	.9232	.9238
8.4	.9243	.9248	.9253	.9258	.9263	.9269	.9274	.9279	.9284	.9289
8.5	.9294	.9299	.9304	.9309	.9315	.9320	.9325	.9330	.9335	.9340
8.6	.9345	.9350	.9355	.9360	.9365	.9370	.9375	.9380	.9385	.9390
8.7	.9395	.9400	.9405	.9410	.9415	.9420	.9425	.9430	.9435	.9440
8.8	.9445	.9450	.9455	.9460	.9465	.9469	.9474	.9479	.9484	.9489
8.9	.9494	.9499	.9504	.9509	.9513	.9518	.9523	.9528	.9533	.9538
9.0	.9542	.9547	.9552	.9557	.9562	.9566	.9571	.9576	.9581	.9586
9.1	.9590	.9595	.9600	.9605	.9609	.9614	.9619	.9624	.9628	.9633
9.2	.9638	.9643	.9647	.9652	.9657	.9661	.9666	.9671	.9675	.9680
9.3	.9685	.9689	.9694	.9699	.9703	.9708	.9713	.9717	.9722	.9727
9.4	.9731	.9736	.9741	.9745	.9750	.9754	.9759	.9763	.9768	.9773
9.5	.9777	.9782	.9786	.9791	.9795	.9800	.9805	.9809	.9814	.9818
9.6	.9823	.9827	.9832	.9836	.9841	.9845	.9850	.9854	.9859	.9863
9.7	.9868	.9872	.9877	.9881	.9886	.9890	.9894	.9899	.9903	.9908
9.8	.9912	.9917	.9921	.9926	.9930	.9934	.9939	.9943	.9948	.9952
9.9	.9956	.9961	.9965	.9969	.9974	.9978	.9983	.9987	.9991	.9996
N	0	1	2	3	4	5	6	7	8	9

TABLE II. Logarithms to Base e

N	.0	.1	.2	.3	.4	.5	.6	.7	.8	.9
1	0.000	0.095	0.182	0.262	0.336	0.405	0.470	0.531	0.588	0.642
2	0.693	0.742	0.788	0.833	0.875	0.916	0.956	0.993	1.030	1.065
3	1.099	1.131	1.163	1.194	1.224	1.253	1.281	1.308	1.335	1.361
4	1.386	1.411	1.435	1.459	1.482	1.504	1.526	1.548	1.569	1.589
5	1.609	1.629	1.649	1.668	1.686	1.705	1.723	1.740	1.758	1.775
6	1.792	1.808	1.825	1.841	1.856	1.872	1.887	1.902	1.917	1.932
7	1.946	1.960	1.974	1.988	2.001	2.015	2.028	2.041	2.054	2.067
8	2.079	2.092	2.104	2.116	2.128	2.140	2.152	2.163	2.175	2.186
9	2.197	2.208	2.219	2.230	2.241	2.251	2.262	2.272	2.282	2.293
10	2.303	2.313	2.322	2.332	2.342	2.351	2.361	2.370	2.380	2.389

TABLE III. Exponential and Hyperbolic Functions

x	e^x	e^{-x}	sinh x	cosh x	tanh x
0	1.0000	1.0000	.00000	1.0000	.00000
0.1	1.1052	.90484	.10017	1.0050	.09967
0.2	1.2214	.81873	.20134	1.0201	.19738
0.3	1.3499	.74082	.30452	1.0453	.29131
0.4	1.4918	.67032	.41075	1.0811	.37995
0.5	1.6487	.60653	.52110	1.1276	.46212
0.6	1.8221	.54881	.63665	1.1855	.53705
0.7	2.0138	.49659	.75858	1.2552	.60437
0.8	2.2255	.44933	.88811	1.3374	.66404
0.9	2.4596	.40657	1.0265	1.4331	.71630
1.0	2.7183	.36788	1.1752	1.5431	.76159
1.1	3.0042	.33287	1.3356	1.6685	.80050
1.2	3.3201	.30119	1.5095	1.8107	.83365
1.3	3.6693	.27253	1.6984	1.9709	.86172
1.4	4.0552	.24660	1.9043	2.1509	.88535
1.5	4.4817	.22313	2.1293	2.3524	.90515
1.6	4.9530	.20190	2.3756	2.5775	.92167
1.7	5.4739	.18268	2.6456	2.8283	.93541
1.8	6.0496	.16530	2.9422	3.1075	.94681
1.9	6.6859	.14957	3.2682	3.4177	.95624
2.0	7.3891	.13534	3.6269	3.7622	.96403
2.1	8.1662	.12246	4.0219	4.1443	.97045
2.2	9.0250	.11080	4.4571	4.5679	.97574
2.3	9.9742	.10026	4.9370	5.0372	.98010
2.4	11.023	.09072	5.4662	5.5569	.98367
2.5	12.182	.08208	6.0502	6.1323	.98661
2.6	13.464	.07427	6.6947	6.7690	.98903
2.7	14.880	.06721	7.4063	7.4735	.99101
2.8	16.445	.06081	8.1919	8.2527	.99263
2.9	18.174	.05502	9.0596	9.1146	.99396
3.0	20.086	.04979	10.018	10.068	.99505
3.1	22.198	.04505	11.076	11.122	.99595
3.2	24.533	.04076	12.246	12.287	.99668
3.3	27.113	.03688	13.538	13.575	.99728
3.4	29.964	.03337	14.965	14.999	.99777
3.5	33.115	.03020	16.543	16.573	.99818
3.6	36.598	.02732	18.285	18.313	.99851
3.7	40.447	.02472	20.211	20.236	.99878
3.8	44.701	.02237	22.339	22.362	.99900
3.9	49.402	.02024	24.691	24.711	.99918
4.0	54.598	.01832	27.290	27.308	.99933
4.1	60.340	.01657	30.162	30.178	.99945
4.2	66.686	.01500	33.336	33.351	.99955
4.3	73.700	.01357	36.843	36.857	.99963
4.4	81.451	.01228	40.719	40.732	.99970
4.5	90.017	.01111	45.003	45.014	.99975
4.6	99.484	.01005	49.737	49.747	.99980
4.7	109.95	.00910	54.969	54.978	.99983
4.8	121.51	.00823	60.751	60.759	.99986
4.9	134.29	.00745	67.141	67.149	.99989
5.0	148.41	.00674	74.203	74.210	.99991

TABLE IV. Trigonometric Functions

Degrees	x-Radians	sin x	cos x	tan x	cot x	sec x	csc x	x-Radians	Degrees
0°	.000	.0000	1.0000	.0000	. . . . .	1.000	. . . . .	1.571	90°
1°	.017	.0175	.9998	.0175	57.29	1.000	57.30	1.553	89°
2°	.035	.0349	.9994	.0349	28.64	1.001	28.65	1.536	88°
3°	.052	.0523	.9986	.0524	19.08	1.001	19.11	1.518	87°
4°	.070	.0698	.9976	.0699	14.30	1.002	14.34	1.501	86°
5°	.087	.0872	.9962	.0875	11.43	1.004	11.47	1.484	85°
6°	.105	.1045	.9945	.1051	9.514	1.006	9.567	1.466	84°
7°	.122	.1219	.9925	.1228	8.144	1.008	8.206	1.449	83°
8°	.140	.1392	.9903	.1405	7.115	1.010	7.185	1.431	82°
9°	.157	.1564	.9877	.1584	6.314	1.012	6.392	1.414	81°
10°	.175	.1736	.9848	.1763	5.671	1.015	5.759	1.396	80°
11°	.192	.1908	.9816	.1944	5.145	1.019	5.241	1.379	79°
12°	.209	.2079	.9781	.2126	4.705	1.022	4.810	1.361	78°
13°	.227	.2250	.9744	.2309	4.331	1.026	4.445	1.344	77°
14°	.244	.2419	.9703	.2493	4.011	1.031	4.134	1.326	76°
15°	.262	.2588	.9659	.2679	3.732	1.035	3.864	1.309	75°
16°	.279	.2756	.9613	.2867	3.487	1.040	3.628	1.292	74°
17°	.297	.2924	.9563	.3057	3.271	1.046	3.420	1.274	73°
18°	.314	.3090	.9511	.3249	3.078	1.051	3.236	1.257	72°
19°	.332	.3256	.9455	.3443	2.904	1.058	3.072	1.239	71°
20°	.349	.3420	.9397	.3640	2.747	1.064	2.924	1.222	70°
21°	.367	.3584	.9336	.3839	2.605	1.071	2.790	1.204	69°
22°	.384	.3746	.9272	.4040	2.475	1.079	2.669	1.187	68°
23°	.401	.3907	.9205	.4245	2.356	1.086	2.559	1.169	67°
24°	.419	.4067	.9135	.4452	2.246	1.095	2.459	1.152	66°
25°	.436	.4226	.9063	.4663	2.145	1.103	2.366	1.134	65°
26°	.454	.4384	.8988	.4877	2.050	1.113	2.281	1.117	64°
27°	.471	.4540	.8910	.5095	1.963	1.122	2.203	1.100	63°
28°	.489	.4695	.8829	.5317	1.881	1.133	2.130	1.082	62°
29°	.506	.4848	.8746	.5543	1.804	1.143	2.063	1.065	61°
30°	.524	.5000	.8660	.5774	1.732	1.155	2.000	1.047	60°
31°	.541	.5150	.8572	.6009	1.664	1.167	1.942	1.030	59°
32°	.559	.5299	.8480	.6249	1.600	1.179	1.887	1.012	58°
33°	.576	.5446	.8387	.6494	1.540	1.192	1.836	.995	57°
34°	.593	.5592	.8290	.6745	1.483	1.206	1.788	.977	56°
35°	.611	.5736	.8192	.7002	1.428	1.221	1.743	.960	55°
36°	.628	.5878	.8090	.7265	1.376	1.236	1.701	.942	54°
37°	.646	.6018	.7986	.7536	1.327	1.252	1.662	.925	53°
38°	.663	.6157	.7880	.7813	1.280	1.269	1.624	.908	52°
39°	.681	.6293	.7771	.8098	1.235	1.287	1.589	.890	51°
40°	.698	.6428	.7660	.8391	1.192	1.305	1.556	.873	50°
41°	.716	.6561	.7547	.8693	1.150	1.325	1.524	.855	49°
42°	.733	.6691	.7431	.9004	1.111	1.346	1.494	.838	48°
43°	.750	.6820	.7314	.9325	1.072	1.367	1.466	.820	47°
44°	.768	.6947	.7193	.9657	1.036	1.390	1.440	.803	46°
45°	.785	.7071	.7071	1.000	1.000	1.414	1.414	.785	45°
Degrees	x-Radians	cos x	sin x	cot x	tan x	csc x	sec x	x-Radians	Degrees

ANSWERS TO EXERCISES

Exercises 0.1

1. *a*) -16 *c*) 1152
2. *a*) $x > 0$ *c*) $x < 0$ *e*) $x > 1$ or $x < 0$
3. *a*) $1/24$ *c*) $7/11$ *e*) 2
5. 2, 3, 5, 7, 11, 13, 17, 19, 23, 29, 31, 37, 41, 43, 47, 53, 59, 61, 67, 71, 73, 79, 83, 89, 97
7. *a*) $x > 3$ *c*) $x > 15/17$
8. *a*) all x *c*) $x \geq 1$ *e*) $-3 < x < -1$
9. *a*) $7/12$ *c*) $(x + 1/x)^3$ *e*) $x^3/(x + 1)$
10. *a*) $x < 17/24$
12. *a*) $2 \times 2 \times 2 \times 5 \times 2 \times 5$ *c*) $5 \times 3 \times 13$

Exercises 1.1

1.

p	q	p if q
T	T	T
T	F	T
F	T	F
F	F	T

3. *a*)

F
F
F
T

4. He did not lie.

5. *a*) valid   *c*) not valid   *e*) not valid   *g*) not valid   *i*) valid

Exercises 1.2

3. *a)* true   *b)* false   *c)* false   *d)* true   *e)* false
4. *a)* $\subset$ *c)* $\overset{?}{=}$ *e)* $\in$ *g)* $\in$ *i)* none of these   *k)* $\subset$ *m)* $\subset$ *o)* $\in$
5. *a)* false   *b)* true   *c)* true   *d)* false   *e)* true   *f)* true
7. *a)* $\emptyset$, $\{1\}$, $\{2\}$, $\{3\}$, $\{1, 2\}$, $\{1, 3\}$, $\{2, 3\}$, A *c)* 2^n
8. *a)* $\not\in B$?   *c)* $A \subset B$ *e)* $x \in B$
9. No. $\emptyset$ is a subset of every set.
11. *a)* yes   *c)* yes   *e)* not necessarily
12. *a)* yes   *c)* yes   *e)* no

Exercises 1.3

1. *a)* true   *c)* true
2. *a)* false   *c)* false   *e)* false   *g)* true   *i)* false   *k)* true
3. *a)* true   *c)* false   *e)* true   *g)* true
4. *a)* $\{x : x \in Q \text{ and } x > 5\}$ *c)* $\{x : x \in R \text{ and } x^2 - 17 = 36\}$
5. $\{\emptyset, \{4\}, \{5\}, \{7\}, \{4, 5\}, \{4, 7\}, \{5, 7\}, A\}$
8. *a)* false   *c)* false   *e)* false   *g)* false
9. *a)* $\{2, 4, 7, 8, 9, 10, 12\}$ *c)* $\{1, 3, 5, 7, 8, 9, 12\}$ *e)* $\{1, 3, 5\}$

Exercises 1.4

1. *a)* false   *c)* false   *e)* true   *g)* true
2. *a)* if $1 \in B$ then $1 \in A$; if $2 \in B$ then $2 \in A$; if $3 \in B$ then $3 \in A$; if $4 \in B$
        then $4 \in A$.
       c) false because $4 \not\in A$
3. *a)* true   *c)* false   *e)* true   *g)* true
4. *a)* true   *c)* true   *e)* true   *g)* false
6. *a)* $\forall x$ if $x \in R$ then $\exists y$ $y \in R$ and $x > y$. (true)
      c) $\forall x$ if x is a man   then $\exists y$ y is a woman and x is married to y. (false)
      e) $\forall x$ if x is an integer   then $\exists y$ $x + y = 0$.
7. *a)* false   *c)* true   *e)* true
8. *a)* undecidable   *c)* undecidable   *e)* undecidable

Exercises 1.5

5. Should read "For all sets A and B, $A \subset B$ and $B \subset A \Rightarrow A = B$."
7. Find a counter example (a situation in which the generalization fails). Prove
   the negation.
8. *a)* false   *c)* false   *e)* true

Exercises 1.6

1. *a)* ∅   *c)* {1, 4, 7, 10}   *e)* {1, 3, 4, 5, 6, 7, 9, 10}
    g) {1, 2, 3, 4, 5, 6, 7, 8, 9, 10}   *i)* {1, 3, 5, 7, 9}   *k)* {4, 5, 6, 10}
2. *a)* $\{x: x > 18\}$ *c)* $\{x: x \geq 3 \text{ or } x < -5\}$ *e)* $\{x: x > 18\}$

Exercises 1.7

1. *a)* $\{x \in Q: x > 5\}$ *c)* $\{x \neq 0: x > -5\}$
2. *a)* $\{x: x \in N \text{ and } x^2 > 7\}$ *c)* $\{x: x \neq 5 \text{ and } x > 2\}$
3. *a)* $\forall x$ if $x \in N$ then $x^2 \geq x$ *c)* $\exists x$ $x \in R$ and $x^2 = 5$
    e) $\forall x$ if $x > 0$ then $x + 2 > 0$
4. *a)* $\forall x \in N$ $2 + x \in N$ *b)* $\exists x \in A$ $6x^3 + 2x - 1 > 0$
    c) $\forall x \in Q$ $x + 5 \in Q$
5. *a)* false, $\exists x \in R$ $x + 1 \not> 0$ *c)* true
    e) false, $\exists x$ $x \in Q$ and $5x \neq 7$ *g)* false, $\exists x > 2$ $x - 1 < 2$
6. *a)* form   *c)* sentence (true)   *e)* form   *g)* form
7. all follow
8. *a)* $\exists x$ $\exists y$ $\forall z$ not-$P(x, y, z)$ *c)* $\exists x > 0$ $\forall n \in N$ not-$P(x, n)$
9. *a)* $\forall x \in S$ x likes Greek $\Rightarrow x$ likes mathematics.
    c) $\forall x$ if x is an instant   than $\exists y$ y is an instant and x is after y.
    e) $\exists x \in J$ x does not like French and x dates both Betty and Glenda.
10. *a)* $\exists x \in R$ $x < 7$ and $x > 3$.   *c)* $\forall x \in R$ $\exists y \in R$ $x < y$
    e) $\forall x \neq 0$ $\forall y \neq 0$ if $x + y = 0$ then $x > 0$ or $y > 0$.
12. *a)* true   *c)* false   *e)* true

Exercises 1.8

1. *a)* {−1}   *c)* {114/7}   *e)* {0}
2. *a)* 10/3   *c)* −2/11
3. *a)* $x > 11/2$

    c) $x > -6$

    e) R

4. *a)* $\{x: x > 8\} \cup \{x: x < -7\}$

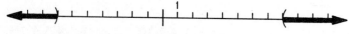

c) $\{x: -3/2 \le y < 1\}$

e) $\{x: x < -4\} \cup \{x: x > 3/2\}$

5. *a)* $\forall x$ (an identity)   *c)* $\forall x \ne 2$ (restricted identity)

     e) $\forall x \ne 1$ (restricted identity)   *f)* $\exists x$ (equation)

7. *a)* $(-\infty, -4] \cup (3/2, 3]$

8. *a)* $[-2, 1]$ *c)* $(-1/2, 4)$ *e)* $(-\infty, -3) \cup (1, 3)$ *f)* $(-1, 1/3] \cup [2, \infty)$

9. *a)* $(-\infty, -1/3) \cup (1/2, \infty)$

Exercises 1.9

2. $A \times B = \{(3, 1), (3, 2), (3, 3), (4, 1), (4, 2), (4, 3), (5, 1), (5, 2), (5, 3)\}$

5. $\{1, 3\} = \{3, 1\}$ but $(1, 3) \ne (3, 1)$

11. $m \times n$

13. *a)* You should have 15 sets of ordered pairs with four elements per set.

     b) You should have 6 sets.

14. *a)* $\{(1, 4), (2, 5), (2, 6)\}$ *c)* $\{(1, 3), (2, 4), (3, 5), (4, 6)\}$

Exercises 1.10

1. T and S

2. *a)* $D_T = \{1, 5, 7, 3\}$ $R_T = \{3, 7, 4\}$ *c)* $D_S = \{5, 9\}$ $R_S = \{5, 9\}$

3. *a)* $T_1[S_1] = \{1, 5\}$, $T_1[S_2] = \{5, 9\}$, $T_1[S_3] = \{1, 5, 9\}$, $T_1[S_4] = \{9\}$,

     $T_3[S_1] = \{1\}$, $T_3[S_2] = \{1\}$, $T_3[S_3] = \{1\}$, $T_3[S_4] = \{1\}$

     b) The functions are T_1, T_3, and T_4.

     c) The functions are T_1^{-1} and T_2^{-1}.

6. $F(1) = 2$, $F(3) = 9$

7. $R_f = \{3, 4, \ldots\}$, f^{-1} is a function

8. $\emptyset$ vacuously satisfies the definition of a function.

9. Yes. For example $f = \{(1, 1), (2, 2)\}$ and $g = \{(1, 2), (2, 1)\}$

12. *a)* 5   *c)* 33   *e)* 145   *g)* 51

13. *a)* 0   *c)* 2   *e)* 4   *g)* $8a - 4$

14. *a)* (5, 7)   *c)* (−1, 7]
15. *a)* [−1, 3)   *c)* [−1, 3]

Exercises 1.11

1. *a)* 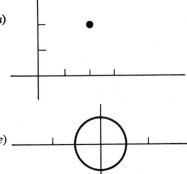   *c)*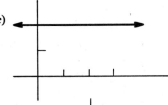

    e)   *g)*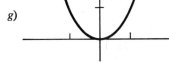

2. *a)* *a, c, d, g*   *b)* a. Domain is {2}, range is {2}. c. Domain is *R*, range is {2}. d. Domain is *R*, range is *R*. g. Domain is *R*, range is [0, ∞).   *c)* All are onto their range, but only *b, d,* and *h* are onto *R*.   *d)* *a, d*   *e)* *a, d*

3. *a)* 1, $2\frac{3}{4}$, 6, 17, 34, 3/4, 2, 9, 22

4. *a)* 2, 1, −2, −7, 1, −2, −7   *b)*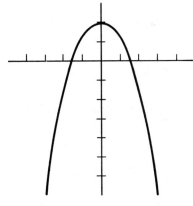

5. *a)* 27   *b)* 13   *c)* 12   *d)* 6
6. *a)* no   *b)* no   *c)* yes   *d)* no   *e)* yes

Exercises 1.12

1. *a)* {(2, 5), (3, 3)}, {(1, 3), (3, 3), (4, 7)}
2. {(1, 1), (5, −23), (6, −34), (7, −47)}

3. *a)* b   *b)* a   *c)* c   *d)* a   *e)* a   *f)* {((a, a), a), ((a, b), b),
((a, c), a), ((b, a), b), ((b, b), a), ((b, c), c), ((c, a), a), ((c, b), c), ((c, c), a)}

4. commutative and associative

6. *a)* 1   *b)* 10   *c)* 9   *d)* undefined

Exercises 1.13

1. {(π, Gurney), (3/4, Glenda), (7, Grant), (21, Ole)} is a *one-one* correspondence between A and B.

4. $f(x) = 25x$ defines a *one-one* correspondence between $[0, 1]$ and $[0, 25]$.

5. *a)* {(5, 7), (6, 7), (7, 5)}   *b)* {(9, 7), (9, 5), (7, 9), (4, 2)}

6. $S \circ T = \{(5, b), (b, b), (b, 9)\}$ $T \circ S = \{(a, 7), (a, 48), (7, 7), (7, 48), (7, 9)\}$

7. *a)* $324x^2 + 324x + 82$ *b)* $54x^2 + 9$

8. *a)* $f \circ g(x) = 18x^2 + 6x + 8$ $g \circ f(x) = 108x^2 + 78x + 15$
   c) $f \circ g(x) = 7x^2 - 4$ $g \circ f(x) = 7x^2 - 4$

9. *a)* $f \circ g(3) = 74$ $g \circ f(3) = 326$
   c) $f \circ g(3) = -3673$ $g \circ f(3) = 2499$

13. yes

21. *a)* $f \circ g(x) = x^2 + 1$ *c)* $f^{-1}(x) = x - 1$, g^{-1} is not a function

22. *a)* $1/x^2 + 2/x + 1$ *b)* $x^4 + 2x^2 + 1$ *c)* $4x^2 + 4x + 1$ *d)* x^2

23. *a)* $1\frac{2}{3}$ *b)* $2x + 1$ *c)* $1\frac{2}{5}$ *d)* 11 *e)* $2x + 1$ and $1/x$

24. *a)* false   *b)* false   *c)* false   *d)* false

Exercises 2.1

1. (1) doesn't follow, (2) does follow, (3) does follow, (4) doesn't follow, (5) does follow.

Exercises 2.3

6. *a)* valid   *b)* valid   *c)* invalid   *d)* invalid
   e) invalid   *f)* valid   *g)* invalid   *h)* valid

Exercises 2.4

1. *a)* 5   1   9   *b)* 5   1   9

2. {(a, 4), (a, 7), (a, b), (4, 7), (4, b), (7, b)} There are 15 others.

3. 512 relations (counting $\emptyset$), 48 order relations, 6 strict orderings.
8. *a)* sup (2, 5] = 5 (in the set)   inf (2, 5] = 2 (not in the set)
   c) sup [1, 5] = 5 (in the set)   inf [1, 5] = 1 (in the set)
   d) sup (2, ∞) does not exist   inf (2, ∞) = 2 (not in the set)
9. {(c, a), (c, e), (c, b), (c, d), (a, e), (a, b), (a, d), (e, b), (e, d), (b, d)}

Exercises 2.5

1. *a)* (0, 1], (0, 2)   *b)* {0}, [0, ∞)   *c)* $\emptyset$, [1, ∞)   *d)* $\emptyset$, [0, ∞) ∩ Q
2. the whole universe

Exercises 2.6

1. *a)* *i)* {{0, 1}}   *ii)* {{0}, {1}}
        i) {(0, 0), (1, 1), (0, 1), (1, 0)}   *ii)* {(0, 0), (1, 1)}
   b) *i)* {{a, b, c}}   *ii)* {{a}, {b, c}}   *iii)* {{a, c}, {b}}
        iv) {{a, b}, {c}}   *v)* {{a}, {b}, {c}}
        i) {(a, a), (b, b), (c, c), (b, c), (c, b), (a, b), (b, a), (a, c), (c, a)}
        ii) {(a, a), (b, b), (c, c), (b, c), (c, b)}
        iii) {(a, a), (b, b), (c, c), (a, c), (c, a)}
        iv) {(a, a), (b, b), (c, c), (a, b), (b, a)}   *v)* {(a, a), (b, b), (c, c)}
5. There are five classes: {..., −5, 0, 5, 10, ...}, {..., −4, 1, 6, 11, ...},
   {..., −3, 2, 7, 12, ...}, {..., −2, 3, 8, 13, ...}, {..., −1, 4, 9, 14, ...}.
6. {(0, 0), (1, 1), (2, 2), (3, 3), (0, 1), (1, 0)}
7. {{0, 1}, {2}, {3}}
8. *a)* {(2, 2), (4, 4), (9, 9), (2, 4), (4, 2)}   *b)* {{2, 4}, {9}}
19. 67

Exercises 2.7

1. *a)* {{1, 2}, {3}, {5}, {1, 2, 3, 5}, {1, 2, 3}, {1, 2, 5}, {3, 5}}
   c) {{1, 2}, {3}, {5}, $\emptyset$}
   e) {{1, 2}, {3}, {5}, {3, 4, 5}, {1, 2, 4, 5}, {1, 2, 3, 4}}
5. *a)* yes   *b)* no   *c)* yes   *d)* no
7. *a)* {{1}, {2}, $\emptyset$, U, {1, 2}}   *c)* {{1, 3}, {1, 5}, $\emptyset$, U, {1}, {1, 3, 5}}
8. *a)* {{1}, {2}, {1, 2}, $\emptyset$, U, {3, 4, 5}, {2, 3, 4, 5}, {1, 3, 4, 5}}
   c) {{1, 3}, {1, 5}, {1, 3, 5}, {3}, {5}, $\emptyset$, U, {1}, {3, 5}, {2, 4, 5}, {2, 3, 4},
       {2, 4}, {1, 2, 4, 5}, {1, 2, 3, 4}, {2, 3, 4, 5}, {1, 2, 4}}

Exercises 2.8

1. a) $\{(a, (x, p)), (b, (x, p)), (c, (x, p)), (a, (x, q)), (b, (x, q)), (c, (x, q)), (b, (y, p)),$
    $(a, (y, p)), (c, (y, p)), (a, (y, q)), (b, (y, q)), (c, (y, q))\}$
    b) $\{((a, x), p), ((b, x), p), ((c, x), p), ((a, x), q), ((b, x), q), ((c, x), q), ((a, y), p),$
    $((b, y), p), ((c, y), p), ((a, y), q), ((b, y), q), ((c, y), q)\}$
    c) $\{(a, x, p), (b, x, p), (c, x, p), (a, x, q), (b, x, q), (c, x, q), (a, y, p), (b, y, p),$
    $(c, y, p), (a, y, q), (b, y, q), (c, y, q)\}$

2. a) no   b) yes   c) yes   d) yes   e) no   f) no

4. a) $\sqrt{2}$ c) $\sqrt{15}$ 5. a) 20

8. a) (7, 2) and 5   c) (4, 4) and 0

9. a) $\sqrt{20}$ c) $\sqrt{405}$

Exercises 3.1

1. a) 66   c) 166   2. a) 17   c) 65

5. a) 6   c) 8   e) 10   g) 10

7. a) $\forall n \in N\, f(n) = F$ or equivalently $f(1) = F$ and $\forall n \in N\, f(k + 1) = f(k)$
    c) $f(1) = f(2) = f(3) = R;\ f(4) = S$ and $f(k + 1) = f(k)$ if $k \notin \{1, 2, 3\}$

11. a) yes   c) yes

Exercises 3.2

1. a) 5   c) 6   e) 7   g) 18

2. a) 20   c) 85   e) 15

3. a) 32   c) 12   4. a) 20   c) 36

5. a) 18   b) 64

9. a) $n = 2$ c) no solution   e) no solution

10. no   11. a) 5, 9, 13, 17, 21   c) 3, 7, 15, 31, 63

Exercises 3.3

1. a) 24   c) 18   2. a) 384   c) 362,880

3. a) 8   c) 12   e) 280   g) 10

    i) 1536   k) 15

4. a) $\sum\limits_{i=1}^{n} 2i$ c) $\sum\limits_{i=1}^{n} (2i + 1)^3$ 5. a) $\{1, 2, 3, 4, 5\}$ c) $\{1\}$

6. a) 9   c) 1440   7. a) $\prod\limits_{i=1}^{5} i^2$ c) $\prod\limits_{k=1}^{5} (1 + k)^k$

8. a) $f(1)g(1)f(2)g(2)f(3)g(3)f(4)g(4)f(5)g(5)$
    c) $(f(1) + g(1))(f(2) + g(2))(f(3) + g(3))$

Exercises 3.4

1. $364 = 9 \times 40 + 4$
2. a) $q = 34, r = 2$ c) $q = 1, r = 5$ e) $q = 53, r = 7$
3. a) $9642 = 9 + 0 \cdot 13 + 5 \cdot 13^2 + 4 \cdot 13^3$ c) $649 = 25 + 24 \cdot 26$
4. 204134   6. a) 16   c) 57
8. $f(0) = R$, $f(1) = L$, and $\forall k$ $f(k + 2) = f(k)$ or equivalently $\forall n \in N_0$
    $f(2n) = R$ and $f(2n + 1) = L$

Exercises 3.5

1. a) 14   c) 21   2. a) no solution   c) $x = 2$
3. a) -60 c) $-3^5 = -243$ e) 0
5. a) 12   c) 7   e) 288
9. b) i) -12 iii) 0

Exercises 3.6

1. a)   4   5   6   7   8
    c) -5 -4 -3 -2 -1 0   1   2   3   4   5
2. a) 14   c) 38   e) 5   g) 16   5. a) yes
7. a) $f(2) = 27$ $f(-2) = 27$ 9. $a = 2$
10. $p = 4, q = -3$
12. a) i) $\{2, -3\}$ ii) $\{x \in Z: x \geq 2 \text{ or } x \leq -3\}$ iii) $\{x \in Z: -3 \leq x \leq 2\}$
     c) i) $\{-1, -3, 2\}$ ii) $\{x \in Z: -3 \leq x \leq -1 \text{ or } x \geq 2\}$
     iii) $\{x \in Z: x \leq -3 \text{ or } -1 \leq x \leq 2\}$

Exercises 3.7

1. a) 9   b) 7   c) 6   d) 11   e) 2   f) a if $a \geq 0$ and $-a$ if $a < 0$
2. a) $\pm 1, \pm 2, \pm 3, \pm 6$ c) $\pm 1, \pm 3, \pm 5, \pm 15$
3. a) composite   c) prime   e) prime   g) prime   i) prime
5. (24, 17), (30, 17), (16, 17), (16, 15), (17, 8), (17, 15), (8, 15)
6. a) $24 = 2 \cdot 2 \cdot 2 \cdot 3$ c) $52 = 2 \cdot 2 \cdot 13$ e) $53 = 53$ 7. a) 3   c) 1

12. *a)* $\pm 1, \pm 2$ *c)* ± 1 13. *a)* 72   *c)* 191,854

16.   2,3,5,7,11,13,17,19,23,29,31,37,41,43,47,53,59,61,67,71,73,79,83,89,97

Exercises 3.8

1. *a)* $\dfrac{1 + 3y^3}{xy^2}$ *c)* $y + z^{-1}$ 3.   yes

4. *a)* $31/24$ *c)* $7\dfrac{17}{24}$ 5. *a)* $x = 4/3$ *c)* $x = -11$

9. *a)* x^3/y *c)* $1/xy$ 13. *a)* $236/921$ *c)* $-50/327$

16. *a)* $3/2$ *c)* $-5/7$

Exercises 3.9

2. *a)* $(-\infty, 3/2)$

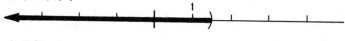

c) $(3/7, \infty)$

e) $(-\infty, 3/14]$

3. *a)* $(-2, 3/2)$ *c)* $\varnothing$ *e)* $(-\infty, -2/3) \cup [-1/3, \infty)$

4. *a)* $(-\infty, -2) \cup (3, \infty)$

c) $(-\infty, 1) \cup (3, \infty)$

6. *a)* $[-4, 4]$ *c)* $\{-6, 6\}$ *e)* Same as *a)*.

7. *a)* $[-5, 9]$ *c)* $[-6, 2]$ *e)* $(-\infty, -33/2) \cup (-9/2, \infty)$

10. *a)* $\{1/2, -2/3\}$ 13. *a)* 2, 3/4, 4/9, 5/16, 6/25

14. *a)* 1/2, 3/4, 7/8, 15/16, 31/32

Exercises 3.10

1. $5^6 = 15,625$ *c)* $(-1/4)^5 = (-1/1024)$

2. *a)* $1/x^6y^4$ *c)* $y^4z^4/x^3 + 1/x^3z^3$ *e)* $x/(xz^3 + y^4z)$

ANSWERS TO EXERCISES

5. *a)* $(x + 3/2)^2 - 1/4$ *c)* $(x - 1/2)^2 - 5/4$
6. *a)* $6(x + 1/4)^2 + 5/8$ *c)* $5(x - 3/10)^2 - 49/20$
7. *a)* $(3x + 7/6)^2 - 85/36$ *c)* $(2x - 1/4)^2 + 15/16$
8. *a)* no solution in Q *c)* no solution in Q
9. *a)* $\{-2, 3/4\}$ *c)* $\{-7/8, 1/3\}$
12. *a)* $\{-4, 6\}$ *c)* no solution   14. *a)* 2   *c)* 5

Exercises 3.11

1. sup $S = 5/9$, inf $S = .5$
2. *a)* sup $S = 1 + 12/99$, inf $S = 1.12$
    b) sup $S = -1.12$, inf $S = -(1 + 12/99)$
3. *a)* $a_1 = 1$, $a_2 = 3/4$, $a_3 = 2/3$, $a_4 = 5/8$, $a_5 = 3/5$
7. *a)* 1   *b)* 0   *c)* 0   *d)* -1
10. *a)* 2, 9/4, 64/27, 625/256, 7776/3125

Exercises 3.12

1. *a)* $2.236 < \sqrt{5}$ (but close!); $2.645 < \sqrt{7}$ (but close!)
    b) $4.881 < \sqrt{5} + \sqrt{7}$ (but close!)   *c)* $2.978 < 1/3 + \sqrt{7}$ (but close!)
6. $16 + \sqrt{2}$ 9. within $1/8$
11. *a)* $\left\{\dfrac{-3 + \sqrt{41}}{4}, \dfrac{-3 - \sqrt{41}}{4}\right\}$ *c)* $\left\{\dfrac{1 + \sqrt{1 + 8\pi}}{4\pi}, \dfrac{1 - \sqrt{1 + 8\pi}}{4\pi}\right\}$
    e) no solution in R
12. *b)* *i)* $|x - (-5)| = 3$ *ii)* $|x - 4| < 2$ *iii)* $|x - 1/2| > 7/2$
13. *a)* 41   *c)* $\left\{\dfrac{-3 - \sqrt{129}}{4}, \dfrac{-3 + \sqrt{129}}{4}\right\}$ *e)* $[-11, 13]$ *g)* $\{-1, 5\}$
14. *a)* $3/2^{1/2}$ *c)* $3^{1/2} + 2/6^{1/2}$ 15. *a)* $\sqrt{10}$ *b)* $\sqrt{13}$

Exercises 3.13

1. *a)* .5   *c)* .333   *e)* .315
3. *a)* 165/999   *c)* $13 + 16769/24975$
4. *a)* .12345   *c)* .005678   *e)* 1.8887
5. *a)* 34/99   *c)* $-83/99$ *e)* $-3156/9999$
6. *a)* 4060   *c)* 5.442   8. 2.2361

ANSWERS TO EXERCISES

Exercises 3.14

1. *a)* $8 - 4i$ *c)* $24 - 52i$ *e)* $24/45 + (27/45)i$
   g) $169/58 - (143/58)i$ *i)* $1/5 + (2/5)i$ *k)* $-2/41 + (23/41)i$
2. *a)* $z = 5/3 - 2i/3$ *c)* $109/17 - (57/17)i$ *e)* $-9/41 - (1/41)i$
5. *a)* $-1, -i, 1, i, -1, -i, 1$ *c)* $-i, -1, i, 1, -i, -1, i, 1$
9. It must be real.

10. $\left\{ \dfrac{-i + \sqrt{23}}{6}, \dfrac{-i - \sqrt{23}}{6} \right\}$

Exercises 3.15

1. *a)* $\sqrt{45}$ *c)* $\sqrt{5}$
3. *a)* the disc of radius 1 with center at 0
   c) the disc of radius 2 with center at $3 + 2i$ 4. $1/5$
12. *a)* $i, -i$ *c)* $8i, -8i$ *e)* $\sqrt{20}\,i, -\sqrt{20}\,i$
13. *a)* $\{-2, 1/2\}$ *b)* $\{1 + \sqrt{3}\,i, 1 - \sqrt{3}\,i\}$
    c) $\left\{ \dfrac{1 + \sqrt{29}}{14}, \dfrac{1 - \sqrt{29}}{14} \right\}$ *d)* $\left\{ \dfrac{-5 + \sqrt{59}\,i}{6}, \dfrac{-5 - \sqrt{59}\,i}{6} \right\}$

Exercises 3.16

2. *a)* $(f + g)(x) = 3x^2 + 5x + 1$; $\ f \cdot g(x) = 15x^3 + 6x^2 - 5x - 2$; $\ f \circ g(x) = 75x^2 + 60x + 11$; $\ g \circ f(x) = 15x^2 - 3$
   c) $(f + g)(x) = 2x^2$; $f \cdot g(x) = x^4 - 16$; $f \circ g(x) = x^4 - 8x^2 + 20$; $g \circ f(x) = x^4 + 8x^2 + 12$
8. *a)* $-1/2$ *b)* $4/3$ *c)* $-b/a$ *d)* 1 and $-5/3$

Exercises 4.1

1. 120   2. *a)* 6   *b)* 20
3. *a)* $3f(1) + 2f(2) + f(3)$ *c)* 27
7. *a)* 58   *c)* $f(1)f(2)f(3)(g(1) + g(2) + g(3))$
8. *a)* $1/990$ *c)* 156   *e)* $63/57$ *g)* $n(n + 1)(n + 2)$ *i)* 10
9. *a)* $S_n = 3^{n-1}$ *c)* $S_n = \displaystyle\sum_{i=1}^{n} \frac{1}{2i} = \frac{2^n - 1}{2^n}$ *e)* $S_n = \dfrac{2^{n-1} n!}{3}$
10. *a)* $S_{nm} = 6m + 1$ *c)* $S_{nm} = 9m^2 + 1$

Exercises 4.2

4. a) $\bigcup\limits_{i=1}^{1} S_i = S_1, \;\; \bigcup\limits_{i=1}^{k} S_i = S_k \cup \left(\bigcup\limits_{i=1}^{k-1} S_i \right)$ 　　 b) $\bigcup\limits_{i=1}^{n} S_i = \bigcup\limits_{i \in \{1, \ldots, n\}} S_i$

5. a) $\{(a, a, a), (a, a, e), (a, b, a), (a, b, e), (a, d, a), (a, d, e), (b, a, a), (b, a, e),$
$(b, b, a), (b, b, e), (b, d, a), (b, d, e), (c, a, a), (c, a, e), (c, b, a), (c, b, e),$
$(c, d, a), (c, d, e)\}$ 　　　 b) $\{a, b, c, d, e\}$ 　　　 c) $\{a\}$

Exercises 4.3

1. a) 8 　　　　　　　　　 c) 2 　　　　　　　　　 e) 4
4. a) $x = -1, y = 1$ 　　　 c) $x = 2, y = -1$ 　　　 e) $x = 1, y = -3$

Exercises 4.4

1. a) $1/2 + -2/7$ 　 c) $1/2 + -4/17$ 　 e) $3/3 + -13/17$ 　 g) $2/3 + -2/5$
2. a) $3/6 + -2/7$ 　　　　　　　 c) $-2/6 + 6/10$
4. a) $1/27 + 2/9 + 1/3$ 　　　 c) $5 + 1/4$ 　　　　　　 e) $6/11^3 + 3/11^2$
6. a) $1 + 1/4^4 + 1/4^3$ 　　　 c) $4/15$ 　　　　　　　 e) $1/8^5 + 1/8^4 + 1/8^2$

Exercises 4.5

1. a) $(12, 24)$ 　　　　　　　　　　　 c) $(-6, 0), (12, 18)$
2. a) $A = (0, 2), B = (0, 1)$ 　　　　　 c) $A = (-2, 4), B = (-2, 4)$
　　 e) $A = (-4, -2) \cup (0, 3) \cup (4, 8), B = (-8, -2) \cup (1, 4) \cup (4, 16)$
3. a) $S = (0, \infty)$ 　 c) $S = (1/2, 2)$ 　　 6. a) $n = -2$ 　 c) $n = 21$
8. a) $\sqrt{2}$ 　　　　　　　　　 c) $-1/2$ 　　　　　　　 e) $-\sqrt{10}$
9. a) $(4, 6)$ 　　　　　　　　　 c) $(-2, 2)$ 　　　　　　 e) $(1/2, 1)$
10. a) $(2, 5)$ 　　　　　　　　　 c) $[1, 5)$ 　　　　　　　 e) $[1, 1 + a^2)$
13. a) $\sup A = 5, \inf A = -\sqrt{5}$ 　　　 c) $\sup C = 2, \inf C = 0$
　　 e) $\sup E = 3, \inf C = 1$

Exercises 4.6

1. a) yes 　　　　　 b) no 　　　　　 c) yes 　　　 d) all integers divisible by 3
　　 e) three 　　　　 f) countable infinity
2. b) yes 　　　　　　　 3. a) seven 　　　　　　 4. n 　　　　 5. $\bar{1}, \bar{0}$

6. $\overline{13}, \overline{13}$

11. when n is prime

12. a) 0   c) 5

13. 0, 1, 2, 4

14. a) 4   b) 3   c) 0   d) all x in Z_5

17. a) 4, 2

c) 6, 5

e) 3, 5

Exercises 5.1

1. a)

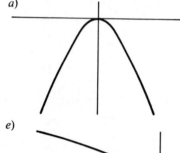

c)

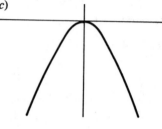

e)

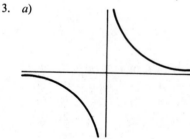

3. a)

c)

4. a) even   c) even   e) odd   g) odd
8. a) nothing   c) symmetry about the ordinate   e) symmetry about the ordinate
9b. a) symmetry about the ordinate   c) symmetry about the ordinate
     e) symmetry about the ordinate
11. c) p is even   14. a) odd   c) even

Exercises 5.2

1. a) $R - \{1\}$ c) $R - \{0\}$

2. *a)*

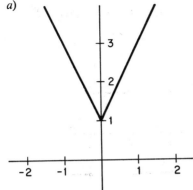

c)

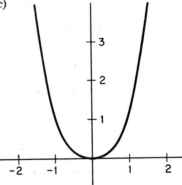

3. *a)*

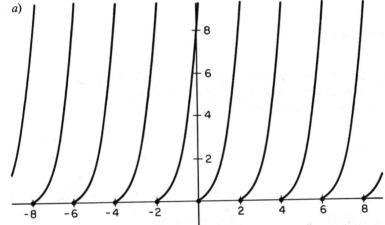

c)

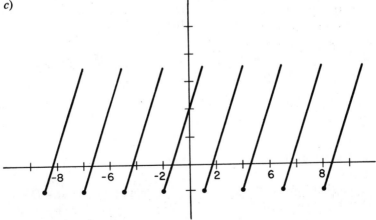

4. *a)* not necessarily periodic   *c)* not necessarily periodic
   e) not necessarily periodic

5. *a)*

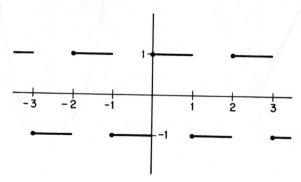

Exercises 5.3

1. *a)* strictly monotonic increasing   *c)* bounded below
   f) strictly monotonic increasing and bounded below
2. Yes, but only if it is a constant.

Exercises 5.4

2. No. Yes.   3. $2^{16} = 65536$ 5. *a)* arithmetic   *c)* neither

6. *c*   8. 157/495   9. *a)* 0   *c)* 1

10. *a)* no limit exists   *b)* no limit exists

12. *a)* decreasing   *c)* decreasing   *e)* increasing

13. *a)* 5/81   *c)* -9 *e)* 242/243

14. $a_6 = 31, a_{10} = 43$ 15. $b_1 = 33, b_{15} = 5$

16. *a)* 6, 8, 10   *c)* 125×126 18. $d_1 = 6, d_{10} = 6/2^9$

19. $r = 1/8\sqrt{2}, h_1 = 5 \cdot 2^{16} = 327680$

20. *a)* 1   *c)* no limit exists   22. *a)* $.05208333\bar{3}$ *c)* $.26\bar{6}$

23. *a)* 0   *b)* $s_1/(1 - r)$ 24. *a)* 21715

Exercises 5.5

1. *a)* does not exist   *c)* 2   *e)* 0

7. *a)* 5/6   *c)* 0

8. *a)* not continuous at 0 and 1.
   e) not continuous on Z.   *c)* not continuous at -1.
                             g) not continuous on $Z - \{0\}$.

Exercises 5.6

1. a) $x = 1/2$

   c) $x = \dfrac{1 + \sqrt{17}}{2}$ and $\dfrac{1 - \sqrt{17}}{2}$

5. $\lim\limits_{x \to a} \dfrac{g(x)}{f(x)}$ does not exist.

7. a) $f \wedge g = \mathcal{O}(x^2 + 2x + 1)$ as $x \to \infty$ c) $f + g = \mathcal{O}(x^2 + 3x + 1)$ as $x \to \infty$
   e) $f \cdot g = \mathcal{O}(x^3 + 2x^2 + x)$ as $x \to \infty$

Exercises 5.7

1. a) slope $m = 3$ c) slope $m = 1/2$
2. a) slope $m = 2$ c) slope $m = 4/3$ e) slope $m = -1/2$
4. a) 7 units   c) 49 units   e) decreases by 14 units
5. at $(0, 2)$ f has slope 0; at $(1, 5)$ f has slope 6; at $(-1, 5)$ f has slope -6
7. a) 9.26   c) 9.10   9. a) -2 c) 0
10. a) $y = -x + 1$ c) $y = 4x + 7$ 11. $y = 8x - 5$
12. a) slope of f at $(1, 2)$ is 0; slope of f at $(b, f(b))$ is $15b^2 - 15b^4$.
    c) slope of f at $(-1, -2)$ is 3; slope of f at $(b, f(b))$ is 3.
13. $y = 32x - 99$ 15. $y = -x + 3$

Exercises 5.8

2. a) $x \geq 1$ or $-2 \leq x < 0$ c) $-2 < x < 1/5$ or $1 < x < 3/2$ or $2 < x$
4. a) $x < -1$ or $1/3 < x < 1$ c) $x \leq -2/7$ or $2 < x < 5$

Exercises 5.9

7. none are linear   10. a) $y = -x + 2$ c) $y = 3$
11. a) $x/1 + y/2 = 1$ c) $x/-3 + y/-2 = 1$

Exercises 5.10

2. i) a) $2 + \log 3.6541$ c) $-3 + \log 2.13$ e) $-9 + \log 2.197$

3. i) a) $\log_{15} 32 = \dfrac{1 + \log 3.2}{1 + \log 1.5}$ c) $\log_{1/2} 5.4 = \dfrac{\log 5.4}{-\log 2}$

4. a) $x = \log 9.51$ c) $x = \dfrac{\log 3.71}{\log 5}$

5. a) $x = 10^{5.103}$ c) $x = 10^{56.102}$

6. a) $x = 4/5$ c) $x = 998$ e) $1 \pm \sqrt{\dfrac{\log 7}{\log 6} - 7}$

7. a) 1.4306   c) .4478

8. a) 12090/6825   c) 1000/12090

Exercises 5.11

9. a) $\cosh a = 5/4$; $\tanh a = -3/5$; $\coth a = -5/3$; $\operatorname{sech} a = 4/5$;
    $\operatorname{csch} a = -4/3$ c) $\sinh a = 12/5$; $\cosh a = 13/5$; $\tanh a = 12/13$;
    $\coth a = 13/12$; $\operatorname{sech} a = 5/13$

12. a) 1.5662   c) .9993

13. a) 246.3745   c) 11013.2093

Exercises 5.12

3. a) $x = 4$ and $y = 0$ c) $x = 0$ and $y = 4$ e) $x = -3$ and $y = -1$

4. a) no simultaneous solutions   c) $\{(x, y): x \in [0, \infty)$ and $y = e^x\}$

5. a) $T = \bigcup\limits_{b \in R} \{(b, y): y \leq 2b + 1\}$

7. a) $(-1/9, 11/9)$ c) no solution

Exercises 5.13

3. no   6. $f[C] = C$

Exercises 5.14

1. a) $\{z: |z - (1 + i)| = 3\} = \{(x, y): (x - 1)^2 + (y - 1)^2 = 9\}$
    c) $\{z: |z - 1| = 2\} = \{(x, y): (x - 1)^2 + y^2 = 4\}$
    e) $\{z: |z - (-1 + 2i)| = \sqrt{7}\} = \{(x, y): (x + 1)^2 + (y - 2)^2 = 7\}$

7. a) $y = 4x - 5$ c) $y = 2x - 5$ e) $y = 3x + 4$

8. a) $(y - 1) = 3(x - 1)$ c) $(y - 2) = 3(x - 4)$

9. a) $(y + 1) = -1/2(x - 2)$ c) $(y + 3) = -1/2(x - 1)$

Exercises 5.15

1. a) 2   c) $1 + i$ e) $4i$ g) $-1 + 9i$

Exercises 6.1

1. 171
3. 125
6. 243
7. *b)* 24
9. *a)* 60
c) 10,080
11. *a)* $8 \cdot 10^6$
12. 2^{16}
14. p_5^{11}
15. *b)* no such x (prove this!)

Exercises 6.2

3. *a)* 2, 6, 4

4. *a)* $\binom{52}{5}$
    c) $\binom{4}{2} \cdot \binom{48}{3}$

6. *a)* 26^3

7. *a)* 3
    b) $p_{10}^{10} = 10!$

10. *b)* only if $r = 0$ or $r = 1$.

12. $\binom{2}{1} \cdot \binom{3}{2}$

13. *a)* $p_3^3 \cdot p_3^3 \cdot p_6^6 \cdot p_4^4$

c) $p_3^3 \cdot p_6^6 \cdot p_4^4$

Exercises 6.3

2. *a)* x^{10} *c)* 5^{10} 3. 24   4. $(x + 2)^{21}$
8. *a)* $32x^5 + 240x^4y + 720x^3y^2 + 1080x^2y^3 + 810xy^4 + 243y^5$
    c) $-(x^{14} + 14x^{12}y + 84x^{10}y^2 + 280x^8y^3 + 560x^6y^4 + 672x^4y^5 + 448x^2y^6 + 128y^7)$

10. *a)* $\binom{10}{4} + \binom{10}{5}$ *c)* $\binom{n}{p} + \binom{n}{k}$ 11. $\left[\binom{10}{4} + \binom{10}{2}\right]\left[\binom{12}{5} + \binom{12}{3}\right]$

Exercises 6.4

2. *a)* $\{\{1, 2, 3, 4, 5\}, \varnothing, \{1, 2\}, \{2, 4\}, \{2\}, \{1, 3, 4, 5\}, \{3, 4, 5\}, \{1, 3, 5\}, \{1, 2, 3, 5\}, \{3, 5\}, \{1\}, \{2, 3, 4, 5\}, \{4\}, \{1, 4\}, \{2, 3, 5\}, \{1, 2, 4\}\}$
3. *b)* $A - B = A \cap \bar{B}$. But $A \in \mathcal{E}$ and $\bar{B} \in \mathcal{E} \Rightarrow A \cap \bar{B} \in \mathcal{E}$

4. *a)* $\binom{48}{5} \Big/ \binom{52}{5}$
    d) $\binom{4}{3} \cdot \binom{48}{2} \Big/ \binom{52}{5}$

5. *a)* $1 \Big/ \binom{11}{2}$ *c)* $\left[\binom{4}{2} + 1 + \binom{5}{2}\right] \Big/ \binom{11}{2}$ *e)* $\binom{4}{1}\binom{7}{1} \Big/ \binom{11}{2}$

7. *a)* 10/16
    c) 12/16
8. *d)* $\{(H, H, H), (H, H, T), (H, T, H), (T, H, H), (H, T, T), (T, H, T), (T, T, H)\}$
    The probability of this event is 7/8.

17. *a)* 0, 1, 2, 3, 4, 5, 6   *c)* $P(i) = \binom{6}{i} \cdot (1/2)^6$ *d)* $P(2, 3, 5) = .64$

ANSWERS TO EXERCISES

Exercises 6.5

2. a) $\dfrac{1}{4} \cdot \dfrac{1}{6}$ c) $\dfrac{1}{2} \cdot \dfrac{4}{6}$ 3. $\dfrac{1}{12} \times \$10$

5. a) $(.312)(5/36)$ c) $(.5)(15/36)$ e) $(.062)(2/36)$

6. a) \$2 7. a) roughly 1/2 9. b) \$(19 × 5/8)

10. a) $1 - \dfrac{\binom{4}{3}}{\binom{11}{3}}$ c) $\$50\left[\dfrac{\binom{7}{2}\binom{4}{1}}{\binom{11}{3}} + \dfrac{\binom{7}{3}}{\binom{11}{3}}\right]$

11. a) $\dfrac{\binom{13}{3}\binom{39}{1}}{\binom{52}{4}} + \dfrac{\binom{13}{4}}{\binom{52}{4}}$

Exercises 7.1

1. a) .3429 c) −.2475 e) −.1493 g) −.798
2. a) .996 c) −.1587 e) −.2585
3.

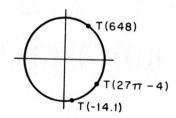

6. a) $t = \pm\pi/3 + 2n\pi$ c) no solution e) $x = \pm\pi/3 + (2n+1)\pi$
   g) $x = \pi/2 + n\pi = (2n+1)(\pi/2)$ i) $(2n+1)(\pi/4)$
   k) $x = .501 + 2n\pi$ or $x = \pi - .501 + 2n\pi = (2n+1)\pi - .501$
   m) $\pm.396 + 2n\pi$
8. a) $\sqrt{2}/2 + \sqrt{2}i/2$ c) $-\sqrt{2}/2 - \sqrt{2}i/2$ e) $-\sqrt{3}/2 + 1/2i$ g) -1
9. a) 1st c) 2nd e) 2nd g) 1st i) 2nd k) 4th

Exercises 7.2

1. a) 56/65 c) 16/65 2. a) 204/325 c) 36/325
3. a) $\sqrt{2} \sin x$ c) $\cos^2 t - \sin^2 t$

718

4. *a)* $3 \sin x - 4 \sin^3 x$

    c) $\pm\sqrt{1 - \cos^2 x}\,(4 \cos^2 x - 1)$ ($+$ in the 1st and 2nd quadrants, $-$ in 3rd and 4th)

5. *a)* $\sin 8t - \sin 2t$ *c)* $\sin 4t + \sin 2t$

6. *a)* $n\pi/2$ for all n *c)* $x = (2n + 1)\pi/2$ *e)* $x = (4n + 3)(\pi/6)$

    g) $x = 6n\pi + 3\pi/4$ or $x = 3(2n + 1)\pi - 3\pi/4$

    i) $x = \pi/6 + 2n\pi$ or $x = 5\pi/6 + 2n\pi$ $x = 3\pi/2 + 2n\pi$

    k) $x = n\pi$ or $x = \pi/3 + 2n\pi$ or $x = 2\pi/3 + 2n\pi$

    m) $x = (2n + 1)(\pi/2)$

    o) $x = n\pi$ or $x = \pi/6 + 2n\pi$ or $x = 5\pi/6 + 2n\pi$

    q) $x \cong \pi \pm .775 + 2n\pi$

    s) $x = \pi/6 + n\pi$ or $x = 4\pi/3 + n\pi$ or $x = n\pi/3$

    u) $x = (2n + 1)(\pi/8)$ or $x = n\pi/2$

Exercises 7.3

7. *a)* $\sqrt{2}/2$ *c)* $-1/2$ *e)* $\dfrac{\sqrt{2+\sqrt{3}}}{2}$ *g)* $\dfrac{\sqrt{2-\sqrt{3}}}{2}$ *i)* $-\sqrt{3}/3$

Exercises 7.4

1. 19.2 inches   3. 15 feet   5. $1000/\pi \cong 318.5$

7. $17/19 \times 180/\pi \cong 51.3$

9. *a)* 70.5   *c)* 57.3   *e)* 18.4

10. *a)* .698   *c)* .1744   *e)* 1.744   11. 648.2 yards

13. $(133/40)\pi$ ft./sec. ($\cong 10.45$ ft./sec.)

Exercises 7.5

1. 1.61 ft.   3. .795 radians or 45.6°   5. 40.89 ft.

6. *a)*

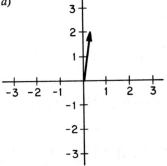

    c)

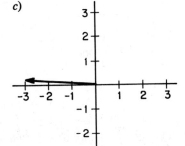

7. all positive real numbers

8. a) $(1, \pi/2)$ c) $(3, \pi/2)$ e) $(4\sqrt{2}, 5\pi/4)$

9. a) $(\sqrt{17}/6, .955)$ c) $(\sqrt{17}, .755)$

11. $\{r \cos \theta + ir \sin \theta : r = 1\}$

13. a) $(-2, 0)$ c) $(4.807, -1.378)$ e) $(\sqrt{2-\sqrt{3}}, \sqrt{2+\sqrt{3}})$

14. a) 2   c) $3\sqrt{3}/2 - 3i/2$ e) $.798 + 1.834i$ g) 6

15. a) $r = 5$ c) $r \sin \theta = -6$

16. a) $x^2 + y^2 = 49$ c) $x^2 + y^2 = 4x$

Exercises 7.6

3. a) $c = \sqrt{7}, \beta = 41.0°, \alpha = 79.0°$ c) $a \cong 8.53, \beta = 35.45°, \gamma = 9.55°$

    e) $c \cong 10, \beta = 23.5°, \alpha = 63.5°$

4. a) 38.2°, 60°, 81.8°   c) 31.9°, 58.1°, 90°

7. a) 13.52 and 7.84   b) 12.15

9. a) $(21/4)\sqrt{11} \cong 17.41$ c) 0   e) $64\sqrt{3} \cong 110.85$

11. 115.6 ft.   13. 45π inches

Exercises 7.7

1. a) $[-1, 1]$ is the domain. $[-\pi/2, \pi/2]$ is the range.

    c) $(-\infty, -1] \cup [1, \infty)$ is the domain. $[0, \pi/2) \cup (\pi/2, \pi]$ is the range.

    e) R is the domain. $(-\pi/2, \pi/2)$ is the range.

2. a) $(9\pi/2, 11\pi/2)$ is the domain. R is the range.

    c) R is the domain. $(9\pi/2, 11\pi/2)$ is the range.

4. a) $\pi/4$ c) .204   5. a) false   c) true   e) true

10. a) $x = \sqrt{2}/2$ 12. a) $-\alpha$ 13. a) $-\alpha$

14. a) 0   c) $\pi/2$ e) π g) $\pi/4$ i) $\pi/6$ k) $\pi/3$ m) $\pi/6$

15. a) 3/4   c) 1/2   e) $-1/4$ g) No such value exists.   i) 5/13   k) 8/17   m) $-3/4$

16. a) $x \cong .730 + 2n\pi$ or $x \cong 2.41 + 2n\pi$

    c) $x \cong 2.22 + 2n\pi$ or $x \cong 4.06 + 2n\pi$

    e) $x = 7\pi/6 + 2n\pi, \quad x = 11\pi/6 + 2n\pi, \quad x \cong .340 + 2n\pi, \quad x \cong 2.80 + 2n\pi$

    g) $x \cong .198 + n\pi, x = .930 + n\pi$

Exercises 7.8

1. *a*) amplitude 2; period 2π

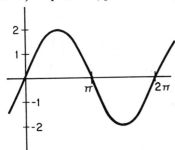

c) amplitude 1/2; period 2π

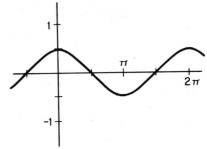

e) amplitude 1; period 4π

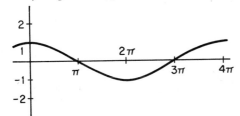

g) amplitude 1; period 2π

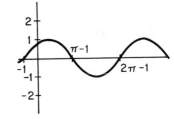

i) amplitude 2; period π

l) not periodic

k) amplitude 1/3; period 4π

2. *a*)

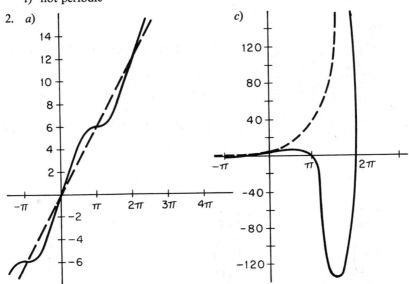

c)

5. 3.18 cm. in the direction the spring was originally stretched.

Exercises 7.9

1. a) $2(\cos 5\pi/4 + i \sin 5\pi/4)$ c) $7(\cos(2+\pi) + i \sin(2+\pi))$

3. a) $1,\ e^{i\pi/3},\ e^{i2\pi/3},\ e^{i\pi},\ e^{i4\pi/3},\ e^{i5\pi/3}$

4. $\sqrt[3]{2}\,e^{i\pi/18},\ \sqrt[3]{2}\,e^{i13\pi/18},\ \sqrt[3]{2}\,e^{i25\pi/18}$

6. a) $2\sqrt{2}\,e^{i\pi/4}$ c) $\sqrt{13}\,e^{i\,\mathrm{Tan}^{-1}3/2}$ e) $-\sqrt{13}\,e^{i\,\mathrm{Tan}^{-1}3/2}$

7. a) $-1 + i$ and $1 - i$ c) $\dfrac{-1+\sqrt{3}}{2}\,i$ and $\dfrac{-1-\sqrt{3}}{2}\,i$

11. a) ie^{2i} c) $-ie^{-5(1+i)}$ e) 1

13. a) $1/4(-3 \pm e^{1/2i\,\mathrm{Arctan}\,8/9})$ c) $-1 \pm e^{1/2i\,\mathrm{Arctan}\,7}$

e) $\dfrac{(7 - 9i) \pm (5 + i)e^{1/2i\,\mathrm{Arctan}\,-16/57}}{52}$

15. a) $\sqrt[7]{2}\,e^{i(\pi/7 + 2n\pi/7)}$ where $n \in \{0, \ldots, 6\}$

Exercises 7.10

2. Any horizontal strip of thickness 2π.

3. a) $(i/2)(e - 1/e)$ c) $1/2(e + 1/e)$ e) $(i/2)(e^\pi - e^{-\pi})$ g) $1/2(e^\pi + e^{-\pi})$

7. a) $a = 3$

Exercises 8.1

5. a point

6. a) The equation $y = mx + b$ can be uniquely solved for x in terms of y, so $f(x) = mx + b$ is 1-1.

   b) Suppose $f_1 = m_1x + b_1$ and $f_2 = m_2x + b_2$. Then $(f_1 \circ f_2)(x) = f_1(f_2(x)) = m_1(m_2x + b_2) + b_1 = mx + b$, where $m = m_1m_2$ and $b = m_1b_2 + b_1$.

8. $r \sin\theta = mr \cos\theta + b$

10. a) $-6 - 12i$ c) $12 - 10i$ 11. a) $-14 + 26i$ c) $-126 - 25i$

Exercises 8.2

1. a) $\begin{pmatrix} 5 \\ 4 \end{pmatrix}$ c) $\begin{pmatrix} 7 \\ 5 \end{pmatrix}$ e) $\begin{pmatrix} 12 \\ 7 \end{pmatrix}$

2. a) $\begin{pmatrix} 7 \\ 6 \\ 19 \end{pmatrix}$ c) $\begin{pmatrix} 4 \\ 3 \\ 13 \end{pmatrix}$ e) $\alpha = \beta = 1/5$

3. *a)* $\alpha = 4, \beta = 1, \gamma = 2$ *c)* There are no such α, β.

5. *a)*

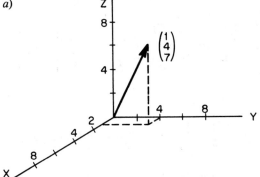

6. *b)* Suppose $A = \begin{pmatrix} a \\ 3a \end{pmatrix}$ and $B = \begin{pmatrix} b \\ 3b \end{pmatrix}$. Then $\alpha A + \beta B = \begin{pmatrix} \alpha a \\ 3\alpha a \end{pmatrix} + \begin{pmatrix} \beta b \\ 3\beta b \end{pmatrix} = \begin{pmatrix} \alpha a + \beta b \\ 3(\alpha a + \beta b) \end{pmatrix} \in S.$

Exercises 8.3

2. $ae^x + be^{-x} = 0 \Leftrightarrow a + be^{-2x} = 0 \Leftrightarrow be^{-2x} = -a \Leftrightarrow a = b = 0$, since if $b \neq 0, e^{-2x} = -a/b$ which is impossible because e^{-2x} is not a constant function. But if $b = 0$, then $be^{-2x} = 0 \Rightarrow a = 0$.

4. *a)* $\begin{pmatrix} 3 \\ 2 \\ -1 \end{pmatrix}$ *c)* $\begin{pmatrix} 2 \\ 5 \\ -1 \end{pmatrix}$ *e)* $\begin{pmatrix} -6 \\ -7 \\ 8 \end{pmatrix}$

5. 26 and 15   7. \$630 and \$810

9. $\dfrac{mn(y - x)}{ym - xn}$ persons each received $\dfrac{xy(n - m)}{nx - my}$ dollars.

11. *a)* $a \neq -2b$

Exercises 8.4

1. *a)* $\begin{bmatrix} 2 & -1 & 1 \\ 1 & -1 & -1 \\ 3 & -2 & -1 \end{bmatrix} \begin{bmatrix} x \\ y \\ z \end{bmatrix} = \begin{bmatrix} 1 \\ 2 \\ -1 \end{bmatrix}$

723

2. a) $3x - 6y + 5z = 9$
    $2x - y + z = -1$
    $x - 2y + 4z = 3$

3. 1a) $\begin{bmatrix} 2 & -1 & 1 & | & 1 \\ 1 & -1 & -1 & | & 2 \\ 3 & -2 & -1 & | & -1 \end{bmatrix}$ reduces to $\begin{bmatrix} 1 & 0 & 0 & | & -9 \\ 0 & 1 & 0 & | & -15 \\ 0 & 0 & 1 & | & 4 \end{bmatrix}$ so the solution

is $\begin{pmatrix} -9 \\ -15 \\ 4 \end{pmatrix}$.

4. a) $AB = \begin{bmatrix} 4 & 10 \\ 3 & 6 \end{bmatrix}$; $BA = \begin{bmatrix} 4 & 6 \\ 5 & 6 \end{bmatrix}$ d) $AB = B$; BA is not defined.

   e) $AB = BA = B$

5. Aa) $a_{14} = 9$ Ad) $a_{32} = 1$ Bb) 1

7. a) $\displaystyle\sum_{i=1}^{n} i^2 = \frac{n(n+1)(2n+1)}{6}$ c) $\begin{bmatrix} 1 & 2 & 3 & \cdots & n \\ 2 & 4 & 6 & \cdots & 2n \\ 3 & 6 & 9 & \cdots & 3n \\ \cdot & \cdot & \cdot & & \\ \cdot & \cdot & \cdot & & \\ \cdot & \cdot & \cdot & & \\ n & 2n & 3n & \cdots & n^2 \end{bmatrix}$

8. d) $B = \begin{bmatrix} 1/a & 0 & 0 & 0 \\ 0 & 1/a & 0 & 0 \\ 0 & 0 & 1/a & 0 \\ 0 & 0 & 0 & 1/a \end{bmatrix}$

Exercises 8.5

1. a) $A + B = B + A = \begin{bmatrix} -1 & 8 \\ -1 & -2 \end{bmatrix}$ c) $\begin{bmatrix} 0 & 33 \\ -3 & -12 \end{bmatrix}$

2. a) $A + B = \begin{bmatrix} 3 & 5 & 7 \\ 5 & 8 & 11 \\ 7 & 11 & 15 \end{bmatrix}$ b) $AB = \begin{bmatrix} 20 & 40 & 60 \\ 26 & 52 & 78 \\ 32 & 64 & 96 \end{bmatrix}$

3. a) 12, 0, 12, 8   c) 540, 480, 0, 0

6. a) $(ABC)(C^{-1}B^{-1}A^{-1}) = (AB)(CC^{-1})(B^{-1}A^{-1}) = (AB)I(B^{-1}A^{-1}) = A(BB^{-1})A^{-1}$
   $= AIA^{-1} = AA^{-1} = I$. Therefore $(ABC)^{-1} = C^{-1}B^{-1}A^{-1}$.

12. See problem 13.   13. $\begin{bmatrix} 1 & 0 \\ 0 & -1 \end{bmatrix}$

Exercises 8.6

2. *a)*

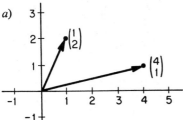

4. $2I_2$

6. $\begin{bmatrix} \cos\theta & \sin\theta \\ -\sin\theta & \cos\theta \end{bmatrix} = 1/2 \begin{bmatrix} 1 & \sqrt{3} \\ -\sqrt{3} & 1 \end{bmatrix}$

8. $\begin{pmatrix} xa - by \\ xb + ya \end{pmatrix} = \begin{bmatrix} a & -b \\ b & a \end{bmatrix} \begin{pmatrix} x \\ y \end{pmatrix}$

Exercises 8.7

1. The system is equivalent to one having the equation $0x + 0y + 0z = 2$.

2. $\begin{pmatrix} 1 - z \\ -2 + z \\ z \end{pmatrix}$ for any $z \in R$.

3. *a)* $\begin{bmatrix} 2 & 3 & 1 \\ 1 & 4 & 1 \\ 0 & 0 & 0 \end{bmatrix} \begin{bmatrix} x \\ y \\ z \end{bmatrix} = \begin{bmatrix} 1 \\ 2 \\ 0 \end{bmatrix}$

4. *a)* $\begin{bmatrix} 1 & 2 & -2 \\ 0 & -1 & 1 \\ 0 & 2 & -1 \end{bmatrix}$

d) $\begin{bmatrix} -5 & -1 & 6 \\ 1 & 0 & -1 \\ 9 & 2 & -10 \end{bmatrix}$

5. *b)* $\begin{bmatrix} 1 & 0 & 0 \\ 0 & 1 & 0 \\ 0 & 0 & 2 \end{bmatrix}$

e) $\begin{bmatrix} 1 & 0 & 0 \\ 0 & 2 & 0 \\ 0 & 1 & -1 \end{bmatrix}$

7. *a)* $\begin{pmatrix} 9/22 \\ 3/22 \\ -5/22 \end{pmatrix}$

c) $\begin{pmatrix} x \\ y \end{pmatrix} = \begin{pmatrix} 2 \\ -1 \end{pmatrix}$

10. 374

Exercises 8.8

1. *a)* -7 *c)* 0

2. *a)* $\begin{bmatrix} 1 & 6 \\ 2 & 1 \\ 4 & 7 \end{bmatrix}$

c) $\begin{bmatrix} i & 1 \\ 2+i & 5 \\ 3i & i \end{bmatrix}$

ANSWERS TO EXERCISES

4. a) $\begin{bmatrix} 0 & 1 & -3 \\ -4 & 0 & -2 \end{bmatrix}$

   c) $\begin{bmatrix} 2 & 3 & 4 \\ 2 & 0 & -3 \end{bmatrix}$

5. a) -32

   c) -25

6. a) $\begin{bmatrix} 3/5 & -1/5 \\ -1/5 & 2/5 \end{bmatrix}$

   c) $\begin{bmatrix} \dfrac{2}{13} - \dfrac{3}{13}i & -\dfrac{1}{13} + \dfrac{3}{26}i \\ 0 & -\dfrac{i}{4} \end{bmatrix}$

11. b) det $H = 1$

12. b) det $H = k$

13. b) det $H = 1$

   c) det $HA =$ det A

   c) det $A^* =$ det A

   c) det $A^* =$ det A

Exercises 8.9

1. a) $\begin{pmatrix} 1 \\ -1 \\ 0 \end{pmatrix}$, $\begin{pmatrix} -1 \\ 2 \\ 1 \end{pmatrix}$, $\begin{pmatrix} 4 \\ 0 \\ 1 \end{pmatrix}$

   c) Since det $A = -3 \neq 0$, the column vectors are independent.

3. a) $1/2 \begin{bmatrix} -3 & 3 & 1 \\ 2 & -2 & 0 \\ 1 & 1 & -1 \end{bmatrix}$

   c) $-1/8 \begin{bmatrix} 0 & -4 & 0 \\ 4 & -8 & -12 \\ 4 & -6 & -8 \end{bmatrix}$

6. a) $-1/21 \begin{bmatrix} -5 & -3 & 1 \\ -2 & 3 & -8 \\ 9 & -3 & -6 \end{bmatrix} \begin{bmatrix} 2 \\ 0 \\ 1 \end{bmatrix} = \begin{pmatrix} 3/7 \\ 4/7 \\ -4/7 \end{pmatrix}$

Exercises 8.10

4. a) $B = \begin{bmatrix} 1 & 0 & 0 & 0 \\ 0 & 1 & 0 & 2 \\ 0 & 0 & 1 & 0 \\ 0 & 0 & 0 & 1 \end{bmatrix}$

   c) $B = \begin{bmatrix} 1 & 0 & 0 & 0 \\ 0 & 1 & 0 & 0 \\ 0 & 0 & 1 & 0 \\ 0 & 2 & 2 & 3 \end{bmatrix}$

5. a) $\begin{pmatrix} -3/4 \\ -1/2 \\ -5/4 \end{pmatrix}$

   c) $\begin{pmatrix} 5 \\ 3 \\ 1 \end{pmatrix}$

7. a)

x	y	R_1	R_2
0	0	3	2
1		-1	1
	-1	0	0
1	-1		

Δx	Δy	ΔR_1	ΔR_2
1	0	-4	-1
0	1	-1	1

Exercises 8.11

1. *a)* convex   *b)* convex   *c)* convex   *d)* convex
6. Yes (consider $\emptyset$ and $\overline{\emptyset}$).
8. *a)*

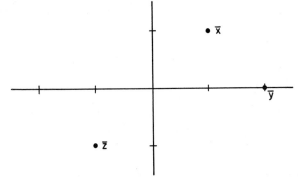

c) $\exists \lambda_1 \in [0, 1]$, $\bar{p} = \lambda_1 \bar{x} + (1 - \lambda_1)\bar{y}$. The segment between $\bar{p}$ and $\bar{z}$ is given by $\{\bar{w} : \bar{w} = \lambda\bar{p} + (1 - \lambda)\bar{z} \text{ for some } \lambda \in [0, 1]\} = \{\bar{w} : \bar{w} = \lambda\lambda_1\bar{x} + \lambda(1 - \lambda_1)\bar{y} + (1 - \lambda)\bar{z} \text{ for some } \lambda \in [0, 1]\}$.

Exercises 8.12

2. *a)*

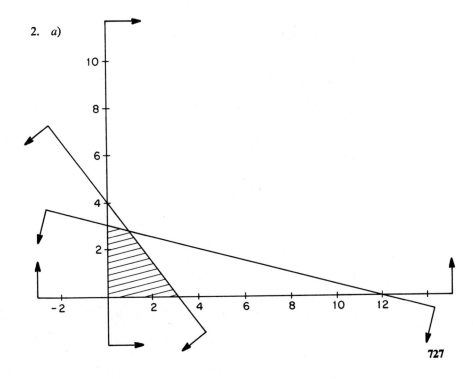

4. *b)*

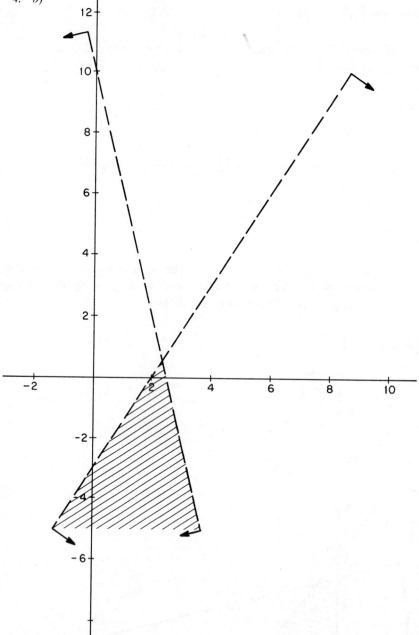

5. *b)* $\begin{bmatrix} 2 & -2 \\ 1 & 5 \\ -1 & -7 \end{bmatrix} \begin{pmatrix} y \\ x \end{pmatrix} \leq \begin{pmatrix} 2 \\ 7 \\ 3 \end{pmatrix}$

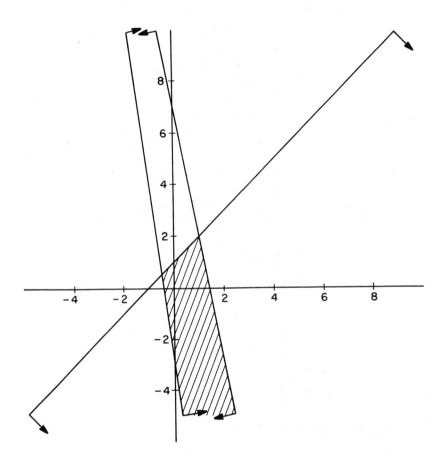

ANSWERS TO EXERCISES

7. a) $\begin{bmatrix} 1 & 0 \\ 0 & -1 \\ -3 & 1 \end{bmatrix} \begin{pmatrix} x \\ y \end{pmatrix} \leq \begin{pmatrix} 1 \\ 0 \\ 0 \end{pmatrix}$

   b) Since the region is not even convex, it cannot be described by a system of linear inequalities.

8. a)

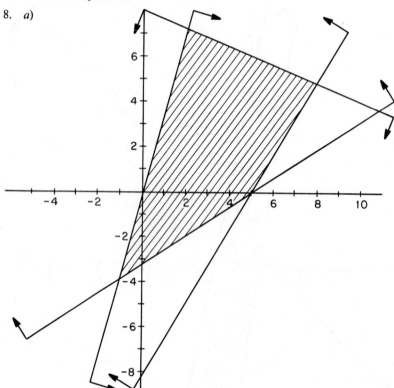

9. Region in first octant bounded by plane.

Exercises 8.13

3. a) 450 yards × 225 yards (longer side parallel to river).
   b) 400 yards × 400 yards
5. Maximum of 5 is attained at (3, 2).
7. The solution set contains any pair (x, y) in the first quadrant such that $x + y = 30$.
9. Use 10 packages of each.
11. 2/7 lb. Zip and 6/7 lb. Go.   12. 350,000 cents

Exercises 9.1

1. *a)* $3 + 7x + 3x^2 + x^3$, $15x + 16x^2 + 12x^3 + 4x^4 + x^5$, $3 + 10x + 3x^2 + x^3$,
   $45x^2 + 48x^3 + 36x^4 + 12x^5 + 3x^6$
2. *a)* $1 + 3x + 3x^2 + x^3$, $2x^2 + 3x^3 + x^4 + x^5$, $1 + x + x^3$, $5x^5 + 3x^6 + x^7$
   c) $f - \varphi \equiv 1 + 3x + x^2 + 3x^4$
4. Z_3 5. *a)* $4i$ *c)* 0 7. *a)* $1, 1, 2$
8. *a)* $a = 0, b = 2, c = 0$ 9. not possible
13. $f: D \to D, a \in D \Rightarrow f(a) \in D = R_f$
15. *a)* $20 - 5i, 3 + 2i, -2 + 7i, 3 + 26i$
16. *a)* $S, F, R, F, R, S, F, R, F, R, \ldots$ *c)* $S, L, F, R, B, S, L, F, R, B, \ldots$

Exercises 9.2

1. 1 2. 3^3 3. *a)* 1 5. *a)* $f \le 2$ *b)* 2
7. *b)* $\deg f \cdot g \le m + n$; $\deg f \circ g \le m \cdot n$
11. *a)* $x^3 + 2x + 1$ *b)* No, since $f(3) \ne 0$.
12. Yes, since $f(1) = 0$. Take $q = 2x^2 + 3x + 3$
13. *a)* no   17. *a)* 77 *c)* 28

Exercises 9.3

1. $q = \frac{3}{2}x^2 + \frac{5}{4}, r = 19/4$ 2. $q = x, r = 2x + 1$

6. Let $f = 1, g = 2$. Then $r = 0$, but there is no q in $Z[x]$ such that $1 = 2q$.
8. *a)* $q = 5x - 12, r = 34$ *c)* $q = 0, r = f$
10. *a)* Impossible, since $\deg f = 4$, but $\deg (ax^3 + bx^2 + cx + d) \le 3$.
11. $a = 0, b = 3, c = 0, d = 2, a_0 = 4$
13. *b)* $\deg f = 2n - 1$ for some $n \in N$. (i.e. $\deg f$ is odd)
14. *a)* No. (Example: suppose $f(x) = \begin{cases} 0 \text{ if } x < 0 \\ 1 \text{ if } x \ge 0 \end{cases}$ and $g = 1 - f$)
15. No, since a non-zero polynomial can have no more zeros than its degree.

Exercises 9.4

1. *a)* No such polynomials exist.
   c) $x^2 + 1, x^2 + \pi, 2x^2 - x + 3, x^2 + 7x + 13$
2. *a)* $2(x - 1)(x - 1/2)$ *c)* $3(x - \sqrt{2})(x + \sqrt{2})(x^2 + 4/3)$

3. *a)* $2\left(x - \dfrac{i(1 + \sqrt{17})}{4}\right)\left(x - \dfrac{i(1 - \sqrt{17})}{4}\right)$

   d) $3\left(x + \dfrac{1 - i2\sqrt{2}}{3}\right)\left(x + \dfrac{1 + i2\sqrt{2}}{3}\right)$

6. *a)* $(1/2, -1), (1/3, -7/9), (2/3, -10/9)$
   c) $(i, -2 - 3i), (-i, -2 + 3i), (i + 1, -3 + i)$
9. *a)* $2 + 4x + 8x^3 + 16x^4 + 3x^5$
   c) $2 + 2x + 2x^2 + 2x^3 + 2x^4 + 2x^5 + 2x^6 + 2x^7 + 3x^8$
10. *a)* $-1, 2, -3$ *e)* $1, -1, 1/2$ *g)* $1/2$

Exercises 9.5

2. *a)* $5/(2x - 3) + 2/(x - 2) - 1/(x + 1)$
   c) $3/(x - 2) + 4/(2x + 3)$
   e) $2/x + 3/(x - 2) + -4/(x + 1)$

3. *a)* $\dfrac{2}{3x - 2} + \dfrac{2x - 1}{x^2 + x + 2}$ *d)* $\dfrac{7/16}{(x + 1)^2} + \dfrac{9/32}{x + 1} + \dfrac{39/16}{(3x - 1)^2} + \dfrac{-27/32}{3x - 1}$

4. *a)* $\dfrac{2}{(x + 1)^2} + \dfrac{3}{x + 1}$ *c)* First use "long division" to obtain

$$\frac{x^5 + x^4 + 4x^3 + 7x^2 - 2x + 19}{(x^2 + 3)(x^2 - x + 2)} = x + 2 + \frac{x^3 + 2x + 7}{(x^2 + 3)(x^2 - x + 2)} \text{ which}$$

reduces to $x + 2 + \dfrac{2x - 1}{x^2 + 3} + \dfrac{-x + 3}{x^2 - x + 2}$

5. *a)* $\dfrac{3}{x} + \dfrac{3x - 2}{2x^2 + x + 1}$ *c)* $\dfrac{1}{x} + \dfrac{-6x - 2}{(2x^2 + 3)^2} + \dfrac{-2x + 1}{2x^2 + 3}$

Exercises 9.6

2. *a)* Yes. Consider a constant function.
3. 0 is a relative minimum.

6. *a)*

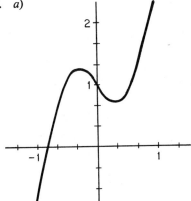

b)

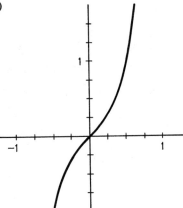

d)

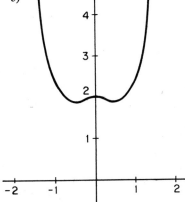

9. *a)*

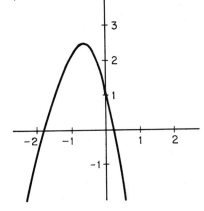

c)

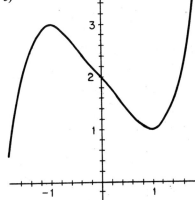

e)

Exercises 9.7

3. Let $y = a_0 + a_1x + a_2x^2$ then

a) $\begin{bmatrix} 1 & 1 & 1 \\ 1 & -1 & 1 \\ 1 & 2 & 4 \end{bmatrix} \begin{pmatrix} a_0 \\ a_1 \\ a_2 \end{pmatrix} = \begin{pmatrix} 1 \\ 0 \\ 1 \end{pmatrix}$, so $\begin{pmatrix} a_0 \\ a_1 \\ a_2 \end{pmatrix} = \begin{pmatrix} 2/3 \\ 1/2 \\ -1/6 \end{pmatrix}$ c) $4 - x - 3x^2$

4. $p(x) \equiv 0; f(x) = x^3 + 2x^2 - 13x + 10 = (x-1)(x-2)(x+5)$

5. a) A relation containing these ordered pairs is not a function, hence there is no polynomial *containing* the points. A "good fit" might be obtained graphically.

c) $7/3 - \dfrac{1}{3}x + \dfrac{1}{6}x^2 - \dfrac{1}{6}x^3$ 7. a) $1 - x + x^2$

INDEX

Notation

This index lists the principal notation used, together with the number of the page where each symbol first appears.